Atam P. Arya

West Virginia University

Fundamentals of
NUCLEAR PHYSICS

Allyn and Bacon, Inc.

Boston

TO MY FATHER

Library of Congress Catalog Card Number: 66-25817

Printed in the United States of America.

First printing . . . . August, 1966
Second printing . . . . April, 1968

PREFACE

This book was written for the student at junior and senior college levels, for the graduate student who requires a thorough grounding in nuclear physics, and for the professional man who has a basic understanding of physics. For the student who is preparing for nuclear engineering, this book will serve well as a text for a prerequisite course. It is assumed that the reader has had a course in atomic physics and is familiar with the basic concepts of quantum mechanics. A good background in mathematics including differential equations will aid him in his understanding of the basic theoretical aspects of nuclear physics.

It is suggested that when the book is used as a text for an undergraduate one-semester, three-hour course, the first nine chapters be covered. When used for first-year graduate study, Chapters 6 through 15 should be covered in a one-semester, three-hour course. Since most of the experimental details are easily understood, they may be assigned as home reading to save classroom time.

I have attempted to cover a number of topics in detail to meet the diverse requirements of the reader. The book is comprehensive and can be read with a minimum of outside help. As a further aid, results of quantum mechanics and relativity are summarized in Appendices A and B.

A balance has been sought between theory and experiments. Most of the formulae given have been derived in the text; for example: Theory of Alpha Decay, Beta Decay, Expression for Stopping Power, etc. Rarely have results been presented without complete derivations.

An important feature is the introduction of certain topics in separate chapters; for example: Chapter 6—Nuclear Size, Chapter 10—Nuclear Models, Chapter 11—Nuclear Reactions, and Chapter 12—Nuclear Forces. Chapter 6 on Nuclear Size, in which different methods under nuclear force radius and nuclear charge radius have been discussed, is unique on this level.

With the increasing importance of high energy nuclear physics, Chapter 15, Fundamental Particles, has been introduced. This chapter acquaints the reader with the status—experimental and, to an extent, theoretical—of the fundamental particles. At the end of each chapter, a complete bibliography with reference to the original work has been provided, along with a shorter list of "Suggestions for Further Reading." Also included are a generous sampling of problems of varying difficulty.

In short, I have tried to present a clear and precise account for the reader who is starting work in any field requiring a strong background in nuclear physics. The book acquaints the reader with problems still mathematically unsolved. The experimenter gains insight for improving experiments and designing new ones to accumulate the necessary data to verify theories. For an applied physicist, a nuclear engineer, for example, it offers the basic fundamentals of nuclear physics.

I am indebted to my colleagues, friends and students, without whose help, advice, and suggestions it would have been difficult to complete this book. My thanks to Professor M. G. Kaushish of Tristate College, Indiana; Professor W. W. Pratt of Pennsylvania State University; Professor J. L. Rodda, Professor C. D. Thomas and Professor D. W. Williamson, of West Virginia University, for their critical examination of the manuscript; to Professor S. Farr for some of the photographs; to my students, Mr. Dennis Chojnacki and Mr. C. D. Henry, for drawing some of the most difficult diagrams; and to Mr. R. D. Wilson and Mr. S. P. Pillai, for proofreading assistance. It has been a pleasure working with Mr. Gary B. Simonsen of Allyn and Bacon in the production of this book.

Finally, my appreciation goes to my wife, Pauline, for her assistance and patience in reviewing and improving upon the manuscript. This book developed through the encouragement of my parents and my wife.

Morgantown, West Virginia
April, 1966

ATAM P. ARYA

CONTENTS

I

THE ATOMIC NUCLEUS

1. INTRODUCTION

Physics may be divided into two primary parts: (a) the macroscopic physics that deals with the phenomena visible to the naked eye and (b) the microscopic physics that deals with the study of both atomic and nuclear physics. The laws governing macroscopic physics were well understood long before the beginning of the present century. The understanding of the general atomic-scale phenomena, however, has developed since 1913, to the extent that definite predictions can be made about the outcome of many experiments. The same is not yet true in the field of nuclear physics.

The beginnings of nuclear physics took place with the discovery of radioactivity by H. Becquerel[1] in 1896, but it was in 1911, when E. Rutherford[2] put forward the nuclear-atomic hypothesis, that a significant study was initiated. Since 1911 many scientists have investigated the many aspects of the nucleus. The results, though encouraging, are far from being complete. The aspects of the nucleus being studied are so numerous and complexly related that it is a formidable task to even list them in any order. A broad division of the study of nuclear physics may be made into the following topics.

1

  (i) The study of the size, mass, and constituents of the nucleus.

 (ii) The formulation of the laws governing types of radiations given out by different nuclei under different circumstances and the interaction of these radiations with matter.

(iii) The study of the arrangement of the constituents inside the nucleus.

(iv) The study of nuclear forces that hold the components of the nucleus together.

These divisions are artificial. The topics are interrelated and overlap to the extent that it is not possible to investigate any one of them independently. For this reason we shall study these topics in the order that seems convenient and natural to follow.

In order to pursue the study of both the experimental and the theoretical aspects of nuclear physics, it is essential to be familiar with the radiation-detection instruments used in different experiments and the mathematical structure necessary to understand and construct theories. Besides the knowledge of elementary mathematics, which we shall use often, it is essential to understand the basic principles of wave mechanics (or quantum mechanics) and relativity. The classical laws of mechanics must be modified in order to understand the behavior of the particles in the microscopic domain, which involves small mass and high speed. When dealing with small mass, use is made of wave mechanics, which predicts the behavior of these particles in terms of probabilities. Still another refinement, a relativistic correction, is necessary when these particles have velocities approaching the velocity of light.

The basic postulates and an outline of wave mechanics to the extent needed in this course are summarized in Appendix A, while the results of the special theory of relativity are stated in Appendix B. It is expected that the student is familiar with these topics. The radiation detectors commonly used in experimental work in nuclear physics will be discussed in some detail in Chapter 3.

The purpose of this chapter will be to discuss in detail the circumstances that led to the establishment of the proton-neutron model of the nucleus.

2. THE NUCLEAR ATOM

In the year 1808, Dalton put forward his atomic theory which did not prove to be completely correct. It was, however, a stepping stone in the investigation of the vast fields of the atom. As late as 1897 the atom was considered to be an indivisible unit, but the discovery of electrons by J. J. Thomson[3] in that year led to the speculation that the atom might be made up of positive and negative charges. Because the atom as a whole is neutral, it was assumed to contain as many positive charges as negative charges. The mass of an electron was found to be very small. It was evident, therefore, that the protons, the positively charged particles, constitute the major part of the atom's mass. According to the Thomson model of the atom, an electron and a proton form a neutral pair, the whole atom being a mixture of such pairs. That the atom consists of protons and electrons was still further confirmed by the discovery of radioactivity by Becquerel[1] in 1896. Becquerel observed that both positively and negatively charged particles were given out by the atom.

The Thomson model of the atom did not remain valid for very long. Conflicts arose in 1909, when H. Geiger and E. Marsden[4] performed experiments on the scattering of alpha particles by thin metal foils. (Alpha particles have a mass of four atomic mass units and a charge of two positive units.) Based on the Thomson model, it was calculated that the alpha particles would be scattered through small angles. Geiger and Marsden found that most of the alpha particles did penetrate the foil and suffered a very small deflection, but that in one out of about 10,000 events, the particles were scattered in the backward direction. There was no apparent way of explaining these rare events. An alpha particle, which has a mass roughly 7,300 times the mass of an electron, cannot collide with a light particle and bounce back. Moreover, because the foil was very thin, a large deflection could not result from several successive alpha-electron collisions.

The most appropriate and satisfactory explanation was given by Rutherford[2] in 1911 and it led to the concept of the nuclear atom. He assumed that most of the mass and positive charge of the atom was concentrated in a very small volume called the nucleus, while the rest of the space in the atom was almost empty. It became possible, therefore, to explain large-angle scattering of alpha particles. The results of similar scattering experiments by Rutherford and his colleagues showed that the radius of the nucleus was of the order of 10^{-13} to 10^{-12} cm as compared to 10^{-8} cm for the radius of the atom. Though this theory of the nucleus was not complete by any means, it had far-reaching consequences.

3. THE PROTON-ELECTRON MODEL OF THE NUCLEUS

Before the discovery of the neutron by J. Chadwick[5] in 1932, it was generally assumed that the nucleus was composed of protons and the necessary number of electrons to give the proper charge and mass. The atom was thought to consist of a nucleus, with A protons and $A - Z$ electrons, with a net positive charge, Z, and the nucleus was assumed to be surrounded by Z electrons in order to form a neutral atom. This theory of the atom looked more promising than others because of the observed emission of alpha particles and beta particles (fast moving electrons) which were supposed to be emitted from the nucleus.

This proton-electron model of the atom did not survive because of its failure to explain the new experimental facts that were then coming into existence. A few of them are discussed below.

A. ANGULAR MOMENTUM OF THE NUCLEUS.   The discovery of angular momentum associated with a nucleus opened new areas of experimenta- tion. Because of the development of spectroscopes of very high resolutions, it was discovered that the spectral lines that looked to be singlets were actually very complex. A spectroscope of poor resolution, for example, showed $3P \to 3S$ transition in sodium as a singlet. Spectroscopes of moderate resolving power, however, showed the doublet nature of the transition found to be due to the spinning of the electron. These are the famous D-lines of sodium and are due to the transitions $3P_{\frac{1}{2}, \frac{3}{2}} \to 3S_{\frac{1}{2}}$. Further study of the spectral lines with high-resolution spectroscopes revealed many new levels, which were very close to each other. These levels had energy differences of $\sim 10^{-5}$ of the main transition. This type of spectrum is called the *hyper- fine structure* and can be attributed to (i) the existence of isotopes in an element and (ii) the nuclear angular momentum.

Let us consider the effect of *isotopes* (elements having the same atomic number, Z, but different mass number, A). If a given element has no isotopes, then the formula for the wave number $\bar{v}$ of a transition in a hydrogen-like atom is given by

$$\bar{v} = \frac{1}{\lambda} = R_M \left(\frac{1}{n_f^2} - \frac{1}{n_i^2} \right) \qquad (1.1)$$

where λ is the wave length associated with the transition resulting from the jump of an electron from an initial level, n_i, to a final level n_f. R_M is the Ryd- berg constant given by

$$R_M = \frac{M}{M + m} R_\infty \qquad (1.2)$$

where $R_\infty = 1.097 \times 10^{-3} \, \text{Å}^{-1}$ is the Rydberg constant if the nucleus is assumed to have infinite mass, m is the mass of the electron, and M is the mass of the nucleus.

If a given element has two or more isotopes, then R_M will differ for each isotope. For example, consider the case of an element having two stable isotopes such as lithium: $A = 6$ and 7 and $Z = 3$. This will result in two constants

$$R_{M_1} = \frac{M_1}{M_1 + m} R_\infty$$

$$R_{M_2} = \frac{M_2}{M_2 + m} R_\infty \qquad (1.3)$$

for the two isotopes, respectively. From Eq. (1.3) we get

$$R_{M_1} - R_{M_2} = \frac{m(M_1 - M_2)}{(M_1 + m)(M_2 + m)} R_\infty \qquad (1.4a)$$

or

$$\Delta R \doteq \frac{m\Delta M}{M_1 M_2} R_\infty \qquad (1.4b)$$

ΔM is small, and m is very small compared to M_1 or M_2, hence ΔR is also very small. This results in two transitions corresponding to the wave lengths λ_1 and λ_2. The difference $\lambda_1 - \lambda_2$ is another very small value. A singlet line, therefore, becomes a close doublet because of the presence of two isotopes. The effect of isotopes on the spectral lines have been observed in many elements[6] with the help of high-resolution spectroscopes.

The hyperfine structure of the spectral lines cannot be explained in all the cases by the isotopic effect. Many elements that have a single isotope also show a hyperfine structure, an example being bismuth[6]. This conflict was resolved by assuming that a nucleus, like an electron, has an angular momentum. The magnitude of the nuclear angular momentum, according to wave mechanics, is given by

$$[I(I + 1)]^{1/2}\hbar, \quad \text{where} \quad \hbar = \frac{h}{2\pi} \qquad (1.5)$$

h is Planck's constant, and I, an integer or half-integer, is the *nuclear spin*. The name "nuclear spin" for I is actually misleading, because the total angular momentum of the nucleus is supposed to be the vector sum of the orbital angular momentum and the spin angular momentum of the particles inside the nucleus. I is a typical nuclear quantum-number, and the maximum value of the component of the angular momentum in any direction is $I\hbar$. Different nuclei as well as different isotopes of the same element can have different values for I. Like atoms, nuclei can also exist in excited quantum states. The nuclear angular momentum vector also exhibits space quantization, i.e., when a nucleus with spin I is placed in an external magnetic field, it can take $(2I + 1)$ different orientations. These orientations are such that the angular momentum vector projected in the direction of the magnetic field has one of the following values (in units of $\hbar$)

$$I, I - 1, I - 2, I - 3, \ldots, -(I - 2), -(I - 1), -I \qquad (1.6)$$

The nuclear angular momentum vector $\mathbf{I}$ adds to the total angular momentum vector $\mathbf{J}$ of the electrons in an atom, to give the resulting angular momentum vector, $\mathbf{F}$;

$$\mathbf{F} = \mathbf{J} + \mathbf{I} \qquad (1.7)$$

(Note that all vectors are shown in boldface type.) If the values of I and J are known, then we can find all the possible values of F that result from the combination of **J** and **I**, (Fig. 1a) and we can thus predict the possible number of transitions between different states. (Selection rules for F are the same as that for J, i.e., $\Delta J = 0, \pm 1$ allowed, $0 \to 0$ not allowed.) In actual practice the reverse procedure is adopted. By counting the number of lines, which will be equal to $2I + 1$ if $I < J$ and equal to $2J + 1$ if $J < I$, and knowing the value of

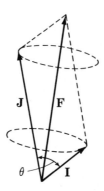

FIG. 1.1   (a) The F vector.

J, it is possible to predict the value of the nuclear spin, I. Besides this method of counting the hyperfine structural lines, other methods have been developed to find $I^{(7)}$. The results of these determinations show a very close relationship between I and the mass number, A, of the nucleus. The relationship implies the following rule:

Nuclei with odd mass numbers have half-integral spins, and those with even mass numbers have zero or integral spins, i.e.,

for odd A, $I = \frac{1}{2}, \frac{3}{2}, \frac{5}{2}, \frac{7}{2}, \dots,$
for even A, $I = 0, 1, 2, 3, 4, \dots,$

Even-even nuclei (nuclei with even number of protons and even number of neutrons) have zero spin. In particular, the spin of the proton is $\frac{1}{2}$, which is the same as that of the electron.

The experimental results given above lead to one of the failures of the proton-electron hypothesis. Consider the case, for example, of $_7N^{14}$ which has a mass number $A = 14$ and atomic number $Z = 7$. According to the proton-electron hypothesis, the $_7N^{14}$ nucleus will have 14 protons and 7 electrons for a total of 21 particles. Because the electron and the proton each have a spin of $\frac{1}{2}$, the $_7N^{14}$ nucleus should have an odd half-integral spin, but experimentally it is found to have an integral spin ($I = 1$). The spin predicted by the proton-electron hypothesis of the nucleus model, therefore, contradicts the stated rule. There are many other isotopes that show this contradiction. Some isotopes, for example, of $Cd(Z = 48)$ and $Pb(Z = 82)$ have odd mass numbers, and according to the above model, these nuclei should have zero or integral spins; experimentally they are found to have odd half-integral spins.

B. MAGNETIC MOMENT. We know from atomic spectra that the rotation of an electron with an angular momentum $1\hbar$ results in a magnetic moment of 1 *Bohr magneton*. This unit of magnetic moment due to the orbital electrons of the atom, μ_B, is given by

$$\mu_B = \frac{eh}{4\pi m_e c} = \frac{eh}{2m_e c} = 0.927 \times 10^{-20} \frac{\text{erg}}{\text{gauss}} \tag{1.8}$$

where e is the electron charge,
  m_e is the mass of the electron, and
  c is the velocity of light.
Because all nuclei have a net charge, and if the spin I is not zero, the motion of the charged particles inside the nucleus should result in a magnetic moment about the nucleus. If the charge distribution of the nucleus is assumed to be spherically symmetric, then the result will be a dipole moment. For the present, we shall assume that the nucleus has a spherically symmetric charge distribution. The same theory may be assumed valid for the protons as that for the electrons.

The proton, whose mass is 1836 times the mass of the electron, will have a magnetic moment of the order of

$$\mu_N = \frac{eh}{4\pi m_p c} = \frac{\mu_B}{1836} = 5.05 \times 10^{-24} \frac{\text{ergs}}{\text{gauss}} \tag{1.9}$$

where m_p is the mass of the proton. μ_N is the *nuclear magneton*, and it is the unit used for expressing nuclear magnetic moments. The actual measured values of the magnetic moments of the nuclei are much smaller than the magnetic moment of the electron. The observed value for the proton, for example, is $+ 2.79353$ μ_N, which is much smaller than the Bohr magneton. If the electrons were to be inside the nucleus, then their magnetic moment, which is of the order of the Bohr magneton, would have been observed experimentally. The measured values of the magnetic moments of the nuclei have always been of the order of μ_N, which is too small to allow electrons to be in the nucleus.

Because the value of μ_I is small, the interaction between the nucleus and the electron is also small. This is the reason for the very small separation in the hyperfine structure of the spectral lines. Actually, the value of μ_I can be calculated from the observed separation in the hyperfine structure components.

The magnetic moment of the nucleus is given by

$$\mu_I = g_I \sqrt{I(I+1)} \frac{eh}{2m_p c} \tag{1.10a}$$

where g_I is the nuclear g factor and, unlike the atomic Lande's g factor, it is completely unpredictable because of the lack of knowledge of the type of particle coupling inside the nucleus. The ratio of the nuclear magnetic moment, μ_I, in terms of the nuclear magneton, to the nuclear angular momentum, in units of $\hbar$, is called the *gyromagnetic ratio*, γ_I, and

$$\gamma_I = \frac{g_I I \hbar \dfrac{e}{2m_p c}}{I\hbar} = g_I \frac{e}{2m_p c} \tag{1.10b}$$

Under the influence of an external magnetic field, the change in the energy, U, is given by

$$U = -\boldsymbol{\mu}_I \cdot \mathbf{H} = -\mu_I H \cos\theta \tag{1.11a}$$

where H is the field acting on the center of the nucleus and θ is the angle between μ_I and H, defined by Fig. 1.1b.

$$\cos\theta = \frac{I(I+1) + J(J+1) - F(F+1)}{2[I(I+1)J(J+1)]^{1/2}} \tag{1.11b}$$

When Eqs. (1.10a) and (1.11a) are combined, we get

$$U = -g_I \sqrt{I(I+1)} \frac{eh}{4\pi m_p c} H \cos\theta \tag{1.12}$$

but

$$\sqrt{I(I+1)} \cos\theta = m_I \tag{1.13a}$$

where

$$m_I = I, I-1, \ldots, -(I-1), -I \tag{1.13b}$$

m_I is introduced because I is space-quantized in an external magnetic field and is called the *magnetic spin quantum number* (Fig. 1.1c). Hence

$$U = -g_I m_I \frac{eh}{4\pi m_p c} H \tag{1.14}$$

Experimentally, therefore, we measure the average value, or the expectation value, of the magnetic moment, given by

$$\langle \mu \rangle_{m_I=I} = g_I I \frac{eh}{4\pi m_p c} \tag{1.15}$$

The order of magnitude of μ_I can be calculated from Eq. (1.11a), knowing H and U. The hyperfine structure is due to the interaction of μ_I with the magnetic field H_e, produced at the center of the nucleus by the orbital electrons. The value of the field H_e varies from 10^5 to 10^7 gauss for different atoms. For our purpose, we can take this value to be of the order of 10^6 gauss. The separations, $\Delta\lambda$, are usually of the order of 1/100,000 of the wavelength

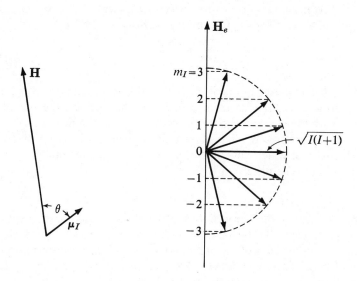

FIG. 1.1   (b) The angle θ between μ_I and H.

FIG. 1.1   (c) The space quantization of I,

$$m_I = \sqrt{I(I + 1)}\cos\theta$$

[H_e is in the direction of J.]

in the visible region. Let the wavelength in the visible region be 6000 Å, which corresponds to a quantum of energy of 2 ev or 3×10^{-12} erg as shown in the following.

$$h\nu = h\frac{c}{\lambda} = \frac{6.6252 \times 10^{-34} \text{ joule-sec} \times 3 \times 10^8 \text{ m/sec}}{6000 \times 10^{-10} \text{ m}}$$

or $h\nu \cong 3 \times 10^{-19} \text{ joule} = 3 \times 10^{-12} \text{ erg} = 2 \text{ ev}$

Because the separation is of the order of 10^{-5} of this amount, therefore

$$U = 3 \times 10^{-17} \text{ erg}$$

Using the relation $U = \mu_I H_e$, where $H_e \simeq 10^6$ gauss, one gets $\mu_I \cong 10^{-23}$ emu.

This value of μ_I is approximately twice that of the nuclear magneton, μ_N, and is $\sim 1/1000$ of the value of the Bohr magneton, μ_B. It is quite clear, therefore, that the magnetic moment of the nucleus is of the order of the nuclear magneton and not that of the Bohr magneton, which demonstrates the absence of the electrons inside the nucleus. If the electrons were present inside the nucleus, they would have contributed to the magnetic moment, but obviously this does not seem to be the case.

C. Wave Mechanics.   From the wave-mechanical point of view, the wavelength of an electron is given by the de Broglie relation

$$\lambda = \frac{h}{p} = \frac{h}{m_e v} \tag{1.16}$$

where p, m_e and v are the momentum, mass, and velocity, respectively, of the electron. In order for the electron to be inside the nucleus, the wavelength associated with the electron should be less than, or at the most equal to, the diameter of the nucleus. We shall show that this will require electrons to have very high energies, which have not been observed experimentally.

According to the uncertainty principle

$$\Delta x \, \Delta p \geqslant h \tag{1.17}$$

where Δx and Δp are the uncertainties in the position and the momentum of the electron, respectively. Because the radius for a typical heavy nucleus of mass number about 200 is of the order of 0.6×10^{-12} cm, the uncertainty in the position of the electron will be $\Delta x = 2R = 1.2 \times 10^{-12}$ cm. From Eq. (1.17), the uncertainty in the momentum of the electron is

$$\Delta p \sim \frac{h}{\Delta x} = \frac{6.6 \times 10^{-27} \text{ erg-sec}}{1.2 \times 10^{-12} \text{ cm}} = 5.5 \times 10^{-15} \frac{\text{erg-sec}}{\text{cm}}$$

Some estimate of the energy E of the electron can be obtained by using the relation

$$E^2 = p^2 c^2 + m_0^2 c^4 \tag{1.18}$$

where $m_0 c^2$ is the rest mass energy of the electron. Assume that the momentum p is not greater than Δp (any larger value of p will give a still larger value of E). Substituting $p = \Delta p$ in Eq. (1.18),

$$\begin{aligned} E^2 &= (5.5 \times 10^{-15})^2 (3 \times 10^{10})^2 + (9.1 \times 10^{-28})^2 (3 \times 10^{10})^4 \\ &= [(16.5 \times 10^{-5})^2 + (6.6 \times 10^{-13})] \text{ ergs}^2 \\ &= [(2.7 \times 10^{-8}) + (6.5 + 10^{-13})] \text{ ergs}^2 \end{aligned}$$

The second term can be neglected in comparison to the first and we get

$$E \doteq (1.65 \times 10^{-4}) \text{ erg} = \frac{1.65 \times 10^{-4} \text{ erg}}{1.6 \times 10^{-12} \text{ erg/ev}} = 10.5 \times 10^7 \text{ ev}$$

and hence

$$E \doteq 105 \text{ Mev}$$

The kinetic energy of an electron inside the nucleus, therefore, would be of the order of 100 Mev. (The values actually would be even larger if $p > \Delta p$.) These values of the energies are much larger than those experimentally observed for the electrons emitted in nuclear decay, which usually have kinetic energies of the order of 2–3 Mev.† This is another proof against electrons inside the nucleus.

Conversely, it is easy to show, by following a similar procedure, that a proton, with a mass larger than that of the electron can exist inside the nucleus. Because the rest-mass energy of the proton is 938 Mev, it can be shown that the protons emitted from some unstable nuclei should have kinetic energies of the order of 2–3 Mev, which is in complete agreement with the experimentally observed values.

D. CONCLUSIONS. All the three arguments lead to the conclusion that the proton-electron model is not the true model for the nucleus. Electrons must exist only outside the nucleus. The final blow to the proton-electron hypothesis came with the discovery of the neutron by Chadwick. It is important at this point to go into the details of the discovery of the neutron, because it led to the establishment of the *proton-neutron* model of the nucleus.

4. DISCOVERY OF THE NEUTRON

The discovery of the neutron was the result of experiments performed by investigators in several different countries. The first indication of the existence of the neutron was given by Rutherford in 1920. According to Rutherford, the neutron consisted of a proton and an electron in close combination. The series of experiments that led to the final discovery of the neutron by Chadwick[5] in 1932, are explained briefly here.

It was shown by W. Bothe and H. Becker[8] in 1930 that some light elements such as beryllium and boron, when bombarded by alpha particles from a natural radioactive source like polonium, emit radiation of great penetrating power. It was further observed that this radiation (a) could penetrate thick sheets of material and (b) did not cause much ionization. The radiation was affected neither by electric nor magnetic fields. In addition, it left no tracks in a cloud chamber. This unknown radiation was thought to be electromagnetic, because it displayed all the properties of electromagnetic radiation, and was thought to consist of high-energy photons. When the

---

† It is possible to explain such a high energy for electrons if we assume that the electrons are in a very deep potential well. But, according to Dirac theory (as we shall see in Chapter 9) the potential well cannot be deeper than $2mc^2$. The potential energy of the electron, therefore, is less than 1.02 Mev.

alpha particles from polonium, for example, which have kinetic energy K_α equal to 5.3 Mev, interact with beryllium, the following reaction was supposed to take place:

$$_4Be^9 + (_2He^4 + K_\alpha) \rightarrow (_6C^{13})^* \rightarrow {_6}C^{13} + h\nu$$

where * indicates the excited state of the nucleus. The alpha particle and $_4Be^9$ combine together to form $(_6C^{13})^*$ which decays to $_6C^{13}$ giving out a photon of energy $h\nu$. The energy of the photon can be estimated from the mass differences.† The decrease in the rest mass, therefore, is

$$= M(_4Be^9) + M(_2He^4) - M(_6C^{13})$$
$$= (9.01505 + 4.00387 - 13.00748) \text{ amu}$$
$$= 0.01144 \text{ amu}$$
$$= 0.01144 \times 931.4 \text{ Mev}$$
$$= 10.7 \text{ Mev}$$

In addition to this 10.7 Mev, the kinetic energy of the alpha particle, which is 5.3 Mev, is also available. A total energy of 16 Mev, therefore, is produced in the reaction with beryllium. The recoil energy of the carbon nucleus $_6C^{13}$ is about 2 Mev. Photons, therefore, will have a maximum energy of 14 Mev. None of the gamma rays given out by natural radioactive elements have such high energy.

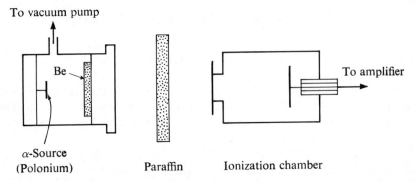

FIG. 1.2 Experimental arrangement for observing ionization caused by protons that are knocked out of paraffin by neutrons.

During the period of 1930–33 several investigators determined the absorption coefficient of different materials for this unknown radiation. In France, I. Curie and F. Joliot[11] reported that if a hydrogenous material, like paraffin, was placed in the path of this radiation, it knocked out protons that caused a high degree of ionization in an ionization chamber. Their experimental arrangement is shown in Fig. 1.2.

† Masses used are those given in "Chart of the Nuclides" by The General Electric Company, enclosed at the end of the book.

When similar experiments were performed with a cloud chamber, the protons knocked out of paraffin produced tracks up to ~ 40 cm long. These experiments were tried with other materials as well, especially with nitrogenous materials. The maximum recoil energies for the proton and nitrogen nucleus were found to be 5.7 Mev and 1.4 Mev, respectively. Whatever the nature of this unknown radiation, it should have explained these recoil energies.

If the unknown radiation is assumed to be a photon of high energy, then the collision can be treated as a Compton collision between a photon and a nucleus. If the incoming photon has energy hv, the energy hv' of the scattered photon from a nucleus of mass m is

$$hv' = \frac{hv}{1 + \dfrac{hv}{mc^2}(1 - \cos \phi)} \tag{1.19}$$

where ϕ is the angle between the scattered photon and the initial direction of the photon. Hence the energy of the recoiled nucleus of mass m will be given by

$$hv - hv' = hv\left(1 - \frac{1}{1 + \dfrac{hv}{mc^2}(1 - \cos \phi)}\right) \tag{1.20}$$

The maximum recoil energy is obtained by letting $\phi = 180°$ so that $\cos \phi = -1$, and

$$hv - hv' = \frac{2}{2 + \dfrac{mc^2}{hv}} \cdot hv \tag{1.21}$$

If this were the true nature of the process taking place, and because we know the recoil energies of the proton and the nitrogen nucleus, it is possible to calculate the energy of the incoming photons (the unknown radiation). From Eq. (1.21), the incoming photon must have energy of about 55 Mev in order to account for the recoiled proton energy of 5.7 Mev. For the nitrogen recoil energy of 1.4 Mev, the incoming photon should have energy of the order of 90 Mev. The available energy of the unknown radiation is only about 12 Mev. The difficulty is increased when we calculate the photon energy necessary to produce the observed recoils of heavier nuclei. Hence the Compton process does not explain the phenomenon, and the incoming radiation does not seem to consist of photons. The correct explanation was given by J. Chadwick in 1932.

THE NEUTRON HYPOTHESIS. According to Chadwick[5], "It is evident we either relinquish the application of the conservation of energy and momentum in these collisions or adopt another hypothesis about the nature of the radiation. If we suppose that the radiation is not a quantum radiation, but consists of particles of mass very nearly equal to that of proton, all the difficulties connected with the collisions disappear,.... In order to explain the great penetrating power of the radiation we must further assume that the particle has no net charge. We may suppose it to consist of a proton and an electron in close combination, the 'neutron' discussed by Rutherford in his Bakerian Lecture of 1920".

It can be shown, by combining the data of the recoil energies of the proton and the nitrogen, that the mass of the neutron is roughly equal to that of the proton. This can be done by considering a head-on collision between a particle of mass m_1 and velocity u with a particle of mass m_2 at rest. Let the velocities of the two after the collision be u_1 and u_2. Because the collision is head-on, we can write equations for the conservation of energy and momentum as

$$\tfrac{1}{2}m_1u^2 = \tfrac{1}{2}m_1u_1^2 + \tfrac{1}{2}m_2u_2^2 \tag{1.22}$$

$$m_1u = m_1u_1 + m_2u_2 \tag{1.23}$$

Eliminating u_1 from these two equations, we get

$$u_2 = \frac{2m_1}{m_1 + m_2}u \tag{1.24}$$

Applying Eq. (1.24) to the case of hydrogen and nitrogen, we get the maximum velocities u_p and u_N respectively for the two as

$$u_p = \frac{2m}{m+1}u \tag{1.25}$$

and

$$u_N = \frac{2m}{m+14}u \tag{1.26}$$

where m is the mass of the neutron and the masses of proton and nitrogen are taken to be 1 amu and 14 amu, respectively. Dividing Eq. (1.25) by Eq. (1.26), we have

$$\frac{m+14}{m+1} = \frac{u_p}{u_N} = \frac{3.3 \times 10^9 \text{ cm/sec}}{4.7 \times 10^8 \text{ cm/sec}} \tag{1.27}$$

which gives

$$m = 1.15 \text{ amu} \tag{1.28}$$

The values substituted for u_p and u_N are those determined from the experiments. The mass of the neutron determined by this method has an error of about 10 percent. Better estimates of the neutron mass were obtained by using the reaction

$$_5\text{B}^{11} + {}_2\text{He}^4 \rightarrow {}_7\text{N}^{14} + {}_0\text{n}^1$$

The mass of the neutron obtained by this method is between 1.005 and 1.008 amu. A recently determined value of the mass of the neutron is (1.008982 ± 0.000003) amu[10] on the O^{16} scale.

It is possible to retain the conservation of energy and momentum under the assumption that the unknown radiation is a neutron of mass equal to that of proton. Consequently, the reaction between the alpha particle and $_4Be^9$ can now be written as

$$_4Be^9 + _2He^4 \rightarrow _6C^{12} + _0n^1$$

Thus the decrease in the mass is

$$= M(_6C^{12}) + M(_0n^1) - M(_4Be^9) - M(_2He^4)$$
$$= 0.00616 \text{ amu} = 5.7 \text{ Mev}$$

This value, combined with 5.3 Mev kinetic energy of the alpha particle, gives a total of 11 Mev as the available energy. This is enough to account for all the recoil energies of different nuclei, as explained in the following paragraph.

It can be shown that if the collision is not head-on, the kinetic energy K_2 transferred to m_2 by a particle of mass m_1 and kinetic energy K is given by

$$K_2 = \frac{4\zeta \cos^2 \phi}{(1 + \zeta)^2} K \qquad (1.29)$$

where $\zeta = \dfrac{m_2}{m_1}$ and ϕ is the angle m_2 makes with initial direction of m_1. For maximum recoil energy,

$$K_2 = \frac{4\zeta}{(1 + \zeta)^2} K \qquad (1.30)$$

For a proton, $\zeta = 1$, and for nitrogen $\zeta = 14$. Therefore, $K_p = K$, and $K_N = \frac{5.6}{2.25} K \simeq \frac{1}{4} K$.

In order to have $K_p = 5.7$ Mev, and $K_N = 1.4$ Mev, K has to be of the order of only 5.7 Mev. This amount of energy is clearly available. The existence of the neutron (having a mass approximately equal to that of a proton and having no charge) was firmly established.

5. THE PROTON-NEUTRON MODEL OF THE NUCLEUS

We have already shown that the proton-electron model of the nucleus could not explain many experimentally observed facts. The main difficulty arose because of the assumed presence of the electrons inside the nucleus. Before the discovery of the neutron, there was no alternate explanation to account for the charge Z of a nucleus of mass number A, except by including $A - Z$ electrons inside the nucleus to neutralize the charge of $A - Z$ protons. This resulted in a net positive charge Z on the nucleus. However, the discovery of the neutron altered the entire picture. In 1932, Heisenberg suggested that the new particle, the neutron, was a fundamental constituent of all matter. According to him, all nuclei are made up of protons and neutrons, with no electrons inside the nucleus. As indicated previously, the mass of the neutron is almost equal to that of the proton, and its charge is zero. Accordingly, the mass of the nucleus would be equal to the sum of the masses of the protons and neutrons inside the nucleus, and the charge would be equal to the total charge of the protons. A common name *nucleon* is given to a proton or a neutron. Hence, if there are A nucleons inside a nucleus, then there will be Z protons and $A - Z$ neutrons. This model of the nucleus is in complete agreement with the experiments. Before going into the detailed explanation, we will list some properties of the neutrons, protons, and electrons.

TABLE 1.1

SOME PROPERTIES OF THE NEUTRON, PROTON, AND ELECTRON

Property	neutron	proton	electron
Mass	1.008982 amu	1.00759 amu	$\frac{1}{1837}$ amu
Charge	0	$+1e$	$-1e$
Spin	1/2	1/2	1/2
Magnetic Moment	$-1.9135\ \mu_N$	$+2.7927\ \mu_N$	$-1.0021\ \mu_B$
g factor	-3.83	5.59	2

It is found that the neutron, like proton and electron, has a spin of $\frac{1}{2}$. Although the neutron has no net charge, it does have a negative magnetic moment, which implies that the spin and the magnetic moment vectors are oppositely directed.

The proton-neutron model of the nucleus overcomes all the difficulties that could not be explained by the proton-electron model, mentioned in Section 3. Firstly, since there are only A particles inside the nucleus, each particle having a spin of $\frac{1}{2}$, the theoretical predictions of the nuclear spins agree with the experimental results, i.e., nuclei with odd mass numbers have half-integral spins and those with even mass number have zero or integral spins. For example, in the case of $_7N^{14}$, according to the proton-neutron model there will be 14 nucleons i.e. 7 protons and 7 neutrons, hence it should have a zero or an integral spin which is in agreement with the experimentally observed value of $I = 1$ for $_7N^{14}$. Secondly, according to the proton-neutron model, there are no electrons inside the nucleus and hence we do not expect the magnetic moment of the nucleus to be of the order of the Bohr magneton. We expect, on the other hand, the nuclear magnetic moment to be of the order of the nuclear magneton. This is in agreement with the experimental values of μ_I. Finally, since the mass of the neutron is approximately equal to the mass of the proton, it is possible for the neutrons to reside inside the nucleus, according to uncertainty principle.

One most important question still remained unanswered. The protons, with positive charges, repel each other, and thus they try to disrupt the nucleus. It was assumed that some type of nuclear forces held these protons, as well as the neutrons, together. The knowledge of these forces is still far from being complete. What is known about nuclear forces can explain some properties of the nucleus. The discussion of the nuclear forces appears in Chapter 12.

PROBLEMS

1. Na^{23} has a nuclear spin of 3/2. Using this value of the nuclear spin, draw the hyperfine structure of the sodium D-lines. Making use of the selection rules, draw all the possible transitions.

2. Derive the expression given in Eq. (1.9) for the magnetic moment of a proton.

3. If the orbital motion of an electron results in a magnetic field at the center of the nucleus of the order of 10^6 gauss, what is the amount of splitting in the case of hyperfine structure of the sodium D-lines of Problem 1? The nuclear g factor for sodium is 1.4, i.e., $g_I = 1.4$.

4. Show from wave-mechanical calculations that, unlike electrons, it is possible for protons and neutrons to exist inside the nucleus.

5. Calculate the minimum amount of kinetic energy needed by an electron to stay inside a nucleus of mass number $A = 100$. (The radius of the nucleus is given by $r = r_0A^{1/3}$ where $r_0 = 1.35 \times 10^{-13}$ cm).

6. Derive Eq. (1.19).

7. Derive Eq. (1.29).

8. If a photon of energy 12 Mev strikes (a) a hydrogen nucleus and (b) a nitrogen nucleus, each assumed to be at rest, what will be the energies of recoiled nuclei if the photons are scattered (a) at 45° and (b) at 90°. Calculate also the maximum recoil energies of the nuclei.

9. If a neutron having a kinetic energy of 5.7 Mev strikes a $_2He^4$ nucleus at rest head-on, what will be the maximum recoil kinetic energy of $_2He^4$?

REFERENCES

1. Becquerel, H., *Compt. Rend.* Paris, **122**, p. 420, (1896).
2. Rutherford, E., *Phil. Mag.*, **21**, p. 699, (1911).
3. Thomson, J. J., *Phil. Mag.*, **44**, p. 293, (1897).
4. Geiger, H. and E. Marsden, *Proc. Roy. Soc.* (London), **A-82**, p. 495, (1909).
5. Chadwick, J., "The Existence of a Neutron," *Proc. Roy. Soc.* (London), **A-136**, p. 692, (1932).
6. White, H. E., *Introduction to Atomic Spectra*. New York: McGraw-Hill Book Company, 1934.
7. Fermi, Enrico, *Nuclear Physics*, ed. by Joy Orear, *et al.*, pp. 9–15. Chicago: The University of Chicago Press, 1950. A brief description of several methods of measuring magnetic moments.
8. Bothe, W. and H. Becker, *Z. Physik* (Berlin), **66**, p. 289, (1930).
9. Curie, I. and F. Joliot, *Compt. Rend.*, **194**, p. 273, (1932).
10. Strominger, D., J. M. Hollander, and G. T. Seaborg, *Revs. Mod. Phys.*, **30**, p. 585, (1958).

SUGGESTIONS FOR FURTHER READING

1. Evans, R. D., *The Atomic Nucleus*, Chapters 1, 4. New York: McGraw-Hill Book Co., Inc., 1955.
2. White, H. E., *Introduction to Atomic Spectra*, Chapter XVIII. New York: McGraw-Hill Book Co., Inc., 1934.
3. Smith, K. F., *Progress in Nuclear Physics*, **VI**, p. 52, 1957.
4. Chadwick, J., "The Existence of a Neutron," *Proc. Roy. Soc.*, (London), **A-136**, p. 692, (1932). (Reproduced in R. T. Beyer, ed., *Foundations of Nuclear Physics*. New York: Dover Publications, 1949.)
5. Halliday, D., *Introductory Nuclear Physics*, Chapter 15. New York: John Wiley & Sons, Inc., 1962.

II

RADIOACTIVITY

1. INTRODUCTION

Most of our knowledge about the physics of the atom and its nucleus started with the discovery of radioactivity by Henri Becquerel[1] in 1896. He was studying the radiation emitted by certain fluorescent salts after being activated by sunlight when he accidentally discovered the phenomenon of radioactivity. By chance he placed a sample of the double sulphate of uranium and potassium, wrapped in a thick paper, near photographic plates in a dark room. When the plates were developed they were found to have been exposed even though they were fully protected against exposure to light. He repeated this experiment and came to the conclusion that some sort of radiation that affected the photographic plates was coming out of the uranium salt. Later, the same radiation was found to cause ionization of air. The radiation emitted by the uranium salt was first given the name *Becquerel Rays*. This name was later changed to include different types of radiations from many different substances.

The emission of radiation was observed from some other substances besides uranium salt. This phenomenon is *radioactivity*, and the elements that exhibit it are *radioactive elements*. In the year 1898, Madame Marie Curie and her husband, Pierre Curie[2], discovered two radioactive elements, polonium and radium. Thorium, actinium, radiothorium, mesothorium, and other radioactive elements, were discovered[3] within a few years. Today hundreds of radioactive isotopes of different elements are known. Radioactive isotopes are quite difficult to separate from the raw ore, and often tons of ore yield only a small fraction of a gram of the radioactive material.

The radioactivity (or simply *activity*) of a sample is not affected by physical and chemical changes, i.e., any changes in the pressure, volume, temperature or chemical form, do not change the rate of emission of the radiation. It was first suggested by E. Rutherford and F. Soddy[4] in 1902 that radioactivity is due to the spontaneous disintegration of atoms, and that the new elements thus formed may have quite different properties from those of the initial elements. Though the disintegration of the atom is a spontaneous process, the activity is a prolonged process, extending over periods from a few seconds to millions of years.

2. IDENTITY OF DIFFERENT TYPES OF RADIATION

Following the discovery of radioactivity, many efforts were directed to the study of the properties of this radiation, especially the (a) penetrating power in different materials, (b) specific ionization in different gases, and (c) behavior under the effects of a magnetic or electric field. Most of the initial researches were conducted by the Curies[1,2,5,6,7], William Crookes[8,9], and Ernest Rutherford and his collaborators at Cambridge[3,4,10−13]. The radiations of natural radioactive substances were classified into three different components, depending upon their penetrating powers. One component, with a very weak penetrating power, was stopped by an ordinary sheet of paper, but caused intense ionization in air. These are *alpha rays*[10], or α-rays, mentioned in chapter I. A second type had less ionization power but was more penetrating than α-rays and could easily pass through thin foils of metal (a few mm thick). These are *beta rays*[10], or β-rays. The third type caused even less ionization but could penetrate through slabs many centimeters thick of different material[14]. These are *gamma rays*, or γ-rays.

F. Giesel[15], and S. Meyer and E. von Schweidler[16] studied the effect of a magnetic field on the radiation. They showed, independently, that certain parts of the radiation could be deflected by the application of a strong magnetic field. Rutherford[12] demonstrated that α-particles showed a small deflection under the influence of a strong magnetic field and behaved as if they were positively charged. β-particles showed much more deflection and behaved as negatively charged particles. R. Strutt[17] showed that the γ-rays were undeflected even in the strongest electric or magnetic fields. The existence of these three types of radiation can be demonstrated by a simple experiment devised by Mme. Curie (Fig. 2.1).

A small amount of a radioactive sample, say radium, is placed at the bottom of a long hole drilled in a lead block. This produces a well collimated beam of radiation. A strong magnetic field is applied at right angles to the

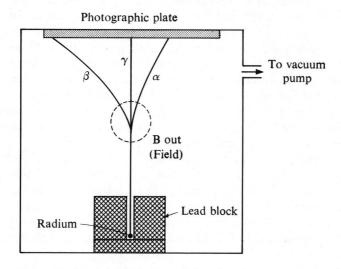

FIG. 2.1 Experimental arrangement showing the deflections of α, β, and γ rays by a magnetic field. α-particles, being positively charged, are deflected to the right; β-particles, being negatively charged, are deflected to the left; and γ-rays, being uncharged, are not deflected by the magnetic field.

plane of the figure; the field points out of the paper. Under these conditions, the positively charged particles will be deflected towards the right, and the negatively charged particles will be deflected towards the left; the uncharged particles will not be deflected at all. The amount of deflection will depend upon the velocity, the amount of charge, and the mass of the particles. A photographic plate, exposed to the deflected beam of radiation, will show points of exposure in various locations: α-particles produce an image at the right, at only one spot, indicating that they are monoenergetic; γ-rays produce an image directly in line with the source; and β-particle-images appear at varying locations to the left of the central portion, because they are of nonuniform intensity and have energies that vary from zero to a certain maximum value.

A. ALPHA-PARTICLES.   Alpha particles cause fluorescence in some substances. If the fluorescence is examined closely with a magnifying glass, it is found to consist of a series of scintillations. These scintillations are produced by the impact of the particles on the fluorescent screen, which proves they are discrete particles.

Alpha particles always ionize the gas through which they travel and in the process of ionization, they lose energy and velocity. Finally, after reaching thermal velocities, when they can cause no further ionization, they capture electrons and thus become neutral atoms. Most alpha particles from radioactive elements are given out with velocities between 1.4×10^9 cm/sec and 2.2×10^9 cm/sec, but any one group of alpha particles from a nucleus always has a definite velocity, and, hence, a definite energy. Very often there is more than one group of alpha particles emitted from any one type of nuclei.

Measurements[18,19,20] of the charge to mass ratio for alpha particles, determined by deflection in electric and magnetic fields, show that $e/m = 4823$ emu/gm. For hydrogen ions the value of $e/m = 9650$ emu/gm. This indicates that the mass of an alpha particle is double that of the hydrogen ion or that the charge of an alpha particle is twice that of a hydrogen ion and its mass is four times that of a hydrogen ion. By measuring both e and e/m it is found that the latter is true, i.e., alpha particles have a mass of 4 amu and a charge of 2 electron units. Thus, they are really fast moving doubly-ionized helium atoms, He^{++}. This is demonstrated by the following experiment.

Fig. 2.2 shows an apparatus for the purpose of spectral identification of alpha particles. A radioactive source, S, which produces alpha particles is placed in a thin glass tube, T. Those alpha particles that escape through the glass are slowed down in the evacuated chamber, C. After capturing electrons, the particles become neutral atoms. When a sufficient number of these neutral atoms has accumulated in the chamber, their optical spectrum is viewed by maintaining a discharge between the two electrodes E and E'. The spectrum is found to be identical with that of helium.

B. BETA-PARTICLES.   Beta particles produce brilliant fluorescence, the color of which depends on the nature of the fluorescent substance, and, which on close observation, appears as discrete scintillations. Beta particles, therefore, like alpha particles, have discrete masses and charges. They cause much less ionization than alpha particles, but are ~ 100 times more penetrating. Beta particles are not stopped by a thin sheet of paper, but a thin foil of aluminum does stop a large fraction of them. Because these particles are very light as compared to alpha particles, they may change their direction on colliding with air molecules. The velocities of β-particles range up to 0.99 c where c is the velocity of light ($c = 3 \times 10^{10}$ cm/sec). A given radioactive element produces beta particles of varying energies, the maximum value of which is called the *end-point energy*. Hence, unlike alpha particles, beta particles have neither homogeneous velocities nor energies.

The deflection of beta particles by electric and magnetic fields is much greater than that of alpha particles. The measurement of e/m and e identifies beta particles to be fast-moving electrons. Because their mass changes with velocity, the value of e/m varies for different velocities. For low-energy (a few kev) beta particles, the value of e/m is $\sim 1.77 \times 10^7$ emu/gm.

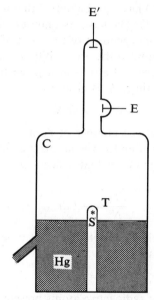

FIG. 2.2 A method of identifying alpha particles as He^{++} by means of spectral lines.

C. GAMMA-RAYS. Gamma rays also produce fluorescence, and they also cause ionization of a gas, but to a lesser degree than that caused by α-rays or β-rays. The penetrating power of γ-rays is ~ 100 times greater than that of β-rays. γ-rays are not stopped by many centimeters of aluminum, but a few centimeters of lead can stop a large fraction of them. Because they carry no charge, they are not deflected by electric or magnetic fields, and they exhibit all the characteristics of electromagnetic waves. In fact, γ-rays are x-rays of very short wavelength, and because γ-rays are electromagnetic waves, they travel at the speed of light, with wavelengths between 1.7×10^{-10} cm and 4.1×10^{-8} cm.

3. THE RADIOACTIVE DECAY LAW

When the nucleus of an atom emits an alpha particle, a beta particle, a gamma ray, or any other particle, or when it captures an electron from an extra-nuclear shell, the process is called *radioactive decay*. Experimental evidence shows that radioactive decay follows an exponential law. It is possible to derive this law, if it is assumed that the decay is statistical in nature. This statistical nature implies that it is not possible to predict which atom will decay in the next second.

Let us assume that each undecayed nucleus (or sometimes we shall use the term "undecayed atom") has a probability λ that it will decay in the next second (assuming that $\lambda \ll 1$). The basic assumption of the statistical theory is that this probability λ is independent of time and of the number and type of other nuclei present. In time dt the probability of decay of each atom will be $\lambda \, dt$. If there are N undecayed atoms at a given time, the number, dN, that will decay in the short time, dt, is given by

$$dN = -\lambda \, dt \, N \qquad (2.1)$$

This equation says that the number of decays in a short time, dt, are proportional to the number of undecayed atoms present, N, and to the length of time, dt. The negative sign means that N decreases as t increases. Eq. (2.1) can be written

$$\frac{dN}{N} = -\lambda \, dt \qquad (2.2)$$

Integrating Eq. (2.2) with the assumption that at time $t = 0$, the number of radioactive atoms present is N_0, gives

$$N(t) = N_0 e^{-\lambda t} \qquad (2.3)$$

where $N(t)$ is the number of radioactive atoms present at time t.

The probability, λ, used in the above equations is called the *disintegration constant* or *decay constant*.

Most of the time one is less interested in knowing the absolute number of radioactive atoms present in a given radioactive sample than in the number of atoms that will decay in a unit time. This is accomplished by using the activity of a radioactive sample, which is defined as the number of disintegrations per second that result from a given sample. From Eq. (2.3), we find

$$\text{activity} = \left| \frac{dN}{dt} \right| = \lambda N_0 e^{-\lambda t} \qquad (2.4)$$
$$= \lambda N$$

Thus the activity of a sample depends on the actual number, N, of radioactive atoms present and the decay constant, λ.

A. HALF-LIFE. Another quantity of importance in radioactivity is *half-life*, denoted by $t_{1/2}$. It is defined as the time interval in which the activity decreases by one-half. Because the activity is proportional to the number of undecayed atoms present, $t_{1/2}$ is also equal to the time interval during which the number of undecayed atoms decreases by one-half. Substitution of $N = \dfrac{N_0}{2}$ and $t = t_{1/2}$ in Eq. (2.3) yields

$$\frac{N_0}{2} = N_0 e^{-\lambda t_{1/2}} \qquad \text{or} \qquad t_{1/2} = \frac{\ln 2}{\lambda} = \frac{0.693}{\lambda} \qquad \text{(2.5)}$$

Because the unit of $t_{1/2}$ is time, the unit of λ is the reciprocal of time, e.g., $\sec^{-1}$.

B. AVERAGE LIFE. The exponential form of the decay makes it evident that it will take infinite time for the complete disappearance of radioactive atoms. We do not know, of course, which atom is going to decay next, and individual atoms may have lifetimes anywhere from zero to infinity. For the statistical nature of this phenomenon, we must define the quantity *average* or *mean life*, τ.

The average life, τ, of a radioactive nucleus can be calculated by summing the lives of all the nuclei and dividing by the total number of nuclei. Suppose dN_1 nuclei have a lifetime t_1, that dN_2 have t_2, that dN_3 have t_3, and so on. The mean life will be, therefore,

$$\tau = \frac{t_1\,dN_1 + t_2\,dN_2 + t_3\,dN_3 + \cdots}{dN_1 + dN_2 + dN_3 + \cdots} \qquad \text{(2.6)}$$

We may write Eq. (2.6) in the integral form

$$\tau = \frac{\displaystyle\int_0^{N_0} t\,dN}{\displaystyle\int_0^{N_0} dN} = \frac{\displaystyle\int_0^{N_0} t\,dN}{N_0} \qquad \text{(2.7)}$$

where $N_0 = dN_1 + dN_2 + dN_3 \cdots$

Substituting for dN from Eq. (2.3) into Eq. (2.7) and integrating yields

$$\tau = \frac{-\displaystyle\int_\infty^0 \lambda t\, N_0 e^{-\lambda t}\,dt}{N_0} = \int_0^\infty \lambda t\, e^{-\lambda t}\,dt = \frac{1}{\lambda} \qquad \text{(2.8)}$$

hence

$$\tau = \frac{1}{\lambda}$$

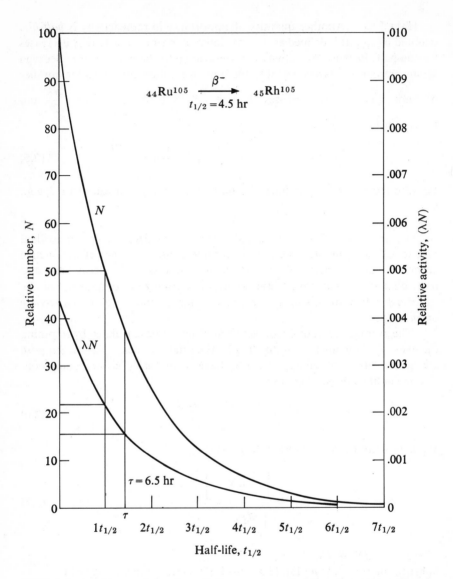

FIG. 2.3 (a) Linear plots of a relative number of radioactive atoms N and activity λN versus time t for $_{44}\text{Ru}^{105}$ ($t_{1/2} = 4.5$ hr) in arbitrary units.

As an illustration, consider the radioactive isotope $_{44}\text{Ru}^{105}$, which decays by electron emission to $_{45}\text{Rh}^{105}$ with a half-life of 4.5 hr.[21,22] The decay constant is, therefore, $\lambda = 4.27 \times 10^{-5}$ sec^{-1} and the mean life $\tau = 6.5$ hr. Making use of Eq. (2.3) we can find N, the number of radioactive atoms present at any time; while the activity from Eq. (2.4) is λN. Fig. 2.3a shows the plot of N and λN versus time in units of half-life on a linear scale; Fig. 2.3b shows the same plot on a semi-logarithmic scale. The ordinates in both the graphs have an arbitrary relative number of counts and activity. The relative number of atoms and activity are shown for both $t_{1/2}$ and τ.

It should be noted that $_{45}Rh^{105}$ itself is radioactive and decays to $_{46}Pd^{105}$ with a half-life of 35 hr. We shall discuss this type of decay in the next section.

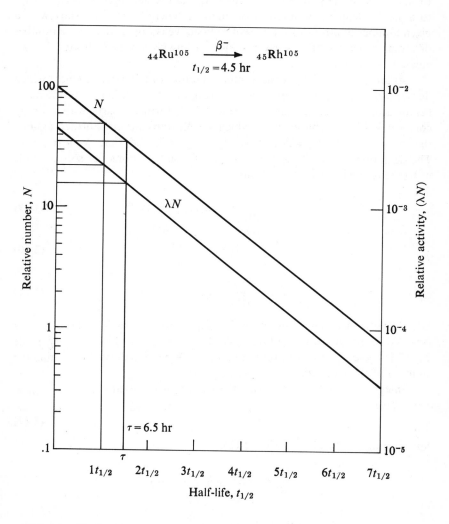

FIG. 2.3 (b) Semilogarithmic plots of a relative number of radioactive atoms N and activity λN versus time t for $_{44}Ru^{105}$ ($t_{1/2} = 4.5$ hr) in arbitrary units.

4. THE LAW OF SUCCESSIVE DISINTEGRATION

Both in the case of naturally occurring as well as artifically produced radio-active isotopes, decay may take place by successive disintegrations. A parent radioactive element decays into a daughter product. If this daughter product itself is radioactive, it will further decay into another element, which is called the grand-daughter, and so on. In most cases this successive decay is limited to the decay of the parent to its daughter, and the daughter, in turn, decays to a stable element. A question of interest, generally, is if we start with a given number of atoms of the parent radioactive isotope, what is the number of atoms of each of the decay products at any given time? This can be calculated as follows:

At any time, t, let N_1 be the number of atoms of the parent element which decays with a decay constant λ_1 into its daughter element. Let N_2 be the number of atoms of the daughter element, which further decays with a decay constant λ_2 into a stable element, which has N_3 stable atoms. Further, assume that at time $t = 0$, $N_1 = N_{10}$, that $N_2 = N_{20} = 0$, and that $N_3 = N_{30} = 0$. The definition of activity as the number of disintegrations per second leads us to the following set of equations:

$$\frac{dN_1}{dt} = -\lambda_1 N_1 \tag{2.9}$$

$$\frac{dN_2}{dt} = \lambda_1 N_1 - \lambda_2 N_2 \tag{2.10}$$

$$\frac{dN_3}{dt} = \lambda_2 N_2 \tag{2.11}$$

Eq. (2.9) gives the rate of decay of N_1, Eq. (2.10) means that the atoms of type N_2 are produced at the rate $\lambda_1 N_1$ and disappear at the rate $\lambda_2 N_2$, while Eq. (2.11) gives the rate of production of N_3. We are interested in finding the solution of these equations.

Integration of Eq. (2.9), with the condition imposed that $N_1 = N_{10}$ at $t = 0$, gives

$$N_1 = N_{10} e^{-\lambda_1 t} \tag{2.12}$$

Substituting Eq. (2.12) into Eq. (2.10),

$$\frac{dN_2}{dt} = \lambda_1 N_{10} e^{-\lambda_1 t} - \lambda_2 N_2$$

or

$$\frac{dN_2}{dt} + \lambda_2 N_2 = \lambda_1 N_{10} e^{-\lambda_1 t} \tag{2.13}$$

Multiplying both sides of Eq. (2.13) by $e^{\lambda_2 t}$, we get

$$e^{\lambda_2 t}\frac{dN_2}{dt} + \lambda_2 N_2 e^{\lambda_2 t} = \lambda_1 N_{10}e^{-\lambda_1 t}\cdot e^{\lambda_2 t}$$

or

$$\frac{d}{dt}(N_2 e^{\lambda_2 t}) = \lambda_1 N_{10}e^{(\lambda_2 - \lambda_1)t} \tag{2.14}$$

Integrating Eq. (2.14) produces

$$N_2 e^{\lambda_2 t} = \frac{\lambda_1}{\lambda_2 - \lambda_1} N_{10}e^{(\lambda_2 - \lambda_1)t} + C \tag{2.15}$$

where C is a constant of integration, the value of which is determined by substituting

$$N_2 = N_{20} = 0, \qquad \text{at} \qquad t = 0$$

$$C = -\frac{\lambda_1}{\lambda_2 - \lambda_1} N_{10}$$

Substituting this value of C into Eq. (2.15), and dividing both sides by $e^{\lambda_2 t}$, we get

$$N_2 = \frac{\lambda_1}{\lambda_2 - \lambda_1} N_{10}(e^{-\lambda_1 t} - e^{-\lambda_2 t}) \tag{2.16}$$

Similarly, solving Eq. (2.11), with the condition that $N_3 = N_{30} = 0$ at $t = 0$, we get

$$N_3 = N_{10}\left(1 + \frac{\lambda_1}{\lambda_2 - \lambda_1} e^{-\lambda_2 t} - \frac{\lambda_2}{\lambda_2 - \lambda_1} e^{-\lambda_1 t}\right) \tag{2.17}$$

Hence Eqs. (2.12), (2.16) and (2.17) completely describe the number of atoms present at any time t. These equations have been derived for the special case when $N_1 = N_{10}$, and $N_{20} = N_{30} = 0$, at $t = 0$. Following this procedure, it is possible to derive the expressions for N_1, N_2, and N_3, even if N_{20} and N_{30} are not zero at $t = 0$. The results of such calculations are

$$N_1 = N_{10}e^{-\lambda_1 t} \tag{2.18a}$$

$$N_2 = \frac{\lambda_1}{\lambda_2 - \lambda_1} N_{10}(e^{-\lambda_1 t} - e^{-\lambda_2 t}) + N_{20} e^{-\lambda_2 t} \tag{2.18b}$$

$$N_3 = N_{30} + N_{20}(1 - e^{-\lambda_2 t}) + N_{10}\left(1 + \frac{\lambda_1}{\lambda_2 - \lambda_1} e^{-\lambda_2 t} - \frac{\lambda_2}{\lambda_2 - \lambda_1} e^{-\lambda_1 t}\right)$$

$$\tag{2.18c}$$

As a practical example of the use of the Eqs. (2.12), (2.16), and (2.17), we consider the successive decay of $_{44}Ru^{105(21,22)}$ which decays to $_{45}Rh^{105}$, and which, in turn, decays to $_{46}\text{Pd}^{105}$, i.e.,

$$_{44}\text{Ru}^{105} \xrightarrow[t_{1/2} = 4.5 \text{ hr}]{\beta^-} {}_{45}\text{Rh}^{105} \xrightarrow[t_{1/2} = 35 \text{ hr}]{\beta^-} {}_{46}\text{Pd}^{105} \text{ (stable)}$$

Fig. 2.4 shows the plot of the decay and growth of N_1, N_2, and N_3 in the case of $_{44}\text{Ru}^{105}$ with $N_{10} = 100$, at $t = 0$ and $N_{20} = N_{30} = 0$, at $t = 0$.

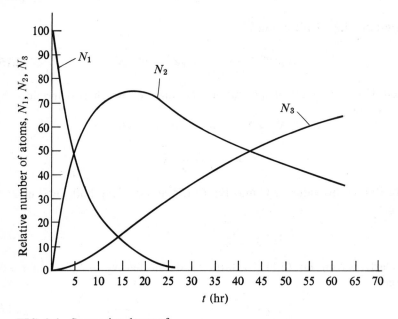

FIG. 2.4 Successive decay of

$$_{44}\text{Ru}^{105} \xrightarrow[t_{1/2} = 4.5 \text{ hr}]{\beta^-} {}_{45}\text{Rh}^{105} \xrightarrow[t_{1/2} = 35 \text{ hr}]{\beta^-} {}_{46}\text{Pd}^{105} \text{ (stable)}$$

The problem of successive decay can be generalized to any number of successive radioactive decays. The differential equations representing the successive decays are

$$
\begin{aligned}
dN_1/dt &= -\lambda_1 N_1 \\
dN_2/dt &= \lambda_1 N_1 - \lambda_2 N_2 \\
dN_3/dt &= \lambda_2 N_2 - \lambda_3 N_3 \\
&\ \vdots \\
dN_n/dt &= \lambda_{n-1} N_{n-1} - \lambda_n N_n
\end{aligned}
\qquad \textbf{(2.19)}
$$

where N_1, N_2, N_3, ..., N_{n-1}, and N_n are the number of atoms of different isotopes present at any time t, and λ_1, λ_2, λ_3 ..., λ_{n-1}, and λ_n are their decay constants, respectively. If we know the initial number of radioactive atoms of different isotopes present, i.e., we know N_{10}, N_{20}, N_{30}, ..., N_{n0} at $t = 0$, it is possible to calculate the values of N_1, N_2, N_3, ..., N_n at any time t, by solving the equations (2.19) in a manner similar to the ones for Eqs. (2.9)–(2.11) given above.

5. RADIOACTIVE EQUILIBRIUM

In this section we shall apply the equations of successive decay to some special cases. The two cases of interest are (i) where $\lambda_1 \simeq \lambda_2$ and (ii) where $\lambda_1 \ll \lambda_2$. The first case leads to what is called the transient equilibrium and the second to the permanent or secular equilibrium.

A. TRANSIENT EQUILIBRIUM. Consider the case of a parent nucleus that decays with a decay constant λ_1 to its daughter element, which in turn decays with the characteristic decay constant λ_2. Suppose the mean lives of the two are of the same order of magnitude, i.e., $\tau_1 \simeq \tau_2$ and, therefore, $\lambda_1 \simeq \lambda_2$. In this case, we shall show that the number of atoms of the daughter element reaches a certain maximum and then starts decreasing at the decay rate of the longer-lived of the two.

Starting with Eq. (2.16)

$$N_2 = \frac{\lambda_1}{\lambda_2 - \lambda_1} N_{10}(e^{-\lambda_1 t} - e^{-\lambda_2 t}) \qquad (2.16)$$

we can find the time t_m in which N_2 reaches a maximum value. Differentiating Eq. (2.16) with respect to time and equating it to zero, gives

$$\frac{dN_2}{dt} = 0 = \frac{\lambda_1}{\lambda_2 - \lambda_1} N_{10}(-\lambda_1 e^{-\lambda_1 t_m} + \lambda_2 e^{-\lambda_2 t_m})$$

or

$$t_m = \frac{1}{\lambda_2 - \lambda_1} \log_e \frac{\lambda_2}{\lambda_1} \qquad (2.20)$$

After time t_m the decay rate of the daughter, i.e., dN_2/dt will be governed by λ_1 or λ_2 whichever is smaller, as follows:

(i) If $\lambda_1 < \lambda_2$, it means the mean life of the parent element is longer than the daughter element. This implies that the term $e^{-\lambda_2 t}$ in Eq. (2.16) will approach zero faster than $e^{-\lambda_1 t}$ and may be neglected. This gives

$$N_2 = \frac{\lambda_1}{\lambda_2 - \lambda_1} (N_{10}e^{-\lambda_1 t})$$

$$= \frac{\lambda_1}{\lambda_2 - \lambda_1} (N_1) \qquad (2.21)$$

or

$$\frac{N_2}{N_1} = \frac{\lambda_1}{\lambda_2 - \lambda_1} \qquad (2.22)$$

while the ratio of the activity of the daughter element to that of the parent element is

$$\frac{dN_2/dt}{dN_1/dt} = \frac{\lambda_2 N_2}{\lambda_1 N_1} = \frac{\lambda_2}{\lambda_2 - \lambda_1} \tag{2.23}$$

Eq. (2.21) states that the daughter element decays with the decay rate of the parent element, i.e., λ_1 determines the decay rate of the daughter element; Eq. (2.22) states that the ratio of N_2/N_1 is constant. In such a case the parent element and the daughter element are said to be in a transient equilibrium.

(ii) If on the other hand $\lambda_2 < \lambda_1$, it can be shown that

$$N_2 = \frac{\lambda_1}{\lambda_2 - \lambda_1} N_{10} e^{-\lambda_2 t} \tag{2.24}$$

which means that after a certain time the daughter element decays with its own decay rate determined by the decay constant λ_2. This holds good even if there is more than one successive decay. After a certain time the parent element disappears and the daughter decays at its own rate.

B. PERMANENT OR SECULAR EQUILIBRIUM. Consider once again Eq. (2.16) of successive decay, and suppose that the half-life of the parent element is very, very long as compared to its daughter element, or, $\lambda_1 \ll \lambda_2$. In such cases, Eq. (2.16)

$$N_2 = [\lambda_1/(\lambda_2 - \lambda_1)]N_{10}(e^{-\lambda_1 t} - e^{-\lambda_2 t}) \tag{2.16}$$

reduces to

$$N_2 = \frac{\lambda_1}{\lambda_2} N_{10}(1 - e^{-\lambda_2 t}) \tag{2.25}$$

because $\lambda_2 - \lambda_1 \simeq \lambda_2$ and $e^{-\lambda_1 t} \cong 1$.

Furthermore, if t is very large as compared to the mean life of the daughter that is, $t \gg \dfrac{1}{\lambda_2}$, then $e^{-\lambda_2 t}$ becomes negligible as compared to 1, and the Eq. (2.25) reduces to

$$N_2 = (\lambda_1/\lambda_2)N_{10} \tag{2.26}$$

which states that the amount, N_2, of the daughter element present is constant. The daughter element is said to be in "permanent or secular equilibrium" with the parent element. Because the half-life of the parent element is very large, its amount is almost constant, $N_{10} = N_1$, and hence

$$N_2 = (\lambda_1/\lambda_2)N_1$$

Thus the condition for the "permanent or secular equilibrium" is

$$\lambda_1 N_1 = \lambda_2 N_2 \tag{2.27a}$$

or

$$N_1/N_2 = \lambda_2/\lambda_1 = \tau_1/\tau_2 \qquad \textbf{(2.27b)}$$

or the amount of the two substances present at a given time is inversely proportional to their decay constants, or directly proportional to their mean lives.

Eq. (2.27b) could have been easily derived by the application of Eq. (2.19). For equilibrium, $dN_2/dt = 0$, the second equation in (2.19) gives

$$\lambda_1 N_1 = \lambda_2 N_2$$

This also implies that $dN_1/dt = 0 = -\lambda_1 N_1$, which is approximately correct, because λ_1 is very small, and hence the product $\lambda_1 N_1 \cong 0$.

For the case of many successive decays in which the parent has a much longer half-life than any of its products, we can write the condition of secular equilibrium from Eq. (2.19) as

$$\lambda_1 N_1 = \lambda_2 N_2 = \lambda_3 N_3 = \ldots = \lambda_n N_n \qquad \textbf{(2.28a)}$$

or

$$N_1/\tau_1 = N_2/\tau_2 = N_3/\tau_3 = \ldots = N_n/\tau_n \qquad \textbf{(2.28b)}$$

As a typical example of secular equilibrium, consider the decay of Ra ($t_{1/2} = 1620$ years) to its daughter radon Rn ($t_{1/2} = 3.82$ days). After a long time t as compared with the half-life of Rn, the amount of Rn becomes constant. This is evident from Fig. 2.5 in which the sum of the ordinates of

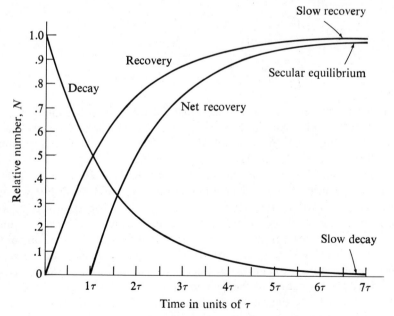

FIG. 2.5 The decay and recovery of radon.

the decay and the growth curves becomes constant after a certain time. When such conditions are reached, the daughter Rn is said to be in permanent or secular equilibrium with its parent Ra.

6. NATURAL RADIOACTIVE SERIES

The search for radioactivity in the naturally occurring isotopes revealed that there are many radioisotopes among the elements with atomic numbers $Z = 81$ to $Z = 92$, because at large Z, the coulomb repulsion between the protons makes the elements less stable. In order to decrease the effect of coulomb repulsion, a nucleus undergoes alpha decay, which results in a loss of two protons and two neutrons. This may lead to excess of neutrons, as usually is the case, and the nucleus undergoes electron (or beta) emission. In the process of β-emission, in order to conserve the total charge, a neutron is converted into a proton. This chain of alpha and beta decay continues until a stable isotope is reached. Such chain reactions are demonstrated very well by four different radioactive series occurring in nature[23].

Depending on the mass number A, all the radioactive isotopes from $Z = 81$ to $Z = 92$ that occur naturally, fall into one of four series. Each of these series is represented by one of the following four classes:

$A = 4n$	Thorium Series
$A = 4n + 1$	Neptunium Series
$A = 4n + 2$	Uranium Series
$A = 4n + 3$	Actinium Series

where n is an integer. It is quite evident that a decay process beginning in one of these classes will remain in the same class, because in alpha decay the mass changes by four units, $\Delta A = 4$, while in the process of beta and gamma decay there is no change in mass.

Figs. 2.6 and 2.7 show the plots of N (where $N = A - Z$) versus Z. These figures also indicate the half-lives, the types of decay and the disintegration energies (those listed are the maximum energies). The existence of such series is due to the fact that the parent element in each series (shown at the top) has a very long life except in the case of neptunium. Because of the comparatively short half-life ($t_{1/2} = 2.2 \times 10^6$ yrs) of the parent element of the neptunium series, these elements do not occur in nature, as they have decayed away since the formation of the elements ($\sim 5 \times 10^9$ years ago). As shown in Figs. 2.6 and 2.8, the names of these series of radioactive isotopes are different from their element names.

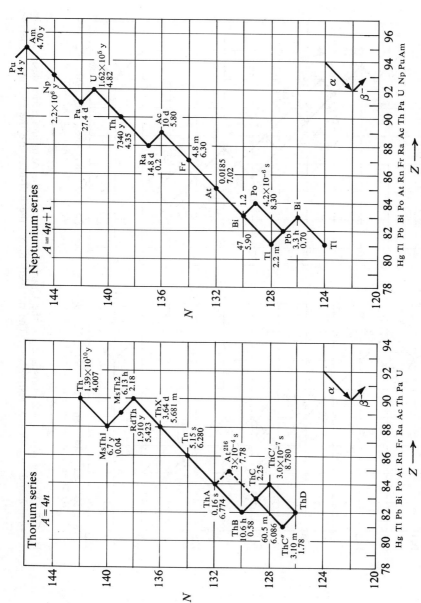

FIG. 2.6 Plot of $N(=A-Z)$ versus Z for the Thorium Series and the Neptunium Series designated by $A=4n$ and $A=4n+1$, respectively. The numbers below the half-lives are the maximum energies in Mev.

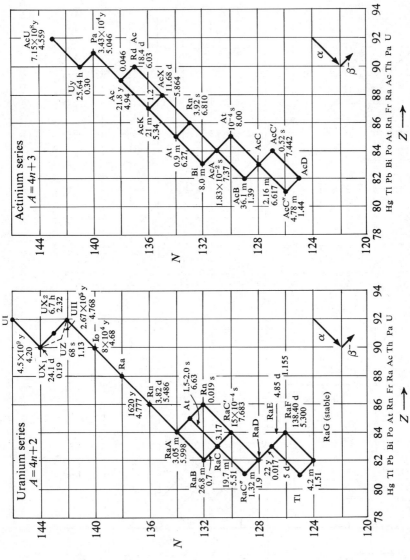

FIG. 2.7 Plot of $N(=A-Z)$ versus Z for the Uranium series and the Actinium Series designated by $A = 4n+2$ and $A = 4n+3$, respectively. The numbers below the half-lives are the maximum energies in Mev.

Excepting the neptunium series, the rest of the series have the following four properties common to them:

1) All of them have a single very long-lived isotope, for example,
   (a) $_{90}Th^{232}$ $t_{1/2} = 1.39 \times 10^{10}$ yrs
   (b) $_{92}U^{238}$ $t_{1/2} = 4.5 \times 10^9$ yrs
   (c) $_{92}U^{235}$ $t_{1/2} = 7.15 \times 10^8$ yrs
   The rest of the isotopes of the series have much shorter half-lives.

2) The stable end-product of all the three series is some isotope of lead, i.e., $_{82}Pb^{208}$, $_{82}Pb^{206}$, $_{82}Pb^{207}$, respectively, for the thorium, uranium, and actinium series.

3) Each has an inert gas occurring at $Z = 86$. The names of the three being thoron ($_{86}Rn^{220}$), radon ($_{86}Rn^{222}$) and actinon ($_{86}Rn^{219}$), respectively, for the thorium, uranium, and actinium series.

4) In all three series, an isotope C disintegrates in a branching process by α and β decay, and the resulting two substances in each case, in turn, transform in such a way as to give a common product D (Fig. 2.8).

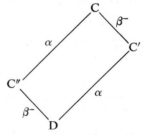

FIG. 2.8 Branching process of disintegration by α and β decay.

Beside the radioisotopes in the heavy elements mentioned here, there are a few isolated radioactive isotopes in the lighter elements. Some of these are listed in Table 2.1.

TABLE 2.1

**NATURAL RADIOISOTOPES IN MEDIUM-
AND LIGHT-WEIGHT ELEMENTS**

Isotope	Half-Life (in years)	Type of Decay
$_{19}K^{40}$	1.2×10^9	β^-, K-capture
$_{37}Rb^{187}$	6.2×10^{10}	β^-
$_{62}Sm^{147}$	1.5×10^{11}	α
$_{71}Lu^{176}$	2.4×10^{10}	β^-
$_{75}Re^{187}$	4.0×10^{11}	β^-

The decay of elements is not limited to the emission of α-, β- and γ-rays. There are some elements that decay by the process of *positron* emission. A positron is a particle of the same mass as the electron, but its charge is equal and opposite to that of the electron. Some elements decay by capturing orbital electrons. Both processes are also called beta decay.

7. UNITS OF RADIOACTIVITY

As already discussed, it is more important to know the number of atoms disintegrating per second than the absolute number of radioactive atoms present in a given sample. Hence, the units for radioactivity are in terms of disintegrations per unit time. There are two different units. Historically, the old unit of radioactivity is the *curie*, defined as the amount of the activity of radon that is in equilibrium with one gram of radium. The value of the curie can be calculated in a simple manner. The half-life of radium is 1620 years and the decay constant is

$$\lambda_{radium} = \frac{0.693}{1.62 \times 10^3 \text{ yrs}} = 13.8 \times 10^{-12} \text{ sec}^{-1}$$

The mass of radium is 226 amu and there are 6.02×10^{23} atoms in one gram-atom of radium, therefore, one gram of radium contains

$$\frac{6.02 \times 10^{23}}{2.26 \times 10^2} = 2.66 \times 10^{21} \text{ atoms.}$$

Hence, the disintegration rate is

$$dN/dt = |\lambda N| = 13.8 \times 10^{-12} \times 2.66 \times 10^{21}$$
$$\cong 3.7 \times 10^{10} \text{ disintegrations/sec}$$

Using different values of $t_{1/2}$ of radium as determined by various experimentors, the number of disintegrations per second obtained varies between 3.4×10^{10} to 3.7×10^{10}. *The curie, however, has been defined to be equivalent to 3.7×10^{10} disintegrations per second.* The sub-units of the curie are the milli-curie denoted by mc and the micro-curie, μc, which correspond to 3.7×10^7 and 3.7×10^4 disintegrations per second, respectively.

Because of the confusion in the definition of the curie, the American National Bureau of Standards has proposed a new unit, called the *rutherford* (rd), which is equal to 10^6 disintegrations per second. The sub-units of the rd are the milli-rutherford (mrd) $= 10^3$ disintegrations per second and the micro-rutherford (μrd) $= 1$ disintegration per second.

8. DETERMINATION OF HALF-LIFE

Most of the methods used for determining half-lives are applicable to all three types of decays, α, β, and γ. Because the three characteristic constants λ, τ, and $t_{1/2}$ of the radioactive isotopes are related to each other, the determination of one gives all three. Usually the half-life $t_{1/2}$ is experimentally determined, while the others can be calculated from it.

A. DETERMINATION OF SHORT HALF-LIVES. For radioactive isotopes with moderately short half-lives (minutes, hours, days, and months) and hence a high λ, the half-life can be determined by plotting the number of counts versus time on semi-logarithmic paper. The plot is a straight line and the absolute value of the slope gives the disintegration constant, λ, that is

$$N = N_0 e^{-\lambda t}$$
$$\ln N = \ln N_0 - \lambda t$$

or

$$y = a - \lambda t$$

where

$$y = \ln N, \text{ and } \ln N_0 = a \text{ (constant)}$$
$$|dy/dt| = \lambda = \text{the slope of the straight line}$$

For a more accurate determination of a short half-life, it is necessary to make a least-square fit of the data, i.e., of the counting rate versus time. If the half-life of a radioactive sample is of the order of a few seconds, it is difficult to use this method. Other methods have been developed[24].

B. DETERMINATION OF VERY LONG HALF-LIVES
 (i) If we know the number, N, of radioactive atoms present in a given substance, then by measuring experimentally the number of disintegrations per unit time, λ can be determined.

$$|dN/dt| = \lambda N$$

$$\lambda = \left(\frac{1}{N}\right) \frac{dN}{dt}$$

This method is applicable to isotopes with half-lives as large as 10^{10} years or more.
(ii) If the two isotopes have reached a secular equilibrium so that

$$N_1 \lambda_1 = N_2 \lambda_2$$

then knowing N_1, λ_1 and N_2, a calculation of λ_2 can be made. An example of the use of the secular equilibrium equation is the determination of the half-life of uranium from the known half-life of radium.

C. A MIXTURE OF ACTIVITIES. In the investigation of the decay characteristics of some radioisotopes, one finds that the plot of activity versus time on a semi-logarithmic paper is not a straight line. Such behavior is an indication of the presence of different radioactive isotopes in the sample under investigation. For simplicity, suppose there are only three different activities present in a mixture. Fig. 2.9 shows the plot of activity versus time (solid circles)

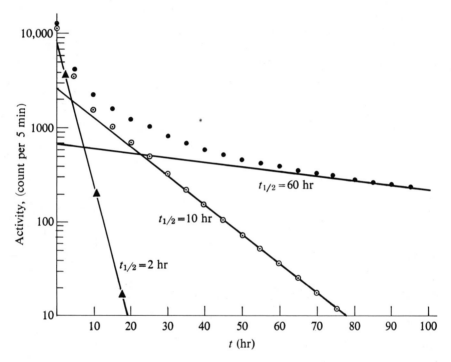

FIG. 2.9 Determination of the half-lives of different components in a mixture. Solid circles show the sum of the unrelated activities versus time as experimentally determined.

which is not a straight line. The half-lives of the different components in the mixture can be determined in the following manner:

(i) Plot the experimentally determined counting rate as a function of time on a semi-logarithmic paper (solid circles, ●).

(ii) Corresponding to large values of time (near the end of the curve) one finds the experimental points to be on a straight line. Draw a straight line passing through these points and extend it to $t = 0$. This straight line represents the decay of the isotope with the longest half-life. From this straight line the half-life can be determined by the method used in determining short half-lives. In this particular case $t_{1/2} = 60$ hr.

(iii) Subtract from the experimental points the activity of the 60-hour half-life sample represented by the straight line in (ii) above. The result of the subtraction is shown by the open circles, ⊙. The process of drawing a straight line through the points lying on the end of the new curve can be repeated again as explained in (ii) and the half-life determined as before, which in this case is 10 hours.

(iv) Repeat the process explained in (iii) to find out the half-life of the third activity. This time subtract the activity represented by the straight line corresponding to the 10-hour half-life from the open circles. The resulting points are represented by solid triangles, ▲. The straight line through these points corresponds to a half-life of 2 hours.

Though the above example is limited to a mixture of three activities, the method can be used for a mixture of a larger number of radioactive isotopes. The following factors impose certain limits on the applicability of the above method.

(a) The different activities must be unrelated, i.e., they must not correspond to successive decay.

(b) The half-lives of the different isotopes must be far apart.

(c) The sample must be strong, or hot, enough (strong in the sense that the disintegration rate is high), so that if there is a very short-lived activity, it will contribute to the counting rate for a considerable interval of time to make the determination of the short half-life sufficiently accurate.

PROBLEMS

1. A sample of radioactive Au^{198} was observed to decay in the following manner:

Time elapsed (hours)	Counts/min	Time elapsed (hours)	Counts/min
0	4810	60	2520
12	4215	72	2211
24	3705	84	1998
36	3281	96	1775
48	2850	108	1502

(a) Find the half-life, decay constant, and mean life.
(b) What will be the activity of this sample after two weeks?
(c) Find the number of undecayed radioactive atoms in the sample after two weeks.

2. A certain radioactive sample was observed to decay by electron emission in the following manner:

Time elapsed (min)	Disintegrations /min	Time elapsed (min)	Disintegrations /min
0	2650	35	690
5	2190	40	570
10	1821	45	460
15	1502	50	380
20	1233	55	310
25	1009	60	260
30	830	65	220

(a) Find the half-life, decay constant, and mean life.
(b) Find the activity after two hours.
(c) Find the number of undecayed radioactive atoms in the sample after two hours.

3. Co^{60} has a half-life of 5.2 years.
(a) Calculate the disintegration constant.
(b) Calculate the activity of a 1-gm sample of Co^{60}, and express this activity in curies and in rutherfords.
(c) Each disintegration is accompanied by an emission of an electron of energy 0.31 Mev and two gamma rays of energies 1.17 Mev and 1.33 Mev. Calculate in ergs per second the rate at which the energy is being given out.

4. If one gram of a radioactive radium sample decays by $(3.60 \pm 0.04) \times 10^{10}$ beta disintegrations per second, calculate its half-life and decay constant.

5. Nd^{147} has a half-life of 11 days. How long will it take for its activity to reduce from 10 curie to 1 curie?

6. The half-life of Po^{210} is 140 days. If 10 milligrams are allowed to decay for two years, what will be its activity at the end of this period?

7. What will be the masses of a 1-curie sample and a 100-rd sample of Ba^{133} if its half-life is 8 years?

8. Calculate the masses of 1 rd of U^{238} and 1 rd of Po^{212}.

9. Natural samarium contains 15 percent Sm^{147}. Sm^{147} is radioactive and decays by alpha decay. What will be the number of disintegrations per gram per second of the natural element? The half-life of Sm^{147} is 1.3×10^{10} years.

10. Radium has a half-life of 1620 years and decays into radon, which has a half-life of 3.82 days. A 10-gm source of radium is sealed, and the radon produced is pumped off every 24 hours. How many millicuries of radon are pumped off each time?

11. Calculate the volume of 1 millicurie of radon gas at normal temperature and pressure ($t_{1/2}$ of $_{86}Rn^{222} = 3.82$ days).

12. Natural uranium is a mixture of U^{235} and U^{238} in the ratio of 1:140. The half-life of U^{235} is 7.1×10^8 years and the half-life of U^{238} is 4.5×10^9 years. If the earth is 4×10^9 years old, what was this ratio at the time of formation of the earth? What will be this ratio 10^{10} years hence, if the sample is undisturbed?

13. The final decay product of U^{238} is Pb^{206}

$$U^{238} \rightarrow 8 \ _2He^4 + \ _{82}Pb^{206} + 6 \ _{-1}e^0$$

How much lead (Pb^{206}) will a 1-kg sample of U^{238} contain after 10 million years if the half-life of U^{238} is 4.5×10^9 years? How can you use this method to find the age of the earth?

14. Derive Eqs. (2.18a), (2.18b) and (2.18c).

15. Consider the following radioactive decay series:

$$Nd^{149} \xrightarrow[t_{1/2} = 1.8 \text{ hr}]{\beta^-} Pm^{149} \xrightarrow[t_{1/2} = 50 \text{ hr}]{\beta^-} Sm^{149} \text{ (stable)}$$

If initially we have 10^6 radioactive atoms of Nd^{149} and none of Pm^{149} and Sm^{149}, plot the number of atoms of Nd, Pm, and Sm as functions of time.

16. Consider the decay series

$$U^{235} \xrightarrow[\lambda = 3.1 \times 10^{-17}/\text{sec}]{\alpha} Th^{231} \xrightarrow[\lambda = 7.6 \times 10^{-4}/\text{sec}]{\beta^-} Pa^{231} \xrightarrow{\alpha} Ac^{227}$$

Assuming that at $t = 0$, U^{235} has stripped off all its decay products, plot the build-up and decay of Th^{231}.

17. In the decay scheme shown below, the radioactive atoms of type 1 decay to 2 and 3 with decay constants λ_1 and λ_4, respectively, while 2, in turn, decays to 3 with a decay constant λ_2. Finally the radioactive atoms of type 3 decay to 4 with a decay constant λ_3.

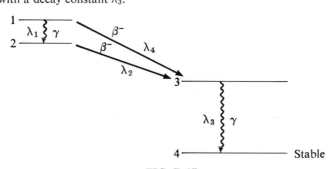

FIG. P-17

(a) Derive expressions for the number of radioactive atoms and the activity of 2, 3, and 4, if at $t = 0$, $N_1 = N_{10}$ and $N_2 = N_3 = N_4 = 0$.
(b) Repeat part (a) for the case when at $t = 0$, $N_1 = N_{10}$ and $N_2 = N_{20}$, while $N_3 = N_{30} = 0$, $N_4 = N_{40} = 0$.
(c) Show that these equations reduce to simpler standard equations if there is no decay from 1 to 3.

18. Consider the following decay in the uranium series

$$RaA \xrightarrow[t_{1/2} = 3.05 \text{ min}]{\alpha} RaB \xrightarrow[26.8 \text{ min}]{\beta^-} RaC \xrightarrow[19.7 \text{ min}]{\alpha}$$

(a) Starting with 10^{10} atoms of RaA, plot the number of atoms of RaA, RaB, and RaC as a function of time.
(b) Find the time in which RaB reaches its maximum value and the time in which RaC reaches its maximum value.
(c) Is it possible to achieve a transient or secular equilibrium?

19. Natural uranium contains 0.72 percent by weight of U^{235} and 99.28 percent of U^{238}. From Fig. 2.7 we see that U^{235} and U^{238} are the parent elements of two series and have much longer half-lives than the subsequent daughters

$$U^{235} \xrightarrow[t_{1/2}=7.1 \times 10^8 \text{ yrs}]{\alpha} Th^{231} \xrightarrow[t_{1/2}=25.64 \text{ hr}]{\beta^-} Pa^{231} \xrightarrow[t_{1/2}=3.43 \times 10^4 \text{ yrs}]{}$$

$$U^{238} \xrightarrow[t_{1/2}=4.5 \times 10^9 \text{ hr}]{\alpha} Th^{234} \xrightarrow[t_{1/2}=24.1 \text{ day}]{\beta^-} Pa^{234} \xrightarrow[t_{1/2}=6.7 \text{ hr}]{}$$

The daughters Th^{231}, Pa^{231} and Th^{234}, Pa^{234} are in secular equilibrium with U^{235} and U^{238}, respectively.
  (a) Calculate the atomic concentration, in parts per billion, of each daughter (Th^{231}, Pa^{231}, Th^{234}, Pa^{234}).
  (b) Can you get some estimate of how long it took to reach this secular equilibrium?

20. Consider the series decay in Problem 15.
  (a) Discuss the type of equilibrium achieved.
  (b) How long did it take to achieve this equilibrium?

21. The counting rate shown here is due to the mixture of two completely un-related activities. Plot the counting rate on a semi-logarithmic paper and find the half-lives of the two activities.

Time elapsed (hours)	Disintegrations /min	Time elapsed (hours)	Disintegrations /min
0	7410	3.5	406
0.5	4108	4.0	322
1.0	2405	4.5	270
1.5	1510	5.0	221
2.0	990	5.5	183
2.5	703	6.0	153
3.0	524	6.5	130
		7.0	110

REFERENCES

1. Becquerel, H., *Compt. Rend.*, **122**, pp. 420, 501, 689, (1896).
2. Curie, P., and M. Curie, *Compt. Rend.*, **127**, pp. 175, 1215, (1898).
3. Rutherford, E., and F. Soddy, *Phil. Mag.*, **5**, pp. 445, 576, (1903).
4. Rutherford, E., and F. Soddy, *Phil. Mag.*, **4**, pp. 569, (1902).
5. Becquerel, H., *Compt. Rend.*, **136**, p. 199, (1903).
6. Curie, M., *Compt. Rend.*, **126**, p. 1101, (1898).
7. Curie, P., M. Curie, and G. Bemont, *Compt. Rend.*, **127**, p. 1215, (1898).
8. Crookes, W., *Proc. Roy. Soc.*, **A-66**, p. 409, (1900).
9. Crookes, W., *Proc. Roy. Soc.*, **A-69**, p. 413, (1902).
10. Rutherford, E., *Phil. Mag.*, **47**, p. 109, (1899).

11. Rutherford, E., *Phil. Mag.*, **5**, p. 95, (1903).
12. Rutherford, E., *Phil. Mag.*, **5**, p. 177, (1903).
13. Rutherford, E., *Nature*, **65**, p. 366, (1903).
14. Villard, P., *Compt. Rend.*, **130**, p. 1178, (1900).
15. Giesel, F. D., *Ann. Phys. Chem.*, **69**, p. 834, (1899).
16. Meyer, S., and E. von Schweidler, *Z. Physik.*, **1**, p. 90, (1899).
17. Strutt, R. J., *Proc. Roy. Soc.*, **A-72**, p. 208, (1903).
18. Rutherford, E., *Phil. Mag.*, **12**, p. 348, (1906).
19. Rutherford, E., and O. Hahn, *Phil. Mag.*, **12**, p. 371, (1906).
20. Rutherford, E. and H. Robinson, *Phil. Mag.*, **28**, p. 552, (1914).
21. *Nuclear Data Sheets*, National Research Council, NRC 58-11-55-60.
22. Duffield, R. B., and M. L. Langer, *Phys. Rev.*, **81**, p. 203, (1951).
23. Strominger, D., J. M. Hollander, and G. T. Seaborg, *Rev. Mod. Physics*, **30**, p. 585, (1958).
24. Rowlands, S., "Methods of Measuring Very Long and Very Short Half-Lives," *Nucleonics*, **3**, No. 3, p. 2, (Sept., 1948).

SUGGESTIONS FOR FURTHER READING

1. Rutherford, E., J. Chadwick, and C. D. Ellis, *Radiation From Radioactive Substances*, Chapter I. New York: Macmillan, 1930.
2. Segre, E., Ed., *Experimental Nuclear Physics*, Vol. III, Part IX. New York: John Wiley & Sons, Inc., 1959.
3. Evans, R. D., *The Atomic Nucleus*, Chapters 15, 25, 26. New York: McGraw-Hill Book Co., Inc., 1955.
4. Siegbahn, K., Ed., *Alpha- Beta- and Gamma-Ray Spectroscopy*, New York: Interscience Publishing, 1965.

III

RADIATION
DETECTORS

1. INTRODUCTION

The radiation detector is the most important instrument in any nuclear physics experiment. This chapter will describe and explain the principles of operation of various detectors used to measure the several types of nuclear radiations. For certain experiments, the standard device may be modified somewhat. For any experiment, however, the choice of a particular detector is guided mainly by two factors: first, the type of radiation present, and second, the type of data to be collected. α-, β- and γ-rays are not the only radiations that one encounters in exploring the many different aspects of an atomic nucleus. These other radiations, as well as specialized detectors applicable to them, will be discussed as we continue our study of nuclear physics.

Statistics is an important tool in the analysis of the experimental data. One must know the accuracy of the data with which one works. For this purpose we shall discuss the kinds of errors encountered, based on the laws of probability. At the end of the chapter, we shall discuss briefly the method of least-square curve fitting, which is a method by which the best fit of experimental points may be made to a theoretical curve.

46

2. TYPES OF DETECTORS

Simple radiation detectors make use of the fact that charged particles and photons create ionization in certain media. Uncharged particles, like neutrons, cause little or no ionization, and, as a result, are difficult to detect. The discussion of neutron detectors will appear in Chapter XIII.

A. ELECTROSCOPE.   The electroscope is one of the earliest instruments used to detect ionizing radiations. It is a simple device that measures the potential of a charge. It is usually composed of two thin gold leaves.

A radioactive material is placed inside the container of a charged electroscope. The radiation given out by the radioactive source causes the gas inside the electroscope to ionize. The charge collected by the leaves make them converge. The rate of this convergence is directly proportional to the amount of ionization and, hence, proportional to the amount of radiation. A modern form of an electroscope whose measurements are more accurate than early models has been designed by C. Lauritsen[1].

B. IONIZATION CHAMBER.   Fig. 3.1a shows an ionization chamber. It is made up of a small volume of gas at about atmospheric pressure contained in a chamber, I, inside of which are two electrodes, E and E', maintained at a high potential difference by means of a voltage source, V. The radiation is allowed to enter the chamber, in which the radiation causes ionization. The ions produced are collected by the respective + and − electrodes. The voltage

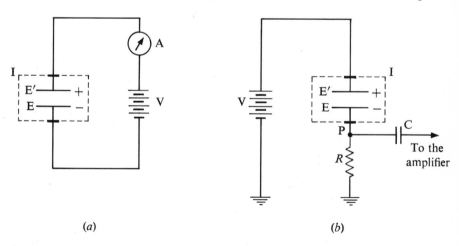

(a)   (b)

FIG. 3.1   (a) Ionization chamber and circuit for detection of a continuous beam of particles or x-rays. (b) Ionization chamber and circuit for detection of individual particles.

is kept high enough so that there is a negligible amount of recombination of charges.

The arrangement shown in Fig. 3.1a is used for intensity measurements of a continuous beam of radiation, like x-rays. The amount of radiation present is proportional to the amount of ionization, which is indicated by a current-measuring device, A, such as an electrometer. This arrangement, however, is not satisfactory for measurements on individual particles, because the current generated by them may not produce a measurable reading on the meter. For individual particles, the arrangement of Fig. 3.1b is employed. The arrival of a particle produces ion pairs in the chamber. (The negative ions reach the electrode before the positive ions.) The effect of both ions is to change the potential of the collector. This produces an ionization current in the external circuit, which results in a potential drop across the resistor, R .

After the passage of a particle, the ionization current and the potential drop across the resistor decreases to zero. The variations in the voltage at a point, such as P, resulting from the changes in the potential drop across R, is an electrical pulse, or a pulse signal. This pulse is amplified and then recorded by a circuit known as a *scalar*. The mean life of the exponential decay of the pulse is equal to the time constant, RC, of the circuit. Fig. 3.2 shows the shape of pulse signals from an ionization chamber for two different time constants[2,3].

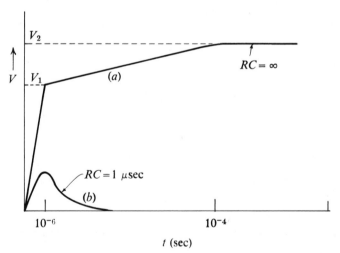

FIG. 3.2 Pulse shapes from an ionization chamber for time constants (*a*) $RC = \infty$, and (*b*) $RC = 1\mu$sec. In (*a*) the fast rise is due to the motion of the electrons (reaching a maximum value V_1); the subsequent slow rise is produced by the motion of positive ions (reaching a final value V_2). [From D. R. Carson and R. R. Wilson, *Rev. Sci. Inst.*, **19**, 207 (1948)].

The disadvantage of this equipment is that the *resolving time*, i.e., the time that will elapse before the chamber is ready to detect another particle, is of the order of several milliseconds, which restricts the use of the chamber to low counting rates.

C. PROPORTIONAL COUNTER.   The proportional counter is a modified form of an ionization chamber, differing from it in two aspects. In the proportional counter, one electrode is a hollow cylinder and the other is a wire that runs

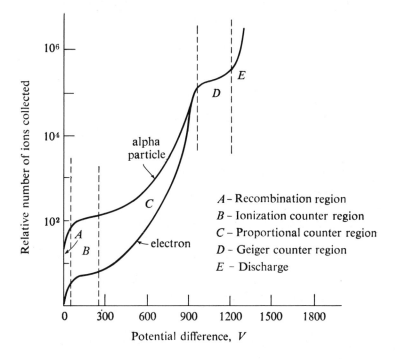

FIG. 3.3   Relative number of ions collected as a function of voltage for a gas-filled detector.

inside the cylinder along its axis. The voltage applied to the electrodes is much higher than that used in an ionization chamber. The size of the pulse increases with increasing voltage up to a certain limit. Below this point, the size of the pulse is directly proportional to the amount of primary ionization of the particle. The voltage region in which this proportionality holds is the *proportional region*, as shown in Fig. 3.3. This proportionality characteristic enables one to use this detector to differentiate between particles of varying ionizing powers and energies.

The electric field strength at a distance r from the wire electrode is given by

$$E = \frac{V}{r \ln (b/a)} \tag{3.1}$$

where V is the voltage applied to the electrodes and a and b are the radii of the wire and the cylindrical electrodes, respectively. If $a = 0.01$ cm, $b = 1.0$ cm, and $V = 1000$ volts, the field in the vicinity of the central wire is of the order of 10^4 volts/cm. An incident particle causes ionization of the gas somewhere in the detector. The resulting electrons in the neighborhood of the central wire gain enough kinetic energy (because of the high field near the center)

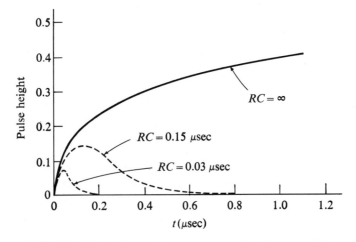

FIG. 3.4 Pulse shapes from a proportional counter for different time-constants of an externally coupled circuit. [From D. R. Carson and R. R. Wilson; *Rev. Sci. Inst.* **19**, 207 (1948).]

to cause additional ionization by further collisions. The electrons so produced cause further ionization, and so on. The overall result is the production of an avalanche of electrons, the size of which is proportional to the initial ionization or energy of the particle if the detector is operating in a proportional region. Initially, if there are n ion-pairs, and these result in the formation of mn electrons and mn positive ions, then m is called the *multiplication factor*. The value of m may be as high as 10^3.

The electrons that are attracted by the wire do not cause a drop in the potential, because their effect is neutralized by the slow-moving positive ions, which are still in the neighborhood of the central wire. It is the drifting away of the positive ions that causes the potential drop. The shape of the pulse, as shown in Fig. 3.4, depends on the time constant of the coupling circuit. Theoretical expressions for the pulse shape and the multiplication factor, m, of the proportional counter have been derived by M. Rose and S. Korff[4], and C. Montgomery and D. Montgomery[5]. There is good agreement between theory and experiment.

One big disadvantage of the proportional counter is the need for an expensive, highly stabilized power supply to maintain the proportionality characteristic.

D. GEIGER-MÜLLER COUNTER.   If the voltage applied to the electrodes of a proportional counter is increased beyond the proportionality region, the device is a Geiger-Müller counter, often called a G.M. counter, or simply a Geiger counter[6,7]. The amplitude of the output pulse-signal becomes independent of the primary ionization (Fig. 3.3). All particles in a G.M. counter, therefore, irrespective of their energy and the amount of primary ionization they may

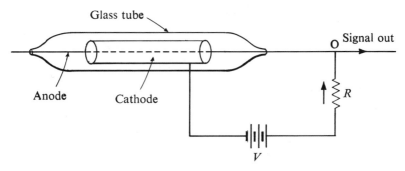

FIG. 3.5   A typical Geiger-Müller counter. A thin mica window may be provided for counting alpha or beta particles.

cause, produce a signal of the same amplitude. This property makes the Geiger-Müller counter well-suited for the detection of individual particles. The workings of the device may be understood from the following brief description.

Just like the proportional counter, the G.M. counter consists of a metal-cylinder electrode and a thin wire electrode fixed inside the cylinder. These work as a cathode and anode, respectively, and are enclosed in a thin glass tube as shown in Fig. 3.5. The tube is filled to a pressure of about 10 cm of Hg with a mixture by weight of 90 percent argon, and 10 percent of some organic vapor (such as ethyl alcohol) or some halogen (such as Cl_2 or Br_2). The advantage of using a low gas pressure in the tube (rather than atmospheric pressure as in the case of the proportional counter) is that the discharge takes place at a lower voltage. The purpose of adding alcohol or halogen will be explained later on.

A charged particle passing through the gas ionizes a gas molecule. The electron is attracted towards the central wire and the positive ion towards the cylindrical cathode. Because of a very high field near the central wire, the approaching electron gains enough kinetic energy to cause ionization of other molecules. The electrons thus emitted will cause still further ionization. In general, if the applied potential is very high (about 1000 volts), the ion multiplication continues, and a complete discharge is set up along the whole length of the electrode. This results in a sudden pulse of current in the external circuit. If the resistance, R, is large, the current creates a potential drop across the resistor, which in turn reduces the potential of the central wire. The drop in the potential extinguishes the discharge and reduces the current to zero. The dropping of the current brings the potential of the central wire back to its original value, and the tube is ready for the next event.

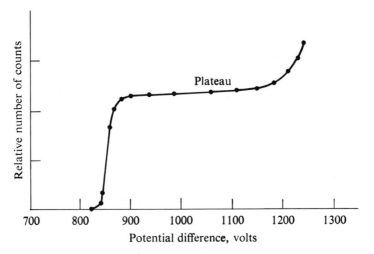

FIG. 3.6 A typical plateau of a G. M. counter is about 200 volts long and has a slope of about 1%.

A big advantage of a Geiger counter is revealed by Fig. 3.6, where a plot of counting rate versus the applied potential is shown. The potential difference at which the counting starts is called the *threshold potential.* After a very sharp rise, the counting rate remains almost constant with increasing voltage. This flat region, the *plateau,* is called the *Geiger region.* Operating the counter in this region eliminates the need for a highly regulated power supply. Most of the discharges start inside the sensitive volume, the volume inside the cylinder, but a few discharges that start outside the sensitive volume contribute to a small slope of about 1 percent per 100 volts to the otherwise flat Geiger region. The shape of the pulse produced depends on the location of the source of ionization with respect to the length of the tube as shown in Fig. 3.7[8].

One big problem in the use of the Geiger counter is the secondary discharge produced once the primary discharge sets in[2]. The 10-percent mixture by weight of the polyatomic gases reduces this unwanted effect.

Because the avalanche of electrons is formed at one spot on the electrode, the discharge does not take place uniformly along the length of the wire. Some of the electrons are absorbed, and photons are emitted. If argon atoms

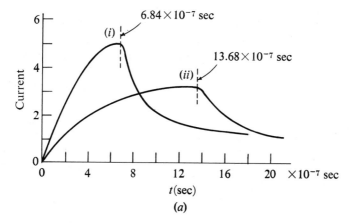

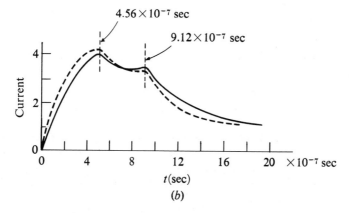

FIG. 3.7 Current pulses obtained from a G. M. counter. (a) Corresponds to the passage of alpha particles (i) from the center of the tube, (ii) from one end of the tube; (b) corresponds to the source placed at a distance of 1/3 the length of the tube measured from one end. The continuous curve is the theoretical curve; the dotted curve is experimental. The cusps in the curves correspond to the arrival of the discharge at the ends. [From Alder, Baldinger, Huber, and Metzgar, *Helv. Phys. Acta* **20**, 73 (1947).]

are the only atoms present in the tube, the photons travel to the cathode and eject electrons, which, in turn, cause secondary avalanches. If polyatomic gas atoms are present, they absorb these photons within a very short distance from the point of their emission. The gas is ionized, and further avalanches are caused, spreading the discharge along the entire length of the wire. It takes about 1 μsecond for the discharge to spread along a wire about 10 cm long.

Let us consider now the positive part of the ion-pair, i.e., the argon ion. In the absence of a polyatomic gas, an argon ion strikes the cathode, with a subsequent emission of electrons from the cathode, and these electrons, in turn, cause secondary avalanches. The polyatomic gas atoms, however, supply the argon ions with electrons, and the argon atoms are neutralized before reaching the cathode.

The positive ions of the polyatomic gas remain in circulation. These positive ions reach the cathode and pull electrons from the metal by field emission and neutralize themselves without dissociation if the polyatomic gas is a halogen, and with dissociation if the polyatomic gas is alcohol. Thus, the polyatomic gas makes the action a self-quenching one.

Note that if we use organic vapors for quenching, the molecules dissociate themselves continuously when the counter is in use, and the supply of the gas decreases. This means that the quenching gas has to be pumped into the tube continuously. On the other hand, the halogen ions are neutralized at the wall without dissociation and they serve as permanent self-quenchers.

E. Cloud Chamber.   Unlike the previously described detectors, the cloud chamber provides visible paths of the charge particles. The cloud chamber, or *expansion chamber*, was invented and first used by C. T. R. Wilson in 1912[9,10]. It is based on the principle of a supersaturated vapor condensing preferentially on charged particles.

Fig. 3.8 shows the sketch of a cloud chamber. The chamber, C, is filled with dust-free air and saturated water vapor at room temperature. The piston is allowed to fall freely resulting in the sudden expansion of the air and water vapor mixture, and hence the temperature falls below ambient room temperature. The water vapor becomes supersaturated. If at this instant a charged particle passes through the chamber producing ion-pairs, the supersaturated vapor condenses on the ions, and a trail of droplets along the path of the charged particle can be seen. The chamber may be illuminated by lights, and a photograph of the track can be taken by a camera. After a photograph is taken, the piston is pushed back to its original position and an electric field is applied to clear the chamber of all the ions. The chamber is then ready for recycling. In most cases arrangements are made so as to repeat the whole cycle automatically.

The *supersaturation ratio*, S, is defined as

$$S = \frac{P_f}{P_i} \tag{3.2}$$

where P_i and P_f are the pressures before and after expansion, respectively, and the *expansion ratio*, E, is defined as

$$E = \frac{V_f}{V_i} \tag{3.3}$$

where V_i and V_f are the volumes of the air in the chamber before and after expansion, respectively. Different gas-vapor mixtures have been prepared

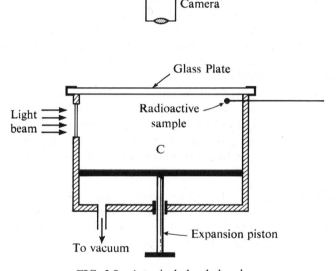

FIG. 3.8   A typical cloud chamber.

with different saturation ratios, S, and different expansion ratios, E, in order for condensation to take place under a variety of conditions. In the case of the air and water-vapor mixture, condensation takes place on the negative ions only if E is between 1.25 and 1.31, or 25 to 31 percent expansion, while condensation takes place on both negative and positive ions if E is between 1.31 and 1.38, or 31 to 38 percent expansion. For $E > 1.38$, dense cloud-formation takes place all over, even in the absence of ions. An expansion ratio of 35 percent gives good results for the air-vapor mixture for either positive or negative ions. On the other hand if the chamber is filled with an argon-alcohol mixture, an expansion of the order of 10 percent is needed to get good tracks for both positive and negative ions.

By adding additional components to the cloud chamber, it can be made more versatile. If a magnetic field is applied soon after expansion takes place in the chamber, the deflection of a particle produces a track whose radius of curvature, r, is given by

$$mv = q_0 Br \qquad (3.4)$$

where m, v, and q_0 are the mass, velocity, and charge of the particle, respectively, and B is the magnetic induction. Eq. (3.4) enables one to calculate the momentum and, hence, the energy of the particle. The direction of deflection of the particle in the magnetic field determines the sign of the charge on the particle. In addition, the energy of the particle may be calculated from its track length.

The pressure of the gas in the chamber can be increased to such an extent that some events will take place inside the chamber. If stereoscopic pictures are taken, the events can be reconstructed in three dimensions for the purpose of studying the details of interactions. These and many other details of the cloud chamber have been discussed by N. Gupta and S. Ghose[11] and by P. Blackett and G. Occhialini [12].

One of the disadvantages of the cloud chamber is that it has a very short *sensitive time* (~ 0.5 sec). This is defined as the period of time after expansion during which ionization by charged particles can cause track formation. It is quite short because the gas that has been cooled by expansion heats up again quickly by heat conducted from the outside of the chamber.

F. DIFFUSION CHAMBER.   The short sensitive time of the cloud chamber has created a need for a diffusion chamber, which is a continuously sensitive type chamber designed by A. Langsdorf[13] in 1936. A sketch of a diffusion chamber is shown in Fig. 3.9, and its principle of operation is explained below.

A chamber having upper and lower plates, is filled with a suitable gas. A container in the upper plate, which is at room temperature, is filled with a liquid whose vapors are readily condensable, such as methyl alcohol or hydrogen. The lower plate is cooled to a temperature of approximately $-60°C$ by a mixture of methyl alcohol and solid carbon dioxide. This establishes a temperature gradient between the two plates. The vapors of the liquid evaporating from the upper plate diffuse downward. Because the temperature in the lower region of the chamber is low, supersaturation of the gas is reached, and condensation will take place on any ions produced by a charged particle passing through this region of the chamber. The resulting track may be readily photographed. The ions are removed from the chamber before recycling by an application of a clearing electric field. The recycling time of the chamber is about 10–20 seconds.

The diffusion chamber in this form has been used by many research-ers[14-17]. It needs, however, more improvement to bring it to a state of perfection. Even though it is continuously sensitive, its sensitive volume is small (the lower 2- to 3-inch depth of the chamber). This makes it unsuitable for the study of cosmic rays, but it can be used successfully in a study involving pulsed accelerators. The density of the gas-vapor mixture can be increased by increasing the external pressure to several atmospheres. Even in such circumstances, the fraction of the total events that take place in the sensitive volume is very small. In the investigation of proton-proton interactions in the high energy range, for example, the diffusion chamber must be filled with hydrogen at 20 atmospheres. And under these conditions only about 4 percent of the total pictures taken show tracks of the nuclear events that took place.

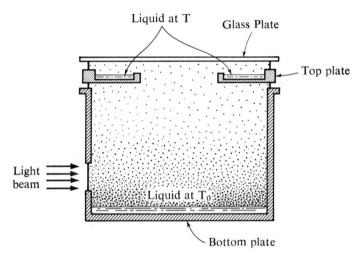

FIG. 3.9 A typical diffusion chamber. [Reprinted with permission from *Prog. Nucl. Phys.* 3, 1 (1953), Pergamon Press Ltd.]

G. BUBBLE CHAMBER[18,19].   The bubble chamber was invented by D. A. Glaser[18] in 1952. It makes use of the instability of a superheated liquid for bubble formation, just as a cloud chamber makes use of the instability of supersaturated vapors for droplet formation. Fig. 3.10 shows a sketch of a bubble chamber. The chamber is filled with a liquid (often hydrogen, deuterium, helium, or xenon) at a temperature varying from $-246°C$ for hydrogen to $-20°C$ for xenon. The liquid is heated above its normal boiling point but is kept in the liquid phase by the application of an external pressure. The first bubble chamber[18] used diethyl ether at $-140°C$ and 20 atmospheres pressure. If the pressure on the liquid is released suddenly, the unstable state of the superheated liquid will exist for a relatively long time before boiling starts. Charged particles passing through the chamber in this interval will produce ionization, and the bubbles will grow on these ions in about 10^{-2} seconds along the path of the particle. A photograph of the tracks may be taken, the ions removed, and pressure again increased before boiling starts throughout the liquid. This reduces the recycling time of the bubble chamber to a few seconds.

All surfaces inside the chamber must be extremely smooth, and there must be no contamination within the fluid, otherwise the sensitive time of the chamber will be reduced to a few milliseconds.

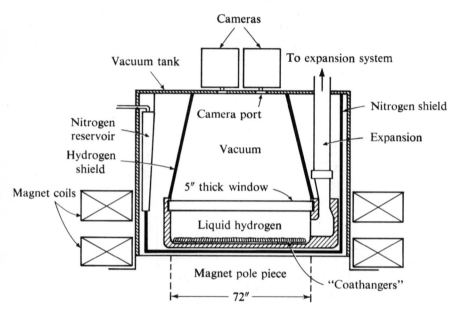

FIG. 3.10 A typical bubble chamber. [Reprinted with permission from D. V. Bugg, *Prog. Nucl. Phys.* **7**, 30 (1959), Pergamon Press Ltd.]

Even though the sensitive time of the bubble chamber is only about 20 milliseconds, it has many advantages: (1) Because of the high density of the liquid, the yield of nuclear events taking place inside the chamber is high, and it becomes possible to investigate the interactions in detail. (2) The chamber has a short recycling time of the order of a few seconds. (3) There is no limit on the depth of the sensitive volume.

H. NUCLEAR EMULSION. The use of nuclear emulsion plates dates back to the discovery of radioactivity in 1896. When an ionizing radiation passes through an emulsion, it affects the silver halide grains embedded in the gelatin. When this is followed by the process of photographic developing the affected silver halide grains are changed into black grains of metallic silver. The unaffected grain can be removed by treating the emulsion chemically in a fixing bath. A permanent image of the path of the charged particle is thus obtained[21]. These paths, though not visible to the naked eye, may be easily viewed through a microscope. The end result is the same as that of the cloud chamber or bubble chamber. With the development and perfection of other types of detectors, the use of emulsion plates was reduced to a minimum. But the progress made in the improvement of the emulsion techniques[22-26] has revived their use, especially in the field of high-energy nuclear physics and cosmic rays. In such work, emulsion-coated glass plates are used, with the emulsion thickness varying from 20 to 600 microns.

The emulsions are usually used for two different purposes. They may be used for counting the number of particles in an incident flux. In some cases, if the incident particles cause little or no ionization, the plates may be loaded with some material that interacts with the radiation to produce charged particles. Slow neutrons, for example, may be detected by loading the emulsion with approximately one percent of lithium or boron. The emulsions are also used for the study of interactions, if the particles are stopped or if they interact with other nuclei in the emulsion. From a knowledge of the grain density of the film and the range-energy relation of the particles (discussed in Chapter VII), the observed tracks can be used to identify the nature and energy of the charged particles. To construct the chronology of events, a stack of emulsions may be used.

There are many advantages to using nuclear emulsions as detectors. (1) They are simple to use, continuously sensitive, and leave a permanent record of the events. (2) They are light in weight, small in size, and low in cost. (3) Emulsions have energy- and velocity-discrimination properties over a wide range. (4) Because emulsions have a high density, they have a high stopping power, which makes them useful for investigating very high-energy particles.

There are, however, two main disadvantages of the use of emulsions as detectors. It takes too much time to scan the emulsions in order to measure the track length and the scattering angles, and because of the short lengths of the tracks inside the emulsion, very high magnetic fields are required to cause any appreciable curvatures in order to make the results reliable[27]. In many cases, especially in connection with high-energy accelerators, the particles are deflected in an external magnetic field before entering the emulsion. Thus, only particles of a fixed ratio of momentum and charge are received on the emulsion plate. Such methods have been employed by C. Powell[28] in the study of mesons.

I. SCINTILLATION COUNTER. Several substances[29], among them sodium iodide, cesium iodide, anthracene, napthalene, and phenanthrene, when struck by a single charged particle, x-ray, or gamma-ray, produce a flash of light. Such substances are called *scintillators*. These light flashes are converted into electrical pulses that may be amplified and counted. This arrangement for detection and counting is known as a *scintillation counter*. Recently, liquid scintillators have been used for special purposes.

The scintillation counters have several advantages over the gas-filled counters. (1) Because the sensitive volume is usually in the form of a solid, the efficiency for the detection of x-rays or gamma rays is very high as compared to the Geiger-counter efficiency of 1 percent (for x-rays). (2) The resolving time of the counter varies from 10^{-6} seconds for some inorganic crystals

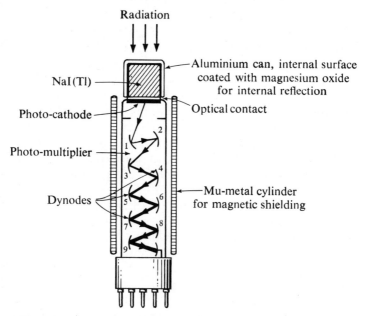

FIG. 3.11   A NaI (Tl) scintillation detector. The number of electrons ejected from the cathode is multiplied as they leave the successive dynodes.

to 10^{-9} seconds for some organic crystals. Such short resolving times allow for high-speed counting without losses. (3) The height of the output pulse from the scintillation counter can be made directly proportional to the energy of incident gamma rays. (4) The use of thin windows is eliminated because the source of radiation may be kept very close to the solid scintillator or sometimes even inside it.

We shall now explain the working of a scintillation counter[30], using a single crystal of NaI(Tl) (sodium iodide, thallium activated) as a scintillator. Because a NaI(Tl) crystal is hygroscopic, it is sealed on all sides with aluminum foil except for one side that has an optical light-tight contact with a photo-multiplier tube (Fig. 3.11). The inside of the foil is coated with magnesium oxide, which serves as a light reflector. The initial ionization caused by a charged particle, or a photon, creates electrons inside the crystal. These electrons, in the process of combination with the atoms and the molecules of the crystal, emit light in the visible region from about 3300 Å to about 5000 Å. Because the scintillators are transparent to their own light[31], the light emitted from the crystal and that reflected from the sides falls on the photocathode of the photomultiplier tube. The surface of the photocathode, made of a thin layer of cesium-antimony alloy, emits photoelectrons because of the light. The photomultiplier operates at a voltage of about 800 to 1500 volts in such a way that there is a successive increase in voltage on each dynode. This results in a successive multiplication of the number of electrons as they travel from the photocathode to the last dynode. A multiplication or an overall gain (i.e., the number of electrons emitted at the last dynode for each electron emitted from the photocathode) of about 10^6 to 10^7 is possible. The pulse height resulting from this burst of electrons is proportional to the energy of the incident particle or photon. These pulses may be amplified and counted by a scalar. In order to suppress the effect of the earth's magnetic field, the photomultiplier is surrounded by a magnetic shield. In some cases where it may be necessary to keep the detector in a strong magnetic field, the light from the scintillator is conveyed to a photomultiplier by means of a plastic light-pipe.

The NaI(Tl) crystal is used most often in the detection of x-rays or gamma rays. This crystal has a very good *energy resolution*—defined as the energy width at the half-maximum divided by the energy at the maximum. With a crystal of 2-inch diameter and 2-inch length, it is possible to get an energy resolution for the 661 kev gamma ray from Cs^{137} of the order of about 8 percent. In some experiments where energy resolution is not the aim but very high counting rates are involved, organic crystals are used. For beta detection, crystals (such as anthracene) that are insensitive to gamma rays may be used.

J. SOLID STATE DETECTOR.   The use of some semiconductor (or dielectric) crystals as detectors was demonstrated by P. Van Heerden[32] in 1945 and D. Wooldridge, *et al.*[33] in 1947. Since then, semiconductors have been used for the detection of charged particles in several ways[34–38]. A germanium P-N junction diode has been used as an alpha-particle detector by K. McKay[34] and R. Bomal, *et al.*[38]. Very recently a diffused-junction silicon detector has been developed[39] and used successfully for charged-particle counting. We shall describe in some detail the workings of such a solid-state detector.

An atom of silicon has four valence electrons and, as a result, it is a poor conductor of electricity at room temperature. The conduction band of silicon lies 1.1 ev above the valence band. If an atom of phosphorous, which has five valence electrons, is introduced into silicon, four electrons are used up in bond formation while the fifth electron goes near the conduction band (Fig. 3.12a). The phosphorous is the donor, and the silicon, thus containing traces of phosphorous, becomes N-type silicon. Similarly, if a boron atom, which. has three valence electrons, is introduced into silicon, one of the valence electrons of silicon jumps to the boron atom, and lies just above the valence band of silicon, thus creating a "hole" in the valence band of silicon (Fig. 3.12b). The boron is the acceptor, and the silicon, thus containing traces of boron, becomes P-type silicon. N-type and P-type silicon are fused together to form a single crystal called a P-N junction. A contact potential is established between the two types of materials, the P-type being at a lower

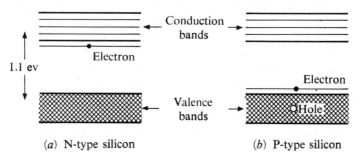

(*a*) N-type silicon   (*b*) P-type silicon

FIG. 3.12   Valence and bound-electron diagram for silicon. (*a*) Silicon containing a trace of phosphorus is called N-type silicon (the donors) and (*b*) silicon containing a trace of boron is called P-type silicon (the acceptor).

potential with respect to N-type. The free electrons of the donor go to the acceptor, thus making the region a nonconductor. This region, the *depletion region*, can be increased still further by the application of an external voltage. The device is shown in Fig. 3.13. The thickness of the depletion region is the sum of the t_N and t_P thicknesses, where

$$t_N = \frac{\epsilon V}{2\pi e N_N} \qquad (3.5)$$

$$t_P = \frac{\epsilon V}{2\pi e N_P} \qquad (3.6)$$

V is the applied voltage, e the electron charge, ϵ the dielectric constant of silicon, and N_N and N_P are the number of N-type and P-type atoms, respectively, in a unit volume of silicon.

When an ionizing particle enters from the N-type layer and stops in the depletion region, free electrons and holes (positive ions) will be formed. The electrons and the holes move at once towards the N-type (positive) and P-type (negative) layers, respectively. This results in a potential drop across the junction, which is conveyed to the amplifier. The size of the pulse produced is proportional to the energy of the incident particle, provided the particle loses all its energy in the depletion region. An important feature of such a detector is that the collection time of the electrons and of the holes is very short (less than 10^{-8} second), because the positive ions do not move bodily. They contribute their share of current by capturing electrons from the neutral atoms, for example, on their right. The neutral atom that has lost an electron to the hole is now a positive ion. Thus, in this process, the hole has moved to the right and the electron to the left.

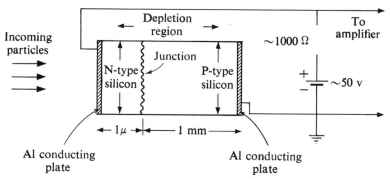

FIG. 3.13   A typical silicon P-N junction detector. The junction is about 1 micron from the surface and the sensitive volume is about 1 mm. [From Friedland, Mayer and Wiggins, Nucleonics **18**, 2, 54 (1960).]

This counter has proved to be useful for detecting heavy charged particles such as protons and alpha particles. A typical energy resolution[39] for 5.3 Mev alpha particles is found to be 0.6 percent in a 300 ohm-cm detector with a 6-volt bias. Crystals having depletion depths of the order of 3 to 6 mm have been used for beta- and gamma-ray spectroscopy as well. For example, a lithum-drifted germanium crystal, when used at a temperature of 77° K, gives a resolution of ~ 6 kev for 661 kev gamma rays of Cs^{137}. For comparison Fig. 3.14 shows a gamma spectrum of Co^{60} obtained by using Li-drifted Ge and the scintillation NaI(Tl) crystals. The excellent resolution of the solid-state crystal (Li-drifted Ge) is quite obvious.

There are several advantages to using semiconductor detectors. (1) They are small in size. (2) They have a fast response. (3) They eliminate the need for a high-voltage supply. (4) They can be designed to give a high-energy resolution response proportional to the incident energy. One big disadvantage of these detectors is that they have a very low efficiency of detection.

K. THE SPARK CHAMBER[40,41].   Unlike other detectors, the development of the spark chamber has been the result of many investigators[40]. In a recently improved form it has proven to be useful in high-energy nuclear physics for the investigation of subatomic particles.

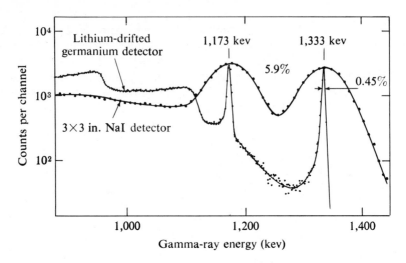

FIG. 3.14   Gamma-ray spectra of Co⁶⁰.

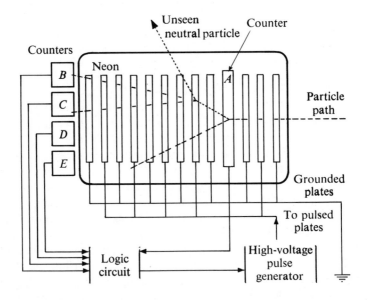

FIG. 3.15   A diagram of a spark chamber consisting of thin metal plates surrounded by neon. The logic circuit triggers the high-voltage pulse generator, which in turn applies a high-voltage pulse to alternate plates. The sparks produced along the path of ionization are photographed. [From G. K. O'Neill, *Scientific American*, August, 41 (1962).]

The first practical spark chamber was constructed by S. Fukui and S. Miyamoto in 1959. Fig. 3.15 shows a sketch of a typical spark chamber. It consists of a series of thin metal plates surrounded by an inert gas, usually neon. Chambers have been constructed with a number of gaps between the plates that ranges from 6 to 128, with the distance between the plates ranging between 2 and 20 mm. One such chamber has a volume of 2 cubic feet with 128 gaps of 3 mm each. A very high voltage, 10 to 15 kv, is applied to alternate plates. The passage of a charged particle leaves a trail of ionization behind it. The sparks are produced along the ionization path that make the track visible. A constant clearing field is applied at all times in order to remove the ions.

Usually, the chamber is provided with one or more counters, and a logic circuit is provided for identifying the arrival of a particle of interest. The logic circuit triggers the generator, which sends a high voltage pulse to alternate plates. Fig. 3.16 shows the path of a particle in a spark chamber. In many cases a magnetic field is applied, and the measurement of the resultant curvature of the path gives an accurate measurement of the momentum.

The spark chamber has the same time resolution as the ionization chamber, scintillation counter, and others. It locates the path of the particles with the excellent spatial resolution common to the visual techniques (cloud chamber, nuclear emulsions). In the field of high-energy physics, the spark chamber has two big advantages over the bubble chamber. First, both the triggering and the decision to photograph selected events can be made after the events have occurred. Triggering is impossible in the case of the bubble chamber. Second, the ions are removed by the clearing field within one to two microseconds, hence the pictures show the events that took place in the previous period of 1 to 2 microseconds. A disadvantage is that the sparks scatter 15 to 20 thousandths of an inch, and their path-uncertainty increases as the path of the particles becomes parallel to the plates.

L. ČERENKOV DETECTOR[42]. It was demonstrated by P. Čerenkov[43] in 1934 that a particle moving through a dielectric medium with a velocity greater than the phase-velocity of light in that medium gives out a very weak radiation in the visible region. This radiation is different in nature from that of fluorescence as well as Bremsstrahlung. Unlike Bremsstrahlung, it does not depend on the atomic number of the material or the mass of the charged particle. The emission of Čerenkov radiation may be explained in the following way.

An electromagnetic pulse (time-varying field) associated with fast-moving charged particles causes polarization of the atoms of the medium by displacing the bound electrons along its path. The time variation of the polarization produced by the field causes the atoms to radiate electromagnetic waves. If the particle is moving slowly, the radiation reaching a distant point interferes

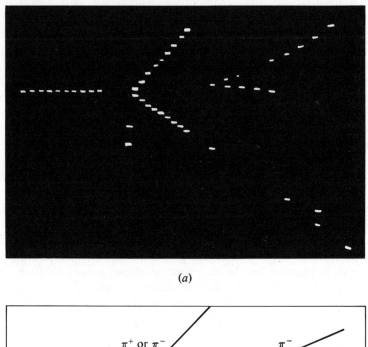

(a)

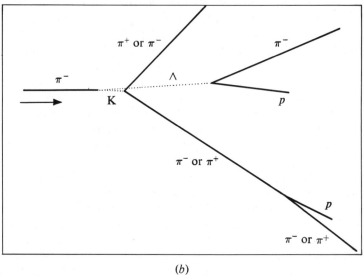

(b)

FIG. 3.16 Tracks of particles in a spark chamber, (a) actual photograph and (b) the schematic outline. [From G. K. O'Neill, *Scientific American*, August, 42 (1962).]

destructively, and the resultant intensity is zero. If the velocity of the particle, however, is greater than the phase-velocity of light, the energy lost is radiated coherently and the resultant intensity at a distant observation point may not be zero. The condition for coherence may be obtained from Huygen's construction, shown in Fig. 3.17. In time Δt, the particle travels a distance

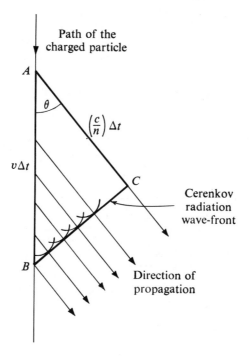

FIG. 3.17 Condition of coherence from a Huygen construction.

$AB = v\Delta t = \beta c \Delta t \left(\text{where } \beta = \dfrac{v}{c} \right)$, while the light travels a distance $AC =$

$(c/n)\Delta t$, where n is the refractive index of the medium. Thus $\cos \theta = \dfrac{AC}{AB}$ is given by

$$\cos \theta = \frac{1}{\beta n} \tag{3.7}$$

Eq. (3.7) puts a limit on β(or v) for the production and detection of Čerenkov radiation.

For a given n,

$$\beta_{min} = 1/n \tag{3.8}$$

and below this value no radiation will take place. The maximum value of θ is obtained when for a given n, β is 1, i.e.,

$$\theta_{max} = \cos^{-1}\left(\frac{1}{n}\right) \tag{3.9}$$

For the case of lucite where $n = 1.5$, $\theta_{max} = 48°$.

Thus the energy lost is radiated in coherence in a cone of half-angle θ, whose axis is the path of the particles. The light emitted, which is in the visible region, is detected by means of a photomultiplier or a photographic recording. Fig. 3.18 shows an improved form of the apparatus used by Mather[44], in

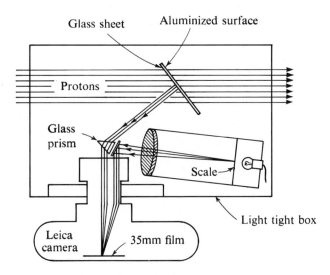

FIG. 3.18 Precision instrument developed by Mather for detection of Čerenkov radiation from protons. [From: R. L. Mather, *Phys. Rev.* **84**, 181 (1951).]

which thin flint-glass, about 2/3 mm thick, of $n = 1.88$ is utilized. The apparatus is designed to minimize the dispersion effects. Fig. 3.19 shows the results of a 340 Mev proton recorded with a microphotometer tracer. The accuracy is about ± 0.8 Mev.

The chief advantages of this counter are as follows. (1) There is no emission of radiation for particles with velocities less than certain minimums given by Eq. (3.8), i.e., $\beta_{min} = \frac{1}{n}$ or $v_{min} = \frac{c}{n}$. Hence, this device may be used as a threshold detector. (2) The pulses obtained from the detector have a very fast rise and decay time (much less than 10^{-10} second). (3) It can discriminate between particles of different masses having either the same energy or range. (4) The velocity of the particle is a function of the angle of emission of radiation.

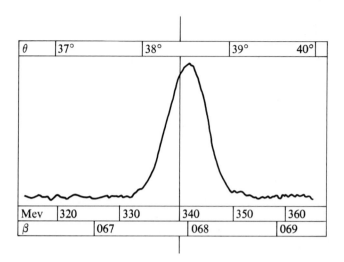

θ	37°		38°		39°	40°

Mev	320		330		340	350		360
β		067			068			069

FIG. 3.19 A densitometer trace for 340 Mev protons
Čerenkov radiation photograph. [From: R. L. Mather, *Phys.
Rev.* **84**, 181 (1951).]

3. STATISTICAL ERRORS

Because of the random nature of the decay process, the statistical fluctuations
in the count rate must be calculated by using the laws of probability. If an
observation is made of the count rate of radiation emitted by a radioactive
sample, subsequent rates will fluctuate from the one observed earlier, even
after making all the corrections due to the decay process. There is no way to
determine the true count rate, but we may talk of the true average count
rate, which is an average of the counting rate made over a very long period of
time.

Let X be the number of nuclei present in a given sample and let $\bar{n}$ be
the average disintegration rate. The probability, $P(n)$, that the observed count
rate will be n may be described in most cases by the Poisson distribution[45]

$$P(n) = \frac{\bar{n}^n e^{-\bar{n}}}{n!} \tag{3.10}$$

The probability gives the fraction of the total number of determinations in
which we may expect to observe n counts. In counting statistics it is simpler to
use a Gaussian or normal distribution rather than a Poisson distribution.
For n sufficiently large, the Poisson distribution given by Eq. (3.10) reduces to
the Gaussian distribution

$$G(n) = \frac{1}{\sqrt{2\pi\bar{n}}} e^{-(\bar{n}-n)^2/2\bar{n}} \tag{3.11}$$

Even for $\bar{n} = 20$, the two distributions are very similar as shown in Fig. 3.20[46].

The probability $G(|\bar{n} - n|)$ that in a determination the error will exceed amount $|\bar{n} - n|)$ is given by

$$G(|\bar{n} - n|) = 2 \int_{|\bar{n} - n|}^{\infty} \left[\frac{1}{\sqrt{2\pi\bar{n}}} e^{-(\bar{n} - n)^2/2\bar{n}} \right] dn \qquad (3.12)$$

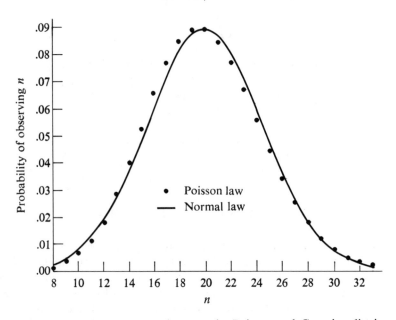

FIG. 3.20   The agreement between the Poisson and Gaussian distributions. [From Alan A. Jarrett, AECU-262.]

The value of $G(|\bar{n} - n|)$ may be evaluated in terms of the number of times the error $|\bar{n} - n|$ exceeds $\sqrt{\bar{n}}$. The quantity $\sqrt{\bar{n}}$ is often denoted by σ; the actual definition of σ, however, is indicated below:

The *standard deviation* or, *root-mean-square deviation*, is a special form of the average deviation from the mean, and is computed by taking the quadratic mean of the deviations from the arithmetic mean, i.e.,

$$\sigma = \sqrt{\frac{\Sigma(\bar{n} - n)^2}{N}} \qquad (3.13)$$

where N is the number of observations. σ may also be defined by

$$\sigma^2 = \int_0^{\infty} (\bar{n} - n)^2 P(n) \, dn \qquad (3.14)$$

which, after substituting for P(n), gives

$$\sigma \approx \sqrt{\bar{n}} \qquad (3.15)$$

Another quantity, beside σ, that is commonly used in describing error is the *probable error*, p, given by

$$p = 0.67\sqrt{\bar{n}} = 0.67\sigma \qquad (3.16)$$

σ, p, and other errors are represented graphically for different counting rates in Fig. 3.21 (Reference 46).

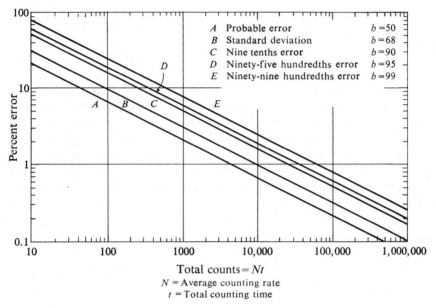

FIG. 3.21   The determination of the error of counting. [From Alan A. Jarrett, AECU-262.]

As an example, suppose 40,000 counts were observed in 10 minutes. The standard deviation is $\sqrt{40,000} = 200$, and the probable error, from Eq. (3.16,), is 134. Thus, the measured value is $(4,000 \pm 20)$ counts/minute, if standard deviation is used; or $(4,000 \pm 13.4)$ counts/minute, if probable error is used.

In a measurement that is a function of two counting rates n_1 and n_2 with standard deviations σ_1 and σ_2, the total deviation σ is given by the following.

For addition or subtraction

$$\sigma = \sqrt{\sigma_1^2 + \sigma_2^2} \qquad (3.17)$$

For multiplication

$$\sigma = n_1 n_2 \sqrt{\left(\frac{\sigma_1}{n_1}\right)^2 + \left(\frac{\sigma_2}{n_2}\right)^2} \tag{3.18}$$

For division

$$\sigma = \frac{n_1}{n_2} \sqrt{\left(\frac{\sigma_1}{n_1}\right)^2 + \left(\frac{\sigma_2}{n_2}\right)^2} \tag{3.19}$$

Further evaluation of Eq. (3.12) and Fig. 3.21 implies that if the error in the observation is one standard deviation, then there is a 31.73% chance that n is outside the limit $n \pm \sigma$. For one p error, the chance is 50% that n lies outside $n \pm p$.

4. LEAST SQUARE FITTING

The *least square method* is used for fitting the best curve to a given set of experimental points. Suppose that it is required to fit a straight line $y = a + bx$ to the experimental points $(x_1, y_1), (x_2, y_2) \ldots (x_n, y_n)$. We want to find the values of a and b that give the best fit to the experimental points. The principle of least squares requires that the sums of the squares of the deviations of the actual from the theoretical values be a minimum. Let d represent the difference between the actual value y and the theoretical value y_t, i.e.,

$$d = y - y_t$$

then according to the principle of least squares we should have

$$\Sigma(d^2) = \text{a minimum}$$

or

$$\Sigma(y - y_t)^2 = \text{a minimum} \tag{3.20}$$

where

$$y = a + bx \tag{3.21}$$

Substituting Eq. (3.21) into Eq. (3.20), differentiating with respect to a and b, and equating the result to zero gives

$$\frac{\delta \Sigma(y - y_t)^2}{\delta a} = 0 = 2Na - 2\Sigma y + 2b\Sigma x$$

and

$$\frac{\delta \Sigma(y - y_t)^2}{\delta b} = 0 = 2b\Sigma x^2 - 2\Sigma xy + 2a\Sigma x$$

or

$$\Sigma y = Na + b\Sigma x \tag{3.22}$$

$$\Sigma(xy) = a\Sigma x + b\Sigma x^2 \tag{3.23}$$

These two equations, called the *normal equations*, may now be solved for the two required constants a and b.

The method may be generalized for any standard equation. The following two steps are necessary to set up the normal equations. Multiply the standard equation by the coefficients of the constants one by one, and sum up the equations so obtained over all the observations. For example, the normal equations for

$$\log y = a + b \log x$$

are

$$\Sigma \log y = Na + b \Sigma \log x$$

$$\Sigma (\log x \log y) = a \Sigma \log x + b \Sigma (\log x)^2$$

PROBLEMS

1. An alpha particle loses all its energy in the gas of an ionization chamber and produces 12,000 ion pairs. (a) What will be the total electric charge of either sign collected on the plates? (b) If the ionization chamber has a capacitance of 50 $\mu\mu f$ and $V = 250$ volts, what change in the potential will result?

2. 4.5-Mev alpha particles are entering an ionization chamber (filled with air) at a rate of 300 per second. If we assume that all the energy is lost inside the chamber, what is the average current in the ionization chamber? Assume that, on the average, the energy loss by an alpha particle to produce an ion pair is 35.2 ev.

3. In the situation of problem 2, what is the value of the resistor that must be put in series with the ionization chamber so that the potential drop across the resistor is (a) 5 volts? (b) 1 volt? (c) 0.1 volt? Which of the three values is preferable, and why?

4. Derive the expression for the electric field E given in Eq. (3.1), i.e.,

$$E = V/[r \ln (b/a)]$$

Also calculate the value of the radius, r, of a cylinder so that half of the electrostatic energy lies inside this cylinder.

5. In problem 4, calculate the force acting on a charge q at a distance d from the center of the wire.

6. A Geiger tube is operating at 1200 volts potential difference between the electrodes. The central wire of the tube has a diameter of 0.3 mm and the outer cylinder has a diameter of 6 cm. What is the electric-field strength at the two electrodes?

7. Alpha particles are incident on the mica window of a Geiger counter at a steady rate of 800 counts per minute. If 10^7 electrons are collected by the tube in each discharge, what is the average steady current in the tube?

8. What is the life time (time in which all the self-quencher will be used up) of a Geiger tube if its volume is 50 cm^3, and it is filled at a pressure of 10 cm of Hg with a mixture of 90% by weight of argon and 10% by weight of ethyl alcohol?

Assume that the Geiger tube is being used for counting 1 Mev electrons (from a 1 μc source), which lose energy, on the average of 26 ev to produce an ion pair.

9. A radioactive source placed inside a cloud chamber emits alpha particles of 5 Mev and electrons of 1.5 Mev. What are the values of the magnetic field required to bend the track of these particles in arcs of radii 5 cm and 10 cm, respectively?

10. In a certain counting determination 548,746 counts were registered in 10 minutes. Calculate the most probable error and the standard deviation. If the background counting rate is 1200 counts per 10 minutes, what will be the standard deviation of the counting determination?

11. The resolving time, 2τ, of a coincidence circuit [Chapters 8, 9] is determined by the expression

$$2\tau = N_a/N_1 N_2$$

where N_a is called the accidental coincidence counting rate and N_1, N_2 are the single count rates. If in a 10-minute period $N_a = 241$, $N_1 = 12,062$ and $N_2 = 20,596$, what is the value of 2τ and its standard deviation?

12. A counter is registering 2575 counts per minute at a steady rate. How long should we count in order to achieve 90%, 95%, 99% accuracy?

13. By the method of least square fitting, calculate the value of a_2 and a_4 in the following equation

$$W(\theta) = 1 + a_2 \cos^2 \theta + a_4 \cos^4 \theta$$

from the following data:

$$W(180°) = 1.330$$
$$W(150°) = 1.101$$
$$W(120°) = 1.042$$
$$W(\ 90°) = 1.000$$

14. By the method of least square fitting, calculate the value of the decay constant, λ, in equation

$$N(t) = N_0\, e^{-\lambda t}$$

(where N_0 is the counts per minute at $t = 0$ and $N(t)$ the number of counts per minute after time t) from the following data:

$N(0)\ \ = 605$	$N(50) = 364$
$N(10) = 530$	$N(60) = 330$
$N(20) = 497$	$N(70) = 297$
$N(30) = 434$	$N(80) = 268$
$N(40) = 402$	

Also determine σ_λ, i.e., the standard deviation of λ.

15. By the method of least square fitting, calculate the value of a_0, a_2, a_4 in equation

$$W(\theta) = a_0 + a_2 \cos^2 \theta + a_4 \cos^4 \theta$$

from the data:

$W(180°) = 1.0392$	$W(120°) = 1.0097$
$W(165°) = 1.0464$	$W(105°) = 0.9990$
$W(150°) = 1.0354$	$W(\ 90°) = 1.0000$
$W(135°) = 1.0286$	

REFERENCES

1. Lauritsen, C. C., *Rev. Sci. Inst.*, **8**, p. 438, (1937).
2. Carson, D. R., and R. R. Wilson, *Rev. Sci. Inst.*, **19**, p. 207, (1948).
3. Rossi, B. B., and H. H. Staub, *Ionization Chambers and Counters*, McGraw Hill Book Co., 1949.
4. Rose, M. E., and S. Korff, *Phys. Rev.*, **57**, p. 850, (1941).
5. Montgomery, C. G., and D. D. Montgomery, *Phys. Rev.*, **57**, p. 1030, (1940).
6. Geiger, H., and W. Müller, *Z. Physik*, **29**, p. 839, (1928), **30**, p. 483, (1929).
7. Rutherford, E., and H. Geiger, *Proc. Roy. Soc.*, **A81**, p. 141, (1908).
8. Alder, A., E. Baldinger, P. Huber, and F. Metzger, *Helv. Phys. Acta*, **20**, p. 73, (1947).
9. Wilson, C. T. R., *Proc. Roy. Soc.*, **87**, p. 277, (1912).
10. Wilson, C. T. R., *Proc. Roy. Soc.*, **104**, p. 1, (1923).
11. Gupta, N. N. Dass, and S. K. Ghosh, *Revs. Mod. Phys.*, 18, p. 225, (1948).
12. Blackett, P. M. S., and G. P. S. Occhialini, *Proc. Roy. Soc.*, **A139**, p. 699, (1933).
13. Langsdorf, A., *Phys. Rev.*, **49**, p. 422, (1936).
14. Needles, T. A., and C. E. Nielsen, *Rev. Sci. Inst.*, **21**, p. 976, (1950).
15. Cowan, E. W., *Rev. Sci. Inst.*, **21**, p. 991, (1950).
16. Shutter, R. P., *Rev. Sci. Inst.*, **22**, p. 730, (1951).
17. Snowden, M., *Prog. Nucl. Phys.*, **3**, p. 1, (1953).
18. Glaser, D. A., *Phys. Rev.*, **91**, p. 762, (1953).
19. Dodd, C., *Prog. Nucl. Phys.*, **5**, p. 142, (1956).
20. Slatis, H., *Nucl. Inst. and Methods*, **5**, p. 1, (1959).
21. Shapiro, M. M., *Revs. Mod. Phys.*, **13**, p. 58, (1941).
22. Lattes, C. M. G., H. Muirhead, G. P. S. Occhialini, and C. F. Powell, *Nature*, **159**, p. 694, (1947).
23. Berriman, R. W., *Nature*, **161**, p. 432, (1948).
24. Spence, J., J. Castle, and J. H. Webb, *Phys. Rev.*, **74**, p. 704, (1948).
25. Brown, R., U. Camerini, P. H. Fowler, H. Muirhead, C. F. Powell, and D. M. Ritson, *Nature*, **163**, p. 47, (1949).
26. J. Rotbalt, *Prog. Nucl. Phys.*, **1**, p. 37, (1950).
27. Dilworth, C. C., S. J. Goldsack, Y. Goldschmidt-Clermont, and F. Levy, *Phil. Mag.*, **41**, p. 1032, (1950).
28. Powell, C. P., *Rep. Prog. Phys.*, **13**, p. 350, (1950).
29. Garlick, G. F. G., *Prog. Nucl. Phys.*, **2**, p. 51, (1952).
30. Siegbahn, K., ed., *Alpha- Beta- and Gamma-ray Spectroscopy*, Chapter V. New York: Interscience Publishers, Inc., 1965.
31. Kallmann, H., *Nature U. Tech.* July, 1947.
32. Van Heerden, P. J., *The Crystal Counter*, Utrecht Dissertation, (1945).

33. Wooldridge, D. E., A. J. Akearn, and J. A. Burton, *Phys. Rev.*, **71**, p. 913, (1947).
34. McKay, K. G., *Phys. Rev.*, **84**, p. 829, (1951).
35. Mayer, J. W., B. R. Gossick, *Rev. Sci. Instr.*, **27**, p. 407, (1956).
36. Walter, F. J., J. W. T. Dabbs, L. D. Robert, and H. W. Wright, ORNL 58-11-99, (1958).
37. McKenzie, J. M., D. A. Bromley, *Phys. Rev. Letters* **2**, p. 303, (1959).
38. Bomal, R., L. Koch, N. Van Dong, and C. L. Schneider, *Electronique Nucleaire*, p. 137. (Vienna: Agence internal de l'energie atomique, 1959.)
39. Friedland, S. S., J. W. Mayer, and J. S. Wiggins, *Nucleonics*, **18**, pp. 2, 54, (1960).
40. O'Neill, G. K., *Scientific American*, August, p. 37, (1962).
41. Beall, E. F., B. Cork, P. G. Murphy, and W. A. Wenzel, *Nuovo Cimento*, **20**, p. 502, (1961).
42. Jelley, J. V., *Prog. Nucl. Phys.*, **3**, p. 84, (1953).
43. Čerenkov, P. A., *C. R. Acad. Sci.* (USSR) **21**, p. 451, (1934); *Phys. Rev.*, **52**, p. 376, (1937).
44. Mather, R. L., *Phys. Rev.*, **84**, p. 181, (1951).
45. Rainwater, L. J., and C. S. Wu, *Nucleonics*, **1**, p. 60, (1947).
46. Jarrett, Alan A., *Statistical Methods Used in the Measurement of Radioactivity*, AECU-262.

SUGGESTIONS FOR FURTHER READING

1. Staub, H., *Detection Methods, in Experimental Nuclear Physics*, ed., E. Segre, Vol. I, Part I. New York: John Wiley & Sons, Inc., 1953.
2. Fretter, W. B., *Introduction to Experimental Physics*. New York: Prentice-Hall, Inc., 1954.
3. Rossi, B. B., and H. S. Staub, *Ionization Chambers and Counters*. New York: McGraw Hill Book Co., 1949.
4. Sharpe, J., *Nuclear Radiation Detectors*. London: Methuen and Co., Ltd., 1955.
5. Price, J. W., *Nuclear Radiation Detection*. New York: McGraw Hill Book Co., 1958.
6. Wilson, J. G., *Principles of Cloud Chamber Technique*. Cambridge University Press, 1951.
7. Slatis, H., On Bubble Chambers, *Nucl. Instrum. and Methods*, **5**, p. 1, 1959.
8. Snowden, M., *The Diffusion Chamber*, *Prog. Nuclear Physics*, **3**, p. 1, 1953.
9. Yuan, L. C. L., and C. S. Wu, Ed., *Methods of Experimental Physics*, **5A**. Academic Press, 1961.
10. Siegbahn, K., (Ed.), *Alpha-, Beta- and Gamma-ray Spectroscopy*. New York: Interscience Publishing, 1965, and Amsterdam, Holland: North Holland Publishing Co.

11. Shive, J. N., *Semi-Conductor Devices*. Princeton, New Jersey: D. Van Nostrand Co., 1959.

12. Dabbs, J. W. T., and F. J. Walter, *Semi-conductor Nuclear Particle Detector*. Washington, D. C.: National Academy of Sciences, National Research Council, 1961.

13. Jarrett, A. A., *Statistical Methods Used in the Measurement of Radioactivity with Some Useful Graphs and Nomographs*, AECU-262.

IV

NUCLEAR
REACTIONS I

1. INTRODUCTION

Chapter II was devoted to the study of the disintegration of natural radioactive elements and the laws that govern these decays. In this chapter we are interested in a process which may be considered the opposite of a decay process. Consider an element that is bombarded by fast-moving particles, such as neutrons, protons, or electrons. We wish to find whether or not certain particles will be captured by target nuclei. It is found experimentally that if these moving particles have sufficiently high energies, irrespective of the charge they carry, they will come close to the nuclei and will be captured. This indicates that when a particle reaches the vicinity of the nucleus, the forces which act between them are attractive forces. A γ-ray or some other particle altogether different from the incident particle may be emitted by the nucleus within a very short time ($< 10^{-13}$ sec) after the capture of the incident particle. This type process is a nuclear reaction. The nucleus, after emitting a particle or gamma ray, may or may not be stable. In case it is unstable, or radioactive, it will decay with a certain half-life and obey the same laws as do the natural radioactive elements.

The nucleus formed after bombardment is, in most cases, different from the target nucleus (it has a different mass number and atomic number). Such a change of the target nucleus is a *transmutation* and the reaction itself is called a *transmutation reaction.*

The importance of the study of nuclear reactions lies in the fact that most of the information about the properties of the nucleus (such as the size, the charge distribution, and the nature of the nuclear forces) is obtained from these investigations. For every nuclear reaction we can write a reaction equation somewhat similar to a chemical equation. The nuclear reaction equation is written as

$$x + X \rightarrow Y + y \tag{4.1}$$

which means that when a particle x strikes a target nucleus X, the outcome of the nuclear reaction is a recoil nucleus Y and a particle y. In many cases more than one type of particle may be given out. The nuclear reaction represented by Eq. (4.1) is also denoted by

$$X (x, y) \ Y \tag{4.2}$$

One example of a nuclear reaction, which we have seen in the history of the discovery of the neutron in Chapter II, is α-particles coming from radioactive polonium bombarding a beryllium ($_4Be^9$) target. A new nucleus $_6C^{12}$ is formed and neutrons are given out.

$$_2He^4 + _4Be^9 \rightarrow _6C^{12} + _0n^1 \tag{4.3}$$

Another reaction we came across in Chapter 2 is

$$_2He^4 + _5B^{11} \rightarrow _7N^{14} + _0n^1 \tag{4.4}$$

The first transmutation of a target was performed by E. Rutherford[1] in 1919, in which a nitrogen target was bombarded by alpha particles obtained from a natural radioactive source.

$$_2He^4 + _7N^{14} \rightarrow _8O^{17} + _1H^1 \tag{4.5}$$

Nuclear reactions can be initiated not only by the particles given out by radioactive elements, as is the case in the examples given above, but also by high energy particles and gamma rays produced by linear accelerators, cyclotrons, nuclear reactors, and other machines producing particles with high energies. The first nuclear reaction using artificially accelerated particles was observed by J. Cockcroft and E. Walton[2] in 1930. This reaction is represented by

$$_3Li^7 + p \rightarrow _2He^4 + \alpha \tag{4.6}$$

The accelerated protons (p or $_1H^1$) strike a lithium target, and the outcome of the reaction is two α-particles (denoted as a recoil helium nucleus and an α-particle).

The nuclear reactions given above are also denoted by $_4Be^9$ (α, n) $_6C^{12}$, $_5B^{11}$ (α, n) $_7N^{14}$, $_7N^{14}$ (α, p) $_8O^{17}$ and $_3Li^7$ (p, α) $_2He^4$, respectively. There are many other types of reactions that have been studied since 1930 and the detailed discussion of some of these will be taken up in later sections.

We are interested in the study of nuclear reactions from two view points:

A. The conditions under which different reactions take place. In many cases it is possible to predict the outcome of a nuclear reaction, but we shall limit ourselves to looking into the conditions necessary to start a nuclear reaction.

B. The determination of the probability of an incoming particle being absorbed by the target nucleus. This probability is called the *cross section* of a given nuclear reaction. The cross section σ has the same significance in nuclear reactions as the decay constant λ has in the decay process.

We shall devote this chapter to the discussion of the experimental aspects of these topics while the theoretical aspects will be discussed in Chapter XI.

2. ENERGY CONSERVATION IN NUCLEAR REACTIONS

As already stated, a nuclear reaction is written, in general, as

$$x + X \rightarrow Y + y \tag{4.1}$$

Let us assume that x and X are far apart and do not exert any force on each other. This implies that the system does not have any potential energy. Let us further say that long before the collision between the incoming particle, x, and the target nucleus, X, their rest masses are m_x and M_X, and their kinetic energies are K_x and K_X, respectively. Thus the total energy, E_i, of the initial system is the sum of the kinetic and rest-mass energies, i.e.,

$$E_i = K_x + m_x c^2 + K_X + M_X c^2 \tag{4.7}$$

Similarly the final energy, E_f, of the system $Y + y$, long after the collision, is

$$E_f = K_Y + M_Y c^2 + K_y + m_y c^2 \tag{4.8}$$

Because there are no external forces acting on the system, the final energy must be equal to the initial energy, i.e.,

$$E_f = E_i$$

or

$$K_Y + M_Y c^2 + K_y + m_y c^2 = K_x + m_x c^2 + K_X + M_X c^2 \tag{4.9}$$

This can be written as

$$[(K_Y + K_y) - (K_X + K_x)] = [(M_X + m_x)c^2 - (M_Y + m_y)c^2] \tag{4.10}$$

This equation states that the net increase in the kinetic energy is equal to the net decrease in the rest-mass energy. This net change in the kinetic energy is called the *disintegration energy* or *Q-value* of the nuclear reaction, i.e.,

$$Q = (K_Y + K_y) - (K_X + K_x)$$
$$= \text{final kinetic energy} - \text{initial kinetic energy} \qquad (4.11)$$

Q is also equal to the change in the rest-mass energies given by

$$Q = (M_X + m_x)c^2 - (M_Y + m_y)c^2$$
$$= \text{initial rest-mass energy} - \text{final rest-mass energy} \qquad (4.12)$$

The value of Q will be positive if the final kinetic energy is greater than the initial energy, which means that the initial rest-mass energy is greater than the final rest-mass energy. Such reactions are called *exoergic reactions*, or exothermic reactions.

The Q-value of the reaction will be negative if the final kinetic energy is less than the initial kinetic energy, which means that the initial rest-mass energy is smaller than the final rest-mass energy. Such reactions are called *endoergic reactions*, or endothermic reactions.

In most experiments the target nucleus is initially at rest, and hence it does not have any kinetic energy. In such cases the Eqs. (4.11) and (4.12) for the Q-value of the reaction become

$$Q = (K_Y + K_y) - K_x$$
$$= (M_X + m_x)c^2 - (M_Y + m_y)c^2 \qquad (4.13)$$

In general, it is not easy to measure accurately the kinetic energy, K_Y, of the recoil nucleus. If we consider the conservation of momentum, it is possible to obtain an expression for the Q-value independent of K_Y. This is done in the following manner.

Consider a particle x of mass m_x moving with velocity v_x that strikes the target nucleus, X, of mass M_X and whose velocity is zero, i.e., at rest. After the nuclear reaction, the recoil nucleus Y makes an angle ϕ with the initial direction of x and has mass M_Y and velocity V_Y, while the particle y makes an angle θ and has mass m_y and velocity v_y. This is shown in Fig. 4.1. From the conservation of momentum, we get

$$m_x v_x = m_y v_y \cos\theta + M_Y V_Y \cos\phi \qquad (4.14)$$

$$0 = m_y v_y \sin\theta - M_Y V_Y \sin\phi \qquad (4.15)$$

or

$$M_Y V_Y \cos\phi = m_x v_x - m_y v_y \cos\theta \qquad (4.14a)$$

$$M_Y V_Y \sin\phi = m_y v_y \sin\theta \qquad (4.15a)$$

Squaring and adding Eqs. (4.14a) and (4.15a), we get

$$M_Y^2 V_Y^2 = m_x^2 v_x^2 + m_y^2 v_y^2 - 2 m_x m_y v_x v_y \cos\theta \qquad (4.16)$$

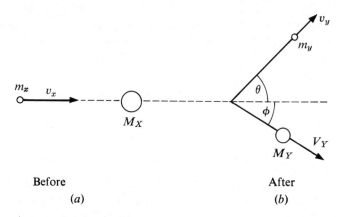

Before   After

(a)   (b)

FIG. 4.1 (a) Shows the incident particle approaching the target nucleus before the reaction. (b) Outgoing particle and the recoiled nucleus after the reaction.

Making use of the relations

$$K_x = 1/2m_xv_x^2, \; K_y = 1/2m_yv_y^2 \text{ and } K_Y = 1/2M_YV_Y^2 \qquad (4.17)$$

in Eq. (4.16) and rearranging the terms, we get

$$K_Y = \frac{m_x}{M_Y}K_x + \frac{m_y}{M_Y}K_y - \frac{2}{M_Y}(m_xm_yK_xK_y)^{1/2}\cos\theta \qquad (4.18)$$

The Q-value of the reaction with $K_X = 0$ is given by Eq. (4.13)

$$Q = (K_Y + K_y) - K_x \qquad (4.13)$$

and substituting the value of K_Y from Eq. (4.18) into Eq. (4.13),

$$Q = K_y\left(1 + \frac{m_y}{M_Y}\right) - K_x\left(1 - \frac{m_x}{M_Y}\right) - \frac{2}{M_Y}(m_xm_yK_xK_y)^{1/2}\cos\theta \quad (4.19)$$

Eq. (4.19) is the general equation for the Q-value of a nuclear reaction. The special case of this equation for negative values of Q will be taken up later on, but for the present it is worthwhile to note the following:

A. (i) Eq. (4.19) does not involve the kinetic energy of the recoil nucleus or the rest-mass energy of the target nucleus.

(ii) The importance of the last term in Eq. (4.19) decreases as the mass, M_X, of the target, and, hence, that of the recoil nucleus M_Y increases. In fact if $M_Y \to \infty$ the last term approaches zero.

(iii) If the outgoing particles are observed at right angles to the direction of the incoming particles, i.e., $\theta = 90°$, $\cos 90° = 0$, then Eq. (4.19) becomes

$$Q = K_y\left(1 + \frac{m_y}{M_Y}\right) - K_x\left(1 - \frac{m_x}{M_Y}\right) \qquad (4.20)$$

This is equivalent to the case in which the target nucleus and, hence, the recoil nucleus are of infinite mass.

(iv) Although we have used nuclear masses in defining Q-values, we may use atomic masses, if the number of electrons is the same before and after a nuclear reaction.

B. In the above derivation it has been assumed that the speeds of the particles are low enough to disregard the relativistic effects. In general the speeds of these particles are less than 5×10^9 cm/sec, and it is possible to regard the motion of these particles as nonrelativistic. If, however, for very accurate work, one takes into account the relativistic correction, the expression for the Q-value (Eq. 4.19) can be derived to be

$$Q = \left(1 + \frac{m_y}{M_Y}\right)K_y - \left(1 - \frac{m_x}{M_Y}\right)K_x + \left(\frac{K_x^2 + K_y^2 - K_Y^2}{2M_Yc^2}\right)$$

$$- \frac{2(m_x m_y K_x K_y)^{1/2} \cos\theta \left(1 + \frac{K_x}{2m_xc^2}\right)^{1/2}\left(1 + \frac{K_y}{2m_yc^2}\right)^{1/2}}{M_Y} \qquad \textbf{(4.21)}$$

C. Before leaving the discussion of the disintegration energy, we shall take up once again Eq. (4.19) and investigate it for the exoergic, or exothermal, reactions from the point of view of bombarding energies.

Rewriting Eq. (4.19), we can express the kinetic energy of the outgoing particle in the following form:

$$(M_Y + m_y)K_y - 2(m_x m_y K_x)^{1/2} \cos\theta\sqrt{K_y} - [K_x(M_Y - m_x) + M_Y Q] = 0$$

which is a quadratic in $\sqrt{K_y}$. Solving it we get

$$\sqrt{K_y} =$$

$$\frac{\sqrt{m_x m_y K_x} \cos\theta \pm \{(m_x m_y K_x \cos^2\theta) + (M_Y + m_y)[K_x(M_Y - m_x) + M_Y Q]\}^{1/2}}{(M_Y + m_y)}$$

$$\textbf{(4.22)}$$

or

$$\sqrt{K_y} = a \pm \sqrt{a^2 + b} \qquad \textbf{(4.23)}$$

where

$$a = \frac{\sqrt{m_x m_y K_x}}{M_Y + m_y} \cos\theta \qquad \textbf{(4.24a)}$$

and

$$b = \frac{K_x(M_Y - m_x) + M_Y Q}{(M_Y + m_y)} \qquad \textbf{(4.24b)}$$

If the *bombarding energy* is almost zero, i.e., $K_x \cong 0$, which happens in the case of reactions initiated by the capture of thermal neutrons, Eq. (4.22) reduces to

$$K_y = \frac{M_Y Q}{M_Y + m_y} \quad \text{For } Q > 0 \tag{4.25}$$

This means that the kinetic energy K_y of the outgoing particle of mass m_y is the same for all angles θ, i.e., the reaction is isotropic. This is true because the total momentum in the laboratory coordinate system is zero since K_x is almost zero.

If $Q > 0$ and $M_Y > m_x$, which usually is the case, only one of the two solutions of K_y, obtained from Eqs. (4.22) and (4.23), will be positive (the negative kinetic energy does not correspond to any physical situation), and is given by

$$\sqrt{K_y} = a + \sqrt{a^2 + b} \tag{4.26}$$

In this case K_y does depend on the angle θ. K_y has a maximum value for $\theta = 0$, minimum for $\theta = 180°$, and for $\theta = 90°$, $K_y = b$, i.e.,

$$K_y = \frac{K_x(M_Y - m_x) + M_Y Q}{(M_Y + m_y)} \tag{4.27}$$

K_y is single valued. Note that it is possible to obtain a double value for K_y under certain circumstances (see problem 9).

3. NUCLEAR REACTIONS IN A CENTER-OF-MASS COORDINATE SYSTEM

In the previous section, we used the laboratory coordinate system (LAB coordinate system) to explain the dynamics of nuclear reactions, but it is usually more convenient from the theoretical view point to use the center-of-mass coordinate system (CMCS). As an example, we shall see, in Section 4, how the center-of-mass coordinate system can be utilized to calculate the minimum energy required by the bombarding particle in order to start an endoergic nuclear reaction. Fig. 4.2 illustrates a collision in the LAB coordinate system as well as in the CMCS.

A. BEFORE COLLISION. If a particle of mass m_x has velocity v_x in the LAB coordinate system while the particle of mass M_X is at rest, the velocity v_c of the center-of-mass of the system is given by the relation

$$(m_x + M_X)v_c = m_x v_x + M_X \cdot 0$$

$$v_c = \frac{m_x v_x}{m_x + M_X} \tag{4.28}$$

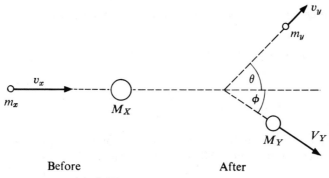

Before | After

(a) **LAB coordinate system**

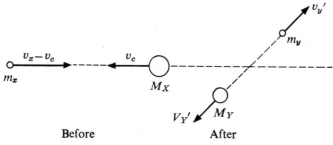

Before | After

(b) **Center-of-mass coordinate system (CMCS)**

FIG. 4.2 A nuclear reaction as observed in (a) the LAB coordinate system, (b) the Center-of-Mass Coordinate System (CMCS).

Let us denote the velocities of m_x and M_X in the CMCS by v'_x and V'_X, respectively, where

$$v'_x = v_x - v_c = v_x - \frac{m_x v_x}{m_x + M_X} = \frac{M_X}{m_x + M_X} v_x \qquad (4.29)$$

and

$$V'_X = 0 - v_c = - \frac{m_x}{m_x + M_X} v_x \qquad (4.30)$$

The kinetic energies, therefore, of the two particles before the collision in the CMCS are given by

$$K'_x = \tfrac{1}{2} m_x v'^2_x = \tfrac{1}{2} m_x \left(\frac{M_X}{m_x + M_X} v_x \right)^2 = \left(\frac{M_X}{m_x + M_X} \right)^2 K_x \qquad (4.31)$$

and

$$K'_X = \tfrac{1}{2} M_X V'^2_X = \tfrac{1}{2} M_X \left(\frac{- m_x v_x}{m_x + M_X} \right)^2 = \frac{m_x M_X}{(m_x + M_X)^2} K_x \qquad (4.32)$$

The total energy K_i' of the system before the collision in the CMCS is given by

$$K_i' = K_x' + K_X' = \left(\frac{M_X}{m_x + M_X}\right)^2 K_x + \frac{m_x M_X}{(m_x + M_X)^2} K_x$$

or

$$K_i' = K_x\left(\frac{M_X}{m_x + M_X}\right) \tag{4.33}$$

where $K_x = 1/2\ m_x v_x^2$ is the kinetic energy of the system (or the particle x) before the collision in the LAB coordinate system.

B. AFTER COLLISION. After the collision in CMCS, let v_y' and V_Y' be the velocities of the masses m_y and M_Y, respectively, and K_f' be the total kinetic energy of the system.

From the conservation of momentum, we have

$$m_y v_y' = M_Y V_Y' \tag{4.34}$$

and the kinetic energies K_y' and K_Y' of m_y and M_Y in CMCS are

$$K_y' = \tfrac{1}{2} m_y v_y'^2 \tag{4.35}$$

$$K_Y' = \tfrac{1}{2} M_Y V_Y'^2 = \tfrac{1}{2} M_Y \left(\frac{m_y}{M_Y} v_y'\right)^2 = \frac{m_y}{M_Y} K_y' \tag{4.36}$$

where Eq. (4.36) has been obtained from Eqs. (4.34) and (4.35). Thus, the total kinetic energy K_f' is given by

$$K_f' = K_y' + K_Y' = \tfrac{1}{2} m_y v_y'^2 + \tfrac{1}{2} M_Y V_Y'^2 \tag{4.37}$$

But we must have

$$K_i' = K_f' - Q \tag{4.38}$$

Substituting for K_i' from Eq. (4.33), we get

$$K_x\left(\frac{M_X}{m_x + M_X}\right) = K_f' - Q$$

$$K_f' = Q + K_x\left(\frac{M_X}{m_x + M_X}\right)$$

$$= Q + K_x\left(1 - 1 + \frac{M_X}{m_x + M_X}\right)$$

or

$$K_f' = Q + K_x\left(1 - \frac{m_x}{m_x + M_X}\right) \tag{4.39}$$

It is interesting to compare this expression for K_f' with K_f, given by

$$K_f = Q + K_x \tag{4.40}$$

Using Eqs. (4.35), (4.36), (4.37), and (4.38), it can be shown that the kinetic energies K_y' and K_Y' after the collision, in the CMCS are given by

$$K_y' = \frac{M_Y}{m_y + M_Y}\left[Q + \left(1 - \frac{m_x}{m_y + M_Y}\right)K_x\right] \tag{4.41}$$

and

$$K_Y' = \frac{m_y}{m_y + M_Y}\left[Q + \left(1 - \frac{m_x}{m_y + M_Y}\right)K_x\right] \tag{4.42}$$

Similarly the kinetic energies of the center-of-mass before the collision and after the collision are (in the LAB system)

$$K_c \text{ (before)} = \left(\frac{m_x}{m_x + M_X}\right)K_x \tag{4.43}$$

$$K_c \text{ (after)} = \left(\frac{m_x}{m_y + M_Y}\right)K_x \tag{4.44}$$

The final result that we are interested in deriving in this section is the relation between the angles in the LAB coordinate system and the CMCS[4]. Let θ_c be the angle which the particle m_y makes with the initial direction after the collision in the CMCS. Let the corresponding angle in the LAB coordinate system be θ_L. To find the relation between θ_c and θ_L, transform the velocity v_y' of m_y after the collision from the CMCS to the LAB coordinate system. This is done as shown in Fig. 4.3, and the velocity transformation equation is

$$\mathbf{v}_y = \mathbf{v}_c + \mathbf{v}_y' \tag{4.45}$$

or in the component form

$$v_y \cos \theta_L = v_c + v_y' \cos \theta_c \tag{4.46a}$$

$$v_y \sin \theta_L = v_y' \sin \theta_c \tag{4.46b}$$

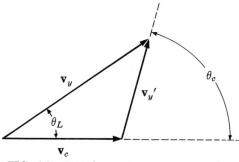

FIG. 4.3 Transform of a velocity vector from the CMCS to the LAB Coordinate System.

Dividing Eq. (4.46b) by Eq. (4.46a), we get

$$\tan \theta_L = \frac{v_y' \sin \theta_c}{v_c + v_y' \cos \theta_c} = \frac{\sin \theta_c}{v_c/v_y' + \cos \theta_c}$$

or

$$\tan \theta_L = \frac{\sin \theta_c}{\gamma + \cos \theta_c} \qquad (4.47)$$

where

$$\gamma = \frac{v_c}{v_y'} = \frac{\text{velocity, } v_c, \text{ of the center-of-mass in the LAB coordinate system}}{\text{velocity, } v_y', \text{ of } m_y \text{ in the CMCS}}$$

$$(4.48)$$

Thus if we know γ as defined by Eq. (4.48), we can find the relation between θ_L and θ_c for different nuclear reactions. With some manipulation, it is possible to show that

$$\gamma = \left[\frac{m_x m_y K_x}{M_Y(m_y + M_Y)Q + M_Y(M_Y + m_y - m_x)K_x} \right]^{1/2} \qquad (4.49a)$$

or, since $\dfrac{Q}{c^2} \ll 1$ amu

$$\gamma \doteq \left[\frac{m_x m_y}{M_X M_Y} \frac{K_x}{Q(1 + m_x/M_X) + K_x} \right]^{1/2} \qquad (4.49b)$$

Eq. (4.47) can be plotted for different values of γ (which is a characteristic of the nuclear reaction) as shown in Fig. 4.4 where θ_c has been plotted against θ_L. There are two special cases of interest in Fig. 4.4.

The case of $\gamma = 0$ corresponds to a very heavy target nucleus, and thus γ is almost equal to zero. From Eq. (4.47), by substituting $\gamma = 0$, we get

$$\theta_c = \theta_L$$

which means that for a heavy target nucleus the angle θ_c is almost equal to θ_L.

The case of $\gamma = 1$, we see from Eq. (4.47) that

$$\theta_c = 2\theta_L$$

This corresponds to the case of neutron-proton elastic scattering in which case $Q = 0$ and $m_x = m_y = m_n$ and $M_X = M_Y = m_p$. Note also that for this case Eqs. (4.47) and (4.48) reduce to

$$\tan \theta_L = \frac{\sin \theta_c}{(m_n/m_p) + \cos \theta_c} \qquad (4.50)$$

and

$$\gamma = m_n/m_p \qquad (4.51)$$

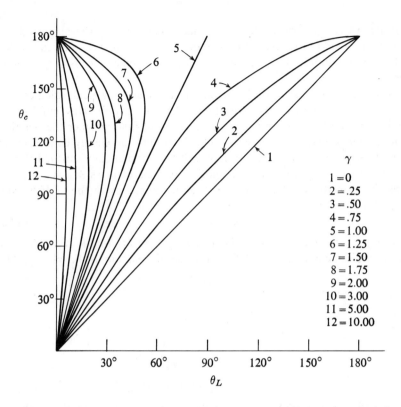

FIG. 4.4 Plot of θ_c versus θ_L for different values of γ (γ is a characteristic of a nuclear reaction).

4. THRESHOLD ENERGY FOR AN ENDOERGIC REACTION

In Section 2 we derived the expression for the Q-value of a nuclear reaction by considering the reaction to be taking place in the LAB coordinate system. As already stated, an endoergic reaction is one for which the Q-value is negative. In this case some of the initial kinetic energy (equal to the Q-value of the reaction) is converted into the rest-mass energy of the final products. At first glance one might be led to the conclusion that an endoergic reaction is possible if the incoming particle m_x has just enough kinetic energy, K_x, to be equal to the Q-value: $K_x = |Q|$. The final products (the outgoing particle and the recoil nucleus) will be produced at rest. Because the initial system has kinetic energy equal to K_x, its momentum will not be zero; the final products that are produced at rest will have zero momentum. This implies that the momentum is not conserved. But this is not possible because the momentum must always be conserved. Hence an energy greater than the magnitude of the Q-value would be required for an endoergic reaction. The minimum value of the energy required for an endoergic reaction to take place is the *threshold energy*.

From the conservation of momentum and energy, we can calculate the threshold energy for endoergic reactions. Because this involves lengthy calculations in the LAB coordinate system, we shall first consider the reaction in the center-of-mass coordinate system. Imposing the energy conditions in the CMCS, the momentum conditions will be automatically satisfied. For a particle of mass m_x approaching another particle of mass M_X at rest with a velocity v in the LAB coordinate system, the energy in the CMCS from Eq. (4.33) is

$$K'_i = \tfrac{1}{2} m_{red.} v^2 \tag{4.52}$$

where $m_{red.}$ is the reduced mass given by $m_{red.} = m_x M_X / (m_x + M_X)$. Thus the energy requirement in the CMCS for an endoergic reaction to take place will be

$$K'_i \geqslant |Q|$$

or from Eq. (4.52)

$$\frac{1}{2} \cdot \frac{m_x M_X}{m_x + M_X} v^2 \geqslant |Q|$$

$$\tfrac{1}{2} m_x v^2 \geqslant \frac{m_x + M_X}{M_X} |Q|$$

$$\geqslant (1 + m_x / M_X) |Q|$$

But $1/2\, m_x v^2 = K_x =$ the kinetic energy of the particle x in the LAB coordinate system; therefore,

$$K_x \geqslant (1 + m_x / M_X) |Q|$$

Hence

$$\text{Threshold energy} = (K_x)_{min} = (1 + m_x / M_X) |Q| \tag{4.53}$$

Thus the threshold energy is greater than the magnitude of the Q-value by a factor of $(1 + m_x / M_X)$ where m_x and M_X are the masses of the incident particle and the target nucleus, respectively.

The results reached in Eq. (4.53) can also be derived by using the LAB coordinate system from Eq. (4.19) or Eq. (4.23) with some interesting conclusions, i.e.,

$$\sqrt{K_y} = a \pm \sqrt{a^2 + b} \tag{4.23}$$

where

$$a = \frac{\sqrt{m_x m_y K_x}}{(M_Y + m_y)} \cos \theta \tag{4.24a}$$

and

$$b = \frac{K_x (M_Y - m_x) + M_Y Q}{(M_Y + m_y)} \tag{4.24b}$$

Here again, as in the case of the exoergic reactions, we shall discuss this equation for different energy ranges.

First of all, for almost zero bombarding energies $K_x \cong 0$, we get

$$a \cong 0, \text{ and}$$
$$b \cong M_Y Q/(M_Y + m_y)$$

and because Q is negative, the quantity $(a^2 + b)$ is negative. This means that $\sqrt{K_y}$ is an imaginary quantity, or K_y is negative, which does not have any physical meaning. Thus the endoergic reactions are not possible with this insufficient amount of kinetic energy.

As the energy K_x of the bombarding particle is increased, the reaction will become possible with a certain minimum value of K_x given by the condition $a^2 + b = 0$, i.e.,

$$(K_x)_\theta = -Q\left[\frac{M_Y + m_y}{M_Y + m_y - m_x - (m_x m_y/M_Y)\sin^2\theta}\right] \tag{4.54}$$

If the outgoing particle of mass m_y is observed at $\theta = 0°$, this leads to

$$(K_x)_{\min} = -Q\left(\frac{M_Y + m_y}{M_Y + m_y - m_x}\right) \tag{4.55}$$

Using the relation

$$M_X + m_x = M_Y + m_y + \frac{Q}{c^2},$$

we get

$$(K_x)_{\min} = -Q\left(\frac{M_X + m_x - Q/c^2}{M_X - Q/c^2}\right) \tag{4.56}$$

Because the energy equivalent of the mass, M_X, is usually very large as compared to Q, we may write Eq. (4.56) as

$$(K_x)_{\min} = -Q\left(\frac{M_X + m_x}{M_X}\right) = -Q\left(1 + \frac{m_x}{M_X}\right) \tag{4.57}$$

which is the same result as obtained in Eq. (4.53) for the threshold energy.

Thus we conclude that if the energy of the incident particles is equal to the threshold energy, the outgoing particles are emitted only in the direction $\theta = 0$ with energy given by the following [from Eq. (4.23)].

$$K_y = (K_x)_{\text{threshold}} \frac{m_x m_y}{(m_y + M_Y)^2} \tag{4.58}$$

As the energy of the bombarding particles is increased beyond the threshold, the outgoing particles are given out at angles greater than $\theta = 0$.

Still another interesting result is the double value of K_y in the case of endoergic reactions. It is quite clear that as the kinetic energy K_x of the bombarding particles is increased beyond the threshold energy, the quantity $(a^2 + b)$ is positive, and hence $\sqrt{K_y} = a \pm \sqrt{a^2 + b}$ will yield double values of K_y in the forward direction, i.e., for $\theta < 90°$. The double-value behavior for the reaction $_7N^{14}(\alpha, p)_8O^{17}$ is shown in Fig. 4.5.

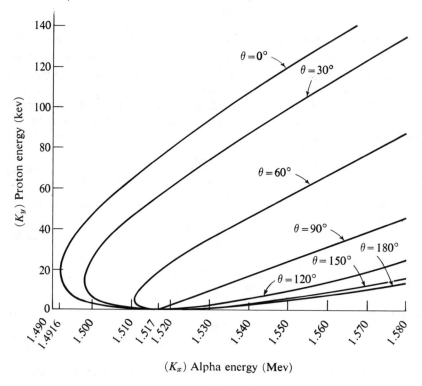

FIG. 4.5   The double-value behavior for the reaction N^{14} (α, p) O^{17} which has a Q-value of -1.16 ± 0.04 Mev. Plots show the proton energy K_y versus the alpha energy K_x. K_y is double valued for $K_x < 1.517$ Mev and $\theta < 90°$.

5. MEASUREMENT OF Q-VALUE

From Eq. (4.11) and (4.12) we have

$$Q = (K_Y + K_y) - (K_X + K_x) \tag{4.11}$$

or

$$Q = [(M_X + m_x) - (M_Y + m_y)]c^2 \tag{4.12}$$

and it is clear that the precise measurement of the Q-value of a nuclear reaction involves very accurate measurement of either the masses or the kinetic energies of the particles. The common practice is to measure the kinetic energies of the particles. As we shall show in the next chapter, one can find the unknown masses very precisely from the accurate determination of the Q-value.

Different methods have been used for the measurement of energies of the bombarding and the outgoing particles, namely: (i) the range-energy

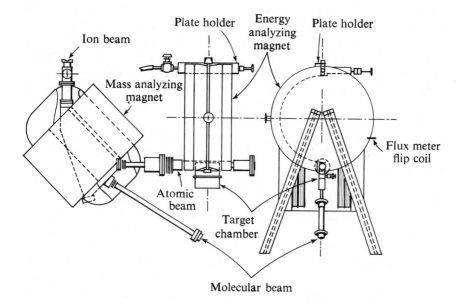

FIG. 4.6   The apparatus used by Buechner *et al.* to investigate nuclear reactions. The charged particles accelerated by the Van de Graaff generator enter as a beam of ions. Particles of the desired mass and energy are separated by the "mass-analyzing magnet." Accurate energy measurement of the particles produced in the reaction is made by the "energy-analyzing magnet" and are detected by the nuclear track plates. [From Buechner *et al.*, *Phys. Rev.* **74**, 1569 (1948).]

relationships, which will be considered in detail in Chapters 7 to 9, (ii) the analysis of the deflection produced by electrostatic fields, or (iii) the analysis of the deflection produced by magnetic fields.

One of the most precise methods for measuring energies by the application of magnetic fields was developed by W. Buechner and his co-workers[6] in 1948, at the Massachusetts Institute of Technology. Fig. 4.6 shows the apparatus used by Buechner *et al.*

We shall describe, somewhat briefly, the essential features of this experimental set-up. The ion beam obtained from an electrostatic accelerator is first analyzed into its various mass components by a 90° deflecting magnet. The resulting beam is brought to a focus on the target, which is located between the poles of a large annular magnet. The design and the dimensions of this magnet are very close to those of the one designed by Cockcroft[7], and used by Rutherford and his collaborators[8] for the precise determination of energies of alpha particles from natural radioactive substances. The magnet produces a uniform field over an annular region having a mean diameter of 70 cm and an annular width of 5 cm. The gap between the pole faces is 14 mm. The targets are contained in a chamber placed in a one-inch wide slot cut through the annular region. In order to define the energy and the position of the beam hitting the target, a slit is placed at the entrance of the target chamber. This target chamber contains a wheel, on the perimeter of which are mounted the targets and the alpha-particle sources for calibrating the magnets. The wheel can be rotated from outside, and different targets can be brought in position for the investigation of different reactions without the necessity of opening the vacuum system of the target chamber.

Nuclear-track photographic plates are placed in a small vacuum enclosure and used for detecting the particles produced in a nuclear disintegration. The photographic plate holder is connected with the target and different plates can be brought into position for exposure. The position of the plates is such that the particles given out in nuclear disintegrations in a direction 90° with the incident beam are focused on the plate by the annular magnetic fields.

In the normal usage of the apparatus, the accelerating voltage and, hence, the energy of the incident particles is kept constant, while each plate is exposed at a different magnetic field strength. Thus each plate covers a certain range in the energy spectrum of the particles given out in a nuclear reaction. The magnetic field strength and the curvature of the path of the particles determine the energy of the particles. Many reaction energies have been measured accurately by E. Strait et $al.$[9] and the results of the reactions $_4Be^9(d, \alpha)_3Li^7*$, $_4Be^9(d, \alpha)_3Li^7$ and $_4Be^9(d, p)_4Be^{10}$ are shown in Fig. 4.7

The number of nuclear reactions that have been investigated so far is so numerous that it is not possible to discuss all of them in this text. The details of most of the reactions can be found in references 10, 11, and 12. A few examples of nuclear reactions with their disintegration energies will be given below. The bombarding particles most frequently used in nuclear reactions are alpha particles (α), protons (p), neutrons (n), deuterons (d), tritons (t) and gamma rays (γ). These particles are also observed as disintegration products. As already mentioned, most of the recoil nuclei are in the excited states and hence are radioactive.

A large number of nuclear reactions are classified by M. Livingston and H. Bethe[10] in the following groups (Z stands for the atomic number and A for the mass number, Z^A before the parenthesis stands for the target and

Z^A after the parenthesis for the recoiled nucleus):

$$Z^A(\alpha, p) \, [Z + 1]^{4+3}, \, Z^A(\alpha, n) \, [Z + 2]^{4+3}, \, Z^A(p, \alpha) \, [Z - 1]^{4-3}$$
$$Z^A(p, d) \, [Z]^{4-1}, \qquad Z^A(p, \gamma) \, [Z + 1]^{4+1}, \, Z^A(p, n) \, [Z + 1]^{4}$$
$$Z^A(d, \alpha) \, [Z - 1]^{4-2}, \, Z^A(d, p) \, [Z]^{4+1}, \qquad Z^A(d, n) \, [Z + 1]^{4+1}$$
$$Z^A(n, \alpha) \, [Z - 2]^{4-3}, \, Z^A(n, p) \, [Z - 1]^{4}, \qquad Z^A(n, \gamma) \, [Z]^{4+1}$$
$$Z^A(n, 2n) \, [Z]^{4-1}, \qquad Z^A(\gamma, n) \, [Z]^{4-1}$$

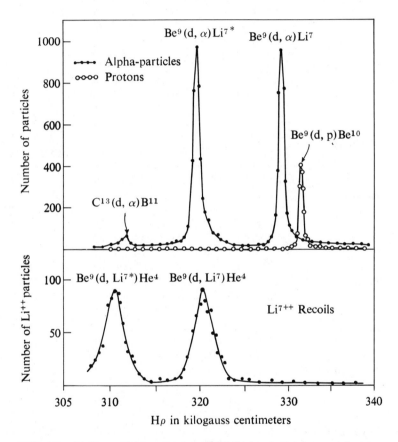

FIG. 4.7 Alpha-particles, protons, and Li^{7++} recoils observed from a beryllium target bombarded by 1.51-Mev deutrons. (H is the field strength in kilogauss and ρ is the radius of curvature in centimeters.) [From Strait *et al.*, *Phys. Rev.* **81**, 747 (1951).]

Table 1 on page 96 gives disintegration values for some nuclear reactions. A more complete list can be found in the paper by D. Van Patter and W. Whaling[12]. The meanings of the abbreviations used are given at the end of the table.

TABLE 1
NUCLEAR DISINTEGRATION ENERGIES[12]

Reaction	Measured Q-Value Mev	Method	Reference	Weighted Average Q-Value (Mev)
1. $B^{10}(\alpha, p)C^{13}$	4.16	cl ch[a]	13	
	3.86	range[b]	14	4.08 ± 0.10
	3.85	ph pl[c]	15	
	4.07 ± 0.2	range	16	
	4.08 ± 0.12	range	17	
2. $Al^{27}(\alpha, n)P^{30}$	-2.8	thresh[d]	18	
	-3.0	thresh	19	-2.9 ± 0.2
	-3.2	thresh	20	
	-3.4	thresh	21	
	-2.93 ± 0.17	ph pl	22	
3. $B^{11}(p, \alpha)Be^8$	8.60 ± 0.10	range	23	
	8.567 ± 0.010	mag. spec.[e]	9	8.585 ± 0.006
	8.574 ± 0.014	mag. spec.	11	
	8.589 ± 0.004	mag. spec.	24	
4. $Be^9(p, d)Be^8$	0.557 ± 0.003	mag. spec.	25	
	0.562 ± 0.004	mag. spec.	9	0.559 ± 0.001
	0.558 ± 0.005	el. spec.[f]	26	
	0.558 ± 0.002	el. spec.	27	
	0.560 ± 0.013	mag. spec.	28	
	0.560 ± 0.003	mag. spec.	26	
5. $Li^7(p, \gamma)Be^8$	17.1	cl ch	29	
	16.7 ± 0.5	cl ch	30	17.1 ± 0.2
	17.2 ± 0.2	pr. spec.[g]	31	
6. $Be^9(p, n)B^9$	-1.85 ± 0.01	thresh	32	-1.852 ± 0.002
	-1.851 ± 0.006	thresh	33	
	-1.852 ± 0.002	thresh	34	
7. $Li^7(d, \alpha)He^5$	14.3	range	35	
	13.43	ph pl[h]	36	14.2 ± 0.1
	14.2 ± 0.1	range	37	
	14.2 ± 0.1	ph pl	38	
8. $Li^6(d, p)Li^7$	5.02 ± 0.12	range	39	5.027 ± 0.003
	5.019 ± 0.007	mag. spec.	9	
	5.028 ± 0.003	mag. spec.	26	
9. $N^{14}(d, n)O^{15}$	5.1 ± 0.2	cl ch	40	
	5.15 ± 0.10	ph pl	41	5.12 ± 0.04
	5.11 ± 0.04	ph pl	42	
	5.1	ph pl	43	
	5.15 ± 0.16	ph pl	44	
10. $Ne^{20}(n, \alpha)O^{17}$	-0.7	cl ch	45	
	-0.80 to 0.85	pulse ht	46, 47	0.75 ± 0.05
	-0.75 ± 0.05	pulse ht	47	

11.	$N^{14}(n, p)C^{14}$	0.62	cl ch	48	
		0.60	cl ch	49	
		0.71	pulse ht	50	0.624 ± 0.004
		0.60 ± 0.03	ph pl	51	
		0.63 ± 0.01	pulse ht	52	
		0.616 ± 0.025	cl ch	53	
		0.630 ± 0.006	pulse ht	54	
		0.610 ± 0.010	pulse ht	55	
12.	$Cl^{35}(n, \gamma)Cl^{36}$	1.07 ± 0.15	pulse ht	56	
		0.97 ± 0.16	pulse ht	57	1.02 ± 0.11
13.	$C^{12}(n, 2n)C^{11}$	$\geqslant -21$	thresh	58	
		$\geqslant -17$	thresh	59	
14.	$Si^{28}(\gamma, n)Si^{27}$	-16.9 ± 0.3	thresh	60	-16.9 ± 0.2
		-16.8 ± 0.4	thresh	61	
		-16.9 ± 0.2	thresh	62	

      (a) cl ch   = cloud chamber
      (b) range   = range-energy relationship
      (c) ph pl   = photographic plate
      (d) thresh   = threshold
      (e) mag. spec. = magnetic spectrograph or spectrometer
      (f) el. spec.   = electrostatic spectrometer
      (g) pr. spec.   = pair spectrometer
      (h) pulse ht   = pulse height

6. CROSS SECTION

In the previous sections we have been considering the energetics of nuclear reactions without considering what fraction of the beam of the incident particles will participate in a reaction. In the field of microscopic physics, theories generally do not predict certainties. The decay of a radioactive atom, for example, was defined in terms of the probability λ. Similarly, in the production of artificial radio-isotopes, absorption, scattering, or nuclear reactions of any kind, we need to find some way of expressing the probability of something happening to the particles of an incident beam when they strike the target nuclei. The concept of the cross section, σ, has been introduced for the purpose of calculating the attenuation of the incident beam.

    Consider a beam of particles of intensity I incident on a thin sheet of material of thickness dt and face area A. As a particle passes through the thin sheet there is some chance that it will be absorbed by a nucleus, if the particle happens to come close to it. Assume that σ is the effective area surrounding an atom, such that if the incident particle falls within this area (Fig. 4.8), the nuclear reaction will take place. Let there be n target nuclei per unit volume of the sheet. It is assumed that the foil is so thin that none of the nuclei overlap each other so as to be equally probable to cause the nuclear reaction with the incident particles. With this notation in mind, we have

$$n \, dt = \text{number of nuclei per unit face area,}$$
$$A \, n \, dt = \text{total number of nuclei in the face area } A.$$

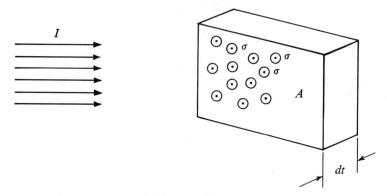

FIG. 4.8   A beam of particles incident on a thin foil.

Because with each nucleus is associated an effective area, σ, the total sensitive area or effective area available for a nuclear reaction is

$$A \, n \, \sigma \, dt = \text{total effective area.}$$

The fractional effective area, f, is given by

$$f = \frac{\text{total effective area}}{\text{total face area}} = \frac{\sigma A n \, dt}{A} = n\sigma \, dt \qquad (4.59)$$

This fractional effective area represents the fractional change in the intensity I of the beam as it passes through the foil. Thus the change in the intensity dI is given by

$$dI = -fI \qquad (4.60)$$

Note that because we are talking in terms of probabilities, f and, consequently, σ have nothing to do with the geometrical size of the atom. Actually σ is proportional to the probability for a nuclear reaction to take place. Combining Eqs. (4.59) and (4.60) we get

$$-\frac{dI}{I} = n\sigma \, dt \qquad (4.61)$$

where the negative sign means that the intensity I decreases as thickness t increases. Assuming $I = I_0$ at $t = 0$ and integrating Eq. (4.61) we get

$$I = I_0 e^{-n\sigma t} \qquad (4.62)$$

Because the number of particles N in the beam is proportional to the intensity of the beam, Eq. (4.62) in terms of the number of particles, can be written as

$$N = N_0 e^{-n\sigma t} \qquad (4.63)$$

where N_0 is the number of particles incident on the foil, and N is the number of particles left after traversing a thickness t of the foil.

The *microscopic-cross-section* or simply the cross section is usually denoted by σ. The unit of the cross section is the barn, or b, where

$$1 \text{ b} = 10^{-24} \text{ cm}^2$$

and a smaller unit is the millibarn, denoted by mb

$$1 \text{ mb} = 10^{-3} \text{ b}$$

The product of n and σ is called the *macroscopic cross section* Σ.

$$\Sigma = n\sigma \qquad (4.64)$$

If we are dealing with absorption only, then sometimes the term *absorption coefficient*, α, is used instead of Σ, where

$$\alpha = n\sigma \qquad (4.65)$$

Eq. (4.63) can be written as

$$N = N_0 e^{-\Sigma t} = N_0 e^{-\alpha t} \qquad (4.66)$$

The meaning of a thin foil can now be made clear. The foil is said to be thin if $\alpha t \ll 1$, which is true either if the foil is sufficiently geometrically thin or if the cross section is sufficiently small. In this case

$$e^{-\alpha t} \doteq 1 - \alpha t$$

$$N \doteq N_0 (1 - \alpha t)$$

Thus the number of particles absorbed while traversing a thickness t, is given by

$$dN = N_0 - N_0 (1 - \alpha t) = N_0 \alpha t = N_0 n\sigma t \qquad (4.67)$$

Note that this is in complete agreement with the definition of fractional effective area $(f = n\sigma \, dt)$.

7. MEAN FREE PATH

It is now possible to derive an expression for the average distance $\bar{x}$ traveled by the particles, i.e., the mean free path, before they are absorbed or scattered. This can be calculated in a manner similar to that used in calculating the average life. Multiply the distance x by the number of particles dN absorbed in distance dx at x, integrate it over all x, and divide by the total number of particles. The mean free path is

$$\bar{x} = \int_0^{N_0} x \, dN \Big/ \int_0^{N_0} dN = \int_0^{N_0} x \, dN \Big/ N_0 \tag{4.68}$$

From Eq. (4.63), and using x instead of t, we get

$$dN = - n\sigma N_0 e^{-n\sigma x} \, dx$$

Substituting the value of dN in Eq. (4.68) we get

$$\bar{x} = \int_0^\infty x n\sigma N_0 e^{-\alpha x} \, dx \Big/ N_0 = \int_0^\infty x n\sigma e^{-n\sigma x} \, dx$$

$$= \frac{1}{n\sigma} \int_0^\infty x n\sigma e^{-n\sigma x} \, d(n\sigma x)$$

$$= \frac{1}{n\sigma} \int_0^\infty y e^{-y} \, dy, \text{ where } y = n\sigma x$$

$$= \frac{1}{n\sigma} \cdot 1$$

$$\therefore \ \bar{x} = \frac{1}{n\sigma} = \frac{1}{\Sigma} \tag{4.69}$$

The mean free path, therefore, is the reciprocal of the macroscopic cross-section. The absorption mean free path is given by

$$\bar{x} = \frac{1}{\Sigma_a} = \frac{1}{\alpha} \tag{4.70}$$

where Σ_a is the macroscopic absorption cross-section.

8. REACTION RATE

In most cases one would like to know, if a beam of particles is incident on a certain material, what is the *reaction rate*, that is, the number of nuclear reactions that take place in unit time.

Let v be the velocity of the particles in a beam having a number density q particles per cm^3. This beam is incident on a foil of thickness t, face area A, and having n atoms per unit volume. The material of the foil has a microscopic cross-section σ. The reaction rate, from our previous definition of fractional sensitive area, is given by

$$\text{reaction rate (R.R.)} = qv(n\sigma t)A \left(\frac{1}{\text{sec}} \right) \tag{4.71}$$

Though this expression for R.R. involves t and A, the final expression, as we shall see, depends only on the total number of nuclei in the material and not on the shape of the material, assuming the foil is thin.

The *flux*, ϕ, is defined as the number of particles crossing a unit area in a unit time. In this case $\phi = qv$. Also $tA = V$, the volume of the material of the foil. Therefore,

$$\text{R.R.} = \phi n \sigma V \qquad (4.72)$$

Because $nV =$ total number of nuclei N, we can write the reaction rate as

$$\text{R.R.} = \phi \sigma N \qquad (4.73)$$

Eq. (4.73) represents the number of events or reactions per second. Also because $n\sigma = \Sigma$, from Eq. (4.72), we can write

$$\text{R.R.} = \phi \Sigma V \qquad (4.74)$$

9. DIFFERENTIAL CROSS-SECTION

When the incoming particles interact with the target nuclei, it is not always necessary that only one kind of nuclear reaction take place. If more than one type of reaction take place, the cross section for each will usually be different. These individual cross-sections are called the partial cross-sections and the total cross-section will be the sum of these. After the nuclear reaction or the scattering has taken place, very often the outgoing particles will have an anisotropic distribution and also different energies at different angles. One might be interested in knowing the number of particles scattered per second into a solid angle $d\Omega$ making an angle θ with the direction of incidence. To make such calculations another type of cross-section, which is angular dependent, is introduced. This new cross-section is called the *differential cross-section* and is defined as the cross-section per unit solid angle. This is denoted by $\sigma(\theta, \phi)$

$$\sigma(\theta, \phi) = \frac{d\sigma}{d\Omega} \text{ (cross-section/steradian)} \qquad (4.75)$$

and the total cross-section σ_T becomes

$$\sigma_T = \int_\Omega \frac{d\sigma}{d\Omega} \, d\Omega \qquad (4.76)$$

The value of the solid angle $d\Omega$ can be calculated with the help of Fig. 4.9.

The solid angle $d\Omega$ is given by

$$d\Omega = \frac{\text{area}}{(\text{distance})^2} = \frac{dA}{r^2} = \frac{(r \, d\theta)(r \sin \theta \, d\phi)}{r^2} = \sin \theta \, d\theta \, d\phi \qquad (4.77)$$

The total solid angle is

$$\Omega = \int_\Omega d\Omega = \int_0^{2\pi} \int_0^\pi \sin\theta \, d\theta \, d\phi = 4\pi \qquad (4.78)$$

The fractional solid angle is

$$\frac{d\Omega}{\Omega} = \frac{A}{r^2} \frac{1}{4\pi} = \frac{A}{4\pi r^2} \qquad (4.79)$$

The total cross-section σ_T can be found by combining Eqs. (4.76) and (4.77).

$$\sigma_T = \int \frac{d\sigma}{d\Omega} \, d\Omega = \int \frac{d\sigma}{d\Omega} \sin\theta \, d\theta \, d\phi \qquad (4.80)$$

If the differential cross-section has no ϕ-dependence, then the total cross-section (after integrating over ϕ) is given by

$$\sigma_T = 2\pi \int \frac{d\sigma}{d\Omega} \sin\theta \, d\theta \qquad (4.81)$$

where $\frac{d\sigma}{d\Omega} = \sigma(\theta)$, the differential cross section.

As an example, Fig. 4.10 shows the variation of the differential cross-section with θ and the mass number A for elastic scattering of neutrons[5]. The usefulness of the measurement of the differential cross-section lies not only in finding the energy dependent partial cross-section, but also in the fact that the directional dependence of the cross section is sensitive to the type of nuclear force. Assuming the type of nuclear force, it is possible to predict the angular distribution of different nuclear reactions. Agreement between the theory and the experiment will give the degree of accuracy of the form of the nuclear force assumed.

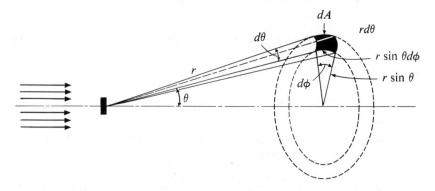

FIG. 4.9   The elements of the calculation of the solid angle $d\Omega$.

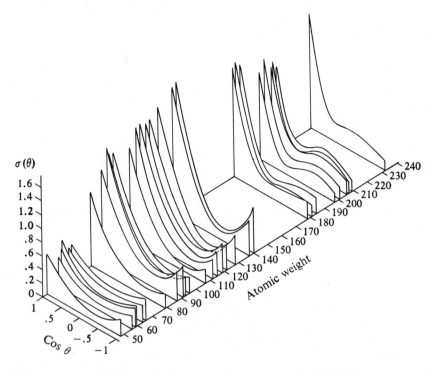

FIG. 4.10   Differential cross-section for elastic scattering of 1 Mev neutrons as a function of the cosine of the scattering angle and of atomic weight. [From Walt *et al.*, *Phys. Rev.*, **93**, 1062 (1954).]

10. RELATION BETWEEN THE CROSS SECTIONS IN CMCS AND LAB COORDINATE SYSTEMS

Let θ_L and ϕ_L denote the angles in the LAB coordinate system, and θ_c and ϕ_c be the angles in the CMCS. The differential cross-sections in the LAB coordinate system and in the CMCS are σ_L and σ_c, respectively. The relation between σ_L and σ_c can be derived from their definitions. The number of particles scattered into the differential solid angle $d\Omega_L$ about θ_L and ϕ_L must be equal to the number of particles scattered into the differential solid angle $d\Omega_c$ about θ_c and ϕ_c, i.e.,

$$\sigma_L(\theta_L, \phi_L) \sin \theta_L \, d\theta_L \, d\phi_L = \sigma_c(\theta_c, \phi_c) \sin \theta_c \, d\theta_c \, d\phi_c \qquad \textbf{(4.82)}$$

Using Eqs. (4.46a), (4.46b), and (4.47)

$$v_y \cos \theta_L = v_c + v_y' \cos \theta_c \qquad \textbf{(4.46a)}$$

$$v_y \sin \theta_L = v_y' \sin \theta_c \qquad \textbf{(4.46b)}$$

$$\tan \theta_L = \sin \theta_c / (\gamma + \cos \theta_c) \qquad \textbf{(4.47)}$$

and because there is no ϕ-dependence

$$\phi_L = \phi_c \tag{4.83}$$

one gets

$$\sigma_L(\theta_L, \phi_L) = \frac{(1 + \gamma^2 + 2\gamma \cos \theta_c)^{3/2}}{|1 + \gamma \cos \theta_c|} [\sigma_c(\theta_c, \phi_c)] \tag{4.84}$$

where γ is given by the Eq. (4.48). Combining Eq. (4.82) and (4.84) one can write

$$d\Omega_c = \frac{(1 + \gamma^2 + 2\gamma \cos \theta_c)^{3/2}}{|1 + \gamma \cos \theta_c|} (d\Omega_L) \tag{4.85}$$

Note that the total cross-section is the same in both coordinate systems because the total number of collisions is independent of the frame of reference used.

PROBLEMS

1. A beam of deuterons incident on Si^{29} causes nuclear reactions. Give the symbol, mass number, and atomic number of the recoil nuclei if the emitted particle is (a) an alpha particle, (b) a proton, or (c) a neutron.

2. Complete the following reactions:

$$C^{13}(d, \alpha)$$
$$C^{13}(d, t)$$
$$C^{13}(d, p)$$
$$C^{13}(d, n)$$

3. Which of the following reactions are exoergic and which endoergic? Calculate their Q-values.

$$O^{18}(p, \alpha)N^{15}, \ Be^9(\alpha, d)B^{11}, \ D^2(d, n)He^3$$
$$O^{18}(\alpha, p)F^{21}, \ Na^{23}(p, \alpha)Ne^{20}, \ Al^{27}(p, \gamma)Si^{28}$$

4. An alpha particle with kinetic energy of 3.5 Mev strikes a B^{10} nucleus at rest. As the result of a nuclear reaction, a proton is given out in the same direction as the original direction of the alpha particle.
   (a) Write the equation for the nuclear reaction.
   (b) What is the Q-value of the nuclear reaction?
   (c) Calculate the kinetic energy of the proton.

5. In many cases fast neutrons are produced in the laboratory by the reaction $H^3(d, n)He^4$, i.e., $_1H^2 + _1H^3 \rightarrow _2He^4 + _0n^1$. Assume that the incident deuteron beam has an energy of 400 kev.
   (a) Calculate the Q-value of this reaction.
   (b) If the kinetic energies of $_1H^2$ and $_1H^3$ can be neglected, what are the kinetic energies of the alpha particles and the neutrons?
   (c) Plot a graph of the kinetic energy of the neutron versus θ in steps of $30°$ from $\theta = 0°$ to $\theta = 180°$.
   (d) What will be the energies of the neutrons at different angles if tritium is bombarded with 4 Mev deuterons.

6. Solve problem 5 for the following reaction, which is another method commonly used for the production of fast neutrons in the laboratory:

$$_1H^2 + _1H^2 \rightarrow _2He^3 + _0n^1 \qquad [H^2(d, n)He^3]$$

7. Apply the principles of conservation of energy and momentum to show that in a nuclear reaction if a light particle is emitted at 90° to the initial direction of the incident particle, the kinetic energy of the light particle emitted is given by the expression

$$K_y = \frac{M_Y}{m_y + M_Y}\left(Q - \frac{m_x - M_Y}{M_Y} K_x\right)$$

8. Alpha particles are given out when carbon nuclei are bombarded by a deuteron beam, according to the reaction

$$_6C^{12} + _1H^2 \rightarrow _5B^{10} + _2He^4$$

   If the energies of the alpha particles measured at angles θ_1 and θ_2 are K_{α_1} and K_{α_2}, respectively, calculate
   (a) the Q-value of the reaction
   (b) the energy of the deuteron beam.

9. The reaction $B^{10}(\alpha, p)C^{13}$ has a Q-value of $+4.0$ Mev. Show that it is possible to get a double value of K_y, where K_y is the kinetic energy of the C^{13} nucleus. What is the physical significance of this result?

10. In problem 7, we derived in the LAB coordinate system the Q-value of a reaction in terms of K_x and K_y for a special case of $\theta = 90°$. Apply an appropriate relativistic correction, assuming that the incident particle and the ejected particles are much lighter than the target and the recoiled nuclei.

11. Derive Eq. (4.21).

12. Derive Eqs. (4.41) and (4.42).

13. Derive Eqs. (4.43) and (4.44).

14. Consider an elastic collision of a particle of mass m and speed v with another particle of the same mass but at rest. (It is the case of proton-neutron scattering or proton-proton scattering.)
   (a) If the incident particle is deflected by 90° in the CMCS, what are the final speeds and directions of each particle in the LAB coordinate system?
   (b) Repeat (a) for 45° deflection of the incident particle in the CMCS.

15. The Q-value of the reaction $Li^7(p, n)Be^7$ is -1.645 Mev.
   (a) What is the threshold energy of the reaction?
   (b) What is the neutron energy at the threshold?
   †(c) Plot a graph of neutron energy versus proton energy for $\theta = 0°$, 60°, 120°, 180°.

16. The Q-value of the reaction $H^3(p, n)He^3$ is -0.764 Mev.
   (a) What is the threshold of the reaction?
   (b) What is the neutron energy at the threshold?
   †(c) Plot a graph of the neutron energy versus proton energy for different values of θ.

† Time consuming. Should be done on a computer.

17. The Q-value of the reaction $F^{19}(n, p)O^{19}$ is -3.9 Mev.
     (a) What is the threshold energy of the reaction?
     (b) What is the mass difference between F^{19} and O^{19}?
     (c) What is the mass of O^{19}?

18. Using the neutrons produced in the reaction $C^{13}(\alpha, n)O^{16}$, is it possible to cause the reverse reaction $O^{16}(n, \alpha)C^{13}$? Explain.

19. Calculate the threshold energy for the photodisintegration of B^{10} in the reaction $B^{10}(\gamma, n)B^9$.

20. The intensity of a thermal neutron beam is reduced to one-half its value by a 5 cm thickness of water. Calculate (a) the absorption coefficient; (b) the effective cross-section in barns, assuming that the absorption is totally due to hydrogen, which is true because the absorption cross-section of oxygen is very small as compared to hydrogen; and (c) the thickness of water needed to reduce the flux to one-tenth. To one-hundredth.

21. The density of aluminum is 2.7 gm/cm³ and its cross-section for 0.02 Mev neutrons is 4.5b. What fraction of neutrons will pass through a foil of aluminum 1 mm thick?

22. Calculate the mean free path of 1 Mev neutrons in graphite ($\sigma = 2.6$b, density $= 2250$ kgm/m³).

23. Calculate the mean free path of thermal neutrons in water. [$\sigma = 0.33$b, density $= 1$ gm/cm³].

24. A Co^{59} wire of 0.1 cm diameter and 1 cm length is bombarded with a flux of 5×10^{12} thermal neutrons per square centimeter per second for 1 hour. How many millicuries of Co^{60} are produced? The thermal capture cross-section is 19b, and the half-life of Co^{60} formed is 5.27 years. Neglect any decay of Co^{60} during the time of bombardment.

25. If the reaction rate is given by

$$N\sigma\phi,$$

     prove that the number of product nuclei, which have a decay constant λ, remaining at the end of a bombardment of duration t seconds is given by

$$N_t = \frac{N\sigma\phi}{\lambda} (1 - e^{-\lambda t})$$

26. In the Pennsylvania State University research-reactor 0.1 gm of natural ruthenium was exposed for 4 minutes at the face of the core in the thermal neutron column where the flux is 10^{13} neutrons/cm²/sec. If the natural abundance of Ru^{104} is 18.6% and its cross-section for thermal neutrons is 0.7 barn, what is the total amount of Ru^{105} produced and its activity soon after exposure. Neglect the decay of Ru^{105} during the exposure time.

$$Ru^{104} + {}_0n^1 \rightarrow Ru^{105} \xrightarrow[4.5h]{\beta^-} Rh^{105} \xrightarrow[30h]{\beta^-} Pd^{105}$$

     What is the percentage error made in neglecting the decay of Ru^{105} during the exposure time?

27. A gold foil 0.01 cm thick and having a 1 sq. cm face area was irradiated for 2 minutes in the thermal neutron flux of a reactor. Au^{198}, which has a half-life of 64.8h, is produced by the reaction $Au^{197}(n, \gamma)Au^{198}$. The activity of the

sample as soon as it is taken out of the reactor is 3 millicuries. The cross-section of Au^{197} for thermal neutrons is 98 barns. Find the thermal-neutron flux. The density of gold is 19.3 gm/cm^3. (This is one of the methods used for measuring neutron flux at different positions in the reactor.)

28. A carbon target is bombarded by deuterons of energy 5 Mev, resulting in the following reaction: $C^{12}(d, n)N^{13}$. The bombardment is carried out for 2 minutes with a deuteron beam current of 200 microamperes. The carbon target has an area of 10 cm^2 and a thickness of 0.004 cm. The reaction cross-section is 0.014 barn.

    (a) Calculate the number of N^{13} atoms produced.

    (b) If the half-life of N^{13} is 10 minutes, what is the activity immediately after the exposure?

REFERENCES

1. Rutherford, E., *Phil. Mag.*, **37**, p. 537, (1919).

2. Cockcroft, J. D., and E. T. S. Walton, *Proc. Roy. Soc.*, **137**, p. 229, (1932).

3. Livingston, M. S., and H. A. Bethe, *Revs. Mod. Phys.*, **9**, p. 263, (1937).

4. Schiff, L. I., *Quantum Mechanics*, pp. 97–99. New York: McGraw-Hill Book Company, 1949.

5. Walt, M., and H. H. Barschall, *Phys. Rev.*, **93**, p. 1062, (1954).

6. Buechner, W. W., E. N. Strait, C. G. Stergiopoulos, and A. Sperduto, *Phys. Rev.*, **74**, p. 1569, (1948).

7. Cockcroft, J. D., *J. Sci. Inst.*, **10**, p. 71, (1933).

8. Rutherford, E., E. C. Wynn-Williams, W. B. Lewis, and B. V. Bowden, *Proc. Roy. Soc.*, **A139**, p. 617, (1933).

9. Strait, E. N., D. M. Van Patter, W. W. Buechner, and A. Sperduto, *Phys. Rev.*, **81**, p. 747, (1951).

10. Livingston, M. S., and H. A. Bethe, *Revs. Mod. Phys.*, **9**, p. 290, (1937).

11. Li, C. W., W. Whaling, W. A. Fowler, and C. C. Lauritsen, *Phys. Rev.*, **83**, p. 512, (1951).

12. Van Patter, D. M., and W. Whaling, *Revs. Mod. Phys.*, **26**, p. 402, (1954).

13. Zlotowski, I., *Compt. Rend.*, **207**, p. 148, (1938).

14. Gentske, W., *Z. Physik*, **41**, p. 524, (1940).

15. Merhaut, O., *Z. Physik*, **41**, p. 528, (1940).

16. Creagan, R. J., *Phys. Rev.*, **76**, p. 1769, (1949).

17. Perkin, J. L., *Phys. Rev.*, **79**, p. 175, (1950).

18. Savel, P., *Ann. Phys.*, **4**, p. 88, (1935).

19. Waring, J. R. S., and W. Y. Chang, *Proc. Roy. Soc.*, **A157**, p. 652, (1936).

20. Polland, E., H. L. Schultz, and G. Brubaker, *Phys. Rev.*, **53**, p. 351, (1938).

21. Pünfer, E., *Ann. Physik*, **32**, p. 313, (1938).

22. Peck, R. A., Jr., *Phys. Rev.*, **73**, p. 947, (1948).

23. Oliphant, M. L. E., A. E. Kempton, and O. M. Rutherford, *Proc. Roy Soc.*, **A150**, p. 241, (1935).

24. Collins, E. R., C. D. McKenzie, and C. A. Ramm, *Proc. Roy. Soc.*, **A216**, p. 242, (1953).

25. Tollestrup, A. V., W. A. Fowler, and C. C. Lauritsen, *Phys. Rev.*, **76**, p. 428, (1949).

26. Carlson, R. R., *Phys. Rev.*, **84**, p. 749, (1951).

27. Williamson, R. M., C. P. Browne, D. S. Craig, and D. J. Donahue, *Phys. Rev.* **84**, p. 731, (1951).

28. Salmon, A. J., *Proc. Phys. Soc.*, **64A**, p. 848, (1951).

29. Gaerttner, E. R., and H. R. Crane, *Phys. Rev.*, **51**, p. 49, (1937).

30. Delsasso, L. A., W. A. Fowler, and C. C. Lauritsen, *Phys. Rev.*, **51**, p. 391, (1937).

31. Walker, R. L., and B. D. McDaniel, *Phys. Rev.*, **74**, p. 315, (1948).

32. Haxby, Shoupp, and Wells, *Phys. Rev.*, **58**, p. 1035, (1940).

33. Hanson, A. O., and D. L. Benedict, *Phys. Rev.*, **65**, p. 33, (1944).

34. Richards, Smith, and Browne, *Phys. Rev.*, **80**, p. 524, (1950).

35. Williams, J. H., W. G. Sheperd, and R. O. Haxby, *Phys. Rev.*, **51**, p. 888, (1937).

36. Lattes, Fowler, and Cuer, *Proc. Phys. Soc.*, **59A**, p. 883, (1947).

37. French, A. P., and P. B. Treacy, *Proc. Phys. Soc.*, **64A**, p. 452, (1951).

38. Cuer, P., and J. Jung, *Compt. Rend.*, **236**, p. 1252, (1953).

39. Cockcroft, J. D., and E. T. S. Walton, *Proc. Roy. Soc.*, **A144**, p. 704, (1934).

40. Stephens, W. E., K. Djanab, and T. W. Bonner, *Phys. Rev.*, **52**, p. 1079, (1937).

41. Gibson, W. M., and D. L. Livesey, *Proc. Phys. Soc.*, **60A**, p. 523, (1948).

42. Mandeville, Swann, Chatterjee, and Van Patter, *Phys. Rev.*, **85**, p. 193, (1952).

43. Rose, Hudspeth, and Heydenburg, *Phys. Rev.*, **87**, p. 382, (1952).

44. Evans, W. H., T. S. Green, and R. Middleton, *Proc. Phys. Soc.*, **66A**, p. 108, (1953).

45. Jaeckel, R., *Z. Physik*, **96**, p. 151, (1935).

46. Graves, E. R., and J. H. Coon, *Phys. Rev.* **70**, p. 101, (1946).

47. Johnson, C. H., C. K. Bockelman, and H. H. Barschall, *Phys. Rev.*, **82**, p. 117, (1951).

48. Livingston, M. S., and H. A. Bethe, *Revs. Mod. Phys.*, **9**, p. 245, (1937).

49. Boggild, J. K., Kgl. Danske. Vindenskab. *Selsk. Mat.-fys. Medd.*, **23**, No. 4, (1945).

50. Barschall, H. H., and M. E. Battatt, *Phys. Rev.*, **70**, p. 245, (1946).

51. Cuer, P., *J. Phys. et Radium*, **8**, p. 83, (1947).

52. Huber, P., and A. Stebler, *Phys. Rev.*, **73**, p. 85, (1948).

53. Jessee, W. P., and J. Sadaukis, *Phys. Rev.*, **75**, p. 1110, (1949).

54. Franzen, W., J. Halpern, and W. E. Stephens, *Phys. Rev.*, **77**, p. 641, (1950).

55. Meyer, P., *Z. Physik*, **128**, p. 451, (1950).

56. Kinsey, B. B., G. A. Bartholomew, and W. H. Walker, *Phys. Rev.*, **85**, p. 1012, (1952).

57. Hamermesh, B., and V. Hummel, *Phys. Rev.*, **88**, p. 916, (1952).

58. Sherr, R., *Phys. Rev.*, **68**, p. 240, (1945).

59. Sommers, H. W., Jr., and R. Sherr, *Phys. Rev.*, **69**, p. 21, (1946).

60. Becket, R. A., A. O. Hanson, and B. C. Diven, *Phys. Rev.*, **71**, p. 466, (1947).

61. McElhinney, A., A. D. Hanson, R. A. Becker, R. B. Duffield, and B. C. Diven, *Phys. Rev.*, **75**, p. 542, (1949).

62. Summers-Gill, R. G., R. N. H. Haslam, and L. Katz, *Can. J. Phys.*, **31**, p. 70, (1953).

SUGGESTIONS FOR FURTHER READING

1. Livingston, M. S., and H. A. Bethe, *Revs. Mod. Phys.* **9**, pp. 245–390 (1937).

2. Evans, R. D., *The Atomic Nucleus*, Chapters 12, 13. New York: McGraw-Hill Book Co., Inc., 1955.

3. Stranathan, J. D., *The Particles of Modern Physics*, Chapters 10, 11. Philadelphia: Blackiston, 1944.

4. Morrison, P., *Experimental Nuclear Physics*, E. Segre, ed., Vol. II, Part IV. New York: John Wiley & Sons, 1953.

V

NUCLEAR MASSES

1. INTRODUCTION

One of the hypotheses of the 1808 atomic theory of Dalton was the identical nature of the atoms of any one element. Other scientists at that time held the view that all the atoms of an element might not necessarily have identical masses. Prout (1815) suggested that the atoms of all the elements were made up of hydrogen atoms. Thus, according to Prout, the mass of any element would be an integral multiple of the mass of a hydrogen atom. Careful determinations, however, showed that the atomic masses of most elements were not integral multiples, and Prout's hypothesis had to be discarded in favor of Dalton's.

Prout's idea was revived again in a different form by Crookes in 1886. According to Crookes, all atoms must have integral atomic masses, and those elements that appear to have nonintegral atomic masses are actually mixtures. He thought, for example, of chlorine, which has an atomic mass of 35.46 amu, as a mixture of atoms having masses of 34, 35, and 36 amu mixed in a certain proportion to give the observed average atomic mass of chlorine. In addition to Crookes' idea, the discovery of radioactivity at the end of the 19th century and the investigation of the properties of radioactive elements gave sufficient experimental evidence to support the suggestion that the atoms of one element need not be identical in mass. Further study of the radioactive elements showed that there were many elements that were chemically identical, but had different atomic masses. This is quite evident from Figs. 2.6 and 2.7. For example, the end product, Pb, of the radioactive series has different atomic mass numbers 206, 207, and 208. Soddy suggested the name "isotopes" (*isos* meaning "equal," *topos* meaning "place") for the elements that were identical in their chemical properties but which had different masses and which occupy the same place in the periodic table.

After the existence of isotopes had been established among the radioactive elements, the search for isotopes among the nonradioactive elements was initiated by J. J. Thomson[1,2] in about 1910. By using electric and magnetic deflections of the positive rays, or positive ions, the first element he successfully investigated was neon, which was found to be a mixture of two isotopes of atomic masses 20 and 22, mixed in such proportions so as to give an average atomic mass of 20.2. The details of this method, called the "parabola method of positive-ray analysis," and other methods, which have been developed since then for very precise measurements, will be discussed in the following sections. At this point we shall define some terms that will be used frequently.

(i) *Isotopes*:–Nuclei with the same atomic number, Z, that have the same number of protons and a different number of neutrons are called isotopes.

(ii) *Isobars*:–Nuclei with the same mass number, A, (the integral number closest to the actual atomic mass) are called isobars.

(iii) *Isotones*:–Nuclei with the same number of neutrons are called isotones.

2. MASS SCALES

For the purpose of measuring atomic mass two different scales are commonly used: (1) the chemical, or atomic, scale and (2) the physical scale. The chemical scale takes the mass of the natural isotopic mixture of oxygen as 16.000000 atomic mass units (amu) [the natural isotopic mixture of oxygen is $_8O^{16}$ (99.76%), $_8O^{17}$ (0.04%) and $_8O^{18}$ (0.20%)]. The physical scale takes the mass of the most abundant isotope of oxygen, $_8O^{16}$ as 16.000000 amu. The ratio of the two scales is:

$$\frac{\text{physical mass scale}}{\text{atomic mass scale}} = 1.000275 \pm 0.000005$$

Masses measured on the chemical mass scale are also referred to as atomic weights of the elements, and those measured on the physical mass scale are referred to as the isotopic weights, or, better, the isotopic masses. Once the isotopic masses are known, the nuclear masses can be evaluated.

Very recently another unit of atomic mass has been suggested. In 1960, the Tenth General Assembly of the International Union of Pure and Applied Physics recommended the exact number 12 as the nuclear mass of the carbon isotope C^{12}. The symbol suggested for this unit is U. The ratio of the two physical mass scales is

$$\frac{O^{16} \text{ mass scale}}{C^{12} \text{ mass scale}} = 0.99968218$$

At present both C^{12} and O^{16} are being used for the physical mass scale. In this text, differentiation will be made between the scales. The masses given in the isotope chart at the end of the book are based on the physical mass scale (C^{12}) and are the masses of the neutral atoms.

3. MEASUREMENT OF ISOTOPIC MASS

Once it was established by Thomson that the nonradioactive elements are also mixtures of isotopes, the next step was to measure these masses accurately. Though the latest methods developed are much more precise than the original method used by Thomson, the principle applied is still the same: the deflection of the positive ions by electric and magnetic fields. By the application of electric and magnetic fields, one can find the value of q/M for the positive ions of the element under investigation and knowing the value of the charge, q, on the ion, can find the mass, M. Because of its originality and its importance, we shall describe briefly the positive-ray analysis. The original method is limited to the study of gases.

A. POSITIVE-RAY ANALYSIS[1,2].   The experimental arrangement is shown in Fig. 5.1a. The positive ions are formed in the gas between the anode, A, and the cathode, C, which are located in the flask, F, thus forming a discharge tube. The cathode consists of a cylinder about 7 cm long, fixed in the neck of the flask. A narrow hole less than 1 mm in diameter is made through the cathode. The cathode is cooled by the water jacket, J. The discharge tube is operated at a potential difference of 30,000 to 50,000 volts. The gas under investigation is allowed to enter at a steady rate through the capillary tube, I, (see Fig. 5.1a) and after circulating around F is pumped out at O. Under a high potential difference the positive ions move towards the cathode, and those passing axially through the narrow tube emerge as a narrow beam. As shown in the figure, pole pieces, PP, of an electromagnet, MM, are located outside the tube near the cathode. These pole pieces are insulated from the rest of the electromagnet by means of thin mica sheets, NN, so that the pole pieces can be used as the plates of a capacitor to produce an electric field in the gap by connecting them to a battery. Thus the beam of positive ions is subjected to parallel electric and magnetic fields simultaneously. The fields are perpendicular to the path of the beam, and they can be made to act simultaneously on the positive ions. After passing through the magnetic and

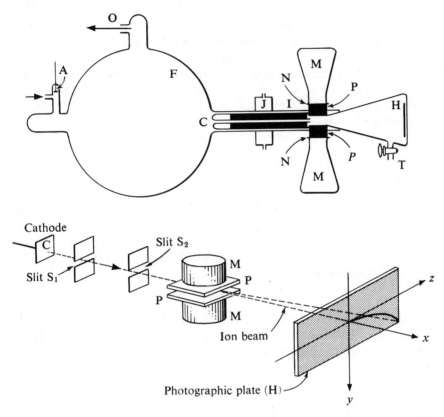

FIG. 5.1   (*a*) Experimental arrangement of the J. J. Thomson method for measuring q/M for the positive ions. (*b*) The path of a beam under the influence of electric and magnetic fields.

the electric fields, the beam is allowed to fall on a photographic plate, H. The plate, after development, shows traces that are parabolas.

The electric field, E, deflects the ions in the plane of the electric field, and the magnetic field, B, deflects them at right angles to this plane. If the values of E and B are held constant, the ions having the same value of q/M, but having different values of the velocity, v, trace a parabola on the photographic plate. The ions having different values of q/M produce different parabolas. The equation of these parabolas can be derived as follows.

Assume the coordinate system to be such that the beam moves in the positive x-direction, and the electric and the magnetic fields are in the positive y-direction (Fig. 5.1b). The effect of the electric field will be to accelerate the positive ions in the y-direction. Thus

$$F_{y\,\text{elec.}} = qE = Ma_y \qquad (5.1)$$

where q is the charge on the positive ions,
  E is the electric field intensity between the plates,
  M is the mass of each ion, and
  a_y is the acceleration in the y-direction produced by the electric field.
If the velocity of the ion before entering the field is v (in the positive x-direction) and the length of the plate is l, then the time t taken by the ion to cross the field is

$$t = l/v \qquad (5.2)$$

Combining Eqs. (5.1) and (5.2), we find the deflection of the ion in the y-direction to be

$$y = \frac{1}{2} a_y t^2 = \frac{1}{2} \frac{qEl^2}{Mv^2} \qquad (5.3)$$

The magnetic field acting on the ion deflects it in a direction perpendicular to both B and v, i.e., in the z-direction. The force accelerating the ion in the z-direction is

$$F_{z\,\text{mag.}} = qvB = Ma_z \qquad (5.4)$$

where B is the strength of the magnetic field and a_z is the acceleration in the z-direction. The deflection in the z-direction is obtained from Eqs. (5.2) and (5.4), (provided the deflection is small) and is given by

$$z = \tfrac{1}{2} a_z t^2 = \frac{1}{2} \frac{qvBl^2}{Mv^2} = \frac{1}{2} \frac{qBl^2}{Mv} \qquad (5.5)$$

Eliminating v from Eqs. (5.3) and (5.5), we get

$$z^2 = \frac{(l^2 B^2 q)}{2EM} y$$

or

$$z^2 = (kq/M)y \qquad (5.6)$$

which is the equation of a parabola, because $k = \dfrac{l^2 B^2}{2E}$ is a constant. Positive ions with the same value of q/M and different velocities, therefore, should form a single parabola. The ions that have the greatest velocity will be least deflected and will be closest to the undeflected spot, O. Reversing the direction of the magnetic field, the other half of the parabola may be traced.

Thomson used this method for several gases, among them H_2, O_2, CO, CO_2, Ne. The results obtained by using this method are shown in Fig. 5.2. It was concluded that neon is a mixture of two isotopes. The value of q/M from Eq. (5.6) is

$$q/M = z^2/ky \qquad (5.7)$$

where $M = 20$ and 22 amu. Because the atomic weight of neon is 20.20 amu, there must be nine times as many neon atoms with atomic mass 20 as there are with atomic mass 22, so that

$$[(9 \times 20) + (1 \times 22)]/(9 + 1) = 20.20$$

Though the parabola method gives clear indications of the existence of isotopes, it does not yield precise values of isotopic masses or their relative

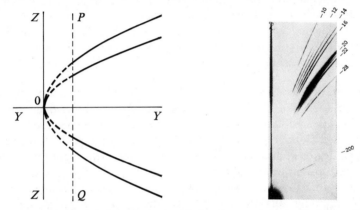

FIG. 5.2 (*a*) Traces of the parabolas due to the two isotopes of neon having mass number 20 and 22. The points of intersection of PQ with the parabolas represent the ions of maximum energies. (*b*) Parabolas obtained by J. J. Thomson method (courtesy of K. T. Bainbridge).

abundance. This is because most of the ion beam is lost in collisions; the beam's total intensity is too small to be photographed with clarity. The beam is also spread over the whole parabola, which contributes to a reduced intensity. The traces on the photographic plate are blurred with no defined edges, and, because of this, it is not possible to get accurate measurements. A precise method was needed to establish, beyond doubt, the existence of isotopes.

This need led to the development of many mass spectrometers and mass spectrographs. The work started by J. J. Thomson was taken over by F. W. Aston. Aston's work[3,4,5,6] is outstanding, and he has possibly accomplished more in this field than any other person. The primary improvements needed were in dispersive power (to increase the separation of the ions of different masses) and in sensitivity of the equipment. These were accomplished by bringing all the ions to focus at a single point, instead of being spread over the parabola. The principle of the method is the application of electric and magnetic fields one after the other and in different directions. First, the electric field produces a dispersion of the positive rays with respect to velocity, and then the magnetic field is applied at right angles to the direction of the electric field, which brings the dispersed rays with a given value of q/M to a common focus. This increases the sensitivity, that is, creates greater intensity, which allows one to use very fine slits to obtain sharp images. The method is also called the *velocity-focusing method*.

The improved form of Aston's mass spectrograph[5] yielded an accuracy of 1 part in 10,000 for isotopic-mass determination. Later instruments, using the same principle, were designed and built by A. Dempster[7], K. Bainbridge and E. Jordon[8], J. Mattauch[9], and A. Nier[10]. The improved designs of these instruments have yielded values of isotopic masses with accuracies of the order of 1 part in 100,000. Nier's mass spectrometer is also well suited for abundance measurements.

B. DEMPSTER'S MASS SPECTROMETER[11,12,13]. Dempster's mass spectrometer is shown in Fig. 5.3(a). It is called a mass *spectrometer*, rather than a *spectrograph*, because the ion current is measured electrically instead of being recorded on a photographic plate as in a mass spectrograph. This instrument has a high degree of accuracy in separating isotopes with slight differences in their atomic masses, provided a steady source of positive ions is available.

The positive rays are obtained either by heating salts on platinum strips or by bombarding salts with electrons; in the latter case the salts are either heated by the bombardment or heated independently while being bombarded. Referring to Fig. 5.3(a), the positively charged atoms produced at F are allowed to fall through a definite potential difference, V, by applying an electric field between the plates, P and Q. A narrow beam is obtained by means of the slit, S_1. These rays are bent into a semicircle by a strong magnetic field, B, applied in a direction perpendicular to the plane of the paper. The radius of the circle must have a certain value so that the positive ions may reach the slit S_2 and be detected by the electrometer, E. A screen, D, is introduced into the analyzing chamber to prevent reflected rays from getting into the slit S_2.

A particle of mass M and charge q, while falling through a potential V, will acquire kinetic energy given by

$$\tfrac{1}{2}Mv^2 = qV \tag{5.8}$$

where v is the velocity of the ions coming out of S_1. The radius, R, of the circle is related to the magnetic field, B, by the relation

$$Bqv = Mv^2/R \tag{5.9}$$

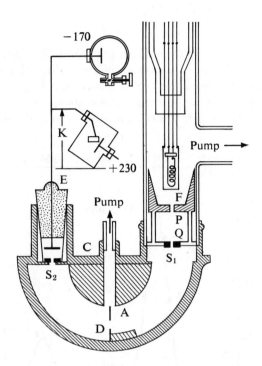

FIG. 5.3 (*a*) Schematic of Dempster's mass spectrometer. [From A. J. Dempster, *Phys. Rev.*, **22**, 631 (1922).]

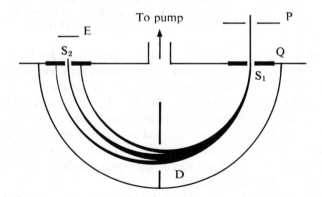

FIG. 5.3 (*b*) The dispersion and focusing of a beam of ions.

Eliminating v from Eqs. (5.8) and (5.9)

$$q/M = 2V/B^2 R^2 \qquad (5.10)$$

which means that if V and B are fixed, the radius, R, depends on the value of q/M as Fig. 5.3(b) shows for three different values of q/M. By changing the magnetic field or the electric field (for maximum reliability, the magnetic field is kept constant while the electric field is changed), the rays having ions with different values of q/M are brought to a focus at the slit S_2 and to the

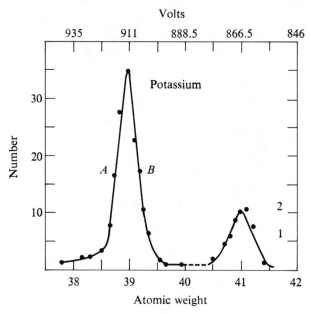

FIG. 5.4 The two isotopes of potassium. Their relative abundances are proportional to the areas under the two peaks. The smaller peak has been multiplied by a factor of 10. [From A. J. Dempster, *Phys. Rev.*, **22**, 631 (1922).]

collector plate of the electrometer, E. The current recorded by the electrometer is proportional to the number of the positive ions reaching E per unit time. Also, because each accelerating potential, V, corresponds to a definite value of M of the particles reaching the plate, E, the current (which is proportional to the intensity) is proportional to the atomic mass. The unknown atomic masses of the isotopes can be found by comparison with some standard atomic masses, while the relative abundance of the isotopes can be found by plotting intensity (proportional to current) versus atomic weights (proportional to the accelerating voltage).

A typical curve obtained by Dempster for potassium is shown in Fig. 5.4. The curve shows the intensity of the rays observed as the accelerating potential is varied to bring various parts of the beam to the slit S_2. There are two isotopes; their atomic weights are 39 and 41 units. The intensity ratio is approximately 18:1, giving a mean atomic weight of 39.10 in agreement with the chemical atomic weight.

C. MATCHED DOUBLET METHOD. The most modern method for a very precise measurement of the masses by using mass spectrography is the matched doublet method. This technique involves the determination of the difference in masses between two ions of the same mass number but which have slightly different masses. For best results the intensities of the two ion beams are matched. The distance between the two lines on the photographic plates represents the difference in the masses of the two ions. Thus, if the mass of one of them is known accurately, the mass of the other can be determined with very high precision. Though the accuracy in the actual measurement is of the order of 1 part in 10^3, the masses can be evaluated with an accuracy of the order of 1 part in 10^6. The procedure for doing such calculations will be clear from the following example.

Consider the three fundamental mass doublets of H, D, C, and O, where $H \equiv H^1$, $D \equiv H^2$, $C \equiv C^{12}$, $O \equiv O^{16}$. The three doublets are (1) $(H_2^1)^+ - (H^2)^+$, (2) $(H_3^2)^+ - (C^{12})^{++}$, and (3) $(C^{12}H_4^1)^+ - (O^{16})^+$. The doubly, triply, and so forth, ionized particles appear at the positions of mass numbers $A/2$, $A/3$, and so forth, respectively. C^{++}, for example, appears at the position of mass 6. If we denote the mass differences of the three doublets given above by α, β, and γ, respectively, we can write

$$A/n = 2; \quad (H_2^1)^+ - (H^2)^+ = 2H - D = \alpha$$
$$A/n = 6; \quad (H_3^2)^+ - (C^{12})^{++} = 3D - \tfrac{1}{2}C = \beta$$
$$A/n = 16; \quad (C^{12}H_4^1)^+ - (O^{16})^+ = C + 4H - O = \gamma$$

If we now assume that the masses are measured on the physical mass scale, so that $O = O^{16} = 16.000000$, then the above three simultaneous equations yield

$$H = H^1 = 1 + \tfrac{3}{8}\alpha + \tfrac{1}{8}\beta + \tfrac{1}{16}\gamma$$
$$D = H^2 = 2 - \tfrac{1}{4}\alpha + \tfrac{1}{4}\beta + \tfrac{1}{8}\gamma$$
$$C = C^{12} = 12 - \tfrac{3}{2}\alpha - \tfrac{1}{2}\beta + \tfrac{3}{4}\gamma$$

Thus, knowing the primary standard of mass, the other secondary mass standards can be established easily.

The measurements on these doublets have been made by many authors[14,15,16,17,18]. Those made by Ewald[18] appear in Table 5.1.

There are many more mass spectrographic doublets, some of which are shown here.

$$C^{12}(H^1)_2 - N^{14}; \quad (N^{14})_2 - C^{12}O^{16}$$
$$(H^2)_2 O^{16} - Ne^{20}; \quad C^{12}O^{16} - Si^{28}$$
$$P^{31}H^1 - S^{32}; \quad (O^{16})_2 - S^{32}$$
$$(H^2)_2 O^{16} - \tfrac{1}{2}A^{40}; \quad Ne^{20} - \tfrac{1}{2}A^{40}$$

TABLE 5.1

MASS DIFFERENCES OF THE THREE FUNDAMENTAL DOUBLETS BY EWALD[18]

A/n	Doublet	Mass Difference ($\times 10^{-3}$ amu)
2	$2H - D$	1.5503 ± 0.0015
6	$3D - \frac{1}{2}C$	42.292 ± 0.012
16	$(C + 4H) - O$	36.371 ± 0.012

Still another method has been developed. The *time-of-flight method* involves the pulsing of the ion source and measuring the time elapsed until the ions reach the detector. The details may be found in the original work[19,20] and also in Chap. 13, Sec. 5.

4. MEASUREMENT OF MASSES FROM NUCLEAR DISINTEGRATION DATA

In Chap. 4, we defined the Q-value of a nuclear reaction by the equation

$$Q = [(M_X + m_x) - (M_Y + m_y)] \, c^2.$$

If the Q-values of the nuclear reactions are known accurately, it is possible to calculate the masses of the nuclei directly in terms of O^{16} without recourse to mass spectrographic results. The calculations of the masses of the light nuclei up to $A = 33$ have been done by C. W. Li, *et al.*[21,22]. This procedure will be explained briefly.

Nuclear reactions can be divided into two classes:

(i) The first class contains those reactions that are independent in the sense that they are not equivalent to any combination of other nuclear reactions.

(ii) The second class contains those reactions, any one of which can be constructed by a suitable combination of two or more of the other reactions in this class. For example, $Na^{23}(d, \alpha)Ne^{21}$ is equivalent to the sum of the two reactions $Ne^{20}(d, p)Ne^{21}$ and $Na^{23}(p, \alpha)Ne^{20}$. These nuclear reactions are said to form cycles. These cycles can be used to determine unknown masses in terms of O^{16} taken as 16.000000 amu, and the values of certain fundamental mass differences.

The calculation of nuclear masses from Q-values is a linear and additive operation. The H^1 mass, for example, is given in terms of O^{16} by

$$H^1 = \tfrac{1}{16}(O^{16}) + \tfrac{1}{16}[-9Q_a + 10Q_b + 5Q_c -$$
$$(Q_1 - Q_2 - Q_3 + Q_4 + Q_5 + Q_6 + Q_7 - Q_8)] \times 1.07394 \times 10^{-3} \text{ (amu)}$$

where

$$Q_a = n - H^1 \qquad\qquad Q_4 = C^{13}(d, \alpha)B^{11}$$
$$Q_b = n + H^1 - H^2 \qquad Q_5 = B^{11}(d, \alpha)Be^9$$
$$Q_c = 2H^2 - He^4 \qquad\quad Q_6 = Be^9(p, \alpha)Li^6$$
$$Q_1 = O^{16}(d, \alpha)N^{14} \qquad Q_7 = Li^6(p, \alpha)He^3$$
$$Q_2 = C^{14}(\beta^-)N^{14} \qquad Q_8 = H^2(d, n)He^3$$
$$Q_3 = C^{13}(d, p)C^{14}$$

It may be pointed out that because there are many more nuclear reactions than unknown masses, the masses are considerably over-determined, and thus it requires the use of adjusted values for Q in order to have internal consistency of the data and to obtain the most probable masses.

Some of the results of such calculations, taken from the work of C. W. Li[22], are tabulated in Tables 5.2 and 5.3 and compared with mass spectroscopic results. The accuracy achieved in this method is better than that in

---

TABLE 5.2

NUCLEAR CYCLES AND FUNDAMENTAL MASS DIFFERENCES

Cycle	Mass difference from experimental Q (Mev)
Group 1. Nuclear cycles giving a sum of zero.	
$Na^{23}(d, \alpha)Ne^{21}$, $Ne^{20}(d, p)Ne^{21}$, $Na^{23}(p, \alpha)Ne^{20}$	0.001 ± 0.015
$Al^{27}(d, \alpha)Mg^{25}$, $Mg^{24}(d, p)Mg^{25}$, $Al^{27}(p, \alpha)Mg^{24}$	0.004 ± 0.014
$P^{31}(d, \alpha)Si^{29}$, $Si^{28}(d, p)Si^{29}$, $P^{31}(p, \alpha)Si^{28}$	0.003 ± 0.017
$Si^{30}(d, \alpha)Al^{28}$, $Al^{27}(d, p)Al^{28}$, $Si^{29}(d, \alpha)Al^{27}$, $Si^{29}(d, p)Si^{30}$	0.020 ± 0.022
Group 2. Nuclear cycles giving $n - H^1$.	
$O^{18}(p, n)F^{18}$, $F^{18}(\beta^+)O^{18}$	0.786 ± 0.009
$F^{19}(p, n)Ne^{19}$, $Ne^{19}(\beta^+)F^{19}$	0.837 ± 0.030
$O^{16}(d, p)O^{17}$, $O^{16}(d, n)F^{17}$, $F^{17}(\beta^+)O^{17}$	0.806 ± 0.024
Group 3. Nuclear cycles giving $n + H^1 - H^2$.	
$F^{19}(d, p)F^{20}$, $F^{19}(n, \gamma)F^{20}$	2.257 ± 0.031
$Al^{27}(d, p)Al^{28}$, $Al^{27}(n, \gamma)Al^{28}$	2.230 ± 0.014
$Si^{28}(d, p)Si^{29}$, $Si^{28}(n, \gamma)Si^{29}$	2.264 ± 0.041
$P^{31}(d, p)P^{32}$, $P^{31}(n, \gamma)P^{32}$	2.236 ± 0.031
$S^{32}(d, p)S^{33}$, $S^{32}(n, \gamma)S^{33}$	2.218 ± 0.023
Group 4. Nuclear cycles giving $2H^2 - He^4$.	
$Ne^{20}(d, p)Ne^{21}$, $Ne^{21}(d, \alpha)F^{19}$, $F^{19}(d, p)F^{20}$, $F^{20}(\beta^-)Ne^{20}$, with $2H^1 - H^2 = (1.443 \pm 0.002)$ Mev	23.815 ± 0.023
$Mg^{24}(d, p)Mg^{25}$, $Mg^{25}(d, \alpha)Na^{23}$, $Na^{23}(d, p)Na^{24}$, $Na^{24}(\beta^-)Mg^{24}$, with $2H^1 - H^2 = (1.443 \pm 0.002)$ Mev	23.812 ± 0.018
$Si^{28}(d, p)Si^{29}$, $Si^{29}(d, \alpha)Al^{27}$, $Al^{27}(n, \gamma)Al^{28}$, $Al^{28}(\beta^-)Si^{28}$, with $n - H^1 = (0.7823 \pm 0.001)$ Mev	23.829 ± 0.022

TABLE 5.3

COMPARISON OF MASSES FROM NUCLEAR DATA AND FROM MASS SPECTROGRAPH MEASUREMENTS

Nuclear Data			Nier (1951)[a]	$\Delta \times 10^6$	Ewald (1951)[b]	$\Delta \times 10^6$
H	1	1.008 142	1.008 165		1.008 141	
		(± 3)	(± 4)	$+23$	(± 2)	-1
H	2	2.014 735	2.014 778		2.014 732	
		(± 6)	(± 8)	$+43$	(± 4)	-3
He	4	4.003 873	4.003 944		4.003 860	
		(± 15)	(± 19)	$+71$	(± 12)	-13
C	12	12.003 804	12.003 842		12.003 807	
		(± 17)	(± 6)	$+38$	(± 11)	$+3$
N	14	14.007 515	14.007 564		14.007 525	
		(± 11)	(± 7)	$+49$	(± 15)	$+10$
N	15	15.004 533			15.004 928	
		(± 12)			(± 20)	$+65$
O	17	17.004 533			17.004 507	
		(± 7)			(± 15)	-26
O	18	18.004 857			18.004 875	
		(± 23)			(± 13)	$+18$
F	19	19.004 456			19.004 414	
		(± 15)			(± 17)	-42
Ne	20	19.998 777	19.998 835		19.998 771	
		(± 21)	(± 43)	$+58$	(± 12)	-6
Ne	21	21.000 504			21.000 393	
		(± 22)			(± 22)	-111
Ne	22	21.998 358			21.998 329	
		(± 25)			(± 19)	-29
Si	28	27.985 767			27.985 792	
		(± 32)			(± 32)	$+25$
P	31	30.983 550			30.983 622	
		(± 39)			(± 23)	$+72$
S	32	31.982 183	31.982 218		31.982 272	
		(± 42)	(± 25)	$+35$	(± 19)	$+89$

[a] A. O. Nier, *Phys. Rev.*, **81**, 624 (1951).
[b] H. Ewald, *Z. Naturforsch.*, **6a**, 293 (1951).

mass spectroscopic determination. There is a good agreement between the two for the light nuclei, though in general, the results obtained by the mass spectroscope are consistently larger than those obtained from the nuclear reactions. But there is an advantage of using nuclear reactions for mass determination of nuclei with short half-lives.

5. NUCLEAR DENSITY

The density of nuclear material can be calculated if we know the mass and the volume of the nucleus. The methods for the determination of nuclear masses have already been discussed in the previous sections. In order to calculate the volume, one has to know the shape and size of the nucleus. Different models have been proposed to explain different characteristics of the nuclei. For our purpose in this chapter, we assume that the nucleus is spherical in shape, and that the protons and the neutrons are arranged in such a way as to give a uniform spherical mass-distribution. This picture of the nucleus is similar to that of a drop of liquid, and the name given to the model is the *liquid-drop model* of the nucleus. The volume, V, of the nucleus, therefore, is given by

$$V = 4\pi R^3/3 \tag{5.11}$$

where R is the radius of the nucleus. The analysis of all the existing experimental data has resulted in the following expression for the nuclear radius

$$R = r_0 A^{1/3} \tag{5.12}$$

where r_0 is a constant, and A is the mass number. As we shall see in Chapter 6, the value of r_0 depends on the experimental technique used for evaluating the nuclear radius. The value of r_0 varies from 1.2×10^{-13} cm to 1.48×10^{-13} cm. For our calculations we may take this value to be

$$r_0 = 1.35 \times 10^{-13} \text{ cm} \tag{5.13}$$

Now we are in a position to calculate the density of the nuclear material. Recalling the definition of density and using Eqs. (5.11) and (5.12), we get

$$\rho = \frac{M}{V} = \frac{M}{\frac{4\pi}{3} R^3} = \frac{M}{\frac{4\pi}{3} r_0^3 A} \tag{5.14}$$

where M is the mass of the nucleus. To get some idea of the numerical value, let us calculate the density of protons. For a proton $A = 1$, $R = r_0 = 1.35 \times 10^{-13}$ cm, and $M = m_p = 1.67 \times 10^{-24}$ gm, the density is

$$\rho = 10^5 \text{ tons/mm}^3 \tag{5.15}$$

6. PACKING FRACTIONS AND BINDING ENERGIES

Accurate measurements of atomic masses of different isotopes of stable elements and of some radioactive isotopes have been made and are given in the *Chart of the Nuclides* at the end of the book. The masses reported are on the physical atomic scale of C^{12}. Included in the chart, as well, are the chemical masses of the atoms. As predicted by the earlier workers, the masses of different isotopes are very close to the whole numbers, but small deviations from whole numbers lead to very important conclusions as we shall see in the following sections. Masses of the isotopes differ very slightly from integral numbers, the maximum deviation being in the case of U^{238}, which has an isotopic mass of 238.12522 amu. This small variation from whole numbers was expressed by Aston in terms of a quantity called the *packing fraction, f*, and is defined as

$$f = \frac{\text{atomic mass of the isotope} - \text{mass number}}{\text{mass number}}$$

or

$$= \frac{M(A, Z) - A}{A} \tag{5.16}$$

where $M(A, Z)$ is the actual mass of a nuclide on the physical atomic scale of C^{12} (or O^{16}), and A is the mass number $Z + N$, Z and N being the number of protons and neutrons, respectively. The numerator in Eq. (5.16)

$$M(A, Z) - A = Af \tag{5.17}$$

is called the *mass defect*. From experiments we find that f is very small for all mass numbers as shown in Fig. 5.5, where f has been plotted against A.

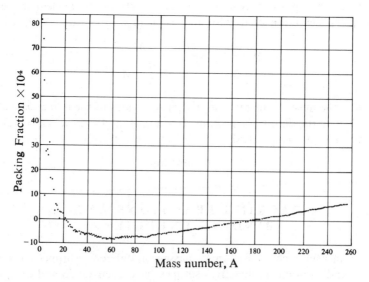

FIG. 5.5 Packing fraction, f, versus mass number A.

The packing fractions for all the nuclei, except for He^4, C^{12}, and O^{16}, fall on or near a smooth curve. For C^{12} the value of f will be zero by definition if we use the physical mass scale of C^{12}. The usefulness of f will appear from the discussion of the binding energies of the nuclei.

One might be tempted to say that because the atom is made up of protons, neutrons, and electrons, the mass of a particular atom will be the sum of the masses of its separate consituents, that is, the sum of the masses of protons, neutrons, and electrons in the free state. But a survey of the atomic masses shows that this is not true. The atomic mass of any isotope is less than the sum of its constituent particles in the free state. This difference in the mass, ΔM, is converted into energy in the process of formation of an atom from protons, neutrons, and electrons. Using the famous mass-energy relation given by Einstein's Special Theory of Relativity, the amount of energy released is

$$E = \Delta M c^2 \tag{5.18}$$

Note that depending upon the mass scale used, 1 amu in terms of the energy units is given by

$$1 \text{ amu } (O^{16}) = 931.145 \text{ Mev}$$
$$1 \text{ amu } (C^{12}) = 931.441 \text{ Mev}$$

Once an atom has been formed from its requisite number of protons, neutrons, and electrons, the same amount of energy will be required to reduce this atom to its constituent particles in the free state. The energy that keeps the nucleons together in a bound state is the *binding energy* of the nucleus and can be calculated in a simple manner. The mass of the constituent particles of an atom $_zX^A$ is the sum of Z protons, $A - Z$ neutrons, and Z electrons. Thus the binding energy is given by

$$BE = [Zm_p + (A - Z)m_n + Zm_e - M(A, Z)]\, c^2 \tag{5.19}$$

where m_p, m_n, and m_e are the masses of the proton, neutron, and electron, respectively. Combining Eqs. (5.19) and (5.17), we may write

$$BE = [Zm_p + (A - Z)m_n + Zm_e - A(1 + f)]c^2 \tag{5.20}$$

As we know, the hydrogen atom is formed by the combination of a proton and an electron, and if we neglect the binding energy of the hydrogen atom, which is very small (a few ev), Eq. (5.19) can be written as

$$BE = [Zm_H + (A - Z)m_n - M(A, Z)]c^2 \tag{5.21}$$

where m_H is the mass of the hydrogen atom.

The average binding energy per nucleon is obtained by dividing the total binding energy of the nucleus by the mass number A. (The binding energies of all the electrons in an atom are very small and may be neglected.) Hence

$$BE/A = [Zm_H + (A - Z)m_n - M(A, Z)]c^2/A \qquad (5.22)$$

Fig. 5.6 shows the plot of the binding energy per nucleon BE/A versus the mass number A. With the exception of He^4, C^{12}, and O^{16} the values of the binding energies per nucleon lie on or close to a single smooth curve. There are some prominent features of this curve.

(i) For low A, the binding energy per nucleon is low and rises rapidly with increasing A.

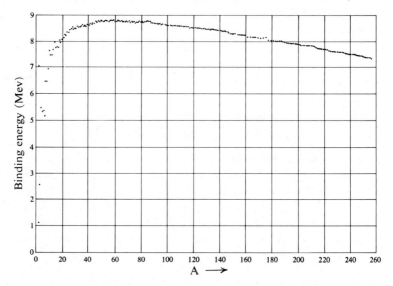

FIG. 5.6   Binding energy per nucleon (BE/A) versus mass number A, in Mev.

(ii) For values around $A = 50$, there is a flat maximum where the binding energy per nucleon is ~ 8.8 Mev, and it gradually drops down to ~ 8.4 Mev at $A = 140$. The average binding energy per nucleon in this region is approximately 8.5 Mev.

(iii) Above $A = 140$, the binding energy per nucleon keeps on decreasing smoothly and reaches a value of 7.6 Mev at $A = 238$ for U^{238}.

The low value of the binding energy per nucleon for small mass numbers can be explained as a surface tension effect on the basis of the liquid-drop model, while the small values at high mass numbers can be explained as due to coulomb repulsion of the protons. These and some other effects will be discussed in detail in the following sections.

7. SURFACE-TENSION EFFECT

The rapid decrease in the value of the binding energy per nucleon at small A can be explained as the surface-tension effect if the nucleus is viewed as a drop of liquid[23]. The nucleons deep inside the nucleus are attracted from every side by the neighboring nucleons while those on the surface are attracted only from one side. This leads to a small value of the binding energy for the surface nucleons. This effect is greater for nuclei with small A because a greater fraction of the nucleons is near the surface as compared to the nuclei with large A. If R is the radius of the nucleus, and S is the coefficient of surface tension, the surface energy E_s is given by

$$E_s = 4\pi R^2 S = 4\pi (r_0 A^{1/3})^2 S$$
$$= (4\pi r_0^2 S) A^{2/3}$$
$$= a_2 A^{2/3} \tag{5.23}$$

where a_2 is a constant equal to $4\pi r_0^2 S$, and as we shall see in Sec. 10, a_2 is approximately equal to 17.80 Mev or $0.019114U$, which results in the value of the coefficient of surface tension S being $\sim 10^{10}$ tons/mm.

8. COULOMB EFFECT

The drop in the binding energy curve at large values of A can be explained by the coulomb effect. According to Coulomb's law, the protons inside the nucleus will repel each other, decreasing the binding energy or increasing the mass of the nucleus. Because the coulomb forces are long range, each proton affects every other proton, not just its immediate neighbors. The repulsive force, therefore, goes on increasing with increasing Z and, hence, with increasing A. This coulomb repulsive force results in two consequences:

(i) The mean binding energy per nucleon will drop as A increases. This is clear from Fig. 5.6, which shows a gradual drop in BE/A at higher values of A.

(ii) The locus of the stable nuclei should depart from the line $N/Z = 1$ towards the direction of a higher number of neutrons as shown in Fig. 5.7.

Fig. 5.7 is an abbreviated form of the *Chart of the Nuclides* given at the end of the book. It shows the neutron number N versus the proton number Z. Each small square represents an isotope and the solid black squares represent stable isotopes. Two smooth curves, one through the stable isotopes and the other for $N = Z$, have been drawn. It is evident from the figure that for low values of N and Z, the stable isotopes have $N/Z = 1$. For the

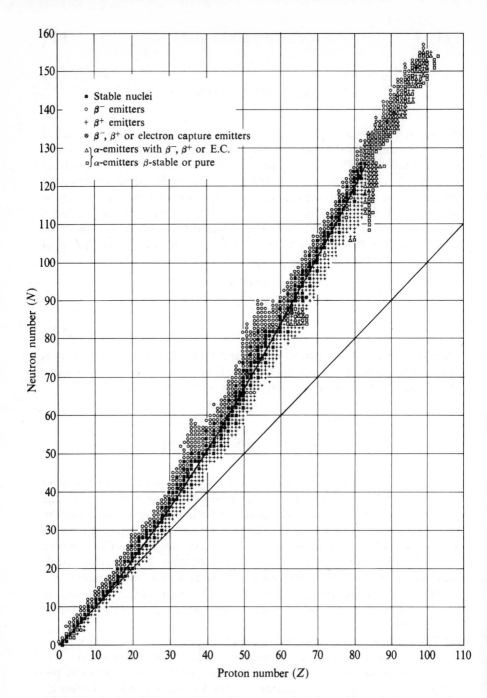

FIG. 5.7 A plot of N versus Z for all known nuclei. The stable nuclei are shown by solid rectangles. A curve through the stable nuclei shows that it starts with $N/Z = 1$ for nuclei of low mass numbers and reaches a value of $N/Z = 1.6$ for high mass numbers. [Drawn from *Chart of Nuclides*.]

heavier elements, the stability curve gradually departs from the $N/Z = 1$ line, reaching a value of $N/Z = 1.6$ for $A = 238$. The isotopes on both sides of the stability curve are radioactive and eventually decay in such a way as to form the final stable isotopes.

The total Coulomb-energy contributed to the binding-energy curve may be calculated in the following manner. We again assume the liquid-drop model of the nucleus even though the drop has a charge of Ze, where Z is the number of protons inside the nucleus, and e is the charge of each proton. Furthermore, if it is assumed that the charge Ze is uniformly distributed throughout the sphere, the charge density ρ is given by

$$\left(\frac{4\pi}{3} R^3\right) \rho = Ze \tag{5.24}$$

or

$$\rho = \frac{3Ze}{4\pi R^3} \tag{5.25}$$

The total electrostatic energy, E, of this uniform spherical charge distribution is given by

$$E = \int_0^R \frac{(4\pi r^3 \rho/3)(\rho 4\pi r^2 \, dr)}{r} \tag{5.26}$$

where r is the radial distance from the center of the nucleus and R is the radius of the nucleus. Integrating Eq. (5.26)

$$E = 16\pi^2 \rho^2 R^5/15 \tag{5.27}$$

and substituting the value of ρ from Eq. (5.25) into Eq. (5.27), one gets

$$E = 3Z^2 e^2/5R \tag{5.28}$$

Note that the above expression for E also includes an extra amount of fictitious self-energy of each proton resulting from the assumption that the proton is spread over the whole volume. Equation (5.28), therefore, needs a correction term. This self-energy for a proton from Eq. (5.28) is $3e^2/5R$ and for Z protons is $Z(3e^2/5R)$. Subtracting $Z(3e^2/5R)$ from E, we get the total Coulomb energy, E_c, given by

$$E_c = \frac{3}{5} \frac{e^2}{R} Z^2 - \frac{3}{5} \frac{e^2}{R} Z$$

or

$$E_c = \frac{3}{5} \frac{e^2}{R} Z(Z - 1) \tag{5.29}$$

which may be written as

$$E_c = \frac{6}{5} \frac{e^2}{R} \frac{Z(Z - 1)}{2} \tag{5.30}$$

Equation (5.30) could have been derived from direct considerations. The coulomb energy between a pair of protons with each having a radius R can be shown to be $6e^2/5R$. The number of proton–proton pairs in a nucleus of atomic number Z (because each of the Z protons interacts with the other $(Z-1)$ protons) is $Z(Z-1)/2$. The factor of $\frac{1}{2}$ comes in because each pair is counted twice. The total coulomb energy, therefore, is as given by Eq. (5.30). If $Z \gg 1$, then $Z(Z-1) \approx Z^2$ and Eq. (5.30) reduces to

$$E_c = \frac{3e^2Z^2}{5R} \qquad (5.31)$$

Substitute for $R = r_0 A^{1/3}$ in Eq. (5.31),

$$E_c = \frac{3e^2}{5r_0}\frac{Z^2}{A^{1/3}} = a_3 \frac{Z^2}{A^{1/3}} \qquad (5.32)$$

where $a_3 = 3e^2/5r_0$ is a constant. The value of a_3 can be calculated if we know e and r_0. The value of a_3 varies from 0.6 Mev to about 0.8 Mev depending on the value of r_0 which may vary from 1.2×10^{-13} to 1.5×10^{-13} cm.

9. ODD-EVEN EFFECT

In addition to other factors, the total binding-energy of a nucleus is determined not only by the ratio of the number of protons and neutrons, but also by whether these numbers are odd or even. Four types of nuclei are possible: even–even, odd–odd, even–odd and odd–even. In each type the first word stands for the number of protons and the second, the number of neutrons. The most stable nuclei tend to have an even number of both protons and neutrons; they are an even–even type. The least stable nuclei are the odd–odd type. The stabilities of the even–odd and odd–even types of nuclei are almost identical and lie intermediate between the other two. This tendency can be seen by classifying the stable nuclei. The results of such a classification are given in Table 5.4, which indicate that even–even nuclei are by far the most abundant, and that there are only five stable odd–odd nuclei.

These five odd–odd nuclei ($_1H^2$, $_3Li^6$, $_5B^{10}$, $_7N^{14}$, $_{73}Ta^{180}$) may be treated as special cases. This table suggests that in the nuclear ground-state there is a tendency for two nucleons of the same type in the same state to join together to form a pair with spins oppositely directed. Thus in the case of even–even nuclei, all the nucleons of both types can be paired off. In the case of even–odd or odd–even nuclei there will be one unpaired nucleon. Because the odd–odd nuclei are most unstable, it suggests that nucleon pairing does not take place between a proton and a neutron; otherwise there

TABLE 5.4

NUMBER OF STABLE ISOTOPES*

A	Z	N	Number of Cases
Even	Even	Even	156
Odd	Even	Odd	50
Odd	Odd	Even	48
Even	Odd	Odd	5
			259

* From: D. T. Goldman, *General Electric Chart of Nuclides and Isotopes* (Rev. 1964, Seventh Ed.).

would be no reason for the odd–odd nuclei not to be as stable as the even–even nuclei. This is illustrated by considering a particular example of $_{14}Si^{30}$.

$_{14}Si^{30}$ which is an even–even nucleus has 14 protons and 16 neutrons. Fig. 5.8 shows a highly schematic energy-level diagram for protons and neutrons that are paired off with opposite spin directions. It is clear from

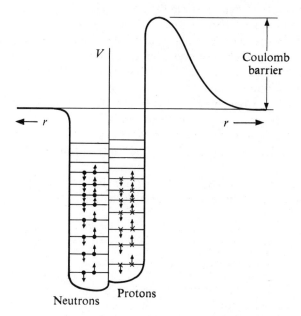

FIG. 5.8 A simplified energy level diagram for protons and neutrons in $_{14}Si^{30}$. Note that because neutrons do not have any charge, there is no coulomb barrier. Nuclear attractive forces are represented by a negative potential.

Fig. 5.8 that the next higher level is either a proton level or a neutron level. If we add a neutron to $_{14}Si^{30}$, it forms $_{14}Si^{31}$ which is unstable and decays by β^--emission with a half-life of 2.62 hours to stable $_{15}P^{31}$. But if we add a proton to $_{14}Si^{30}$, it forms a stable $_{15}P^{31}$. If to $_{15}P^{31}$ we add another proton, it forms a stable $_{16}S^{32}$, while an addition of a neutron to $_{15}P^{31}$ forms $_{15}P^{32}$, which is unstable and decays by β^--emission with a half-life of 14.5 days to a stable $_{16}S^{32}$. Further addition of two neutrons results in stable products, while the addition of protons results in unstable isotopes. This argument indicates that the same type of nucleons pair together.

Another important consequence of the odd–even effect is the isobaric effect which we shall discuss in Sec. 11.

10. THE SEMIEMPIRICAL ATOMIC-MASS FORMULA

By analogy with the liquid drop it is possible to write the semiempirical mass-formula for any atom having mass $M(A, Z)$. Like the intermolecular forces in a liquid, the forces between the nucleons of a nucleus are short range and have saturation properties. Such an analogy predicts most of the important terms in the mass formula. Use will be made of the surface-tension effect, coulomb repulsion, and odd–even effect as previously explained. This formula can be used to predict the stability of nuclei with respect to the emission of radiation.

The procedure to evolve the mass formula for $M(A, Z)$ is to first write the masses of the constituents of the atom, and then apply the necessary corrections. This results in the familiar Weizsäcker[24,25] semiempirical mass formula. The different terms needed in the formula follow.

A. MASS OF THE CONSTITUENTS. The first term is the mass of the constituents of the atoms, the protons, neutrons, and electrons.

$$M_0 = m_p Z + m_n(A - Z) + m_e Z$$

or

$$M_0 = m_H Z + m_n(A - Z) \tag{5.33}$$

where we have neglected the binding energy of the electron and the proton to form the hydrogen atom.

B. SPECIFIC NUCLEAR BINDING ENERGY. From M_0 we must subtract the binding energy of the nucleons. This is equivalent to the heat of condensation in a liquid drop. As we have already seen, the binding energy per nucleon is almost constant and, therefore, the correction term is proportional to the number of particles in the nucleus and is given by

$$M_1 = -a_1 A \tag{5.34}$$

The negative sign means that as A increases more mass is converted into energy in order to increase the total binding energy. The value of the constant a_1 will be evaluated later on.

C. SURFACE TENSION. The correction term M_1 has been over-estimated, because the nucleons near the surface are not as firmly bound as those inside the volume. This introduces the surface-tension effect as already discussed in Sec. 7. The surface tension correction term is proportional to the surface area and is positive

$$M_2 = +a_2 A^{2/3} \tag{5.35}$$

where a_2 is a constant to be determined.

D. COULOMB REPULSION. The effect of coulomb repulsion because of the positive charge on the protons was discussed in Sec. 8. It results in an addition of a mass term M_3 given by

$$M_3 = (a_3) Z^2 / A^{1/3} \tag{5.36}$$

where $a_3 = 3e^2/5r_0$ is a constant and its value varies from 0.0006 U to 0.0008 U depending on the value of r_0.

E. PAIRING OF NUCLEONS. This term depends on the relative number of protons and neutrons. A survey suggests that the stable nuclei tend to form themselves of neutron-proton pairs; the nuclei will be most stable and, hence, more strongly bound if $A = 2Z$. Any deviation from $A = 2Z$ should decrease the binding energy. Thus, a positive mass-correction term for the number of unpaired nucleons is applied in the following form

$$M_4 = a_4 \left(\frac{A}{2} - Z \right)^2 \Big/ A \tag{5.37}$$

where a_4 is a constant to be evaluated. There is a good theoretical justification[26,27] for the expression in Eq. (5.37), as we shall see in Sec. 10.4.

F. ODD–EVEN EFFECT. Another important factor that affects the binding energy of a nucleus and, hence, its mass, is whether the numbers of protons and neutrons are odd or even. As already discussed in Sec. 9, the even–even nuclei are the most stable, while the odd–odd nuclei the least stable. This results in an addition of another term $\delta(A, Z)$ to the mass formula. This term is given by

$$\delta(A, Z) = \begin{cases} -f(A) & \text{for } A \text{ even, } Z \text{ even} \rightarrow \begin{bmatrix} \text{most stable} \\ \text{nuclei} \end{bmatrix} \\ 0 & \text{for } A \text{ odd} \longrightarrow \begin{bmatrix} \text{moderately} \\ \text{stable nuclei} \end{bmatrix} \\ +f(A) & \text{for } A \text{ even, } Z \text{ odd} \rightarrow \begin{bmatrix} \text{least stable} \\ \text{nuclei} \end{bmatrix} \end{cases} \quad \textbf{(5.38a)}$$

The theoretical justification for the $\delta(A, Z)$ correction term is as follows. The spin of each nucleon is $\frac{1}{2}$, and, therefore, the spin can point either up or down. This means each state of the proton or neutron is two-fold degenerate and gives a sudden change in the binding energy every time a proton or a neutron is added. But in all the other mass terms it has been assumed that $M(A, Z)$ varies smoothly as N or Z changes. This points out the need for the correction term $\delta(A, Z)$. Though the theoretical considerations give the value of $\delta(A, Z)$ of the form

$$\delta(A, Z) = \alpha/A \qquad \textbf{(5.38b)}$$

where α is a constant, the best experimental fit gives

$$\delta(A, Z) = a_5 A^{-3/4} \qquad \textbf{(5.39)}$$

as we shall see below.

G. SUMMATION FOR THE FORMULA.   Adding all the six terms given above, we get the following expression for the mass of an atom

$$M(A, Z) = m_{\rm H} Z + m_n(A - Z) - a_1 A + a_2 A^{2/3} + \frac{a_3 Z^2}{A^{1/3}} + a_4 \frac{[(A/2) - Z]^2}{A}$$
$$+ \delta(A, Z) \qquad \textbf{(5.40)}$$

The values of a_1, a_2, a_3, a_4, and $\delta(A, Z)$ can be found by making Eq. (5.40) fit the experimental values of $M(A, Z)$. This equation must satisfy the following three conditions as well, which in turn can be used to evaluate the constants[26,27].

(i) The plot of $M(A, Z)$ versus Z for a fixed value of A should give a parabola, as experimentally observed. The minimum of this parabola should correspond to a stable isobar.

(ii) The plot of $M(A, Z)$ must give the correct N versus Z curve for the stable elements ($N/Z = 1$ for low mass numbers and $N/Z \simeq 1.6$ for high mass numbers).

(iii) Because δ (A odd) $= 0$, this curve must give the mass of odd-A elements. δ (A even), however, must be adjusted to give $M(A, Z)$ for even A.

If we impose condition (i) on Eq. (5.40), the stable isobars are given by

$$\frac{\partial M}{\partial Z} = 0 = (m_H - m_n) + 2a_3 \frac{Z}{A^{1/3}} - 2a_4 \frac{(A/2) - Z}{A} \qquad (5.41)$$

Because $(m_H - m_n) = 0.00083U$ is very small as compared to the other terms in Eq. (5.41), it may be neglected. Rearranging Eq. (5.41) we get

$$Z = \frac{A}{2 + (2a_3/a_4)A^{2/3}} \qquad (5.42)$$

According to condition (ii) this must represent the nuclear stability curve given in Fig. 5.7. The best value of $2a_3/a_4$ that fits the curve is given by[28,29]

$$2a_3/a_4 = 0.014989 \qquad (5.43)$$

Now we can use condition (iii) to find all the other constants. First of all, we use experimentally determined masses of the odd-A stable isotopes and find[28,29] (in atomic mass units on the carbon-12 scale)

$$a_1 = 0.0169123U, \quad a_2 = 0.019114U$$
$$a_3 = 0.0007626U, \quad a_4 = 0.10175U \qquad (5.44)$$

Note that the value of a_3 due to the coulomb correction agrees with the one derived in Sec. 8. The stable elements of even mass-number A can now be used to determine the value $f(A)$. The best fit gives

$$f(A) = 0.036A^{-3/4} \qquad (5.45)$$

Thus the complete expression for $M(A, Z)$ in Eq. (5.40) becomes (on C^{12} scale)

$$M(A, Z) = 1.008665A - 0.000839Z - 0.0169123A + 0.019114A^{2/3}$$
$$+ 0.0007626 \frac{Z^2}{A^{1/3}} + 0.10175 \frac{[(A/2) - Z]^2}{A} + \delta(A, Z) \quad (5.46)$$

where the value of $\delta(A, Z)$ is given by

$$\delta(A, Z) = \begin{cases} -0.036\ A^{-3/4} & \text{for even-}A, \text{ even-}Z \\ 0 & \text{for odd-}A \\ +0.036\ A^{-3/4} & \text{for even-}A, \text{ odd-}Z \end{cases} \qquad (5.47)$$

In order to test the accuracy of Eq. (5.46) it is more convenient to express it in the form of the binding energy per nucleon so that any small disagreement may not be masked by the first two terms, which are the most dominant. Thus rearranging Eq. (5.46) and using the conversion $1U = 931.441$ Mev, we get

$$BE/A = 15.753 - (17.804/A^{1/3}) - (0.7103Z^2/A^{4/3})$$
$$- (94.77) \frac{[(A/2) - Z]^2}{A^2} - \left(\frac{\delta(A, Z)}{A}\right) \qquad (5.48)$$

where $\delta(A, Z) = \pm 33.6\, A^{-3/4}$ or 0. For isotopes of $A \geqslant 15$ Eq. (5.48) agrees with experimentally determined values to better than 1 per cent. A different set of values for the constants are needed in order to fit the data for $A < 15$.

Lately, many improvements[30-34] have been made on this formula so as to cover the whole range of mass numbers by using one set of constants. This results in the addition of new constants and the rearrangement of the basic formula given in Eq. (5.46). The standard expression for the mass excess, $\Delta M_{\text{stan.}}(A, Z)$, in Mev/$c^2$ is

$$\Delta M_{\text{stan.}}(A, Z) = 8.3674N + 7.5845Z - \alpha A + \left(\beta - \frac{\eta}{A^{1/3}}\right)\left(\frac{I^2 - 2|I|}{A}\right)$$

$$+ \gamma A^{2/3} + 0.8076\frac{Z^2}{A^{1/3}}\left(1 - \frac{0.7636}{Z^{2/3}} - \frac{2.29}{A^{2/3}}\right) \quad (5.49)$$

where $I = N - Z$.

Other recent improvements have been made by P. A. Seeger[35] who has taken into consideration the effects of nuclear deformation and the shell structure. This results in the subtraction of a term $S_{jk}(N', Z')$ from the standard formula for the mass excess given in Eq. (5.49). The correct mass excess $\Delta M_0(A, Z)$, therefore, is given by

$$\Delta M_0(A, Z) = \Delta M_{\text{stan.}}(A, Z) - S_{jk}(N', Z') \quad (5.50)$$

where

$$\alpha = 17.06 \qquad \beta = 33.61$$
$$\gamma = 25.00 \qquad \eta = 59.54 \quad (5.51)$$

$S_{jk}(N', Z')$ is a function of N and Z as given by Seeger and shown in Fig. 5.9. The results of the calculations for the masses and the binding energies are tabulated in reference 35.

11. ISOBARIC EFFECT

As already mentioned, elements having the same mass number A are called isobars. The three-dimensional plot of Z, N, and Mc^2 for each nucleus gives what is called the *energy surface*. Actually there are three surfaces, but we are interested in the *isobaric energy surface*, which is one for which the value of A is constant. It is found that the isobaric energy surfaces result in parabolas for the plot of $M(A, Z)$ versus Z. This is predicted by the semiempirical mass formula given in Eq. (5.46) as explained below:

(i) For odd A, the term $\delta(A, Z)$ is zero, and the plot of $M(Z, A)$ versus Z gives a parabola as shown in Fig. 5.10. Eq. (5.46) predicts that there is only

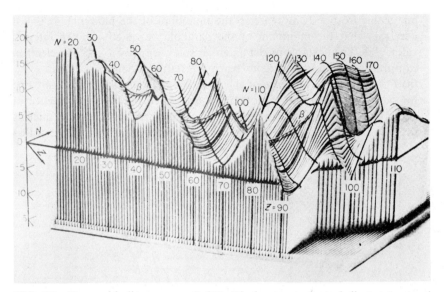

FIG. 5.9 Excess binding energy $S_{jk}(N', Z')$ due to nuclear shell structure and deformation as given by Seeger plotted versus N and Z. Each strip of the model is a constant A. The lines of constant N are perpendicular to those of constant Z. The path of the line of beta-stability is indicated by the line $\beta\beta$. [From P. A. Seeger, *Nuclear Physics*, **25**, 1 (1961).]

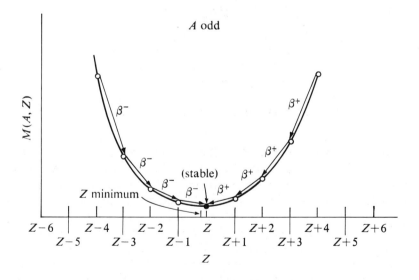

FIG 5.10 $M(A, Z)$ versus Z for odd A.

one stable isotope lying close to the minimum of the parabola. It is not necessary that the minimum of the parabola be exactly on the integral value of Z. The unstable nuclei on either side decay (by β^-, β^+, or electron capture) in such a way so as to reach the stable nucleus.

(ii) For even A the presence of the term $\delta(A, Z)$ gives two parabolas, one for odd–odd nuclei and the other for even–even nuclei. The presence of the term $\delta(A, Z)$ also ensures that there may be more than one stable nucleus for even A and even Z, that is, for even–even nuclei. In Fig. 5.11 the dotted

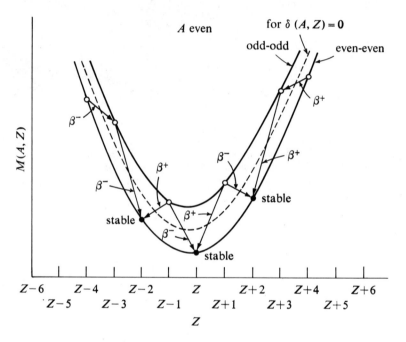

FIG. 5.11 $M(A, Z)$ versus Z for even A.

curve represents the plot of $M(A, Z)$ versus A for $\delta(A, Z) = 0$. The $M(A, Z)$ for odd–odd nuclei lies above this curve while for even–even nuclei it lies below. Since for $A > 15$ there are no odd–odd stable nuclei (except $_{73}Ta^{180}$), all the nuclei lying on the odd–odd curve decay to one or more stable nuclei on the even–even curve. This is also shown in Fig. 5.11.

As a practical example of the above two cases, Fig. 5.12 and Fig. 5.13 show the parabolas for $A = 111$ and $A = 112$, respectively. There is only one stable nucleus, $_{48}Cd^{111}$, that corresponds to $A = 111$ and two stable nuclei, $_{48}Cd^{112}$ and $_{50}Sn^{112}$, corresponding to $A = 112$, as experimentally found, and are in agreement with the above predictions.

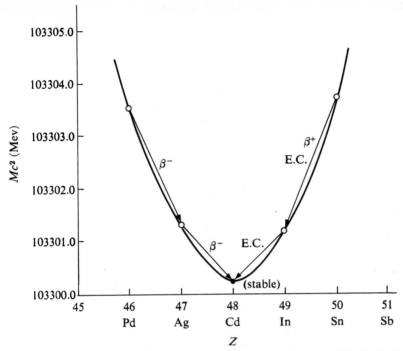

FIG. 5.12 Energy surface diagram for odd mass-number, $A = 111$. Parabola shows the plot of MC^2 versus Z. The only stable isotope is $_{48}$Cd.

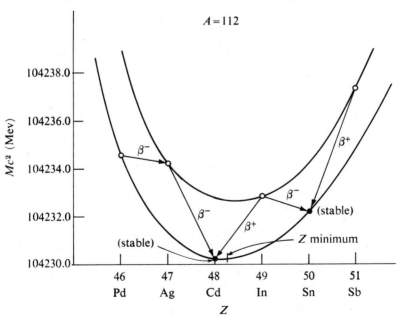

FIG. 5.13 Energy surface diagram for even mass-number, $A = 112$. MC^2 is plotted versus Z. The stable isotopes are $_{48}$Cd and $_{50}$Sn. Note that there are no stable isotopes corresponding to the odd–odd nuclei.

PROBLEMS

1. Show that in a mass spectrometer the behavior of the doubly ionized atom will be the same as that of a singly ionized atom with half the actual mass.

2. The stable isotopes of zinc, their percentage abundances, and mass excesses on the C^{12} physical scale, are

Isotope	Abundance %	Mass Excess $\times 10^6\ U$
Zn^{64}	48.89	$-70\ 855$
Zn^{66}	27.81	$-73\ 952$
Zn^{67}	4.11	$-72\ 851$
Zn^{68}	18.57	$-75\ 135$
Zn^{70}	0.62	$-74\ 652$

Calculate the atomic weight of zinc.

3. Locate the position of the collector plates for singly ionized ions with mass numbers 16, 17, and 18 that have been accelerated through a potential difference of 2000 volts, after which they enter a uniform magnetic field of 2000 gauss perpendicular to the beam.

4. A beam of singly ionized lithium atoms, after being accelerated through a potential difference of 2000 volts, enters a uniform magnetic field of 0.3 weber/m² perpendicular to the beam. The lithium ions then impinge on a photographic plate (Fig. 5.3b). What will be the absolute separation of Li^{6+} and Li^{7+} ions on the photographic plate?

5. Singly charged positive ions ($q = 1.602 \times 10^{-20}$ emu) of a certain material are accelerated through a potential difference of 1500 volts. They then enter a uniform magnetic field of 2000 gauss perpendicular to the beam. These ions are deflected into a circular path of radius $R = 38.2$ cm. Calculate the speed of the ions, the mass of the ions, and the mass number.

6. Protons, after being accelerated through a potential difference of 2000 volts, enter a uniform magnetic field of 5000 gauss perpendicular to their path. Following a circular path of radius R in the magnetic field, the protons impinge on a photographic plate. If now a beam of doubly ionized helium atoms is used and
   (a) keeping the electric field fixed, what should be the value of the magnetic field in order to receive the helium ions on the same spot as in the case of the protons?
   (b) keeping the magnetic field fixed, what should be the value of the electric field in order to receive the helium ions on the same spot?

7. Use is made of the Dempster mass spectrograph for the purpose of measuring the mass difference of the doublet $(H_2^1)^+ - (H^2)^+$. Find an expression for the mass difference in terms of the absolute separation $\Delta r = r_1 - r_2$ and the average distance $\bar{r} = (r_1 + r_2)/2$ where r is as shown in the figure.

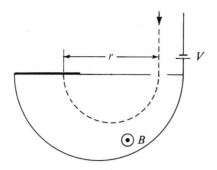

FIG. P.7

8. Neir [*Phys. Rev.*, **81**, p. 507 (1951)] has measured the mass differences of the following doublets (using mass spectroscopes):

$$2H^1 - H^2 = \alpha = 1.552 \times 10^{-3} \text{ amu}$$
$$C^{12}(H^1)_4 - O^{16} = \beta = 36.478 \times 10^{-3} \text{ amu}$$
$$(D_2O)^+ - A^{++} = (H^2)_2O^{16} - \tfrac{1}{2}A^{40} = \gamma = 41.967 \times 10^{-3} \text{ amu}$$
$$2[(H^2)_2O^{16} - \tfrac{1}{2}A^{40}] - [(C^{12})_3(H^1)_4 - A^{40}] = 15.057 \times 10^{-3} \text{ amu}$$

If the mass of $O^{16} = 16.00000$, find the masses of H^1 and C^{12}.

9. The results of the mass spectroscopic measurements by Neir for different doublets are

$$C^{12}(O^{16})_2 - C^{12}S^{32} = \alpha = 17.782 \times 10^{-3} \text{ amu}$$
$$\tfrac{1}{2}[(C^{12})_3(H^1)_8 - C^{12}(O^{16})_2] = \beta = 36.484 \times 10^{-3} \text{ amu}$$
$$(C^{12})_6(H^1)_4 - C^{12}(S^{32})_2 = \gamma = 87.326 \times 10^{-3} \text{ amu}$$

Show that the mass of hydrogen is given by

$$H = 1 + \tfrac{1}{3}(4\alpha + 5\beta - 2\gamma)$$

Evaluate this and compare it with the value given in the nuclear chart.

10. DuMond and Cohen [*Phys. Rev.*, **82**, p. 555 (1951)] have computed from nuclear data the mass differences of the following doublets

$$(O^{16})_2 - S^{32} = 17.818 \times 10^{-3} \text{ amu}$$
$$(C^{12})_4 - S^{32}O^{16} = 33.034 \times 10^{-3} \text{ amu}$$
$$C^{12}(H^1)_4 - O^{16} = 36.372 \times 10^{-3} \text{ amu}$$

Calculate the masses of S^{32}, C^{12}, and H^1 using $O^{16} = 16.00000$. How does this value of H^1 compare with the one obtained from the mass spectroscopic results given in problem 9. What will be the values of these masses on the C^{12} scale?

11. Consider the following nuclear cycle

$$Na^{23}(d, \alpha)Ne^{21}, \ Ne^{21}(d, p)Ne^{22}$$
$$Ne^{22}(d, p)Ne^{23}, \ Ne^{23}(\beta^-)Na^{23}$$

The Q-values of these reactions are Q_1, Q_2, Q_3, and Q_4, respectively. If the mass difference of $2H^1 - H^2 = \Delta(\Delta = 1.443 \text{ Mev})$, obtain the value of mass difference $(2H^2 - He^4)$ in terms of the Q's and Δ. Assume $O^{16} = 16.00000$.

12. Consider the following nuclear cycle $[n + H^1 - H^2 = \Delta(\Delta = 2.25 \text{ Mev})]$.

$$F^{19}(p, \alpha)O^{16}, \ O^{16}(d, \alpha)N^{14}, \ N^{14}(d, p)N^{15}$$
$$O^{18}(p, \alpha)N^{15}, \ O^{18}(p, n)F^{18}, \ Ne^{20}(d, \alpha)F^{18}$$
$$Ne^{20}(d, p)Ne^{21}, \ Ne^{21}(d, \alpha)F^{19}$$

Obtain the mass difference $(2H^2 - He^4)$ in terms of $Q_1, Q_2, Q_3, Q_4, Q_5, Q_6, Q_7, Q_8,$ and Δ.

13. Express the binding energy per nucleon BE/A in terms of the packing fraction f and $(A - 2Z)/A$.

14. Calculate the binding energy of the last proton in He^4, Be^8, C^{12}, O^{16}, and S^{32} by making use of the atomic masses. Compare these values with the binding energy per nucleon.

15. Calculate the binding energy of a neutron added to $_{92}U^{235}$ and $_{92}U^{238}$. How does this compare with the average binding energy per nucleon?

16. In the alpha-particle model of the nucleus, the C^{12} nucleus consists of 3 alpha particles. What is the difference between the binding energy of C^{12} and the sum of the binding energies of the 3 alpha particles?

17. Using the values of the constants given in the text, evaluate the surface tension effect for the following nuclei and plot this versus the mass number A.

$$_2He^4, \ _8O^{16}, \ _{16}S^{32}, \ _{20}Ca^{40}, \ _{50}Sn^{120}$$
$$_{60}Nd^{150}, \ _{74}W^{184}, \ _{82}Pb^{206}, \ _{92}U^{238}.$$

18. Using the values of the constants given in the text, evaluate the coulomb repulsion effect for the nuclei given in problem 17, and plot this versus the mass number A.

19. Using Eqs. (5.42) and (5.43), find Z for the most stable nuclei for the mass numbers $A = 16, 32, 50, 80, 100, 150, 200,$ and 230. How do these agree with the experimental results?

20. According to Eq. (5.42), which isotopes of $_{60}Nd$, $_{61}Pm$, and $_{62}Sm$ should be most stable.

21. Using the semiempirical mass-formula given by Eq. (5.46), calculate the binding energy of the alpha particle emitted from $_{92}U^{235}$ and $_{92}U^{238}$. Compare these values with the experimentally determined values.

22. Draw the parabolas (Mc^2 versus Z) for the mass numbers $A = 147$ and $A = 148$. Predict the most stable nuclei from these plots and show their agreement with the experimentally found stable nuclei.

REFERENCES

1. Thomson, J. J., *Phil. Mag.*, **13**, p. 561, (1907); *Phil. Mag.*, **21**, p. 225, (1911); *Phil. Mag.*, **24**, pp. 209, 669, (1912).

2. Thomson, J. J., *Rays of Positive Electricity*, 2nd Ed. London: Longmans, Green & Co., 1921.

3. Aston, F. W., *Phil. Mag.*, **39**, p. 449, (1920).
4. Aston, F. W., *Phil. Mag.*, **38**, p. 707, (1919).
5. Aston, F. W., *Proc. Roy. Soc.*, **A115**, p. 484, (1927).
6. Aston, F. W., *Proc. Roy. Soc.*, **163**, p. 391, (1937).
7. Dempster, A. J., *Proc. Am. Phil. Soc.*, **75**, p. 755, (1935).
8. Bainbridge, K. T., and E. B. Jordan, *Phys. Rev.*, **50**, p. 282, (1936).
9. Mattauch, J., *Phys. Rev.*, **50**, p. 617, (1936).
10. Nier, A. O., *Rev. Sci. Instr.*, **18**, p. 398, (1947).
11. Dempster, A. J., *Phys. Rev.*, **11**, p. 316, (1918).
12. Dempster, A. J., *Phys. Rev.*, **18**, p. 415, (1921).
13. Dempster, A. J., *Phys. Rev.*, **20**, p. 631, (1922).
14. Mattauch, J., *Phys. Rev.*, **57**, p. 1155 (1940).
15. Cohen E. R., and W. F. Hornyak, *Phys. Rev.*, **72**, p. 1127L, (1947).
16. Bainbridge, K. T., *Isotopic Weights of the Fundamental Isotopes*, Natl. Research Council Nuclear Science Report, **1**, (1948).
17. Li, C. W., W. Shaling, W. A. Fowler, and C. C. Lauritsen, *Phys. Rev.*, **83**, p. 512, (1951).
18. Ewald, H., *Naturfrosch*, **6a**, p. 293, (1951).
19. Goudsmit, S. A., *Phys. Rev.*, **74**, p. 622, (1948).
20. Richards, P. I., E. E. Hays, and S. A. Goudsmit, *Phys. Rev.*, **85**, p. 630, (1952).
21. Li, C. W., W. Whaling, W. A. Fowler, and C. C. Lauritsen, *Phys. Rev.*, **83**, p. 512, (1951).
22. Li, C. W., *Phys. Rev.*, **88**, p. 1038, (1952).
23. Wick, G. C., *Nuovo Cimento*, **11**, p. 227, (1934).
24. Von Weizsäcker, C. F., *Z. Physik*, **96**, p. 431, (1935).
25. Von Weizsäcker, C. F., *Naturwiss*, **24**, p. 813, (1936).
26. Enrico Fermi, *Nuclear Physics* (revised edition). University of Chicago Press, p. 22, (1950).
27. Feenberg, E., *Revs. Mod. Phys.*, **19**, p. 239, (1947).
28. Green, A. E. S., *Nuclear Physics*. New York: McGraw Hill Book Co., 1955.
29. Elton, L. R. B., *Introductory Nuclear Theory*, p. 111. New York: Interscience Publishers, Inc., 1949.
30. Bethe, H. A., and R. F. Becker, *Revs. Mod. Phys.*, **96**, p. 367, (1935). Von Weizsäcker, C. F., *Z. Physik*, **96**, p. 431, (1935).
31. Feenberg, E., *Rev. Mod. Phys.*, **19**, p. 239, (1947).
32. Blatt, J. M., and V. F. Weisskopf, *Theo. Nucl. Phys.*, p. 225, (1952).
33. Brandt, Werner, Wakano, Fuller, and Wheeler, *Proc. Intern. Conf. on Nuclear Masses*, Univ. of Toronto Press, (1960).
34. Mozer, F. S., *Phys. Rev.*, **116**, p. 970, (1959).
35. Seeger, P. A., *Nuclear Physics*, **25**, p. 1, (1961).

SUGGESTIONS FOR FURTHER READING

1. Evans, R. D., *The Atomic Nucleus*, Chapters 3, 8, 9. New York: McGraw-Hill Book Co., Inc., 1955.

2. Bainbridge, K. T., *Experimental Nuclear Physics*, ed., E. Segré, Vol. I. New York: John Wiley & Sons, 1955.

3. Thomson, J. J., *Rays of Positive Electricity and Their Application to Chemical Analysis*. London: Longmans, Green & Co., 1921.

4. Inghram, M. G., *Advances in Electronics*, Vol. I. New York: Academic Press, 1948.

5. Feather, N., *Nuclear Stability Rules*. Cambridge University Press, 1952.

6. Hintenberger, H., ed., *Nuclear Masses and Their Determination*. London: Pergamon Press, 1957.

7. *Proceedings of the Hamilton Conference on Nuclear Masses*. Toronto: University of Toronto Press, 1960.

VI

NUCLEAR SIZE

1. INTRODUCTION

In the previous chapter on nuclear masses we have invariably used the radius R of the nucleus given by the formula $R = r_0 A^{1/3}$, where r_0 is a constant, and A is the mass number. No justification for arriving at such a result has been previously stated. The purpose of the present chapter is to discuss different experimental methods for determining the size of the nucleus that will lead to the above formula. Before we get into the details of these methods, it must be made clear at this stage that there is no way, at least at present, to measure the size of the nucleus by a direct method. The only size we can talk about is derived by indirect means. The value of the size will depend upon the assumptions made and the type of experiment. These experiments can be divided into two main classes: (a) the nuclear methods, and (b) the electromagnetic methods.

The radius of the nucleus obtained by the first method is called the *nuclear force radius* and is defined as the distance from the center of the nucleus at which an incoming particle comes under the influence of the nuclear force. Even though the nuclear forces are short-range, they may extend a little beyond the actual physical size, if there is any, of the nucleus. The radii obtained by these methods, therefore, will be somewhat higher, as we shall see later in this chapter.

The radius of the nucleus obtained by the electromagnetic methods is called the *charge radius*. Because the picture of the nucleus as a point charge does not hold, the charge inside the nucleus (the total charge of the protons) is assumed to have some sort of distribution. The most satisfactory distribution is the one in which it is assumed that the charge density is uniform from the center of the nucleus up to a certain distance, beyond which the charge density, instead of falling sharply to zero, trails off as shown in Fig. 6.1.

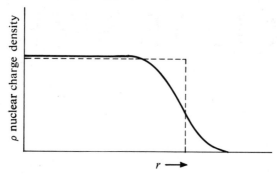

FIG. 6.1 Variation of nuclear density with the distance from the center of the nucleus. The dotted curve is for a uniform spherical charge distribution. The distribution represented by the continuous curve indicates a lower density near the surface of the nucleus.

The experimental methods, under the above two headings, which we shall discuss in detail are:

(a) Nuclear Methods
    1. alpha scattering
    2. lifetimes of alpha-emitters
    3. scattering of fast neutrons

(b) Electromagnetic Methods
    1. electron scattering
    2. mesic atoms (x-ray energies of μ-mesonic atoms)
    3. mirror nuclei
    4. proton scattering
    5. isotope effect (isotopic shift of spectral lines)

It is not possible to give the theoretical and experimental details of all the methods in this book. The theoretical interpretation requires a good background in quantum mechanics. We will limit ourselves to the details that will make the subject understandable. The best single reference for this subject is "International Congress on Nuclear Sizes and Density Distributions"[1].

2. SCATTERING OF ALPHA PARTICLES

H. Geiger and E. Marsden[2] were the first to perform experiments on the scattering of alpha particles. An effort to explain the scattering of the alpha particles through large angles led Rutherford[3] to suggest a nuclear structure for the atom. Rutherford's theory gave the relationship between the scattering cross-sections with regard to its dependence upon (a) the thickness of the scatterer, (b) alpha-particle energy, (c) scattering angle and, (d) atomic number (or nuclear charge) of the target material. His theory was based on Coulomb's law and was verified in subsequent years[4,5]. The cross sections obtained are called the coulomb scattering cross-sections.

The first evidence of departure from coulomb scattering was obtained by E. Bieler[6]. He observed the angular distribution of alpha particles of Ra (B + C) scattered by Mg and Al. The ratio of the observed cross-section to the coulomb cross-section σ/σ_{coul} for Al was found to decrease from 1.0 at small angles to about 0.6 at 110°. These results were further verified by Rutherford and Chadwick[7]. The difference between the coulomb cross-section and the observed cross-section $(\sigma_{coul} - \sigma)$ is called the noncoulomb cross-section. Detailed investigations of the noncoulomb cross-sections were not possible at that time because of the limited range of alpha-particle energies available from natural radioactive sources. Later, with the availability of the versatile machines for the production of high energy particles, extensive studies in the measurement of the noncoulomb cross-section have been carried out. The variation of σ/σ_{coul} with the energy of the alpha particle and different scattering target materials has led the way to the prediction of the nuclear size.

Before taking up the determination of the nuclear radius, it is desirable to discuss coulomb scattering. Classical methods of dealing with Rutherford coulomb cross-sections are given in a number of textbooks[8], but we shall give a more simple and direct method presented by M. Gordon[9].

We shall study the scattering problem under two headings: (A) coulomb scattering or Rutherford scattering, and (B) noncoulomb scattering or elastic scattering.

A. COULOMB SCATTERING [or Rutherford Scattering].   The derivation given below is after Gordon[9], and is significant in the respect that it demonstrates the special nature of the inverse-square-law force in classical scattering theory. Fig. 6.2 shows the scattering of incoming particle by a nucleus at point O, which is the center of the repulsive force. The incoming particle has a mass m, velocity v_0, and charge q. Its momenta, long before and long after collision, are $\mathbf{P}_i$ and $\mathbf{P}_f$, respectively, where $|\mathbf{P}_i| = |\mathbf{P}_f|$. This particle has an impact parameter b and is deflected through an angle, θ, after scattering. The scattering center, the nucleus, has charge Q.

Consider a conservative central force, $\mathbf{F}(r)$, without assuming any special form for it. The application of the impulse-momentum theorem gives

$$\Delta \mathbf{P} = \int \mathbf{F}(r)\, dt \qquad (6.1)$$

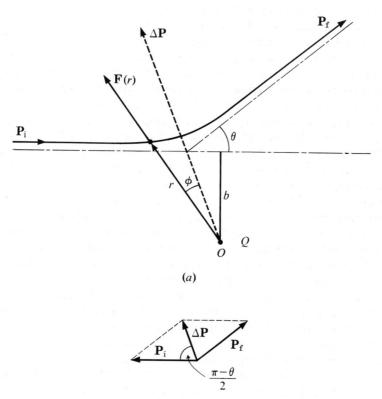

(a)

(b)

FIG. 6.2 Scattering of an alpha particle by a conservative central-force center (repulsive force).

where $\Delta \mathbf{P} = \mathbf{P}_f - \mathbf{P}_i$ is the total change in the momentum vector, the integration extends from $-\infty$ to $+\infty$, and r is a function of t. If θ is the scattering angle, then from Fig. 6.2(b) one finds that

$$|\Delta \mathbf{P}| = 2mv_0 \sin(\theta/2). \qquad (6.2)$$

In order for the angular momentum to be conserved, $\Delta \mathbf{P}$ must point directly towards or away from the center of force. The force, $\mathbf{F}(r)$, between the nucleus and the particle makes an angle ϕ with the direction of $\Delta \mathbf{P}$. Only those components of $\int \mathbf{F}(r)\,dt$ that are parallel to $\Delta \mathbf{P}$ add up to $\Delta \mathbf{P}$; all other components add up to zero. Thus, combining Eq. (6.1) and (6.2), one gets:

$$2mv_0 \sin(\theta/2) = \int_0^\infty |\mathbf{F}(r)| \cos \phi \, dt \qquad (6.3)$$

and

$$0 = \int_0^\infty |\mathbf{F}(r)| \sin \phi \, dt \qquad (6.4)$$

Because there is no external torque on the particle around the nucleus, the angular momentum must be conserved. The initial value of the angular momentum (long before the collision) is $mv_0 b$, where b is the impact parameter; the angular momentum at any other time during scattering is $mr^2\omega$, where ω is the angular velocity given by $\omega = d\phi/dt$. These two must be equal, that is,

$$mr^2\omega = mv_0 b \qquad (6.5)$$

Eq. (6.3) may be written in the form

$$2mv_0 \sin(\theta/2) = \int_{-(\pi-\theta)/2}^{+(\pi-\theta)/2} |\mathbf{F}(r)| \cos \phi \, \frac{dt}{d\phi} \cdot d\phi \qquad (6.6)$$

Changing the variables from dt to $d\phi$ and the limits of integration to $-(\pi - \theta)/2$ and $+(\pi - \theta)/2$ and combining with Eq. (6.5) we get

$$2mv_0^2 b \sin(\theta/2) = \int r^2 |\mathbf{F}(r)| \cos \phi \, d\phi \qquad (6.7)$$

In the above equation r is now a function of ϕ, not of t. Making the substitution $Z = \sin \phi$, we get

$$2mv_0^2 b \sin(\theta/2) = \int_{-\cos(\theta/2)}^{+\cos(\theta/2)} r^2 |\mathbf{F}(r)| \, dZ \qquad (6.8)$$

The limits of integration in Eq. (6.8) are the same for the attractive as well as the repulsive force law. Eq. (6.8) applies to conservative central forces in general. In order to know $b = b(\theta)$, we must know the dependence of r on ϕ, i.e., $r = r(\phi)$. But for a special case of the inverse-square-law force it is not necessary to know $r(\phi)$ because

$$r^2 |\mathbf{F}(r)| = \text{constant } C = qQ. \qquad (6.9)$$

Combining Eqs. (6.8) and (6.9), we get

$$b = \left(\frac{C}{mv_0^2}\right) \cot \frac{\theta}{2} = \left(\frac{qQ}{mv_0^2}\right) \cot \frac{\theta}{2} \qquad (6.10)$$

Looking at Fig. 6.3, we note that the particles that are incident on the target with an impact parameter between b and $b + db$ will be scattered in a cone of solid angle $d\Omega$ at θ and $\theta + d\theta$. Thus if $\dfrac{d\sigma}{d\Omega}$ is the differential cross-section, then

$$\frac{d\sigma}{d\Omega} d\Omega = (2\pi b |db|) \tag{6.11a}$$

or

$$\frac{d\sigma}{d\Omega} = \frac{2\pi b |db|}{2\pi \sin\theta \, d\theta}. \tag{6.11b}$$

Substituting the value of b and db from Eq. (6.10) into Eq. (6.11b), one gets

$$\frac{d\sigma}{d\Omega} = \left(\frac{qQ}{2mv_0^2}\right)^2 \operatorname{cosec}^4(\theta/2) \tag{6.12}$$

which is the famous *Rutherford Scattering Formula*. Eq. (6.12) can be written in a slightly different form as

$$\sigma(\theta) = \left(\frac{qQ}{4K_\alpha}\right)^2 \frac{1}{\sin^4(\theta/2)} \tag{6.13a}$$

$$= \left(\frac{qQ}{2K_\alpha}\right)^2 \frac{1}{(1 - \cos\theta)^2} \tag{6.13b}$$

where $\sigma(\theta) = \dfrac{d\sigma}{d\Omega}$, and K_α is the kinetic energy of the alpha particle. Eq. (6.13b) fits very well with the experimental data at low values of K_α and proves that the nucleus is condensed in a very small volume as suggested by Rutherford.

Consider Eq. (6.7) once again. $r^2 F(r)$ will diverge as $r \to \infty$. This means that unless $|F(r)|$ falls off to zero at least as fast as r^{-2} at the limits of integration, the integral will diverge. Thus the inverse-square-law is the limiting case

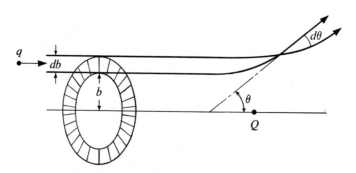

FIG. 6.3 The particles that enter the shaded area, that is, with impact parameter between b and $b + db$, are scattered between θ and $\theta + d\theta$.

for $\mathbf{F}(r)$ in the asymptotic limits. The meaning of this will become clear if we calculate the total cross-section σ_T.

$$\sigma_T = \int_\Omega \sigma(\theta) \, d\Omega = 2\pi \int_0^\pi \sigma(\theta)\sin\theta \, d\theta$$

or

$$\sigma_T = 2\pi \int_0^\pi \frac{K}{(1-\cos\theta)^2}\sin\theta \, d\theta \qquad (6.14)$$

where $K = (qQ/2K_a)^2$. Let $\mu = \cos\theta$ and $d\mu = -\sin\theta \, d\theta$.

Therefore,

$$\sigma_T = 2\pi \int_{-1}^1 \frac{K}{(1-\mu)^2} \, d\mu$$

or

$$\sigma_T = \infty \qquad (6.15)$$

That is, σ_T diverges if $V(r) \propto \dfrac{1}{r}$, where $V(r)$ is the potential function. This means that every particle is scattered and the cross section is infinite except when b is infinite. The plot of the cross section, $\sigma(\theta)$, versus θ is as shown in Fig. 6.4. This difficulty of having an infinite value of the cross section can be overcome by considering the shielding due to electrons that will reduce the effective charge of the nucleus. Consider the charge of different electrons in different orbits to be replaced by an equivalent effective charge at some distance

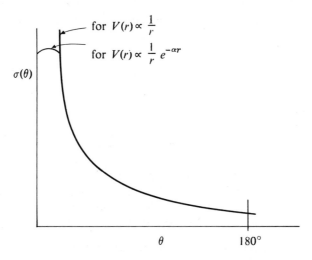

FIG. 6.4 Variation of $\sigma(\theta)$ with θ for fixed energy of alpha particles.

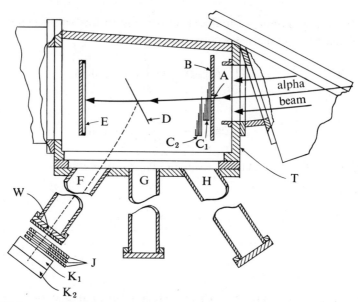

FIG. 6.5 Plan view of the apparatus used by Farwell, *et al.* for the study of scattering of alpha particles. A: aperture in plate B for defining the alpha-particle beam; C_1, C_2: remotely controlled absorbers for reducing beam energy; D: thin foil target; E: Faraday cup; F, G, and H: observation ports; W: thin foil exit window; J: variable aluminum absorber for differential-range proportional-counter telescope K_1, K_2. [From Farwell, *et al.*, *Phys. Rev.*, **95**, 1212 (1954).]

r_{screen} from the nucleus. Then the potential function takes the form

$$V(r) = \frac{qQ}{r} e^{-\alpha r} \tag{6.16}$$

where $\frac{1}{\alpha} \cong r_{\text{screen}}$ and $\alpha > 0$.

Using $F(r) = -\dfrac{dV}{dr}$, we get for σ_T

$$\sigma_T \propto 1 \Big/ \left[1 - \cos\theta + \left(\frac{C}{r_{\text{screen}}} \right)^2 \right]^2 \tag{6.17}$$

where $C = qQ \cdot \sigma_T$ is finite and is as shown in Fig. 6.4.

Thus we have established the form of the coulomb scattering cross-section. The measurement of the elastic scattering cross-section, which we shall discuss below, gives us a method of measuring the nuclear radius.

B. NONCOULOMB SCATTERING (or Elastic Scattering). Fig. 6.5 shows the apparatus used by Farwell, *et al.*[10] for the study of the elastic scattering of alpha particles both in the coulomb and the noncoulomb region.

The deflected alpha-particle beam of the University of Washington 60-inch cyclotron enters the evacuated target chamber, T. Part of the beam passes through the defining aperture, A, in plate B. Variable absorbers C_1 and C_2 are made of copper foils 0.35 mil and 1.5 mils thick, respectively, and are arranged in steps. These absorbers reduce the alpha-particle energy in steps of 1 Mev, from 43 Mev down to 13 Mev. The alpha particles strike the

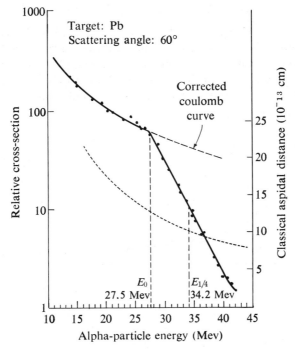

FIG. 6.6 Elastic scattering of alpha particles by lead at 60° in the LAB coordinate system. Relative cross-section versus alpha-particle energy is plotted. The critical energy, E_0, corresponds to the intercept of the straight-line portion of the experimental curve with the corrected coulomb curve. [From Farwell, *et al.*, *Phys. Rev.*, **95**, 1212 (1954).]

thin foil target, D, made of material under investigation. Except for a small fraction of the beam that is scattered, the rest of the beam is transmitted and hits the Faraday cup. The scattered particles pass through the tube, F, and are detected by a set of two proportional counters, K_1 and K_2, which are contained in a common envelope filled with argon gas at a pressure of about one-fourth of an atmosphere. The results obtained by Farwell, *et al.* for a Pb target at 60° angle are shown in Fig. 6.6.

It is clear from Fig. 6.6, which is a plot of the relative cross-section versus energy, that the measured cross-sections agree well with the predicted coulomb cross-section up to an energy of about 26 Mev. At energies higher than 26 Mev, there is a sharp drop in the measured cross-section. The energy at which this drop in the cross section takes place is the critical energy, E_0. At energies above the critical energy, the dependence of the cross section on the energy is well represented by the simple empirical formula[11]

$$\sigma(E) = \sigma(E_0)e^{-K(E-E_0)} \tag{6.18}$$

where K is the slope parameter which decreases slightly with increasing Z.

The drop in the relative cross-section at higher energies can be explained in the following manner. If the coulomb force were the only repulsive force involved in the scattering problem, the variation of the potential $V(r)$ with r would have been as shown in Fig. 6.7(a) and there would have been a complete

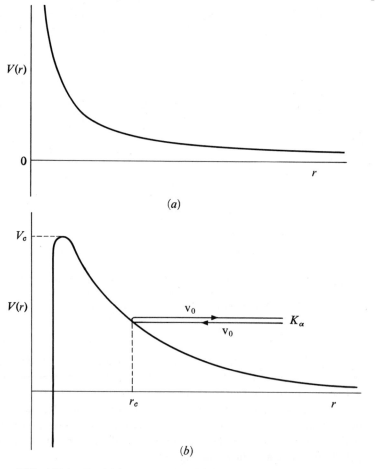

(a)

(b)

FIG. 6.7(a)   Repulsive coulomb potential. (b) Repulsive coulomb potential and attractive nuclear potential shown combined together.

agreement between theory and experiments. But as the energy of the incoming particle is increased, the particle comes closer and closer to the nucleus. If the alpha particle comes close enough, it is attracted by the short-range nuclear force. Thus the potential $V(r)$ does not vary as shown in Fig. 6.7(a),

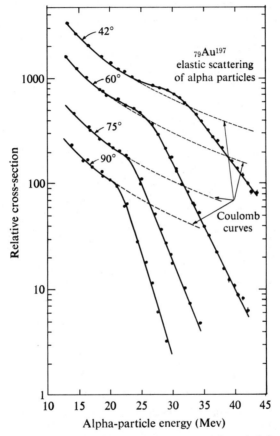

FIG. 6.8(a)   The results of elastic scattering of alpha particles. The plots show the relative cross-sections versus alpha-particles energies. [From Kerlee, *et al.*, *Phys. Rev.*, **107**, 1343 (1957).]

but takes the form shown in Fig. 6.7(b). If the kinetic energy of the incoming particle is greater than V_c, it will probably come within a distance short enough to be influenced by the nuclear attractive force and will follow the cross section given by Eq. (6.18). If, on the other hand, the energy of the particle is less than V_c, we get the familiar coulomb scattering.

The critical energy, E_0, corresponds to the distance of closest approach, not the nuclear radius, because it is possible that the particle may experience the nuclear force before it actually reaches the nuclear surface. Thus, R

obtained by using E_0 may not give the true radius. The method used by Farwell and Wegner[10] (called the quarter-point recipe) for calculating the nuclear radius is to calculate the R that corresponds to the energy $E_{1/4}$, where $E_{1/4}$ is the energy at which the experimental cross-section is one-fourth of the corresponding coulomb cross-section. The distance evaluated at this energy is actually the sum of the nuclear and alpha particle radii. The value of the nuclear radius can now be calculated. The results obtained by Farwell, *et al.* (where $r_0 = 1.5 \times 10^{-13}$ cm in the formula $R = r_0 A^{1/3}$), are somewhat higher than those obtained by other methods.

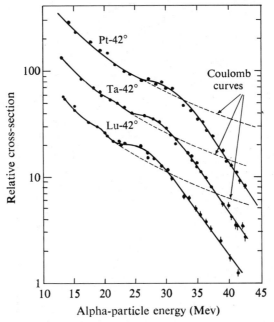

FIG. 6.8(b) The results of elastic scattering of alpha particles by Pt, Ta, and Lu, all at 42°. The plots show the relative cross-sections versus alpha-particles energies. [From Kerlee, *et al.*, *Phys. Rev.*, **107**, 1343 (1957).]

Detailed investigations have been made by Kerlee, *et al.*[12]. They have covered a wide range of elements and energies and have analyzed their data by a sharp cutoff model[11], in which a pure coulomb barrier is assumed beyond a cutoff radius, R, defining a surface that is totally absorbing. Some of the results of the investigations are shown in Fig. 6.8(a) and 6.8(b). Fig. 6.8(b) clearly shows the dependence of E_0 on the mass number A. Instead of using the "*One-Quarter-Point Recipe*," they[12] have used the so-called "*Cross-Over-Point Recipe*" where $E_c = 0.388 E_0$. The plot of the interaction radius $R_{A\alpha}$ (sum of the radius of the nucleus and the alpha particle) versus $A^{1/3}$ is shown in Fig. 6.9, which is a straight line. The results obtained are

$$R_{A\alpha} = (1.414 A^{1/3} + 2.190)10^{-13} \text{ cm}$$

and hence

$$R = 1.414 \times 10^{-13} A^{1/3} \text{ cm} \qquad \text{(6.19a)}$$

therefore

$$r_0 = 1.414 \times 10^{-13} \text{ cm.} \qquad \text{(6.19b)}$$

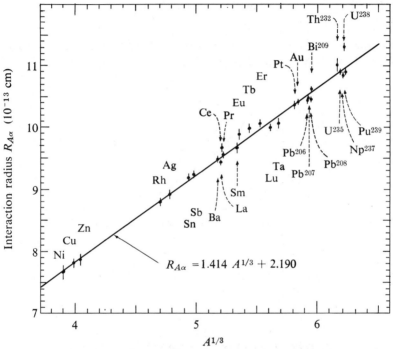

FIG. 6.9   The points ($\blacklozenge$) represent the interaction radius $R_{A\alpha}$ for elastic scattering of alpha particles versus $A^{1/3}$ where A is the atomic number of the target. The solid line represents the least square fit of these points and results in

$$R_{A\alpha} = 1.414 A^{1/3} + 2.190$$

[From Kerlee, *et al.*, *Phys. Rev.*, **107**, 1343 (1957).]

3. LIFETIME OF ALPHA EMITTERS

The spontaneous alpha decay of a nucleus is represented by an equation of the form

$$_Z X^A \rightarrow _{Z-2} Y^{A-4} + _2 He^4$$

This process of alpha decay is very common in nuclei with mass numbers greater than 208. An interesting observation of alpha decay is that a small change in the energy of the alpha particle results in a very large change in the half-life or the decay constant of the alpha emitter. For example, the data

	E_α	$t_{1/2}$	λ
Th^{238}	4.05 Mev	1.39×10^{10} yr	1.5×10^{-18} sec^{-1}
Em^{218}	7.25 Mev	0.019 sec	36.4 sec^{-1}

shows that a change of energy by a factor of 2 changes $t_{1/2}$ or λ by a factor of 10^{20}. This strong energy dependence was explained simultaneously by G.

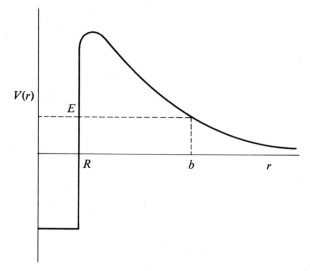

FIG. 6.10   The plot of $V(r)$, the interaction potential between the daughter and the alpha particle, versus r, the distance between them.

Gamow[13] and by R. Gurney and E. Condon[14]. Before emission, both the alpha and the daughter nuclei exist as separate entities which form the parent nucleus. The alpha particle, in an attempt to separate from the daughter nucleus, faces the coulomb barrier of the daughter as shown in Fig. 6.10. Fig. 6.10 shows $V(r)$ as a function of the distance r between the daughter nucleus and the alpha particle. At distances greater than R, the forces are all coulomb forces between a nucleus of charge $(Z - 2)$ and an alpha particle of charge 2. At a distance R, the nuclear forces that are attractive forces come into play. This distance R is defined as the nuclear radius. Using quantum mechanics, one can derive the expression for the probability of an alpha particle of energy E to escape the potential barrier, and, therefore, one can calculate the decay constant in terms of the transmission probability. The results are

$$\lambda = \omega P \qquad (6.20a)$$

and

$$P = \exp \left\{ -2 \int_R^b \sqrt{\frac{2M}{\hbar^2} [V(r) - E]} \, dr \right\} \qquad (6.20b)$$

where P is the probability of an alpha particle penetrating the coulomb barrier and $\omega = v/R$, v being the velocity of the α-particle. This result is derived in Chap. VII. It is quite clear that the decay constant, λ, is a function of E, the barrier height $V(r)$ and the width of the barrier.

This theoretical expression gives an excellent agreement with the experimental values of the decay constant as a function of energy for the even-even nuclei, by assuming a certain functional form of the nuclear radius. I. Perlman and T. Ypsilantis[15] have obtained a consistent function for nuclear radii by applying the quantitative treatment of the alpha decay process to even-even isotopes of the heavy elements. They have used the following expression, which is essentially the same as Eq. (6.20), that relates the decay constant, decay energy, atomic number, and nuclear radius[16]:

$$\log_{10}\lambda = 21.843 + 1/2 \log_{10}E + \log_{10}R + 0.217 \frac{4}{A-4}$$
$$- 1.104 \frac{(Z-2)}{\left\{ E \left[1 + \left(\frac{4}{A-4} \right) \right] \right\}^{1/2}} (\alpha_0 - \sin \alpha_0 \cos \alpha_0) \qquad (6.21a)$$

where

$$\cos \alpha_0 = 0.5893 [Er/(Z-2)]^{1/2} \qquad (6.21b)$$

The method used to evaluate the radius starts with a plot of λ or $t_{1/2}$ versus energy, E, for a given value of the nuclear radius. The variable Z is eliminated by joining points of the same Z. This results in smooth curves. By comparing the theoretical results with the experimental values of λ and E for different nuclei, a functional dependence of the radius R is obtained that gives the best fit. This was done for 25 even-even nuclei by Perlman and Ypsilantis[15] and their results are shown in Fig. 6.11. The value obtained for the nuclear radius is

$$R = 1.48 \, A^{1/3} 10^{-13} \text{ cm} \qquad (6.22a)$$

with

$$r_0 = 1.48 \times 10^{-13} \text{ cm} \qquad (6.22b)$$

Small deviations from smooth curves for certain points can be explained by the small inaccuracy in the energy determination of alpha particles emitted by these elements, because the nuclear radius is sensitive to the alpha energy but not very sensitive to the decay constant.

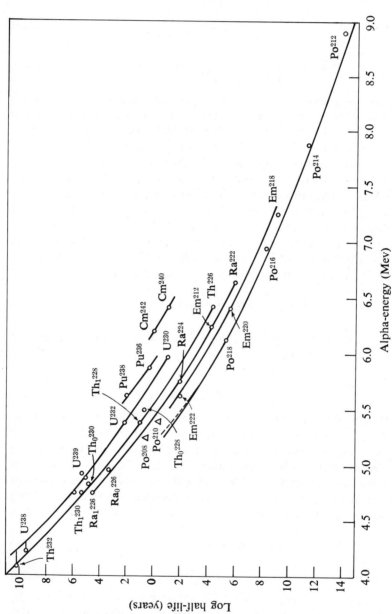

FIG. 6.11 Calculated curves and experimental points for the half-life versus decay-energy relationship. ○ represents alpha-emitters which may have normal nuclear radii. △ represents alpha-emitters having abnormally small nuclear radii. [From Perlman and Ypsikantis, *Phys. Rev.*, **79**, 30 (1950).]

4. SCATTERING OF FAST NEUTRONS

The neutron has proved to be very useful for obtaining information about the structure of the nucleus. Because the neutron has no charge, it does not interact with the extra-nuclear electrons, and, therefore, there is no coulomb force that acts on the neutron. However, as soon as it nears the surface of the nucleus, the neutron interacts with the nucleus and experiences the nuclear force. Thus the radius obtained by the scattering of fast neutrons will be the force radius, because the neutron may come under the influence of the nuclear force before actually reaching the nuclear surface. Many experiments have been done on the scattering cross-section measurements of fast neutrons,

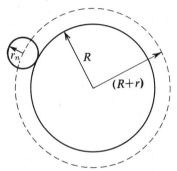

FIG. 6.12   Area enclosed by the dotted circle is the sensitive area available for the collision.

and different interpretations have developed at different stages for calculating the nuclear size from the measured cross-sections[17,18]. We shall develop this subject briefly in this section.

Consider the scattering of fast neutrons by a thin foil. Let R be the radius of the scattering nucleus and r_n be the radius of the neutron, and if the neutron comes within a distance $(R + r_n)$ from the center of the nucleus, it will be absorbed or deflected by the nuclear potential. This picture is true only if the nucleus is considered to be a completely opaque sphere (with potential $V = \infty$) and the comparative size of the neutron to be very small. This is true for high energy neutrons (15 to 20 Mev), as the de Broglie wave associated with them becomes small as compared to the radius of the nucleus. Thus, from the measurement of the attenuation of the neutron beam, it is possible to calculate the collision cross-section of the nucleus. On the basis of this simple picture, if we consider the area of a circle of radius $(R + r_n)$ as the sensitive area available for collision, (Fig. 6.12), then the relation between the cross section and the geometrical size will be given by

$$\sigma_c = \pi(R + r_n)^2 \tag{6.23}$$

Equation (6.23) is based on the assumption that both the nucleus and the neutron are rigid spheres of radii R and r_n and when projected on a plane, have geometrical areas πR^2 and πr_n^2, respectively. Thus, by determining σ_c (or the total cross section, σ_T) experimentally R can be calculated, if r_n is known.

There is some truth in the above description. The measured total cross-sections for fast neutrons have been found to be of the order of twice the target area $2\pi R^2$. The justification for this and further improvements on the nuclear size interpretations have come through the development of wave mechanics where the neutron is treated as a wave instead of a rigid sphere. The interaction between the incoming neutron and the nucleus is represented by a

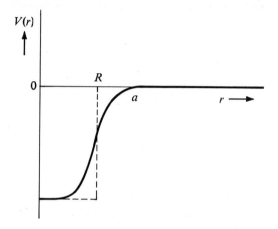

FIG. 6.13 The broken curve represents the square-well potential, and the thick continuous curve represents a potential that corresponds more closely to the actual potential.

finite attractive potential. According to this treatment[19], the neutron sees the nucleus as an attractive potential well given by

$$V(r) = -V_0, \qquad \text{for } r < R$$
$$V(r) = 0, \qquad \text{for } r > R \qquad \text{(6.24)}$$

(Fig. 6.13, broken curve) where $R = r_0 A^{1/3}$ is the radius of the square well. Elastic scattering, reflection, and transmission can be easily explained with the help of this potential well, but other processes occur which cannot be explained by this model.

It was pointed out by R. Serber[20] that to a high-energy bombarding particle the nucleus appears partially transparent, because at high energies (~ 100 Mev) the scattering mean free path for a neutron or a proton traversing nuclear matter becomes comparable to the nuclear radius. S. Fernback, R. Serber, and B. Taylor[21] have treated the problem by considering the nucleus as a sphere with a complex refractive index. From optical analogy, the nucleus is assumed to have the same type of properties as optical material, hence the name *optical model* of the nucleus. The scattering of the neutron wave by a sphere of nuclear material is characterized by (a) an absorption coefficient and (b) an index of refraction, both of which are functions of the neutron momentum. The index of refraction is also determined by the mean potential V of the neutron inside the nucleus. When an incoming neutron wave strikes the nucleus it is either absorbed or diffracted. The absorption corresponds to inelastic collisions while diffraction corresponds to elastic collisions. This model has been very successful[17] in explaining the neutron scattering and absorption for neutron energies of 42 Mev to 1.4 Bev.

Assuming such a picture of the scattering of neutrons, Fernback, *et al.*[21] have calculated the inelastic and elastic scattering cross-sections in the following form

$$\sigma_a = \pi R^2 \left\{ 1 - \frac{1 - (1 + 2KR)e^{-2KR}}{2K^2 R^2} \right\} \tag{6.25}$$

and

$$\sigma_d = 2\pi \int_0^R |1 - e^{(-K + 2ik_1)s}|^2 \rho \, d\rho \tag{6.26}$$

where σ_a and σ_d are the absorption and the diffraction cross-sections, respectively (inelastic and elastic scattering cross-sections, respectively), R is the nuclear radius and K is the absorption coefficient of the nuclear material. If $k = \sqrt{2mE}/\hbar$ is the propagation vector of the neutron wave outside the nucleus, its propagation vector inside the nucleus will be $k + k_1$, where $k_1 = k[(1 + V/E)^{1/2} - 1]$. ρ is the distance from a line through the center of the sphere to where the portion of the wave strikes the sphere and $2s$ is the distance traveled by the wave in the sphere before emerging.

J. De Juren and N. Knable[22] have shown that both σ_a and σ_d are almost equal in magnitude at high energies of the incoming neutrons. This means that the total cross-section is

$$\sigma_T = (\sigma_a + \sigma_d) = 2\sigma_a = 2\sigma_d \tag{6.27}$$

Thus if the classical theory of an opaque sphere is used,

$$\sigma_T = 2\sigma_a = 2\pi(R + r)^2$$

or replacing r by λ, (i.e., wavelength divided by 2π) which is true for high energies, one gets

$$\sigma_T = 2\pi(R + \lambda)^2 \tag{6.28}$$

Fernback, *et al.*[21] using the experimental results of L. Cook *et al.*[23] for the total cross-sections of neutrons and making use of Eqs. (6.25) and (6.26) have calculated the nuclear radius. The results of their calculations are shown in Fig. 6.14. The value of the nuclear radius obtained by them is

$$R = 1.37 A^{1/3} \times 10^{-13} \text{ cm} \qquad (6.29\text{a})$$

and

$$r_0 = 1.37 \times 10^{-13} \text{ cm} \qquad (6.29\text{b})$$

Fernback and co-workers have determined $k_1 = 2.85 \times 10^{12} \text{ cm}^{-1}$ and $K = 3.0 \times 10^{12} \text{ cm}^{-1}$ to give the best straight-line fit for the radius calculated from the total cross-sections when R is plotted as a function of $A^{1/3}$.

As already mentioned, the above described model gives a good agreement for neutron energies above 42 Mev[17]. The difficulties arise when we apply this to low energy neutrons (a few Mev) because the neutron mean free path

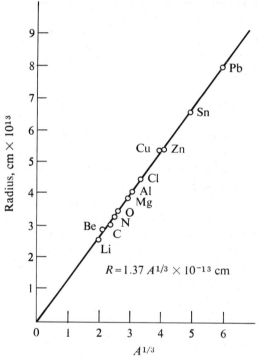

FIG. 6.14 The points represent the plot of nuclear radii, deduced from the total cross-section measurements, versus the cube roots of the mass numbers. The straight line through these points is given by

$$R = 1.37 \ A^{1/3} \times 10^{-13} \text{ cm}.$$

[From Fernbach, *et al.*, *Phys. Rev.*, **75**, 1352 (1949).]

is very small and the "compound nucleus" formation occurs (See Chap. XI). However, it is shown by H. Feshbach, C. Porter, and V. Weisskopf[24] and V. Weisskopf[25] that even in this energy range the optical model can be used to describe the average behavior of various cross-sections. They assume that the interaction of an incoming nucleon with the nucleus can be described by replacing the nucleus by an average optical potential, which has a real as well as an imaginary part,

$$V = V_0(1 + i\xi), \qquad \text{for } r \leqslant R = r_0 A^{1/3} \qquad \textbf{(6.30)}$$
$$V = 0 \qquad , \qquad \text{for } r > R$$

where $V_0 = -42$ Mev, $\xi = 0.03$ and $r_0 = 1.42 \times 10^{-13}$ cm. This model, the so-called *cloudy crystal ball* was successful in explaining the qualitative features of the total cross-section and angular distribution experiments, the real part explaining the elastic scattering and the imaginary part the inelastic scattering.

The latest experiments[18] in this low energy range have been interpreted in terms of the latest optical model calculations[25] using the round edge potential well instead of the one given in Eq. (6.30). The value of r_0 obtained[18] is $(1.35 \pm .04) \times 10^{-13}$ cm, which is in agreement with the value given in Eq. (6.29b).

5. HIGH ENERGY ELECTRON SCATTERING

In Chap. I, while discussing the proton-electron hypothesis of the nucleus, we showed that because the energies of the electrons emitted by the nuclei are only of the order of a few Mev, it is not possible for the electrons to be inside the nucleus. By assuming a certain size of the nucleus and making use of the relation

$$E^2 = p^2c^2 + m_0^2 c^4 \qquad \textbf{(6.31)}$$

we showed that the electrons must have energies of the order of $\gtrsim 100$ Mev. On the other hand, we can bombard the nucleus with very high energy electrons so that it will be possible for the electrons to go inside or near the nucleus. From such scattering of electrons of high energies it should be possible to get some idea of the nuclear size, which will depend on the way the charge is distributed inside the nucleus. The wave length associated with such high energy electrons can be calculated as follows:

From Eq. (6.31) because $E >> m_0 c^2$

$$E^2 = p^2 c^2$$

or

$$p = \frac{E}{c}$$

and

$$\lambda = \frac{h}{p} = \frac{hc}{E} \tag{6.32}$$

which for 150 Mev electrons gives

$$\lambda \approx 8 \times 10^{-13} \text{ cm}$$

It was first pointed out by E. Guth[26] that whenever the electron wavelength is of the order of nuclear dimensions, the results of the electron scattering expected by assuming the nucleus to be a point charge will show large deviations as compared to the case if the nucleus is assumed to have a finite size. The first such experiments that indicated deviations from the point charge scattering were performed by E. Lyman, et al.[27] who used 15.7 Mev electrons which correspond to $\lambda = \lambda/2\pi \approx 1.25 \times 10^{-12}$ cm. Their experimental data proved to be consistent with a uniformly charged distribution model of the nucleus in which $R = r_0 A^{1/3}$ with $r_0 = 1.45 \times 10^{-13}$ cm.

Theoretical calculations of the differential cross-sections of the elastic scattering of electrons by the nucleus have been presented very well by D. Yennie, D. Ravenhall, and R. Wilson[28]. The differential cross-section is given by

$$\frac{d\sigma}{d\Omega} = \sec^2(\theta/2)|f|^2 \tag{6.33}$$

where f is the amplitude of the scattered electron wave. The value of f, beside some other factors, depends on the energy of the incoming electrons and the type of charge distribution of the nucleus. Some of the results of their calculations are shown in Fig. 6.15 where the following shapes of the charge distributions have been assumed

Point charge	$\rho(x) = \rho_0,$	at $x = 0$	
	$= 0,$	$x > 0$	(6.34a)
Uniform	$\rho(x) = \rho_0,$	$x < kR$	
	$= 0,$	$x > kR$	(6.34b)
Exponential	$\rho(x) = \rho_0 \exp[-(x/a)]$	where $a = 1.06$	(6.34c)
Gaussian	$\rho(x) = \rho_0 \exp[-(x/b)^2]$	where $b = 2.12$	(6.34d)

where $\rho(x)$ is the density of the charge distribution at a distance x from the center, k is the propagation vector $2\pi/\lambda$, and R is the nuclear radius. One important feature of the uniform charge distribution shown in Fig. 6.15 (curve 2) is the appearance of maxima and minima in the diffraction of electrons. As explained below, these diffraction patterns are observed experimentally, and this leads to the uniform charge distribution model of the nucleus.

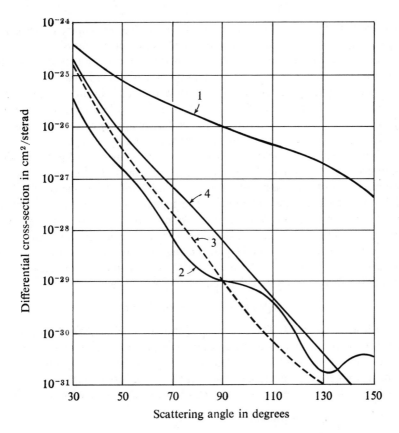

FIG. 6.15 Differential cross-sections for 150 Mev. electrons scattered by gold. The plots show $\frac{d\sigma}{d\Omega}$ versus θ for, 1. point charge distribution, 2. uniform charge distribution, 3. exponential charge distribution, and 4. Gaussian charge distribution. [From Yennie, *et al.*, *Phys. Rev.*, **95**, 500 (1954).]

The total charge contained within the nucleus is thus given by

$$q(R) = \int_0^R 4\pi x^2 \rho(x)\, dx$$

The scattering of high energy electrons has been studied in detail by various groups [29,30,31,32,33]. The apparatus used by R. Hofstadter, *et al.*[29] is shown in Fig. 6.16. A monoenergetic beam of electrons, obtained from the main beam of the Stanford linear accelerator, is deflected by a system of two magnets. Fields produced by these magnets are of the order of 12 or 13 kilogauss. The position of the slit, S, determines the width of the accepted energy band of the electron beam. There are 2×10^8 electrons per pulse, and 60 pulses per second are produced with each pulse lasting about 0.5

microsecond. The focused beam of electrons is directed towards a scattering target, which is a thin foil of the material under investigation. These foils are put in a scattering chamber built in the form of a large bell-jar. Both the deflecting system and the scattering chamber are evacuated to a high vacuum. The scattering chamber is provided with a thin aluminum window (0.006 inch thickness) that extends from $-150°$ to $150°$ and has a vertical height of 3 inches. The scattered electrons from the target are detected, after passing through the collimator (not shown), at several angles.

Some results of these experiments[30] are shown in Fig. 6.17. The continuous curve is the theoretical result obtained by Yennie, *et al.*[28], assuming a uniform charge distribution model for the nucleus. The solid circles are the experimental points. The agreement seems to be excellent. The point charge, the Gaussian or the exponential models, do not agree with the experiments. The observed diffraction structure in Fig. 6.17 can be explained only by a finite boundary of the charge distribution. Fig. 6.17 shows the distributions for $_{79}Au^{197}$ and $_{82}Pb^{208}$, which implies a nuclear radius for a uniformly charged model given by $R = r_0 A^{1/3}$, where

$$r_0 = (1.1 \pm 0.1) \times 10^{-13} \text{ cm}$$

for both lead and gold. The value of r_0, though smaller than that predicted by other methods, gives a good agreement between theory and experiment.

Later experiments and calculations by Hofstadter[32] for different elements and electron energies, based on the procedure described by Yennie, *et al.*[28], where the Fermi smoothed-uniform-model (as shown in Fig. 6.18)

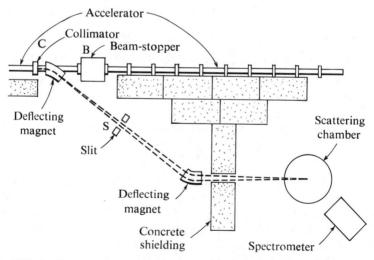

FIG. 6.16 The experimental arrangement of the electron-scattering system by Hofstadter. [From Hofstadter, *et al., Phys. Rev.*, **92**, 978 (1953).]

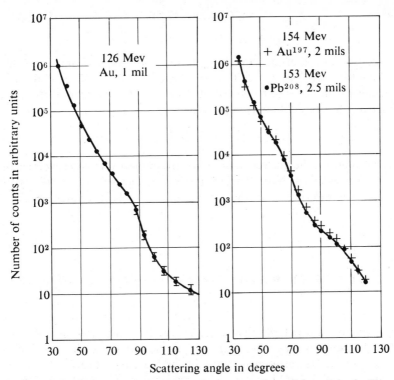

FIG. 6.17 The elastic scattering of electrons by gold and lead. The continuous curves are the theoretical results of a uniform charge-distribution model of the nucleus. Solid circles are the experimental points. (The arrows mark an estimate of the angular position of diffraction washed-out minima.) [From Hofstadter, *et al.*, *Phys. Rev.*, **95**, 512 (1954).]

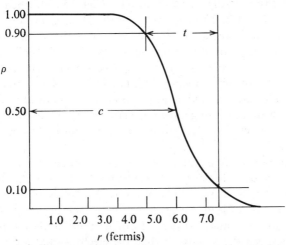

FIG. 6.18 The Fermi model for the charge distribution where c is the distance to the half-density point and t is the skin thickness (1 fermi = 10^{-13} cm).

is employed, show that the value of r_0 in $R = r_0 A^{1/3}$ varies from $r_0 = 1.32 \times 10^{-13}$ cm for $_{20}Ca^{40}$ to $r_0 = 1.20 \times 10^{-13}$ cm for $_{83}Bi^{209}$. Thus, if the value of the nuclear radius is to be described by $R = r_0 A^{1/3}$, then the electron scattering experiments yield an average value

$$r_0 \cong 1.26 \times 10^{-13} \text{ cm} \tag{6.35}$$

Thus the value for the nuclear radius obtained by electron scattering is smaller than the force radius. Note that we have not taken inelastic scattering into account. It is shown[28] that the contribution of inelastic scattering is negligible.

6. NUCLEAR RADII FROM MESONIC ATOMS

The μ^--meson is a particle that has a charge (e^-) and spin $(\frac{1}{2}\hbar)$, the same as the electron, but has a mass that is about 210 times the mass of the electron. Accurate measurements have limited the mass between[34] $(206.77 \pm 0.04)m_e$ and $(207.1 \pm 0.11)m_e$ with an average value of $(206.84 \pm 0.12)m_e$[35], where m_e is the mass of an electron. When a μ^--meson is slowed down to rest within a target material through loss of its kinetic energy to the electrons, it is captured in Bohr-type orbits around a nucleus, thus forming what is called the *mesonic atom*. These captured mesons cascade to lower orbits first by collisions and Auger transitions (see Chap. 8) and then by radiative transitions (for $Z > 15$). The mesons reach the 2P state in most materials in about 10^{-14} to 10^{-13} sec after capture. The 2P $\rightarrow$ 1S meson transition, with the emission of x-rays, occurs with a lifetime of 10^{-18} sec and is of particular interest because the 1S level is very sensitive to the nuclear charge distribution, and is thus sensitive for deducing the charge radius. Two competing mechanisms, natural beta-decay and nuclear capture, account for the disappearance of the mesons without causing any appreciable broadening of the x-ray peaks because their characteristic decay time has been measured to be much longer than 10^{-8} sec.

    The great sensitivity of the μ^--meson as a "probe" for the nucleus was first pointed out by Wheeler[36]. The advantage of the μ^--meson over the electron is its larger mass, which allows the μ^--meson to penetrate the nucleus. In the case of lead, for example, the μ^--meson in its lowest atomic state spends approximately 50 per cent of its time inside the nucleus. The main force between the μ^--meson (like the electron) and the nucleus is an electrostatic one, the nature of which is well known. If there is any non-electromagnetic interaction at all, it is very small. These are the properties that make the μ^--meson a useful probe for nuclear electromagnetic properties.

Fitch and Rainwater[37] have developed a new technique of x-ray spectroscopy for measuring the energies of the x-rays produced when a μ^--meson undergoes transitions between Bohr orbits about nuclei of various values of Z. The μ^--mesons are obtained as follows[37]. The 385-Mev protons rotating clockwise in a cyclotron chamber (Columbia University 164-inch *Nevis* cyclotron) strike a thin Be target (Fig. 6.19) and produce various reaction products including fast neutrons, and other elementary particles, π^+ (pi-plus, π^- (pi-minus), and π^0 (pi-zero) mesons, which are emitted in all directions. The π^0-mesons decay to photons near the target. The π^--mesons of approximately 100-Mev kinetic energy have a mean free path of approximately 10 meters. The π^--mesons decay into μ^--mesons and neutrinos (particles of

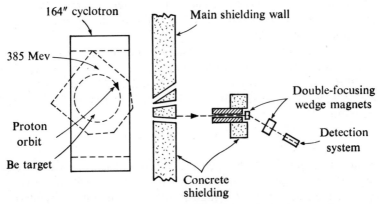

FIG. 6.19 Experimental arrangement for the study of x-rays from μ^--mesonic atoms. The figure shows the location of cyclotron shielding, focusing magnets, and detection system. A typical meson path is also shown. [From Fitch and Rainwater, *Phys. Rev.*, **92**, 789 (1953).]

charge zero, rest mass almost-zero, and spin $\frac{1}{2}\hbar$), i.e., $\pi^- \to \mu^- + \nu$. Because the intensity of π^--mesons is highest near the target, a certain fraction of them decays to μ^--mesons. A beam analysis indicates that about 10 percent of the beam particles are μ^--mesons having approximately the same momentum as the π^--mesons. A typical useful path is indicated in Fig. 6.19. The detector is placed in position as shown and mainly consists of a NaI(Tl) crystal mounted on a 5819 phototube.

The samples under investigation are placed in front of the detector one by one. The μ^--mesons form mesonic atoms which in turn emit x-rays. The energies of these x-rays are measured by the NaI detector. Fitch and Rainwater[37] have studied the x-rays resulting from the 2P → 1S transition when μ^--mesons are stopped in Al, Si, Ti, Cu, Zn, Sb, Pb, Hg, and Bi ($Z = 13$, 14, 22, 29, 30, 51, 82, 80, and 83, respectively) and form mesonic atoms. The x-ray energies vary from about 0.35 Mev for Al to 6.0 Mev for both Pb and Bi.

According to Fitch and Rainwater if we consider the nucleus as a point charge, the radius of the nth Bohr orbit is given by

$$r_{\text{Bohr}} = 2.82 \times 10^{-13} \frac{m_e 137^2}{\mu Z} n^2 \text{ cm} \qquad (6.36)$$

where m_e and μ are the masses of the electron and the μ^--meson, respectively, and n is the number of the Bohr orbit. The μ^--mesonic orbit, therefore, will be smaller than the corresponding electron orbit by the mass factor of about 207. In the case of Pb this gives $r_1 = 3.07 \times 10^{-13}$ cm for $n = 1$, which is well inside the nucleus, and $r_2 = 1.23 \times 10^{-12}$ cm for $n = 2$, which is just outside the nuclear surface. Also, in the case of Pb, the predicted $2P_{3/2} \rightarrow 1S_{\frac{1}{2}}$ transition energy for a point nucleus is 16.41 Mev, whereas the measured energy of this transition is 6.02 Mev. Thus the picture of the nucleus as a point charge is not correct.

Assuming a nuclear model of constant proton density inside a spherical nucleus of radius $R = r_0 A^{1/3}$, with a sharp edge and zero density outside, Fitch and Rainwater have obtained $r_0 = 1.17, 1.21, 1.22,$ and 1.17×10^{-13}cm for $Z = 22, 29, 51,$ and 82, respectively. Thus we obtain for the nuclear charge radius,

$$r_0 \cong 1.2 \times 10^{-13} \text{ cm} \qquad (6.37)$$

It may be pointed out here that the transition energy is mainly sensitive to the meson mass rather than the nuclear size for low Z, and it is mainly sensitive to the nuclear size for high Z. As pointed out by Henley[35,38], some other corrections such as nuclear polarization and radiative corrections may be taken into consideration. The contribution by these corrections is small, as in the case of lead it changes $r_0 = 1.17 \times 10^{-13}$ cm to $r_0 = 1.18 \times 10^{-13}$ cm, which is still small compared to the force radius. We shall take the value of r_0 given by Eq. (6.37) as approximately the correct value.

7. NUCLEAR SIZE DETERMINATION FROM MIRROR NUCLEI

Two nuclei are said to form a *mirror nuclei pair* or *Wigner pair* if they satisfy the condition $2Z = A \pm 1$, i.e., if they have the same mass number A but differ in the sense that the number of protons in one is equal to the number of neutrons in the other and vice versa. Thus a typical mirror pair can be represented by $_Z X^A$ and $_{Z+1} Y^A$, which shows that one nucleus has one more neutron than the number of protons while its isobar has one more proton than the number of neutrons. These pairs occur for $Z \leqslant 21$ where

$A \cong 2Z$. At least one member of the pair must be beta-active, as will be evident from the stability rule. Following are a few examples of mirror pairs:

$$(_1H^3, \, _2He^3); \, (_2He^5, \, _3Li^5); \, (_3Li^7, \, _4Be^7); \, (_4Be^9, \, _5B^9);$$

$$(_5B^{11}, \, _6C^{11}); \, (_6C^{13}, \, _7N^{13}); \, (_7N^{15}, \, _8O^{15}) \cdots$$

$$\cdots (_{11}Na^{23}, \, _{12}Mg^{23}) \cdots$$

$$\cdots (_{19}K^{39}, \, _{20}Ca^{39}); \, (_{20}Ca^{41}, \, _{21}Sc^{41}).$$

It was first pointed out by Bethe[39] that the differences in the coulomb energies between adjacent members of a pair of mirror nuclei may be interpreted as the coulomb-energy difference for homogeneously charged spheres of appropriate charges. The radius of such a sphere is then a measure of the nuclear radius. It may be pointed out that a given pair has the same number of n-p bonds but different numbers of n-n and p-p bonds. We assume that the nuclear forces are charge symmetric, i.e., the n-n forces are equal to the p-p forces and they do not contribute to the difference in the energies of the mirror nuclei (a detailed discussion will be taken up in Chap. XII).

Assuming the charge symmetry of the nuclear forces, the nuclear radius can be calculated as follows. Let the mirror nuclei $_ZX^A$ and $_{Z+1}Y^A$ have atomic masses M_Z and M_{Z+1} respectively. The difference in the masses $(M_Z - M_{Z+1})$ is due to: (i) The mass of $_ZX^A$ is greater than $_{Z+1}Y^A$ by an amount $(m_n - m_p)$, where m_n and m_p are the masses of the neutron and the proton, respectively, because a neutron in $_ZX^A$ is replaced by a proton in $_{Z+1}Y^A$. In terms of energies

$$\Delta mc^2 = (m_n - m_p)c^2 \tag{6.38}$$

(ii) There is a difference in the Coulomb energies of the pair because they have a different number of protons. It has already been shown in the previous chapter that the Coulomb energy of a nucleus having Z protons is

$$E_c = \frac{3e^2}{5} \frac{Z(Z-1)}{R} \tag{6.39}$$

Thus the coulomb energy-difference ΔE_c between $_{Z+1}Y^A$ and $_ZX^A$ is given by the following expression

$$\Delta E_c = (3e^2/5R) \, [(Z+1)Z - Z(Z-1)] = 6e^2Z/5R \tag{6.40}$$

Combining Eqs. (6.38) and (6.40),

$$(M_{Z+1} - M_Z)c^2 = \Delta E_c - \Delta mc^2$$

or

$$(M_{Z+1} - M_Z)c^2 = (6e^2Z/5R) - (m_n - m_p)c^2 \tag{6.41}$$

Eq. (6.41), on solving for R gives

$$R = 1.2e^2Z[(M_{Z+1} - M_Z)c^2 + (m_n - m_p)c^2]^{-1} \tag{6.42}$$

Thus, knowing the masses of the mirror nuclei, and after taking into consideration the maximum energy of beta decay in the case of the member which is
unstable, one can calculate R from Eq. (6.42). Since Bethe's first application
of this method, it has been used several times[40]. The results of such calculations give the nuclear charge radius (electromagnetic radius) $R = (1.4–1.5) \times
10^{-13}A^{1/3}$ cm, i.e., $r_0 = (1.4–1.5) \times 10^{-13}$ cm. This value of r_0 is higher
than the ones obtained by other electromagnetic methods such as electron
scattering. If we assume that the results obtained for r_0 from the mirror
nuclei method, which is applicable for $Z \leqslant 21$ are correct, then this will seem
to imply that the other electromagnetic methods for the determination of r_0
were satisfactory only for heavy elements, because they yield a smaller value
of r_0 for light elements than the mirror nuclei method does. However, it has
been shown by Cooper and Henley[38], and O. Kofoed-Hansen[41] that such
an assumption need not be made. Using a quantum-mechanical approach
and refined models for the proton charge distribution, they have found[41]
$R = (1.28 \pm 0.05) \times 10^{-13}A^{1/3}$ cm, or

$$r_0 = (1.28 \pm 0.05) \times 10^{-13} \text{ cm} \tag{6.43}$$

which is in agreement with other electromagnetic methods.

More recently Wallace and Welch[42] have measured the beta spectra
of mirror nuclei in the range of $19 \leqslant A \leqslant 39$. They have taken into consideration the shell structure of the nuclei. The value of r_0 obtained by them is in
agreement with other experiments such as electron scattering and μ^--mesonic
atoms. The value of r_0 also agrees with the one given in Eq. (6.43).

8. OTHER METHODS

Without going into the details we shall discuss briefly two more methods,
mentioned in Sec. 1, for the determination of the nuclear radius.

A. PROTON-SCATTERING. One of the most intensively investigated nuclear
reactions is the elastic scattering of protons by atomic nuclei. The reasons for
this are (i) the ease with which a well-defined proton beam in any energy
range up to billions of electron volts can be obtained, and (ii) the protons,
because they are heavy, charged particles, are easy to detect. A brief review of
the subject has been given by Glassgold[43]. The scattering of protons over
a wide range of energies can be explained with the help of the optical model,

or the independent-particle potential. The results of such experiments give the value of r_0 in the expression $R = r_0 A^{1/3}$ as

$$r_0 = (1.25 \pm 0.05) \times 10^{-13} \text{ cm} \qquad \textbf{(6.44)}$$

B. Isotopic Shift of Spectral Lines.   If we consider two isotopes of an element, they will have the same number of protons but a different number of neutrons, and, therefore, the proton distribution in the nuclei of the two isotopes will be different. Thus, if the nucleus has a finite size, the atomic electrons of the two isotopes will find themselves in slightly different electrostatic fields. This results in the shift of the spectral lines of the isotopes. Such studies have been made[44,45] and the results of the investigation give the value of r_0[45]

$$r_0 = 1.20 \times 10^{-13} \text{ cm} \qquad \textbf{(6.45)}$$

which agrees with the other electromagnetic methods.

9. SUMMARY

In concluding this chapter, we shall summarize the results of nuclear radii measurements by different methods for the sake of comparison. As shown in Table 6.1, the nuclear force radius, in general, is greater than the charge radius. After one has established the order of the nuclear size, it is possible to investigate other properties of the nucleus, such as the nuclear interactions. These, in turn, give some information about the nuclear force as we shall see in later chapters.

TABLE 6.1

THE VALUE OF r_0 IN $R = r_0 A^{1/3}$
BY DIFFERENT METHODS

Methods	r_0 in Terms of 10^{-13} cm
A. Force radius	
1. Alpha scattering	1.414
2. Alpha decay	1.48
3. Scattering of fast neutrons	1.37
B. Charge (or Electromagnetic) radius	
1. Electron scattering	1.26
2. Mesonic atom	1.2
3. Mirror nuclei	1.28 ± 0.05
4. Proton scattering	1.25 ± 0.05
5. Isotopic shift	1.20

PROBLEMS

1. Using the equations of conservation of angular momentum and energy, show that the impact parameter b is given by

$$b = r_c \sqrt{\left(1 - \frac{qQ}{r_c K_\alpha}\right)}$$

where r_c is the distance of closest approach and K_α is the kinetic energy of the incident alpha particle.

2. Show that for an attractive force, the limits of integration in Eq. (6.6) will change from

$$\int_{-(\pi-\theta)/2}^{+(\pi-\theta)/2} \quad \text{to} \quad \int_{-(\pi+\theta)/2}^{+(\pi+\theta)/2}$$

3. Calculate the height of the coulomb barrier of lead ($Z = 82$) and gold ($Z = 79$) for (a) alpha particles and (b) protons.

4. Calculate the distance of closest approach of 8-Mev alpha particles scattered from U^{238} at an angle of $135°$ in the LAB coordinate system.

5. (a) Calculate the distance of closest approach of 5.3-Mev alpha particles from Po^{210} in a head-on collision with a $_{79}Au^{197}$ target. What estimate do you obtain for the maximum size of the nucleus?
   (b) Repeat the calculations for 8.78-Mev alpha particles given out by $_{84}Po^{212}$ and compare the results with (a).

6. Alpha particles emitted from $_{84}Po^{210}$ having kinetic energies of 5.3 Mev are incident on a gold foil of thickness 2×10^{-7} cm. Calculate the fraction of alpha particles scattered through angles greater than (a) $30°$, (b) $60°$ and (c) $90°$.

7. Calculate the width of the potential barrier in the case of (a) silver and (b) gold targets for the 4.180-Mev alpha particles from $_{92}U^{238}$, by making use of the distance of closest approach r_c and the radius of the nucleus $R = 1.414 \times 10^{-13} A^{1/3}$ cm.

8. If the scattering of alpha particles from a given target is isotropic, what fraction of these will strike a detector of area A, at a distance of r, and placed at an angle θ?

9. Express $\sigma(\theta)$ given by Eq. (6.13b) in the CMCS.

10. Calculate the width of the potential barrier through which the 8.78-Mev alpha particles must pass in the disintegration of $_{84}Po^{212}$.

11. What will be the value of r_0 in $R = r_0 A^{1/3}$, if the height of a potential barrier of gold for alpha particles is 19 Mev?

12. High-energy alpha particles are incident on a heavy target; assume that the collisions are head on. Plot the potential and the force as functions of distance, if the positive charge of the target nucleus is assumed to be (a) a point charge, (b) uniformly distributed in a sphere of radius 10^{-8} cm, (c) confined in a nucleus of radius $R = r_0 A^{1/3}$, and (d) the charge density varying as $\rho(x) = \rho_0 e^{-x/a}$, where a is a constant.

13. Using Eq. (6.25), plot σ_c versus $A^{2/3}$ for $K = 3 \times 10^{-12}$ cm^{-1}.

14. Express the value of r_0 in turns of K and σ_c.

15. Very high-energy electrons are incident on a target. Calculate the recoil energy of the target nucleus as a function of E and θ. Calculate this for 200-Mev electrons incident on a S^{32} target nucleus.

16. If we assume that the charge density of the nucleus is given by Eq. (6.34c), i.e.,

$$\rho(x) = \rho_0 e^{-x/a}$$

show that the rms value of the radius is given by

$$R_{rms} = a\sqrt{12}$$

17. Assuming the nucleus to be a point charge, calculate the radius of the nth Bohr orbit for the μ-mesonic atom in the case of lead and gold. Assuming that the radius is given by $R = r_0 A^{1/3}$, where $r_0 = 1.35 \times 10^{-13}$ cm, which orbits of lead and gold lie inside the two nuclei, respectively?

18. Is it possible to have mirror nuclei with $A \gtrsim 41$, and why?

19. Consider the mirror pairs $(_5B^{11}, {}_6C^{11})$, $(_{11}Na^{23}, {}_{12}Mg^{23})$, and $(_{19}K^{39}, {}_{20}Ca^{39})$. The second member of each pair decays with a β^+ emission having maximum energies of 0.98 Mev, 2.95 Mev, and 5.49 Mev respectively. Calculate the value of nuclear radii in all three cases, and compare the value of r_0.

20. What different methods do you suggest for measuring radii of nuclei with (a) $A < 50$, (b) $50 < A < 150$, and (c) $A > 150$.

REFERENCES

1. "International Congress on Nuclear Sizes and Density Distributions," *Revs. Mod. Phys.*, **30**, p. 412, (1958).

2. Geiger, H., and E. Marsden, *Proc. Roy. Soc.*, **A82**, p. 495, (1909).

3. Rutherford, E., *Phil. Mag.*, **21**, p. 669, (1911).

4. Geiger, H., and E. Marsden, *Phil. Mag.*, **25**, p. 604, (1913).

5. Chadwick, J., *Phil. Mag.*, **40**, p. 734, (1920).

6. Bieler, E. S., *Proc. Roy. Soc.*, **A105**, p. 434, (1924).

7. Rutherford, E., and J. Chadwick, *Phil. Mag.*, **50**, p. 889, (1925).

8. Goldstein, H., *Classical Mechanics*, pp. 81–85. Cambridge: Addison-Wesley Press, Inc., 1951.

9. Gordon, M. M., *Am. J. of Phys.*, **23**, p. 247, (1955).

10. Farwell, G. W., and H. E. Wegner, *Phys. Rev.*, **95**, p. 1212, (1954).

11. Blair, J. S., *Phys. Rev.*, **93**, p. 356, (1954); *Phys. Rev.*, **95**, p. 1218, (1954).

12. Kerles, D. D., J. S. Blair, and G. W. Farwell, *Phys. Rev.*, **107**, p. 1343, (1957).

13. Gamow, G., *Z. Physik*, **51**, p. 204, (1928).

14. Gurney, R. W., and E. U. Condon, *Nature*, **122**, p. 439, (1928).

15. Perlman, I., and T. J. Ypsilantis, *Phys. Rev.*, **79**, p. 30, (1950).

16. Bethe, H. A., *Revs. Mod. Phys.*, **9**, pp. 69, 161, (1937).

17. Fernbach, S., *Revs. Mod. Phys.*, **30**, p. 412, (1958).

18. Seth, K. K., *Revs. Mod. Phys.*, **30**, p. 442, (1958).

19. Bethe, H., *Phys. Rev.*, **47**, p. 747, (1935).

20. Serber, R., *Phys. Rev.*, **72**, p. 114, (1947).

21. Fernback, S., R. Serber, Lt. B. Taylor, *Phys. Rev.*, **75**, p. 1352, (1949).

22. De Juren, J., and Norman Knable, *Phys. Rev.*, **77**, p. 606, (1950).

23. Cook, L. J., E. M. McMillan, J. M. Peterson, and D. Sewell, *Phys. Rev.*, **75**, p. 7, (1949).

24. Feshbach, H., C. E. Proter, and V. F. Weisskopf, *Phys. Rev.*, **96**, p. 448, (1954).

25. Weisskopf, V., *Physica*, **18**, p. 952, (1956).

26. Guth, E., *Wiener Anzeiger Akad Wissenschaften*, **24**, p. 229, (1934).

27. Lyman, E. M., A. D. Hanson, and M. B. Scott, *Phys. Rev.*, **84**, p. 626, (1951).

28. Yennie, D. R., D. G. Ravenhall, and R. N. Wilson, *Phys. Rev.*, **95**, p. 500, (1954).

29. Hofstadter, R., H. R. Fechter, and J. A. McIntyre, *Phys. Rev.*, **92**, p. 978, (1953).

30. Hofstadter, R., B. Hahn, A. W. Knudsen, and J. A. McIntyre, *Phys. Rev.*, **95**, p. 512, (1954).

31. Pidd, R. W., C. L. Hammer, and E. C. Raka, *Phys. Rev.*, **92**, p. 436, (1953).

32. Hofstadter, R., *Revs. Mod. Phys.*, **28**, p. 215, (1956).

33. Ravenhall, D. G., *Revs. Mod. Phys.*, **30**, p. 430, (1958).

34. Koslov, S., V. Fitch, and J. Rainwater, *Phys. Rev.*, **95**, pp. 291, 625, (1954); Cohen, E. R., K. M. Crowe, and J. W. M. DuMond, *Phys. Rev.*, **104**, p. 266, (1956).

35. Henley, E. M., *Revs. Mod. Phys.*, **30**, p. 438, (1958).

36. Wheeler, J. A., *Revs. Mod. Phys.*, **21**, p. 133, (1949).

37. Fitch, V. L., and J. Rainwater, *Phys. Rev.*, **92**, p. 789, (1953).

38. Cooper, L. N., and E. M. Henley, *Phys. Rev.*, **92**, p. 801, (1953).

39. Bethe, H. A., *Phys. Rev.*, **54**, p. 436, (1938).

40. Wigner, E. P., *Phys. Rev.*, **56**, p. 519, (1939); Wilson, R. R., *Phys. Rev.*, **88**, p. 350, (1952); Peaslee, D. C., *Phys. Rev.*, **95**, p. 717, (1954).

41. Kofoed-Hansen, O., *Revs. Mod. Phys.*, **30**, p. 449, (1958).

42. Wallace, R., and J. A. Welch, Jr., *Phys. Rev.*, **117**, p. 1297, (1960).

43. Glassgold, A. E., *Revs. Mod. Phys.*, **30**, p. 419, (1958).

44. Ritter, F., and H. Feshbach, *Phys. Rev.*, **92**, p. 837, (1953).

45. Brix, P., and H. Kopfermann, *Revs. Mod. Phys.*, **30**, p. 517, (1958).

SUGGESTIONS FOR FURTHER READING

1. Evans, R. D., *The Atomic Nucleus*, Chapter 2. New York: McGraw-Hill Book Co., Inc., 1955.

2. International Congress on Nuclear Sizes and Density Distributions, *Revs. Mod. Phys.*, **30**, p. 412, (1958).

3. Preston, M. A., *Physics of the Nucleus*, Chapter 3. Massachusetts: Addison-Wesley Publishing Co., Inc., 1962.

VII

ALPHA DECAY

1. SPONTANEOUS DECAY

Alpha decay is a process in which the parent nucleus disintegrates into a daughter nucleus and an alpha particle. It was shown in Chap. II that alpha particles are doubly ionized helium ions, He^{++}, moving with very high speeds. In the process of spontaneous alpha decay, therefore, the parent nucleus loses two protons and two neutrons, so that its mass decreases by four units and its charge by two units, i.e., $\Delta A = -4$ and $\Delta Z = -2$. The nuclear disintegration may be represented by the equation

$$_ZX^A \rightarrow _{Z-2}Y^{A-4} + _2He^4(\alpha) \qquad (7.1)$$

Because the daughter nucleus $_{Z-2}Y^{A-4}$ has a different atomic number from its parent $_ZX^A$, the chemical nature of the daughter is also different.

A. CONDITIONS FOR SPONTANEOUS DECAY. Consider a nucleus $_ZX^A$ of mass M_p that decays into another nucleus $_{Z-2}Y^{A-4}$ of mass M_d and an alpha particle of mass m_α. Because the parent nucleus is at rest before the decay, the daughter and the α-particle must leave in opposite directions after the decay in order to conserve momentum (Fig. 7.1). Let E_i and E_f be the total energies of the system before and after decay. From the conservation of energy principle

$$E_i = E_f \tag{7.2}$$

or

$$M_p c^2 = M_d c^2 + K_d + m_\alpha c^2 + K_\alpha \tag{7.3}$$

where K_d and K_α are the kinetic energies of the daughter nucleus and the alpha particle, respectively. Thus the disintegration energy, Q, of this process is given by the following:

$$Q = K_d + K_\alpha = (M_p - M_d - m_\alpha)c^2 \tag{7.4}$$

For a spontaneous decay, Q must be positive. From Eq. (7.4), therefore, we conclude that α-decay will take place only if the rest mass of the parent nucleus

M_p

(a) Before

V_d M_d m_α v_α

(b) After

FIG. 7.1   (a) The parent nucleus at rest before decay. (b) The daughter and alpha particles emitted in opposite directions in order to conserve linear momentum.

is greater than the sum of the rest masses of the daughter nucleus plus the alpha particle. Such nuclei, as may be seen from the nuclear decay chart, happen to be in the region of high mass numbers, i.e., for $A \gtrsim 200$.

The usual practice is to express the Q-values in terms of atomic masses instead of nuclear masses. By adding and subtracting Zm_e (where m_e is the mass of the electron) from the right-hand side of Eq. (7.4), we get

$$Q = [M(A, Z) - M(A - 4, Z - 2) - m(4, 2)]c^2 \tag{7.5}$$

B. KINETIC ENERGY OF THE ALPHA PARTICLE.   From the conservation of momentum and energy, we have (see Fig. 7.1)

$$m_\alpha v_\alpha = M_d V_d \tag{7.6}$$

and

$$Q = K_d + K_\alpha = \tfrac{1}{2} M_d V_d^2 + \tfrac{1}{2} m_\alpha v_\alpha^2 \tag{7.7}$$

where v_α and V_d are the velocities of the alpha particle and daughter nucleus, respectively. Substituting for V_d from Eq. (7.6) into Eq. (7.7), we get

$$Q = \tfrac{1}{2}M_d(m_\alpha v_\alpha/M_d)^2 + \tfrac{1}{2}m_\alpha v_\alpha^2$$

$$= \tfrac{1}{2}m_\alpha v_\alpha^2\left(\frac{m_\alpha}{M_d} + 1\right)$$

or

$$Q = K_\alpha\left(\frac{m_\alpha}{M_d} + 1\right) \tag{7.8}$$

or

$$K_\alpha = \frac{Q}{1 + (m_\alpha/M_d)} \tag{7.9}$$

If A and $A - 4$ are the mass numbers of the parent and the daughter nuclei, respectively, $m_\alpha/M_d \doteq 4/(A - 4)$, and Eq. (7.9) takes the form

$$K_\alpha \doteq \frac{A - 4}{A}|Q| \tag{7.10}$$

For large A, therefore, $\dfrac{A - 4}{A}$ is almost unity, and the alpha particle, as a result, will take most of the disintegration energy, Q, but not all.

2. MEASUREMENT OF THE ENERGY OF ALPHA PARTICLES

Accurate determination of the energies of alpha particles is important in two respects; first, to improve the theories governing alpha decay, and second, to construct exact nuclear energy-level schemes. Many techniques, using different relationships, have been employed for the measurement of the energies of alpha particles. The methods whose descriptions follow, in fact, can be used for any heavy charged particles such as protons, deuterons, and the like. The different methods can be described under the following three categories: (a) magnetic deflection, (b) range-energy relationship, and (c) pulse-height analysis.

A. MAGNETIC DEFLECTION.   One of the oldest and most precise methods for the determination of energies is the measurement of the deflection of the path of alpha particles under the influence of a magnetic field. When a charged particle moves in a plane at right angles to the direction of a magnetic field, it describes a circular path of radius r given by

$$qvH = mv^2/r \tag{7.11}$$

where H is the strength of the magnetic field, and q and m are the charge and mass of the particle, respectively. The velocity is given by

$$v = \frac{q}{m}(Hr) \tag{7.12}$$

and the kinetic energy is

$$K = \tfrac{1}{2}mv^2$$
$$= \tfrac{1}{2}m\left(\frac{q}{m}Hr\right)^2 \tag{7.13}$$

Knowing m, H, r, and the charge-to-mass ratio, q/m, one can calculate K from Eq. (7.13).

If, for more accurate work, the relativistic effects are taken into consideration, Eq. (7.12) and (7.13) take the following forms

$$v = \frac{q}{m_0}Hr\left(1 - \frac{v^2}{c^2}\right)^{1/2} \tag{7.14}$$

and

$$K = m_0 c^2\left[\frac{1}{\sqrt{1 - (v^2/c^2)}} - 1\right] \tag{7.15}$$

where $m_0 c^2$ is the rest-mass energy of the particle.

The general principle of construction of an alpha-ray spectrometer is the same as that of a beta-ray spectrometer. The only difference is that the magnetic fields required for deflection of alpha-rays are much greater than those for beta-rays. We shall describe very briefly two spectrometers for the measurement of alpha particle energies.

(i) Fig. 7.2 shows a "180° focusing spectrograph." S is a source of alpha particles. A well-collimated beam of alpha particles is obtained by making

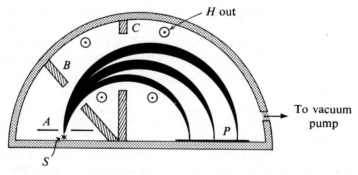

FIG. 7.2   Schematic diagram of a 180° focusing spectrometer. Field H is applied perpendicular to the plane of the figure pointing out. A, B, and C are the defining slits.

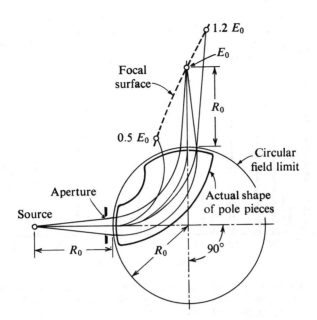

FIG. 7.3 Schematic diagram of a 90° broad range magnetic spectrograph. [From: Buechner, W. W. *Prog. Nucl. Phys.*, **5**, 1, (1955).]

use of a slit. This beam enters a magnetic field applied normal to the plane of the paper. The alpha particles, after deflection, are received on a photographic plate, P, where they leave a permanent impression. H is usually of the order of 10,000 gauss while r, depending on the energies of the alpha particles, varies from 30 to 50 cm. From the measurement of the radius, we can calculate the energy. Primary standards of energy are based on this simple method, which involves accurate measurements of r and H (H is measured by nuclear resonance methods). The energy can be measured with a precision of 1 part in 5,000[1], while the energy resolution ($\Delta E/E$) of about 0.1 percent can be obtained in a typical case of $r \approx 35$ cm.

The disadvantages of this method are that it needs sources of very high activity, which are difficult to handle; there is a lack of uniformity of the field, which introduces error; and the method is very costly.

(ii) For measurement of the energies of alpha particles given out in nuclear reactions, a "90° broad range magnetic spectrograph" shown in Fig. 7.3 has been adopted by Buechner[2] and others. A sector-shaped magnetic field is used, resulting in deflections of less than 180°. The particles are received on a nuclear emulsion, which records a broad range of alpha-particles in one exposure. Typical results obtained are shown in Fig. 7.4. In such a spectrometer, an accuracy of 1 part in 1,000 is possible with a resolution of 0.06 percent at $r \approx 50$ cm.

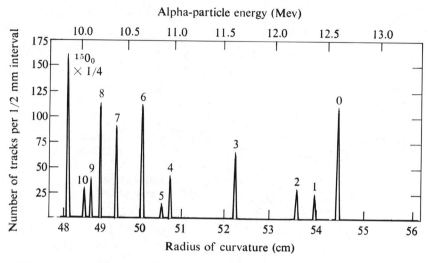

FIG. 7.4 Spectrum of alpha particles from $Al^{27}(He^3, \alpha) Al^{26}$ obtained by using 90° broad range magnetic spectrograph. [From: Hinds S. and R. Middleton, *Proc. Phys. Soc.*, **73**, 501, (1959).]

B. RANGE-ENERGY RELATIONSHIP. The ranges of alpha particles can be measured by making use of a cloud chamber, nuclear emulsion plates, or an ion chamber. Fig. 7.5 shows a photograph of the tracks of alpha particles in a cloud chamber[3]. Fig. 7.6 shows the path of an alpha particle in a nuclear emulsion plate[4]. If these ranges are measured, it is possible to obtain the

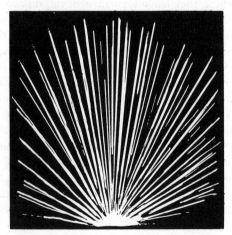

FIG. 7.5 Tracks of alpha particles from thorium $(C + C')$ in a Wilson Cloud Chamber showing the two ranges. Rutherford, Chadwick, and Ellis, *Radiation From Radioactive Substances*, New York: Cambridge University Press, 1930.]

energy of alpha particles from the range-energy relationships, which we shall discuss in some detail in the next section. A modified form of the ionization chamber (also discussed in the next section) is a convenient device to measure the ranges of alpha particles.

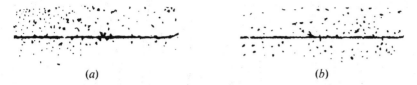

(a)   (b)

FIG. 7.6   Tracks of alpha particles of about 50μ range in various emulsion plates: (a) Ilford C2 emulsion, (b) Ilford E1 emulsion. [From: Robalt, J. *Prog. Nucl. Phys.*, **1**, 42, (1950).]

C. PULSE-HEIGHT ANALYSIS.   The principle of this method is based on the fact that the size of the electrical pulse produced is proportional to the energy of the alpha particle. This may be accomplished in three different ways:
  (i) by using a total-ionization method in which the particle is made to lose all its energy in an ionization chamber or proportional counter,
 (ii) by using a solid-state counter, and
(iii) by using scintillation counter. Fig. 7.7[5] and Fig. 7.8[6] show alpha

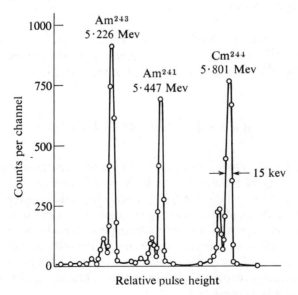

FIG. 7.7   Pulse-height spectra of alpha particles from a source containing Am^{241}, Am^{243}, and Cm^{244}, obtained by using a solid-state detector of 25 mm² sensitive area. [From: Blankenship, J. L. and C. J. Borkowski, *I.R.E. Trans.*, **NS-8**, 17, (1961).]

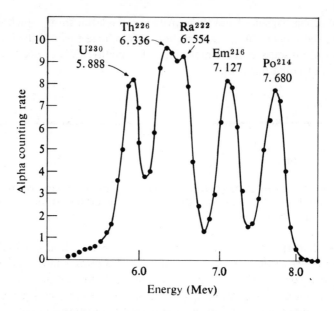

FIG. 7.8 Pulse-height spectra of alpha particles from the U^{230} series, obtained by using a NaI crystal. [From: Stephen, F. Jr., F. Asaro, and I. Perlman, *Phys. Rev.*, **96**, 1568, (1954).]

spectra of (Am^{241} + Am^{243} + Cm^{244}) and the U^{230} series obtained by using a solid-state counter and a scintillation counter, respectively. Note a marked difference in the resolutions of the two detectors.

3. RANGE AND IONIZATION

Measurement of the range constitutes an easy and accurate method of determining the energy of a charged particle. A charged particle moving through an absorber loses its kinetic energy by electromagnetic interaction with the electrons of the atoms of the absorbing material. If, in a collision, an electron gains enough energy, it may completely detach itself from the atom. Otherwise the electron is left in an excited bound-state. In the following discussion the term "ionization" will mean both bound and unbound degrees of excitation. The average energy needed for ionization is called the *average ionization potential*, and it is denoted by $\bar{I}$.

The *range* of an alpha particle may be defined as the distance it travels from the source to the point where its kinetic energy is zero. Depending on the method of measurement, the value of the range will differ slightly. We shall, therefore, later define three types of range: extrapolated range, mean range, and ionization range. The value of the range depends on the initial kinetic energy of the charged particle, as well as the type of absorbing material. The standard absorber is taken as air at 15°C and 760 mm Hg.

A. MEASUREMENT OF THE RANGE OF ALPHA PARTICLES.   A modified form of an ionization chamber for accurate measurement of the ranges of alpha particles in air was designed by Holloway and Livingston[7] in 1938 and is shown in Fig. 7.9. It consists of a shallow (1 to 2 mm deep) screen-wall ionization chamber. The depth of the chamber may be varied by mounting the back plate on a screw of 1 mm pitch, which determines the depth to an accuracy of better than 0.05 mm. The movable back plate, which is connected to an amplifier, is a brass disk 3/4-inch in diameter and is surrounded by a guard ring. The front face, which forms a high potential electrode, is a closely woven nickel screen with rectangular apertures of 0.20 × 0.40 mm. The source of alpha particles is mounted between the mechanical guides perpendicular to the face of the chamber. The distance between the chamber and the source may be varied by moving the steel screw. The source and its backing are made thin enough so as to neglect any self-absorption and scattering. Slits are placed in front of the source to get a collimated beam of alpha particles.

Individual alpha particles reaching the chamber produce ionization. An electrical pulse resulting from the ionization is communicated to an amplifier and then to a scaler. The counting rate is measured for different distances between the source and the chamber face. Curve A in Fig. 7.10 shows a *number-distance curve* for the case of Po^{210} alpha particles (only the end portion of the curve is shown). It shows that the number of alpha particles reaching the chamber remains constant to a distance of about 3.7 cm, after which the counting rate falls very sharply to about 3.85 cm and then steadily goes to zero. *Extrapolated range, R_e,* is defined as the distance from the origin

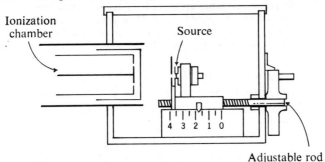

FIG. 7.9 Schematic diagram of a shallow ionization chamber. [From: Holloway, M. G. and M. S. Livingston, *Phys. Rev.*, **54**, 18, (1938).]

to the point where the tangent drawn to the curve A, at its point of inflection, intersects the distance axis. As shown in Fig. 7.10 for Po^{210} alpha particles, $R_e = 3.897$ cm.

Curve B in Fig. 7.10 is called the *differential range curve* and is obtained by taking the derivative of the number-distance curve A at different distances. The resulting curve shows a maximum at the point of inflection of A. The *mean range*, $\bar{R}$, is defined as the distance from the origin to the maximum

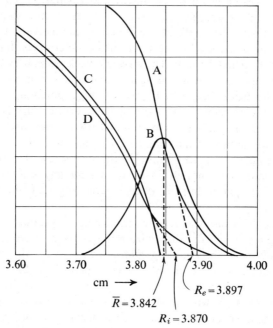

FIG. 7.10   Relative ionization versus distance curves for Po^{210} alpha particles. (A) number-distance curve, (B) differential range curve, (C) differential ionization curve of a single particle, and (D) average ionization or Bragg curve. [From: Holloway, M. G. and M. S. Livingston, *Phys. Rev.*, **54**, 18, (1938).]

of the differential range curve. In this case $\bar{R} = 3.842$ cm. An important significance of the mean range is that half of the alpha particles have ranges more than $\bar{R}$ and half less than $\bar{R}$. The mean range is used more commonly than the extrapolated range.

B. STRAGGLING[7]. As already mentioned, the alpha particles lose their energy by the process of ionization and excitation. The energy loss, therefore, occurs in discrete amounts and will show statistical fluctuations about a mean, or most probable range. This is quite clear from the curves A and B of

Fig. 7.10, which show that all alpha particles do not have the same range. If all alpha particles had exactly the same range, there would have been a very sharp drop at the end. This fluctuation in the range is called *range straggling*. The range-straggling effects are also evident from Fig. 7.5, which shows that all the tracks do not have exactly the same length. The distribution curve B may be closely approximated by a Gaussian function, i.e.,

$$f(x)\,dx = (1/\sqrt{\pi}\alpha)e^{-(\bar{R}-x)^2/\alpha^2}\,dx \qquad (7.16)$$

where $f(x)\,dx$ is the fraction of the total number of particles having a range ending between x and $x + dx$, $\bar{R}$ is the mean range, and α is the range-straggling parameter. The latter is defined as the half-width of the distribution curve at $1/e$ of the maximum, and $\alpha/\bar{R}$ is the dimensionless range-straggling coefficient which is denoted by ρ.

Using Eq. (7.16), we can show that the quantity S, which is defined as the difference between the mean and the extrapolated range, is given by

$$S = \bar{R} - R_e = \tfrac{1}{2}\sqrt{\pi}\alpha \qquad (7.17)$$

For Po^{210} alpha particles, the experimental value of $\alpha = 0.060$ cm gives $S = 0.055$ cm.

S may also be calculated directly from the difference between $\bar{R}$ and $\bar{R}_e$, which, under standard conditions of temperature and pressure, gives $S = 0.070$ cm. As calculated from the slopes of the straight lines used in interpolating the value of half-maximum count, $S = 0.079$ cm. Therefore, the mean value is $S = 0.074$ cm. Thus, a total straggling parameter for Po^{210} alpha particles is given by

$$\alpha_t = 0.074/\tfrac{1}{2}\sqrt{\pi} = 0.084 \text{ cm} \qquad (7.18)$$

This total observed straggling is actually the sum of many separate straggling effects, some of which are[8]: (i) range straggling, (ii) noise straggling, (iii) ionization straggling, (iv) angular straggling, (v) chamber-depth straggling, and (vi) source straggling. The theoretical discussion of straggling is given by Bethe and Ashkin[9].

C. IONIZATION RANGE.   The measure of the range and the ionization along the path of an alpha particle can be used to calculate its initial energy. We define *specific ionization* as the amount of ionization per unit length of the path of the beam. The relative specific-ionization produced by a beam of alpha particles at different distances from the source can be measured with the help of the shallow ionization chamber previously described. For this purpose, the amplifier of the ionization chamber is designed so that the height of the output-voltage pulse is proportional to the number of ion pairs formed in the chamber. A plot of specific ionization versus distance from the end of

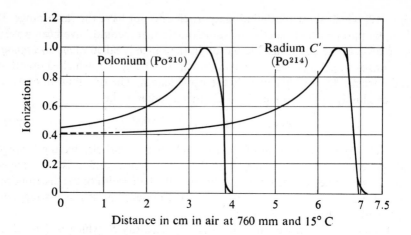

FIG. 7.11 Bragg curves for Po²¹⁰ and Po²¹⁴ alpha particles. [Reprinted by permission from Rutherford, Chadwick, and Ellis, *Radiation From Radioactive Substances*, New York: Cambridge University Press, 1930.]

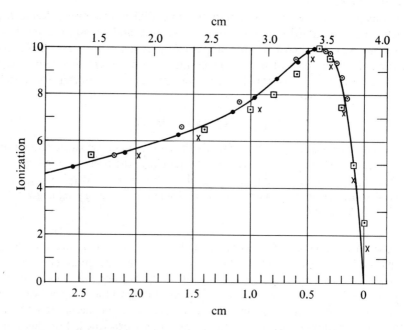

FIG. 7.12 Corrected Bragg curve for a single alpha particle (continuous curve). The points are the results of experiments by different groups. [From: Holloway, M. G. and M. S. Livingston, *Phys. Rev.* **54**, 18, (1938).]

the range is called a *Bragg curve*. Two such curves for Po^{210} and Po^{214} alpha particles[10] are shown in Fig. 7.11. (Curve D in Fig. 7.10 is also a Bragg curve.) These curves show that the relative specific-ionization remains constant up to a certain distance, then rises rapidly and is followed by a sharp drop. (Such a behavior can be explained by the fact that as the alpha particles reach the end of the range, they spend more time near the atoms because of their lower velocities, and, thus, they cause increased ionization. A further decrease in velocity results in the capture of the electrons by the alpha particles forming helium atoms.) The *ionization extrapolated range*, R_i, is defined as the distance from the origin to the point where the tangent to the ionization curve, at the point of inflection, intersects the distance axis. From curve D in Fig. 7.10 we get $R_i = 3.870$ cm.

The effect of straggling is evident at the end of these curves. It is possible to correct for different types of stragglings[7] and to draw a specific ionization curve for a single particle. Such a curve is drawn in Fig. 7.12[7] where the correction has been made for the finite chamber depth. In this connection we define the *differential specific ionization* as the value approached by the specific ionization, as the chamber is made infinitesimally thin.

In all our previous discussions, we have excluded one particular type of collision. When a heavy charged particle with a high energy collides head-on with an electron, a large fraction of the energy is given to the electron in a single collision. The fast electrons produced in this way are called *delta rays*.

4. STOPPING POWER AND RANGE

Another quantity of importance in dealing with the absorption of charged particles is the *stopping power*, which is defined as the amount of energy lost per unit length by a particle in a given material, i.e.,

$$S(E) = -dE/dx = \omega I \qquad (7.19)$$

where $S(E)$ is a function of the kinetic energy, E, of the particle and is different for different materials. I is the average specific-ionization in terms of the number of ion pairs formed per unit length, and ω is the energy required to produce an ion pair. If the value of the stopping power is known, the mean range can be calculated.

$$\bar{R} = \int_0^R dx = \int_0^E \left(-\frac{dE}{dx} \right)^{-1} dE = \int_0^E \frac{dE}{S(E)} \qquad (7.20)$$

On the other hand, if the mean range $\bar{R}$ of the alpha particle in a medium of stopping power $S(E)$ is known, its energy may be calculated.

$$E = \int_0^R \omega I \, dR = \int_0^{\bar{R}} \left(-\frac{dE}{dx} \right) dR \qquad (7.21)$$

It is also possible to find the stopping power of a given material, if one knows the range as a function of energy in that material, i.e.,

$$dR/dE = 1/S(E) \qquad (7.22)$$

The importance of the stopping power lies in the fact that it is not necessary to measure it experimentally for different absorbers, because it can be calculated theoretically either from classical mechanics or quantum mechanics. Such an expression for the stopping power will be derived in the next section, while the results are mentioned here. The energy lost by a non-relativistic particle per unit length of its path is given by

$$S(E) = -dE/dx = (4\pi z^2 e^4/mv^2)NZ \ln (2mv^2/\bar{I}) \qquad (7.23)$$

where v is the velocity of the particle, ze its charge, and m is the mass of the electron. N, Z, and $\bar{I}$ are, respectively, the number of atoms per unit volume, atomic number, and average ionization energy of the absorber.

As is obvious from Eq. (7.23), the stopping power is a function of the velocity. *Relative stopping power*, which is independent of the velocity, is defined as the ratio of the stopping power of a given absorber to that of some standard absorber. If subscript 0 refers to the standard substance, then

$$\text{relative stopping power (RSP)} = \frac{S(E)}{S_0(E)} = \frac{Z \ln (2mv^2) - \ln \bar{I}}{Z_0 \ln (2mv^2) - \ln \bar{I}_0} \qquad (7.24)$$

Also

$$\text{RSP} = \frac{S(E)}{S_0(E)} = \frac{\text{range of } \alpha\text{-particles in air}}{\text{range of } \alpha\text{-particles in the absorber}} \qquad (7.25)$$

In experimental work, we may be more interested to know the thickness of a material that will be needed to absorb the alpha particles. This is commonly expressed in terms of the *equivalent thickness* in units of mg/cm² defined as

$$\text{equivalent thickness in mg/cm}^2 = \text{range} \times \text{density} \times 1000 \qquad (7.26)$$

If the relative stopping power of a material, and hence the range in air is known, the equivalent thickness may be calculated by using Eqs. (7.25) and (7.26).

5. THEORY OF STOPPING POWER

A heavy charged particle passing through an absorber loses most of its energy in ionizing the atoms of the absorber. The energy loss per unit length, i.e., the stopping power, can be calculated theoretically. The first such expression for stopping power based on classical mechanics was derived by N. Bohr[11] in

1915. H. Bethe[12,13] in 1930 deduced an approximate expression from a quantum mechanical treatment. A more exact expression, also based on quantum mechanics, was derived by F. Bloch[14] in 1933 and includes the results of Bohr and Bethe as the limiting cases. We shall derive the expression from the classical viewpoint and then discuss the changes which must be incorporated from the use of quantum mechanical treatments.

An incident charged particle of mass M has a charge ze and velocity v. Let A, Z, and ρ be the mass number, atomic number, and density, respectively, of the absorber. Consider an electron of mass m at a distance b, the impact

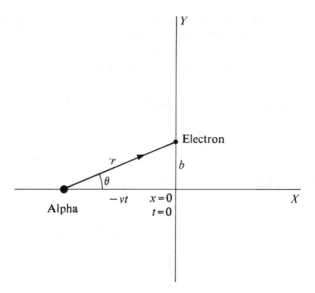

FIG. 7.13 Interaction of an alpha particle with an electron of an atom.

parameter, from the path of the charged particle as shown in Fig. 7.13. Also, $t = 0$ represents the time when the charged particle is at the origin. To make the derivation simple, we make the following assumptions:

(i) The charged particles are heavy and, because of high velocities, their paths in the absorbers are straight lines. They lose their energy only in ionizing and exciting the atoms of the absorber along their path. We also assume that the motion of the charged particles is governed by classical mechanics, and no relativistic corrections are needed. This is true for alpha particles of energies less than 10 Mev.

(ii) The electron in the absorber is free and is initially at rest during the collision. Also the motion of the electron during the collision is so small that the electric field may be calculated as if the electron were not displaced from its position. This is true only if the velocity of the charged particle is much greater than the electronic velocities in the atoms.

From the symmetrical nature of the problem (see Fig. 7.13) the net x-component of the impulse given to the electron is zero. This is true because the contribution to the x-component of the impulse when the particle is approaching 0 cancels the contribution when the particle is receding from 0, i.e.,

$$\int_{-\infty}^{0} F_x \, dt = \int_{0}^{\infty} F_x \, dt \qquad (7.27)$$

where F_x is the x-component of the force $F = ze^2/r^2$. The y-component of the impulse (momentum) given to the electron is

$$p_y = \int_{-\infty}^{\infty} F_y \, dt = \int_{-\infty}^{\infty} (ze^2/r^2)\sin \theta \, dt \qquad (7.28)$$

Introducing a change of variables (from Fig. 7.13)

$$\sin \theta = b/r \qquad -vt/b = \cot \theta$$
$$dt = (b/v) \csc^2 \theta \, d\theta$$

into Eq. (7.28) and integrating, we get

$$p_y = 2ze^2/bv \qquad (7.29)$$

The energy given to a single electron at a distance b, therefore, is

$$E_e = \frac{p_y^2}{2m} = \frac{2z^2e^4}{mb^2v^2} \qquad (7.30)$$

If N_A is Avogadro's number, there are $(Z\rho N_A)/A$ number of electrons per unit volume of the absorber. Because of the cylindrical symmetry of the problem, the number of electrons in a shell of radii b and $b + db$ and length dx as shown in Fig. 7.14 is

$$dN = 2\pi b \, db \, dx(Z\rho N_A/A) \qquad (7.31)$$

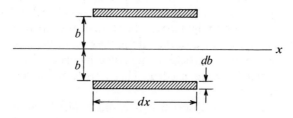

FIG. 7.14   The shaded area represents a cylinder of radius b, thickness db, and length dx.

Combining Eqs. (7.30) and (7.31), the energy loss to the shell of length dx at b and of thickness db is

$$-dE(b) = 2\pi b \; db \; dx \frac{Z\rho N_A}{A} \cdot \frac{2z^2 e^4}{mb^2 v^2} \tag{7.32}$$

Therefore, the total loss in energy per unit length to the electrons in all the shells bounded by the minimum impact parameter, b_{min}, and the maximum impact parameter, b_{max}, is

$$-\frac{dE}{dx} = \frac{4\pi z^2 e^4 N_A \rho Z}{mv^2 A} \int_{b_{min}}^{b_{max}} \frac{db}{b} = \frac{4\pi z^2 e^4 N Z}{mv^2} \ln \frac{b_{max}}{b_{min}} \tag{7.33}$$

where we have replaced $\frac{\rho N_A}{A}$ by N, the number of atoms per unit volume of the absorber. Thus, if we can calculate the values of b_{min} and b_{max}, we shall have an expression for the stopping power S. This can be done by various means, but we shall consider the simple classical method:

(i) The minimum value of b can be calculated from the fact that classically the maximum velocity that can be imparted to an electron in a head-on collision is $2v$. Its energy, therefore, is given by

$$E_e \leqslant \tfrac{1}{2} m(2v)^2 = 2mv^2 \tag{7.34}$$

From Eqs. (7.30) and (7.34)

$$b_{min} = ze^2 / mv^2 \tag{7.35}$$

(ii) The maximum value of b can be calculated from the nonvalidity of the assumption that the electron is free during the collision. The electrons are essentially bound, and there is some average minimum excitation energy, $\bar{I}$. Thus b_{max} is not infinity but is given by (from Eq. 7.30)

$$\bar{I} = 2z^2 e^4 / mb_{max}^2 v^2$$

or

$$b_{max} = ze^2 / v(2/m\bar{I})^{1/2} \tag{7.36}$$

[An alternative expression† for b_{max}/b_{min} can be derived from an approximate quantum-mechanical approach.

(a) Value of b_{min}: The wave packet associated with an electron of mass m and velocity v is given by

$$\lambda = \hbar/p = \hbar\sqrt{1 - \beta^2}/m_0 v$$

The classical treatment is valid, therefore, only if the Coulomb field due to the incident particle does not vary over the dimensions λ of the electron, i.e., $b \geqslant \lambda$, or

$$(b_{min})_{QM} \approx \hbar\sqrt{1 - \beta^2}/m_0 v$$

† Fermi, E., *Nuclear Physics* (Chicago: The University of Chicago Press, 1950) pp. 28–29,.

(b) Value of b_{max}: From the relativistic point of view, the time τ during which the pulse is given to the electron in a direction perpendicular to the path of the particle is

$$\tau \approx b\sqrt{1 - \beta^2}/v$$

If $\dfrac{1}{\tau} < v$, which is the frequency of the electron, the electron does not absorb any energy. For energy absorption, therefore,

$$1/v > \tau \approx b\sqrt{1 - \beta^2}/v$$

or

$$b_{max} = v/\bar{v}\sqrt{1 - \beta^2}$$

where $\bar{v}$ is an average frequency of the electrons. It can be shown that the ratio of b_{max}/b_{min} obtained from this treatment is the same as that of the classical.]

By combining Eqs. (7.33), (7.35), and (7.36), we get

$$S = -\frac{dE}{dx} = \frac{4\pi z^2 e^4}{mv^2} NZ \ln\left(\frac{2mv^2}{\bar{I}}\right)^{1/2} \tag{7.37}$$

The more complete quantum-mechanical treatments[13,14,15] give different values of the limits of b, and the expression obtained for the stopping power is given by Eq. (7.38) (which is essentially the same except for the ln term).

$$S = -\frac{dE}{dx} = \frac{4\pi z^2 e^4}{mv^2} NZ \ln\left(\frac{2mv^2}{\bar{I}}\right) \tag{7.38}$$

If the relativity correction that occurs at high energies is taken into consideration, the following expression[16] is obtained.

$$S = -\frac{dE}{dx} = \frac{4\pi z^2 e^4}{m_0 v^2} NZ \left[\ln\left(\frac{2m_0 v^2}{\bar{I}}\right) - \ln\left(1 - \frac{v^2}{c^2}\right) - \frac{v^2}{c^2}\right] \tag{7.39}$$

where m_0 is the rest mass of the electron. Note that the mass of the incoming charged particle does not occur in these equations.

The results derived above are true for all heavy charged particles such as alphas, deuterons, protons, mesons, and so forth. In order to compare the theoretical expression for the stopping power given by Eq. (7.38) with the experimental results, we consider the case of alpha particles where $z = 2$, for which Eq. (7.38) takes the form

$$S(E) = -\frac{dE}{dx} = \frac{16\pi e^4}{mv^2}\, NZ \ln\!\left(\frac{2mv^2}{\bar{I}}\right)$$ (7.40)

or, rewriting this, we get

$$S'(E) = -\frac{mv^2}{16\pi e^4 N}\frac{dE}{dx} = Z \ln\!\left(\frac{2mv^2}{\bar{I}}\right)$$ (7.41)

Thus $S'(E)$ is a function of Z. Fig. 7.15[17] shows a plot of $S'(E)$ versus Z. The solid line is a plot of Eq. (7.41) while the open circles are the experimental points. The agreement between the theory and the experiment seems to be excellent. Using the above expression, A. Beiser[18] has calculated the stopping power for different charged particles as a function of energy. The results are plotted in Fig. 7.16, for alpha-particles, deuterons, protons, pi-mesons, mu-mesons, and electrons, using air as an absorber.

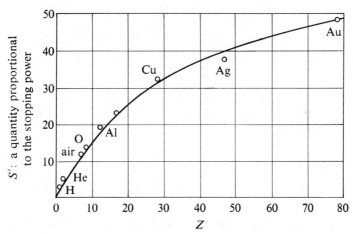

FIG. 7.15 Verification of the expression for the stopping power $S(E)$. Continuous curve for $S'(E)$ is calculated from Eq. (7.41), while the points are the results of experimental measurements. [From: Kaplan, I., *Nuclear Physics*, Reading, Mass.: Addison-Wesley Publishing Co., Inc., 1963, p. 315.]

The expression for the stopping power derived above cannot be relied upon for slow-moving charged particles. For example, it does not hold for alpha particles of energies less than 5 Mev and protons of energies less than 1.3 Mev. The disagreement of the theoretical expression for the stopping power at low energies is due to the fact that the capture and the loss of electrons, which become prominent at low energies, has not been taken into consideration.

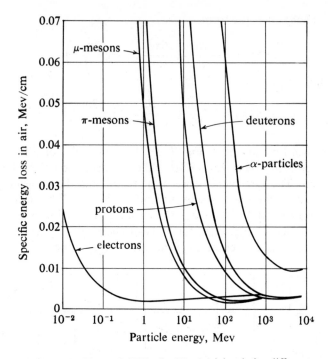

FIG. 7.16 Plots of dE/dx (in Mev/cm) in air for different charged particles. [From: Beiser, A., *Revs. Mod. Phys.*, **24**, 273, (1952).]

6. RANGE-ENERGY RELATIONSHIP

We have already seen that the range and energy of an alpha particle are related by Eqs. (7.20) and (7.21), i.e.,

$$\bar{R} = \int_0^{\bar{R}} dx = \int_0^E (-dE/dx)^{-1} \, dE \qquad (7.20)$$

and

$$E = \int_0^R \omega I \, dR = \int_0^R (-dE/dx) \, dR \qquad (7.21)$$

It is useful in the study of nuclear reactions to have range-energy curves for all energies. It is easier to measure a range of an alpha particle and then calculate its energy from the range-energy curves. These curves may be drawn either from experimental data or from theoretical calculations. For approximate calculations the energies of the alpha particles with ranges between

extent. Witcher[9] showed that the best focus for the electrons emitted from a point source, located on the axis, is a ring perpendicular to the axis[5].

Consider a point source, S, placed at a point on the axis of a homogeneous magnetic field produced by a long solenoid (Fig. 8.5a). The electrons of momenta p emitted at an angle α with the axis will follow a helical path before intersecting the axis again at F. The surface generated by all these electrons[10] is shown in Fig. 8.5b. The distance, SF, may be calculated by the following procedure.

The velocity, v, of the particle may be resolved into two components; $v \sin \alpha$, perpendicular to the field, and $v \cos \alpha$, along the field. The helical path, therefore, is the resultant of uniform circular motion with velocity

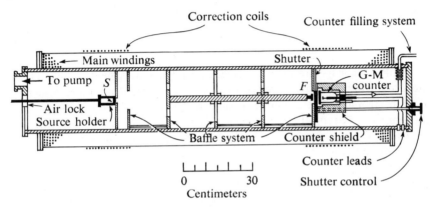

FIG. 8.5 (a) Outline sketch of a magnetic lens spectrometer. [From Wu, C. S., *Revs. Mod. Phys.*, **22**, 386, (1950).]

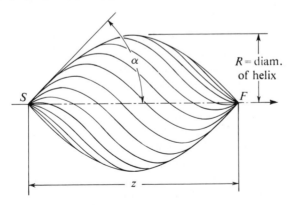

(b) Surfaces generated by electrons of specified θ in the magnetic-lens spectrometer. SF is one full turn of helix. [From Du Mond, J. W. M., *Revs. Sci., Instr.*, **20**, 160, (1949).]

$v \sin \alpha$ in a plane perpendicular to the magnetic field, and linear uniform motion of velocity $v \cos \alpha$ along the direction of the magnetic field. Equations representing these motions are

$$mv \sin \alpha = eH\rho \qquad (8.21)$$

and

$$z = (v \cos \alpha)t \qquad (8.22)$$

For $t = T$, the time period for one complete revolution, $z = SF$. T can be calculated from Eq. (8.21)

$$T = \frac{2\pi}{\omega} = \frac{2\pi}{(v \sin \alpha)/\rho} = \frac{2\pi}{eH/m} = \frac{2\pi m}{eH} \qquad (8.23)$$

Therefore

$$SF = (v \cos \alpha)T = (2\pi mv/eH)(\cos \alpha) \simeq \frac{2\pi p}{eH}\left(1 - \frac{\alpha^2}{2}\right) \qquad (8.24)$$

This type of spectrometer, in which a strong magnetic field is applied over the whole volume, is called a *long-lens spectrometer* (or solenoid spectrometer). This spectrometer has a unique feature in that its resolution increases with transmission. A typical resolution of this spectrometer is 1.25 percent, and the transmission is 5 percent. The figure of merit, (T/R), therefore, is ~ 4.

Although this spectrometer has the best performance, it has a few disadvantages, as well.

(i) It requires a large power supply for an air-cored coil. Iron may be used in the core, but this makes the field, H, nonlinear with current.

(ii) The source and the detector are both in a high magnetic field, which makes it difficult to use two such spectrometers, back to back, for coincidence work[3].

These difficulties were overcome by the development of a *short-lens spectrometer*[4] (or simply lens spectrometer) first designed by O. Klemperer[11] and improved by M. Deutsch, *et al.*[12] (Fig. 8.6). This is essentially the same as the long-lens spectrometer except that the magnetic field is applied over a very small region. It consists of a large coil, which acts as a magnetic lens. A source of electrons and a detector (a Geiger counter) are placed at the opposite ends of an evacuated tube passing through the coil. Beside the slit defining the beam, many other baffles are used to prevent scattered electrons from reaching the detector. A piece of lead is placed along the axis in order to stop the gamma rays from reaching the detector. A typical source-detector distance is 100 cm. The source is a few mm in diameter, and the inner and outer coils have diameters of 20 and 60 cm, respectively.

Deutsch, *et al.*[12] have worked out the theory of this spectrometer. The focal length, f, of this magnetic lens is given by

$$f = K(p/ni)^2 \qquad (8.25)$$

where p is the momentum of the electron, i the current in the coil, n the number of turns of the focusing coil, and K a constant that depends on the dimensions of the coil. The focal length, f, is related to u and v, the source and the counter distances, respectively, from the coil, by the familiar formula of optics

$$\frac{1}{f} = \frac{1}{u} + \frac{1}{v}$$ (8.26)

From Eq. (8.25), the power of the lens is proportional to $(i/p)^2$.

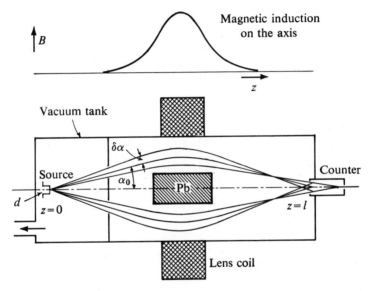

FIG. 8.6   Schematic of a short-lens spectrometer. [From Du Mond, J. W. M., *Rev. Sci. Instr.*, **20**, 160, (1949).

     In a typical case of a lens spectrometer, $R \sim 2$ percent and $T \sim 1$ percent. The figure of merit, (T/R), is ~ 0.5. The lens spectrometer has the following advantages: (a) high performance, (b) because H is linear with current, momentum is also linear with current, and (c) the source and counter are in a field-free region.

     Although the lens spectrometer has a high transmission as compared to a semicircular spectrometer, some investigations of internal conversion and level schemes of medium and light nuclei require spectrometers having very high R and T. Such requirements have been met by the double-focusing spectrometer.

     (3) *Double-Focusing Spectrometer.* As the name indicates, both the electrons that are emitted in one plane and the electrons that make an angle with the plane are brought to focus in this spectrometer. The double-focusing

property, or the space focusing, is achieved by the use of an inhomogeneous magnetic field; the spectrometer, therefore, is also called an *inhomogeneous-field spectrometer*. The double-focusing spectrometer has the high resolution of the semicircular focusing spectrometer and high transmission coefficient of the lens spectrometer. The first such spectrometer was developed by N. Svartholm and K. Siegbahn[13,14]. Other instruments of this type have been constructed by F. Kurie, *et al.*[15] and by F. Shull[16]. Figure 8.7 shows a double-focusing spectrometer and the path of the electrons in the magnetic field.

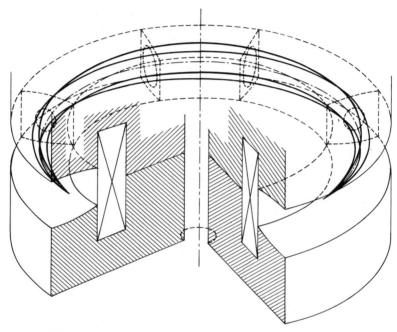

FIG. 8.7 Schematic of a double-focusing spectrometer. [From Svartholm, N., and Siegbahn, K., *Ark. Math. Ast. Fys.*, **A33**, 21, 22, (1946).]

This spectrometer is based on the behavior of the free oscillations of a charged particle in an axially symmetrical magnetic field varying with the radius[17]. Let us say that the applied magnetic field has the form

$$H = H_0(r_0/r)^n \qquad 0 < n < 1 \tag{8.27}$$

where H_0 is the value of H at the source located at a distance r_0 from the axis of symmetry. The electrons emitted from the source in a plane perpendicular to the z-axis will describe orbital motion with frequency

$$\omega_0 = v/r_0 = eH_0/m \tag{8.28}$$

where m is the relativistic mass. If the electrons are given out at small angles α with the plane, they will oscillate with radial frequency ω_r and axial frequency ω_z, given by[17,18]

$$\omega_r = (1 - n)^{\frac{1}{2}}\omega_0 \tag{8.29}$$

and

$$\omega_z = n^{\frac{1}{2}}\omega_0 \tag{8.30}$$

respectively. If $n = \frac{1}{2}$, the radial and axial frequencies are equal, i.e., for $n = \frac{1}{2}$,

$$H \propto r^{-\frac{1}{2}} \tag{8.31}$$

and

$$\omega_r = \omega_z = \omega_0/\sqrt{2} \tag{8.32}$$

This means that both the oscillations are in phase, and they will be in focus after half the oscillation. Because $\omega_0 = \sqrt{2}\omega_r$, the focusing will occur at an angular distance of $2\pi/\sqrt{2} = 254°6'$ as shown in Fig. 8.8.

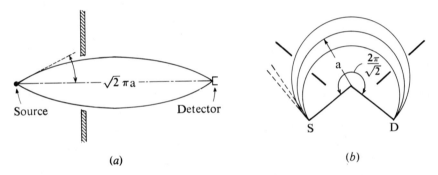

(a)   (b)

FIG. 8.8   (a) Double-focusing transverse field. (b) Focusing occurring at an angle of $2\pi/\sqrt{2}$.

A typical spectrometer has $R = 0.3$ percent and $T = 0.3$ percent. The figure of merit, therefore, is unity for the double-focusing spectrometer as compared to $\sim 1/2$ for a short lens spectrometer and $\sim 1/10$ for a semi-circular focusing spectrometer.

B. ELECTROSTATIC SPECTROMETERS.   Electrostatic spectrometers have been constructed[19–21] for low-energy electrons. It is possible to get a good figure of merit at low energies, but at high energies (> 1.5 Mev) the variation in the mass of the electrons results in poor focusing. The use of the instrument, therefore, is limited, and not much work has been done to improve it.

C. OTHER METHODS.   Other methods that have been utilized for measuring the energy of β-particles are the scintillation counter, solid state detector, the absorption method, and the cloud chamber. These methods do not compare in accuracy with the magnetic spectrometers, but a little sacrifice in accuracy simplifies the measurements to a great extent.

4. ENERGY LOSS BY ELECTRONS[22]

The process by which electrons lose their energy in traversing a medium is more complicated than the energy loss by heavy charged particles. These complications arise for the following reasons:

  (i) Because of the small mass and high velocity of the beta particles, it becomes necessary to consider the relativistic effects.

 (ii) As contrary to the heavy particles, an electron may lose a large fraction of its kinetic energy in a single collision. This not only causes greater straggling, but it also makes it difficult to distinguish between the incident electron and the target electron. The one that has higher energy after collision is called the *incident* (or primary) electron.

(iii) Collisions between the electrons and the atoms, in which the electrons are merely deflected without a loss of energy (i.e., elastic collisions), are of frequent occurrence. Such multiple scattering confuses the problem of energy-loss measurement still further.

 (iv) The most important effect that becomes prominent at very high velocities is the energy loss by radiation—so much so that at extremely high velocities of the beta particles, the energy loss by ionization and excitation becomes negligible as compared to the energy loss by radiation.

  (v) The electrons emitted in the process of beta decay do not have a homogeneous energy; they have a continuous energy distribution between zero and a maximum.

All these factors make it difficult to predict theoretically the energy lost by electrons. For relatively low-energy electrons, the energy loss is due mainly to the excitation and ionization of the electrons in the atoms of the stopping material. In fact, the energy loss per centimeter by a proton does not differ much from that by an electron of the same low velocity. For high-energy electrons, we shall consider the energy loss by the following processes:

A. ENERGY LOSS BY INELASTIC COLLISIONS. The expression for the stopping power for heavy charged particles derived in Chap. VII, i.e.,

$$-\frac{dE}{dx} = \frac{4\pi e^4 z^2}{mv^2} NZ \ln\left(\frac{2mv^2}{\bar{I}}\right), \qquad (7.37)$$

must be modified for two different reasons. (a) Because the reduced mass of the two-electron system is $\frac{1}{2}m$, the term $\log 2mv^2$ must be replaced by $\log mv^2$.

(b) The identification of the higher energy electron as the primary electron emerging from a collision limits the maximum energy-loss in any collision to $\frac{1}{4}mv^2$ instead of $\frac{1}{2}mv^2$. These corrections lead to the following expression for electrons with $E \ll mc^{2}$[(23)]

$$-\frac{dE}{dx} = \frac{4\pi e^4}{mv^2} NZ\left[\ln\left(\frac{mv^2}{2\bar{I}}\right) + 0.15\right] \qquad \text{(8.33)}$$

For the case of relativistic electrons, the following expression has been derived by H. Bethe[(23)]

$$-\frac{dE}{dx} = \frac{2\pi e^4}{mv^2} NZ\left\{\ln\left(\frac{mv^2 E}{2\bar{I}^2(1-\beta^2)}\right) - (2\sqrt{1-\beta^2} - 1 + \beta^2)\ln 2 + 1 - \beta^2\right.$$
$$\left. + \tfrac{1}{8}(1 - \sqrt{1-\beta^2})^2\right\} \qquad \text{(8.34)}$$

where E is the kinetic energy of the incident electron and $\beta = v/c$. For the case of slow electrons, in which $\beta \ll 1$, Eq. (8.34) is almost equivalent to Eq. (8.33). For the case of extremely relativistic particles Eq. (8.34) reduces to

$$-\frac{dE}{dx} = \frac{2\pi e^4 NZ}{mc^2}\left\{\ln\left(\frac{E^3}{2mc^2\bar{I}^2}\right) + \frac{1}{8}\right\} \qquad \text{(8.35)}$$

$$\text{for } E \gg mc^2.$$

B. ENERGY LOSS OF FAST ELECTRONS BY RADIATION (Bremsstrahlung). According to classical electromagnetic theory, an accelerated charged particle radiates electromagnetic energy at a rate given by

$$dE/dt = 2e^2a^2/3c^3 \qquad \text{(8.36)}$$

Whenever a charged particle, such as an electron or proton, moves in the field of the nucleus, it is accelerated and radiates electromagnetic waves; this radiation is called *Bremsstrahlung*. It is clear from Eq. (8.36) that the energy radiated is directly proportional to the square of acceleration a. Therefore, the energy radiated is inversely proportional to the square of the mass because $a = F/m$, where F is the force, and m is the mass of the charge particle. This explains why the radiation effects must be taken into consideration in the case of fast-moving electrons and may be neglected for heavy charged particles, such as protons, alpha particles, mesons, and the like. Because the force is proportional to the charge of the nucleus, we can say that the rate of energy loss by radiation is proportional to Z^2, where Z is the atomic number of the absorbing material. Note that the energy loss by radiation is proportional to Z^2 and increases linearly with energy, while the energy loss by ionization is proportional to Z and increases logarithmically with energy. At high energies, therefore, the radiation loss is predominant.

If the energy loss by radiation is most predominant, the *radiation length* is defined as the path length of the absorber in which the electron emerges with $1/e$ of its initial energy. The *critical energy*, E_c, is defined as the electron energy at which the energy loss by ionization equals the radiative loss. It has been shown by H. Bethe and W. Heitler[24] that

$$E_c \approx 1600 \ mc^2/Z \tag{8.37}$$

and the ratio of the radiative loss to the ionization loss is given by

$$\frac{(dE/dx)_{rad}}{(dE/dx)_{coll}} \approx \frac{EZ}{1600 \ mc^2} \tag{8.38}$$

where $mc^2 = 0.51$ Mev.

As an example, Fig. 8.9 shows the total and the individual energy losses[25] for electrons in lead; where

$$\left(-\frac{dE}{dx}\right)_{total} = \left(-\frac{dE}{dx}\right)_{coll} + \left(-\frac{dE}{dx}\right)_{rad} \tag{8.39}$$

Another point that we have not discussed is that the energy loss by radiation takes place not only in the field of the nucleus but also in the field of the electrons, and the latter must be included in the total radiative loss. Another energy loss that occurs at high energies is by Čerenkov radiation as discussed in Chap. III, but this loss is almost negligible compared with the radiative loss.

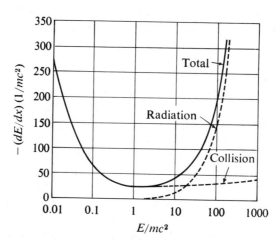

FIG. 8.9 Rates of energy loss by electrons in lead. The total, radiation, and collision losses are shown. The electron energy is expressed in units of mc^2. [From Heitler, W., *The Quantum Theory of Radiation*, New York: Oxford University Press, (1944).]

5. ABSORPTION AND RANGE-ENERGY RELATION[26]

As already mentioned in Chap. II, beta particles travel much longer distances in air (or in any gas) than the alpha particles of the same energy. For this reason, metals in the form of thin foils, commonly aluminum, are used for the absorption of beta particles. The exponential law of absorption holds approximately for nuclear beta-rays. Over a limited region the intensity of the beam is given by

$$I = I_0 e^{-\mu x/\rho} \qquad (8.40)$$

where μ/ρ is an *apparent mass-absorption coefficient* in cm^2/mg, and x is the absorber thickness in mg/cm^2; I_0 is the initial intensity, and I is the intensity after passing through a thickness x of the absorber.

The intensity of the β-rays transmitted through an absorber can be measured experimentally by a simple setup[27] shown in Fig. 8.10. Thin foils of Al are placed between the source and the detector. The signals from the detector are conveyed to the amplifier and the counting circuit. The counting

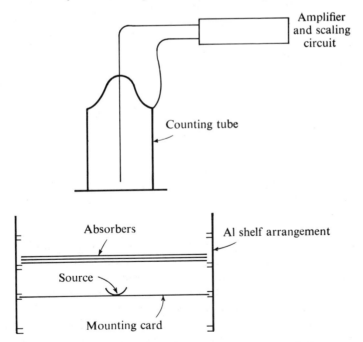

FIG. 8.10   Experimental setup for the measurement of electron-absorption coefficients. [From Glendenin, L. E., *Nucleonics*, **2**, 12, (1948).]

rate is observed for different thicknesses of foils by adding one foil of given thickness at a time. Fig. 8.11 shows the plot of percentage transmission of β^+-particles versus thickness of Al in mg/cm^2. (The β^+-particles are obtained from Cu^{62}, which decays with a half-life of 9.9 min and has an end point

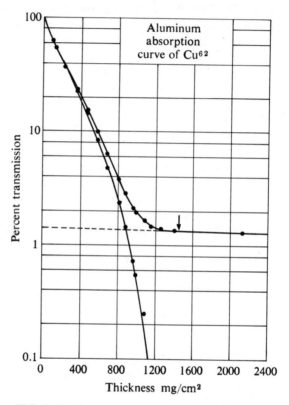

FIG. 8.11 Percentage transmission of β^+-particles (of 2.7 Mev) versus thickness of aluminum in mg/cm^2. [From Katz, L. and A. S. Penfold, *Revs. Mod. Phys.*, **24**, 28, (1952).]

energy of 2.91 Mev.) The point where the absorption curve meets the background, due to gamma rays accompanying the decay of the nucleus and cosmic rays, is called the *range*, R_β, of the nuclear β-rays.

There is a considerable difference in the shapes of the absorption curves for the case of nuclear β-particles (electrons that are produced by nuclear decay and have a continuous energy spectrum) and the homogeneous electrons (that are produced artificially or by conversion). The nuclear β-particles do not have a linear region in the absorption curve, while the homogeneous electrons' absorption-curves have a long straight portion and a long tail at low intensities going into the background. For comparison, this is shown in Fig. 8.12. In Fig. 8.12(a), R_β is the range of the nuclear β-particles as defined above. From Fig. 8.12(b) the range of the homogeneous β-particle is defined as the point where the extension of the straight portion meets the background and is called the *practical range*, R_p, while the point where the curve itself meets the background is called the *maximum range*, R_0. Another point to be noted is that the end portions of these curves of different energy groups of homogeneous electrons are all similar as shown in Fig. 8.12(c). The reason for this is that after traversing a small thickness of the absorber, the beam is completely diffused, and hence it gives the same shape at the end of the curve.

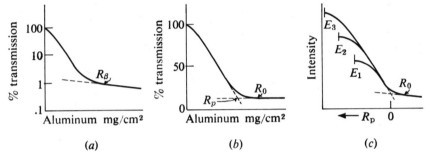

(a)   (b)   (c)

FIG. 8.12   Percentage transmission versus thickness of aluminum (mg/cm^2) of (a) nuclear beta rays and (b) homogeneous electrons. Figure (c) shows the end portion of the range of homogeneous electrons of different initial energies. [From Katz, L., and A. S. Penfold, *Revs. Mod. Phys.*, **24**, 28, (1952).]

The absorption method may be used for the determination of energies of the nuclear β-particles as well as monoenergetic electrons. Though the absorption method is not as accurate as the method using the β-ray spectrometer and does not present the details of the spectrum, it has the advantage of being simple and speedy. Also, as opposed to the β-ray spectrometer, the absorption method does not need a very high intensity source. The accuracy with which the β-ray energies can be measured by the absorption method depends upon two factors: (i) the accurate determination of the range, and (ii) the knowledge of the range-energy relation. The accurate determination of the range involves the precise location of the point where the absorption curve meets the background. The visual inspection method is the simplest of all but the least reliable. Many methods[26] have been developed for accurate determination of the end point.

Once the range has been determined, the next step is to convert it into energy by the use of a proper range-energy relation. Because of the complications mentioned in the beginning of Sec. 4, it is not possible to use the theoretical expression for the energy loss by ionization. Empirical range-energy relations have been obtained by the following procedure. An accurate determination of β-ray energies[28] is made with a β-ray spectrometer for different groups. The range determination is made and interpreted by comparing it with some standard material (usually with RaE beta-particle with an end-point energy of 1.17 Mev which is assigned a range of 508 mg/cm² in Al). The curves that fit these experimental points represent the range-energy relation and are shown in Fig. 8.13. These curves are represented by the

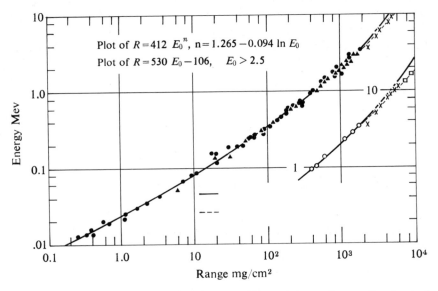

FIG. 8.13 Range-energy curve for electrons. The points are the results of actual measurements by different investigators. The solid curve represents the empirical relation given by Eq. (8.41), for energies below 2.5 Mev. The dashed line, which is given by Eq. (8.42), holds for energies greater than 2.5 Mev. [From Katz, L., and A. S. Penfold, *Revs. Mod. Phys.*, **24**, 28, (1952).]

following equations giving the empirical relation between range (mg/cm²) and energy (Mev)[26].

$$R = 412E_0^{1.265 - 0.094 \ln E_0} \qquad \text{for } E_0 < 2.5 \text{ Mev} \qquad (8.41)$$

and

$$R = 530E_0 - 106 \qquad \text{for } E_0 > 2.5 \text{ Mev} \qquad (8.42)$$

These relations have proved to be very useful and result in an accuracy of 2 to 10 percent. Fig. 8.13 reveals that there is no difference between (i) the ranges of monoenergetic electrons and nuclear β-particles and (ii) the positrons and the electrons, of the same energy. Another point worth noting is that for the energy range between 0.01 and 20 Mev the experimental curve for $(dE/dx)_{coll}$ is nearly parallel to the theoretical curve but is 25 percent larger. The reason for such a discrepancy is not known.

6. THE CONTINUOUS BETA-RAY SPECTRUM AND NEUTRINO HYPOTHESIS

We shall discuss in detail the characteristics of a beta-ray spectrum and show that beta decay is not a two-body problem; it is a three-body problem. This will necessitate the introduction of a new particle, the neutrino, which accompanies the process of beta-decay.

A. CHARACTERISTICS OF BETA-RAY SPECTRA.   Figures 8.14, 8.15, 8.16 and 8.17 show some typical beta-ray spectra that have been observed by different investigators[29-31] using different instruments as discussed in Sec. 3 of

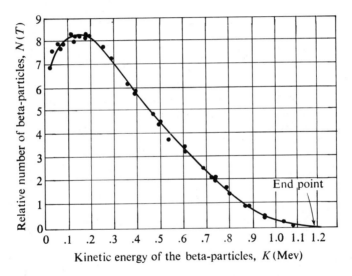

FIG. 8.14   Beta spectrum of RaE. [From Neary, G.J., *Proc. Roy. Soc.*, **A175**, 71, (1940).]

this chapter. All of these figures indicate that the electrons emitted in beta decay have a continuous distribution and energies ranging from zero to a certain maximum value. Because RaE decays by β^--emission without the emission of gamma rays, there are no conversion-electron lines superimposed on the continuous spectrum, Fig. 8.14. On the other hand, the decays of Au^{198} and Cs^{137} do not take place from ground-state to ground-state and the nuclei are left in the excited states. These nuclei subsequently de-excite by gamma emission or by emitting conversion electrons that show up as line spectra superimposed on the continuous spectra of Au^{198} and Cs^{137}, respectively, as shown in Fig. 8.15 and Fig. 8.16. In many cases the spectrum is more complicated as shown in Fig. 8.17 for Cl^{38}. The complexity of this

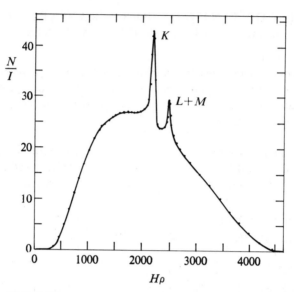

FIG. 8.15 Beta spectrum of Au^{198}. Line spectrum, superimposed on the continuous spectrum, is due to the conversion electrons. [From Fan, C. Y., *Phys. Rev.*, **87**, 258, (1952).]

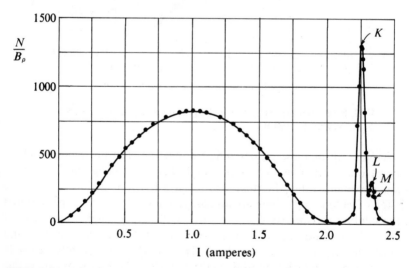

FIG. 8.16 Beta spectrum of Cs^{137}. [From Langer, L. M., *Phys. Rev.*, **77**, 50, (1950).]

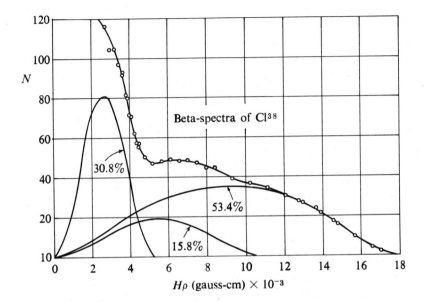

FIG. 8.17   Beta spectrum of Cl^{38}. Cl^{38} decay by emission of three different end-point energy groups of beta particles. The three groups are shown separated. [From Langer, L. M., *Phys. Rev.*, **77**, 50, (1950).]

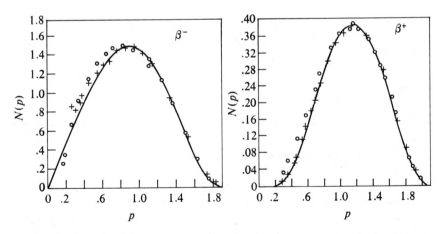

FIG. 8.18 Cu^{64} decays by β^-, β^+, and E.C. processes: (a) shows the β^- spectrum and (b) shows β^+ spectrum. The difference in the shape of the distribution in the two cases is obvious. [From Reitz, J. R., *Phys. Rev.*, **77**, 50, (1950).]

spectrum is due to the fact Cl^{38} decays with three different groups of beta particles having end-point energies of 1.11 Mev, 2.77 Mev, and 4.81 Mev with intensities 38.8, 15.8, and 53.4 percent, respectively. When these three groups are separated, they show simple spectra similar to Au^{198} and Cs^{137}.

Another point to be noted is that at the low energy region of the beta-ray spectrum, the shapes of the distributions are slightly different for the electrons and the positrons. This is shown in Fig. 8.18[32] for Cu^{64} which decays by β^-, β^+, and E.C. processes.

Regardless of whether the nucleus decays by β^--emission or β^+-emission, the continuous β-spectrum has the following characteristics.

(a) There is a definite maximum in the distribution, and its corresponding energy depends upon the type of nucleus undergoing beta-decay.

(b) There is a definite end-point energy that is almost equal to the disintegration energy available. Again, the maximum end-point energy is a function of the decaying nucleus.

(c) The continuous spectrum is observed for β^- and β^+, both for natural as well as artificial beta emitters.

Because the number of beta particles emitted is different at different energies, it is sometimes convenient to talk in terms of average energy. The average energy $\bar{E}$ is defined as

$$\bar{E} = \frac{\int_0^{E_0} N(E)E \, dE}{\int_0^{E_0} N(E) \, dE} \tag{8.43}$$

where $N(E) \, dE$ is the number of electrons having energies between E and $(E + dE)$, and E_0 is the end-point energy. In most cases the average energy is about one-third of the maximum available, i.e., of the end-point energy. RaE, for example, which has an end-point energy of 1.17 Mev, will have an average energy of 0.34 Mev.

B. NEUTRINO HYPOTHESIS.   Let us see what happens if we apply the following conservation laws to beta decay.

(1) conservation of energy

(2) conservation of linear momentum

(3) conservation of angular momentum

The parent and the daughter nuclei are in definite energy states. The maximum energy available is equal to the difference in these two energy states and is equal to the end-point energy. The average energy taken by the beta particles is only one-third of the end-point energy. The recoil energy of the daughter nucleus is very small and may be neglected. The question that arises now is this: What happens to the remaining two-thirds of the available energy? Apparently, the energy is not conserved in beta decay.

In order to overcome this difficulty, different explanations were tried. One such explanation was to assume that there may exist continuous energy states for the daughter nucleus. This implies that the daughter nucleus is left in the excited state and decays to the ground state by gamma emission. If this is the case, a continuous gamma spectrum should accompany beta decay. No such spectrum has definitely been established and hence excludes this hypothesis of continuous final states. (There are indications that *internal Bremsstrahlung* is such a spectrum, but it is not intense enough to explain the energy discrepancy.) Another explanation proposed was that all the electrons are emitted with the same energy, equal to the end-point energy, but in the process of coming through the atomic electrons they lose energy by collisions with electrons and in other processes. If this is true, the microcalorimetric experiments should be able to confirm this hypothesis, because any energy absorbed by the atomic electrons should show up in the form of heat energy. Such experiments were performed[33,35] using RaE and the average energy per disintegration was found to be[34] 0.34 ± 0.02 Mev, and not 1.17 Mev, which is the maximum end-point energy. Thus this explanation also fails.

Conservation of linear momentum requires that if there is a definite amount of energy available to be distributed between two bodies (the recoil nucleus and electron), they should have definite energies and not a continuous energy distribution. The alternative is to give up the law of conservation of energy. Even if we assume this to be the case, though not very reasonable, the angular momentum is not conserved as explained below.

According to the proton-neutron model of the nucleus, if there are A nucleons in a nucleus, its spin will be an integral or half-integral depending upon whether A is even or odd. The conservation of angular momentum requires that the spin of the system changes by integral numbers. Thus, in the case of beta decay the daughter nucleus has the same number of nucleons as the parent nucleus, but the emission of a beta particle adds an angular momentum of $\frac{1}{2}\hbar$. The motion of the daughter nucleus and the beta particle about their common center of mass results in a rotational angular momentum, which, according to quantum mechanics, is an integral multiple of $\hbar$. Thus the emission of a beta particle changes the spin of the system from an integral to a half-integral and vice versa. This also leads to the nonconservation of statistics, because the systems with integral spins obey Bose-Einstein statistics, while half-integral spin systems obey Fermi-Dirac statistics. If the system changes its spin by an integral, the statistics will not change, but the change in spin of a half-integral, as in the above case, will change the statistics from Bose-Einstein to Fermi-Dirac and vice versa. (Note that the electron has a spin of $\frac{1}{2}$ and obeys Fermi-Dirac statistics.)

It seems unlikely that we should give up all the conservation laws in order to explain beta decay. All the difficulties were overcome when, in 1934, Pauli put forth a neutrino hypothesis. He suggested that an additional particle, called a neutrino (denoted by v), is also emitted in the process of beta decay and takes away the missing energy. The properties assigned to the neutrino were such as to satisfy the requirements of beta decay.

(a) The neutrino must have zero charge, because the charge is already conserved without the neutrino.

(b) Because the maximum energy carried away by electrons is equal to the maximum available energy, or end-point energy, the neutrino must have zero, or almost zero, rest mass.

(c) The conservation of angular momentum requires the neutrino to have an intrinsic spin of 1/2, so that the total change of angular momentum due to a beta particle and neutrino together will be zero or $1\hbar$ as required.

(d) A neutrino does not cause any appreciable amount of ionization, and so it passes undetected. This means that the neutrino has a very weak interaction with matter and has a very small, or nearly zero, magnetic moment. Actually, it has none of the electromagnetic properties.

Thus the final system consists of three bodies: the daughter nucleus, the electron, and the neutrino. The beta decay is, thus, essentially a three-body problem (except E.C.), which makes it possible to explain the continuous momentum distribution. The neutrino, like the electron or positron, cannot stay inside the nucleus and is created at the time of decay.

The neutrino hypothesis was successfully applied by Fermi[36] in developing a theory of beta decay that explained the shape of the beta spectrum. According to this theory there exists an interaction (with a very small range, or may be even a point interaction) between nucleons, electrons, and neutrinos that transforms a neutron into a proton and vice versa, and causes a simultaneous emission or absorption of an electron and a neutrino. Thus the three beta decay processes may be written as

$$n \rightarrow p + \beta^- + \bar{\nu}$$
$$p \rightarrow n + \beta^+ + \nu$$
$$p + e^- \rightarrow n + \nu \qquad (8.44)$$

where $\bar{\nu}$ is called an anti-neutrino and is the counterpart of a neutrino ν, as a positron (β^+) is a counterpart of an electron (β^-). The detailed study of the neutrino and the antineutrino will be taken up in subsequent sections.

It is worthwhile to note that free neutrons have been observed to decay with a half-life of[37] $t_{1/2} = 12.8 \pm 2.5$ min, while the free decay of a proton is energetically not possible.

7. NEUTRINO-ANTINEUTRINO EXPERIMENTS

Indirect evidence for the existence of a neutrino was afforded by the success of Fermi's theory of beta decay, which we shall discuss in Sec. 8.9. The purpose of this section is to discuss the experiments that directly establish the existence of the neutrino and antineutrino and to confirm that only one neutrino is emitted in a single disintegration. Before we do so it will be worthwhile to clearly define the difference between the neutrino and the antineutrino.

As already mentioned, a positron is the counterpart of an electron (a negatron), or we may say that a positron is the antiparticle of a negatron. A new law called the *conservation of leptons* (*leptons* are light particles such as electrons, positrons, neutrinos, and the like) has been put forth, according to which the difference in the number of leptons and antileptons in a given system remains constant. If we adopt the hypothesis that the creation of a particle must accompany the simultaneous creation of an antiparticle, a neutrino will be emitted simultaneously with the emission of a positron, and an antineutrino

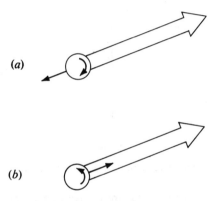

(a)

(b)

FIG. 8.19 Representation of (a) the neutrino and (b) the antineutrino.

with an electron. A real difference between the neutrino and the antineutrino may be stated in this manner: A neutrino, v, a *left-handed* particle, is defined as a particle with its spin vector antiparallel to its momentum vector (or velocity vector) as in the sense of a left-handed screw (Fig. 8.19a). An antineutrino, $\bar{v}$, a *right-handed* particle, is defined as a particle with its spin vector parallel to its momentum vector (or velocity vector) as in the sense of a right-handed screw (Fig. 8.19b). *Helicity* or *spirality* is defined as the cosine of the angle between the spin angular-momentum vector and the linear-momentum vector. Accordingly, the neutrino has -1 helicity while the antineutrino has $+1$.

The choice of names for the neutrino and antineutrino is arbitrary. Note that the mass of these particles is very small (or zero), and they travel almost with the velocity of light. This implies that they travel in the same direction in all Lorentz frames, and it is impossible to transform to a frame that is moving faster than the neutrino (cannot overtake the neutrino) to give it an apparent backward direction. Thus the simple relativistic transformation cannot convert the above defined neutrino into an antineutrino and vice versa.

We can, however, convert a neutrino into an antineutrino and vice versa by reflection. When a neutrino looks into a mirror it thinks it is an antineutrino (Fig. 8.20) and vice versa. This is because the mirror reverses the direction of the momentum, but not the direction of the spin.

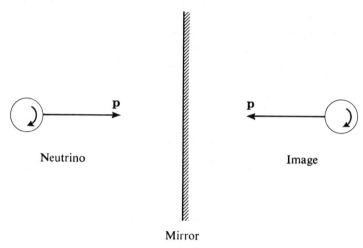

FIG. 8.20   A Mirror reflection of a neutrino is an antineutrino.

Having defined neutrino and antineutrino, we shall now discuss the experiments that fall into the following categories: (a) neutrino mass measurements, (b) neutrino recoil experiments, and (c) neutrino capture experiments (direct evidence).

A. NEUTRINO MASS MEASUREMENTS.   There are two different types of experiments that have been used to estimate the neutrino rest mass. The first method involves the comparison of the maximum energies of the beta-ray spectra with the known available decay energies. The second method which was pointed out by Fermi[36] is to investigate the shape of the beta spectrum near the end point.

According to the first method, the maximum kinetic energy, E_{max}, that a beta particle can have in a negatron emission is

$$E_{max} = (\Delta M - m_{v0})c^2 \tag{8.45}$$

where ΔM is the difference in the masses of the parent and the daughter nuclei, and m_{v0} is the rest mass of the neutrino. For positron emission, the maximum energy is given by the following equation

$$E_{max} = (\Delta M - 2m_0 - m_{v0})c^2 \tag{8.46}$$

where m_0 is the rest mass of the electron. Note that the atomic binding energies are very small and have been neglected. The value of E_{max} is determined from the observed end-point energies in beta decay, while ΔM can be determined either from an accurate measurement of the Q-values of nuclear reactions or from the atomic masses as determined with a mass spectroscope as discussed in Chaps. IV and V, respectively. The best results are obtained by considering those reactions that are just the reverse of the beta decay, i.e., one combines the results of (p, n) reactions with positron emission and (n, p) reactions with negatron emission. Examples of such reactions are: (1) C^{13} (p, n) N^{13} with $Q = -3.003 \pm 0.003$ Mev, and the maximum positron energy in the decay of N^{13} is $E_{max} = 1.200 \pm 0.003$ Mev; (2) H^3 (p, n) He^3 with $Q = -0.764 \pm 0.001$ Mev and the maximum end-point energy in the negatron emission of H^3 is $E_{max} = 0.0181 \pm 0.002$ Mev. The neutrino rest mass $m_{\nu 0}$ calculated from these two examples is $(-0.002 \pm 0.01)\, m_0$ and (0.0 ± 0.03) m_0, respectively. Such calculations have been made for about a dozen cases and they all indicate that $m_{\nu 0} < 0.01\, m_0$, i.e. less than 5.1 kev.

The other method involves a comparison of the theoretical spectrum shape in Fermi's theory of beta decay with the experimental spectrum shape near the end point. We shall discuss this method in detail after we have developed Fermi's theory. The results indicate that $m_{\nu 0} \leqslant 5 \times 10^{-4}\, m_0$.

In conclusion we may say that all the experimental evidence indicates the neutrino rest-mass to be less than $10^{-3}\, m_0$.

B. NEUTRINO RECOIL EXPERIMENTS. In addition to indirectly confirming the existence of the neutrino, the recoil experiments are performed to confirm the emission of a single neutrino in a beta decay (by proving the conservation of energy and momentum simultaneously) and to investigate the type of interaction by performing angular-correlation experiments between the electron and the neutrino. In order to establish a momentum balance, one has to measure the recoil velocity of the nucleus. Because of the very large mass of the nucleus as compared to the electron and neutrino masses, the recoil velocity of the nucleus is very small, which makes it difficult to measure. The measurements are still further complicated if the decaying nuclei are in the form of a solid or if the nucleus is a part of a molecule. Again, because it is a three-body problem, the nuclei will show a continuous velocity spectrum, because the final velocities depend on the final directions and these directions vary from decay to decay.

All these difficulties are overcome and the problem is simplified if we consider a monoatomic gas that decays by electron capture. Because, in the process of K-capture, the decay products are only the daughter nucleus and the neutrino, the beta decay process reduces to a two-body problem. In order to conserve linear momentum, the neutrino and the daughter nucleus are always emitted in the opposite direction to each other with constant velocities inversely proportional to their masses. Thus, if only one neutrino is emitted, the recoiling atom should have a single energy. The decay that satisfies all the conditions mentioned above and is best suited for such experiments is A^{37}.

$$A^{37} + {}_{-1}e^0{}_k \rightarrow Cl^{37} + \nu \qquad (8.47)$$

The experimental setup and the result obtained are discussed below.

The apparatus used by G. Rodeback and J. Allen[38] is shown in Fig. 8.21. The chamber is filled with A^{37}, and a constant pressure of $\sim 10^{-5}$ mm

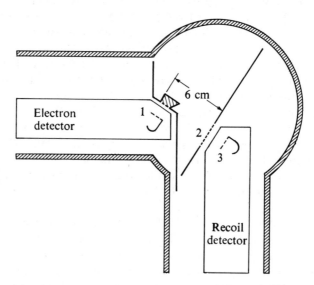

FIG. 8.21   The time-of-flight apparatus used by Rodeback and Allen for the study of neutrino recoils in the electron-capture decay of A^{37}. [From Rodeback, G. W., and J. S. Allen, *Phys. Rev.*, **86**, 446, (1952).]

Hg is maintained. The effective source-volume is defined by using baffles, and the region is simultaneously seen by both the detectors. All shield-baffles and all grids except grid 3 are maintained at zero potential. Grid 3 is at -4500 volts. The capture of a K-electron by A^{37} results in the formation of Cl^{37} and the emission of Auger electrons. The Auger electrons are detected by an Allen-type photomultiplier. The recoil nuclei are accelerated between grid 2 and 3 and are recorded by the photomultiplier. Delayed coincidences are observed between the fast Auger electrons and the recoiled ions. The results are shown in Fig. 8.22. After making all corrections, the maximum time of flight of the ion to travel 6 cm distance is (8.9 ± 0.9) μsec. A sharp peak in the time of flight spectrum corresponds to an energy of (9.7 ± 0.8) ev of the recoil ion. This confirms the emission of a single neutrino with energy (0.8 ± 0.1) Mev, which is in good agreement with the Q value, (0.816 ± 0.004) Mev for the reaction Cl^{37} (p, n) A^{37}. The values of the recoil energies by other independent experiments are (9.6 ± 0.2) ev[39] and (9.65 ± 0.05) ev[40].

Many other recoil experiments using A^{37}, Be^7, and Cd^{107} have been performed[41], and they all confirm the above-stated hypothesis of a single

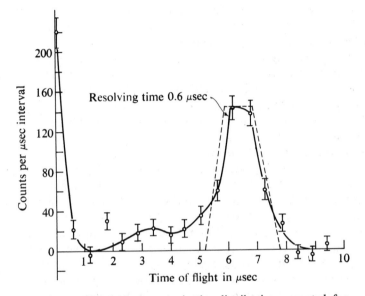

FIG. 8.22 The dashed curve is the distribution expected for monoenergetic recoils of A^{37}. The agreement with the experimental results (continuous curve through the experimental points) is good. [From Rodeback, G. W., and J. S. Allen, *Phys. Rev.*, **86**, 446, (1952).]

neutrino emission in a beta decay. Improvements have been made to investigate the electron-neutrino correlation and are discussed in some length in reference 41.

C. NEUTRINO CAPTURE EXPERIMENT. Though there were no doubts as to the existence of the neutrino, curiosity continued until direct evidence was presented. Such a search was started by F. Reines and C. Cowan, Jr.[42] in 1952 and was successfully completed in 1960[43]. The reaction they investigated is the reverse of a neutron decay, i.e.,

$$p^+ + \bar{\nu} \rightarrow {}_0 n^1 + \beta^+ \tag{8.48}$$

In order to perform such a nuclear reaction one needs a very large flux of antineutrinos, because they do not interact strongly and hence have a very small cross-section. With the construction of powerful nuclear reactors it has become possible to obtain such high fluxes of antineutrinos. Fission products produced in nuclear reactors decay by β^--emission and antineutrinos. A large antineutrino flux was obtained from the nuclear reactor at Savannah River.

An outline of the apparatus used by Reines and Cowan is shown in Fig. 8.23. It consists of five large tanks. The two outer ones and the center one, which have the dimensions 1.9 m × 1.3 m × 0.61 m, are filled with liquid scintillators consisting of terphenyl and PoPoP (a wavelength shifter) dissolved in triethylbenzene and serve as detectors. The other two tanks, having the dimensions 1.9 m × 1.3 m × 0.075 m, are filled with water, containing a small amount of cadmium chloride dissolved in it and serve as targets. Each scintillation tank is viewed by 110 photomultiplier tubes in line from the ends. An antineutrino from the nuclear reactor interacts with a water molecule and results in the formation of a neutron and a positron (Fig. 8.24). The positron disappears at once, giving out two gamma rays of 0.51 Mev each in opposite directions to each other. (This process is called annihilation and will be explained in Chap. IX on γ-decay.) The emission of these prompt gamma rays is signaled by a single coincidence pulse. The neutron collides, scatters, and slows down within 1 to 26 μsec. The slow neutron is captured by the cadmium, which in turn de-excites by the emission of gamma rays with a total energy of 9.1 Mev. Scintillations produced by these gamma rays are also detected. The pulses produced by these delayed gamma rays and prompt gamma rays as viewed in an oscilloscope are shown in Fig. 8.23. In order to confirm that the prompt, as well as the delayed, gamma rays come from the same nuclear reaction, their counting rate is related to the power level of the reactor. With a total running time of 1371 hours, (with the reactor off and on) the final result was a maximum signal rate of (2.88 ± 0.22) counts/hr. This confirms directly the existence of the antineutrino.

The above counting rate gives the cross section for the reaction $\bar{\nu}(p, n) \beta^+$ to be $(11 \pm 2.6) \times 10^{-44}$ cm². A particle with this cross section has very little chance of colliding while passing through the sun and will take lead of 92 light years thickness to reduce its flux by only one-third!

Another experiment that has been studied by Davis[44] is the following reaction

$$\bar{\nu} + Cl^{37} \rightarrow A^{37} + \beta^- \qquad \text{(8.49)}$$

He placed 1000 gallons of carbon tetrachloride in front of the antineutrino flux. If the neutrino and the antineutrino are really different from each other, the antineutrino should not induce this reaction. The cross section obtained is so small (the upper limit is 0.2×10^{-45} cm²) that it confirms this hypothesis.

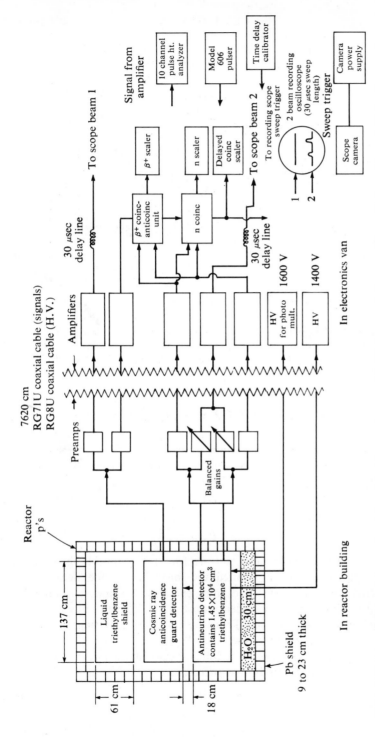

FIG. 8.23 An outline of the antineutrino detection system used by Reines, F., and C. L. Cowan, Jr., *Phys. Rev.*, **90**, 492, (1953); **113**, 273, (1959).]

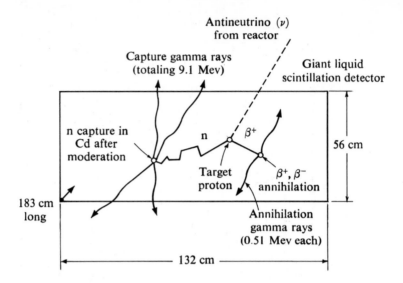

FIG. 8.24 Schematic representation of an antineutrino reaction with a proton used for detection of the antineutrino by Cowan and Reines. [From Reines, F., and C. L. Cowan, Jr., *Phys. Rev.*, **90**, 492, (1953); **113**, 273, (1959).]

8. BETA-DECAY SYSTEMATICS

Analogous to the Geiger and Nuttall law in alpha decay, relations exist between the half life, decay constant, and end-point energy of different beta emitters. It was first pointed out by B. Sargent[45] that the life time, $t_{1/2}$, and the end-point energy, E_{max}, in beta decay are roughly correlated by an equation of the form

$$\log_{10} t_{1/2} = -C_1 \log_{10} E_{max} + C_2 \qquad (8.50)$$

where C_1 and C_2 are constants and are found by adjusting them to fit the experimental data. Sargent plotted the logarithm of the decay constant versus the logarithm of the end-point energies as shown in Fig. 8.25 for natural beta emitters. As is evident, most of the actual points group themselves along two straight lines. These are called Sargent diagrams and have the following two characteristics:

(a) The slope of these lines is ~5, which means that λ varies approximately as the fifth power of the end-point energy, i.e.,

$$\lambda \propto E_{max}^5 \qquad (8.51)$$

(b) For a given value of end-point energy, the upper curve gives a value of λ which is about 100 times as large as the corresponding value on the lower curve. This implies that the transformations on the upper curve are 100 times more likely than the transformations on the lower curve. Accordingly, the upper curve is said to represent *allowed transitions* and the lower curve is said to represent *forbidden transitions*. The terms "allowed" and "forbidden" are used completely in a relative sense and represent the degree of probability of disintegration.

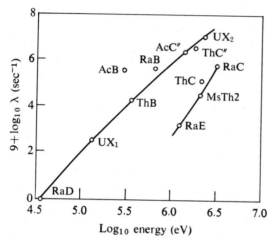

FIG. 8.25 A Sargent diagram showing the relation between the disintegration constant and the maximum end-point energy of the naturally occurring heavy beta-emitters. [From Sargent, B. W., *Proc. Roy. Soc.* A139, 659, (1953).]

Sargent plots have been extended to include the artificial beta emitters and separate curves have been drawn for light, intermediate, and heavy nuclides[46]. Such regularities in the experimental results mean that the theory of beta decay not only has to explain the properties of continuous beta spectra, but also has to account for the relative probabilities of disintegrations.

9. ELEMENTARY THEORY OF BETA DECAY

According to Pauli's neutrino hypothesis, the basic transformations involved in beta decay are

$$n \rightarrow p + \beta^- + \bar{\nu}$$
$$p \rightarrow n + \beta^+ + \nu$$
$$p + {}_{-1}e^0 \rightarrow n + \nu$$

Based on this hypothesis, Fermi[36] in 1934 gave a complete descriptive theory of beta decay, which explained satisfactorily beta spectral shapes, life-times, recoil and angular correlation experiments, and the like. A modern theory of beta decay that takes into account the nonconservation of parity (see Sec. 8.13) was introduced by T. Lee and C. Yang[47] in 1956. This theory is more complicated and involves the use of relativistic wave mechanics, which is beyond the scope of this book. But all the constants used in the modern theory can be expressed in terms of the constants used in the Fermi theory. For the sake of clarity and simplicity we shall limit our development to the simplest form of the theory, based essentially on Fermi's theory. Also we will refer only to β^--decay although this theory holds for β^+-decay as well. The discussion of electron capture will be taken up separately.

Fermi's theory[36,48,49,50] of beta decay is based on the following assumptions:

(a) Because the electron and the neutrino cannot exist inside the nucleus, they must be created at the time of disintegration. According to Fermi there exists an interaction between the nucleon, electron, and neutrino that causes the transformation of a neutron into a proton with a simultaneous emission of an electron and a neutrino. A beta transition is analogous to a gamma transition with the "electron-neutrino field" acting in place of the electromagnetic field.

(b) The interaction is very weak and has a very short range. At most the range is of the order of nuclear dimensions, or it may be a "point" interaction. This interaction may depend on the spin states of the particles but not on their linear or angular momentum. The interaction is completely symmetric in emission and absorption, as well as in the sign of the charge.

Because there is no way of developing beta-decay theory by classical means, strict quantum-mechanical methods have been used. In nuclear physics a transition from one level to another is described in terms of the *transition probability per unit time*, ω. The expression for ω is given by "Golden Rule No. 2," derived by making use of the time-dependent perturbation theory[51]. Thus

$$\omega = \frac{2\pi}{\hbar} \left| \int \Psi_f^* H_{op} \Psi_i \, dv \right|^2 dn/dE \qquad (8.52)$$

or

$$\omega = \frac{2\pi}{\hbar} |H_{if}|^2 \, dn/dE \qquad (8.53)$$

where

$$H_{if} = \int \Psi_f^* H_{op} \Psi_i \, dv \qquad (8.54)$$

where Ψ_i and Ψ_f are the wave functions of the initial and the final states, respectively, H_{op}, the Hamiltonian operator, is the operator associated with the interaction energy that causes the transition, H_{if} is the expectation value,

dv is a small volume, and dn/dE is the statistical factor that indicates the number of states per unit energy, or the energy density of the final states per unit volume of real space.

Thus from Eq. (8.52) we may write the probability per unit time for the emission of a beta particle within the momentum range p to $(p + dp)$ as $N(p)\, dp$, i.e.,

$$N(p)\, dp = \frac{2\pi}{\hbar} \left| \int \psi_f^* H_{op} \psi_i\, dv \right|^2 dn/dE_\beta \tag{8.55}$$

where ψ_i and ψ_f are the time-independent wave functions of the initial and the final states, respectively, of the nuclear system. In order to evaluate $N(p)$, we shall proceed first to derive an expression for the statistical weight-factor, dn/dE_β, by the methods of statistical mechanics.

The total number of states available to a particle that is ejected with a momentum between p and $(p + dp)$ is proportional to the volume of a spherical shell in momentum-space of radius p and thickness dp, i.e., $4\pi p^2\, dp$. According to the Heisenberg uncertainty principle $(\Delta x \Delta p \cong h)$, the uncertainty in the location of a particle is given by

$$\Delta x \Delta y \Delta z \Delta p_x \Delta p_y \Delta p_z \cong h^3$$

We assume further that the interaction takes place in a unit volume, i.e., $\Delta x \Delta y \Delta z = 1$; then $\Delta p_x \Delta p_y \Delta p_z = h^3$, where h^3 is called the volume of a unit cell. Thus, the number of unit cells available in a volume $4\pi p^2\, dp$, which is precisely the number of states in the thin spherical shell considered above, is given by $4\pi p^2\, dp/h^3$. The number of ways (or the number of possible states available for occupation) in which an electron may be emitted with a momentum between p_β and $(p_\beta + dp_\beta)$ and a neutrino with a momentum between p_ν and $(p_\nu + dp_\nu)$ are given by

$$dn_e = 4\pi p_\beta^2\, dp_\beta/h^3 \tag{8.56}$$

and

$$dn_\nu = 4\pi p_\nu^2\, dp_\nu/h^3 \tag{8.57}$$

respectively. The total number of states, dn, available in a disintegration to an electron of momentum between p_β and $(p_\beta + dp_\beta)$ and a neutrino of momentum between p_ν and $(p_\nu + dp_\nu)$ are

$$dn = \frac{16\pi^2}{h^6} (p_\beta^2 p_\nu^2\, dp_\beta\, dp_\nu) \tag{8.58}$$

Because of the conservation of energy, p_β and p_ν are not independent but are related by

$$E_\beta + E_\nu = E_{max} \tag{8.59}$$

Assuming that the neutrino rest-mass is zero, E_ν takes the form

$$E_\nu = p_\nu c \tag{8.60}$$

and substituting in Eq. (8.59), we get

$$(m_0^2 c^4 + p_\beta^2 c^2)^{1/2} + p_\nu c = (m_0^2 c^4 + p_{\beta max}^2 c^2)^{1/2} \tag{8.61}$$

From Eqs. (8.59) and (8.60), we get

$$dE_\nu = c \, dp_\nu = - dE_\beta \tag{8.62}$$

Combining Eqs. (8.59) to (8.62) with Eq. (8.58), we get the following expression for the statistical weight factor dn/dE_β

$$\frac{dn}{dE_\beta} = \frac{p_\beta^2 (E_{max} - E_\beta)^2 \, dp_\beta}{4\pi^4 c^3 \hbar^6} \tag{8.63}$$

In order to evaluate the probability in Eq. (8.55), because we know dn/dE_β from Eq. (8.63), we have to know the expectation value H_{if} of the operator H_{op}, which is given by

$$H_{if}^2 = \left| \int \psi_f^* H_{op} \psi_i \, dv \right|^2 \tag{8.64}$$

At present there is no way of knowing the wave functions, ψ_i and ψ_f, of the initial state and the final state of the nucleus. The whole theory depends, therefore, on the choice of the perturbation energy H_{op}. From analogy with the electrostatic field

$$V = e\phi \tag{8.65}$$

where V is the electrostatic interaction energy, e is the charge, and ϕ is the wave function representing the electrostatic field potential, we may write the expression for H_{op} as

$$H_{op} = g\phi_\beta \phi_\nu \tag{8.66}$$

where g is a constant of the weak interaction (as is e for the electrostatic field); ϕ_β and ϕ_ν are the time-independent wave functions that characterize the electron and the neutrino fields.

We can treat the neutrino as a free particle because it interacts weakly, and, being neutral, it is not affected by the nuclear Coulomb-field. We write the time-independent wave function of the free neutrino normalized to one particle per unit volume as

$$\phi_\nu = e^{i\mathbf{q} \cdot \mathbf{r}} \tag{8.67}$$

where $\mathbf{q} = \mathbf{p}_\nu/\hbar$ is the neutrino propagation constant. Similarly, for high velocity electrons, one may ignore the electrostatic effect of the nucleus and treat the electron created in the disintegration process as a free particle. A time-independent normalized wave-function for the electron is

$$\phi_\beta = e^{i\mathbf{k}\cdot\mathbf{r}} \tag{8.68}$$

where $\mathbf{k} = \mathbf{p}_\beta/\hbar$ is the electron propagation constant. Combining Eqs. (8.64), (8.66), (8.67), and (8.68), we get

$$H_{if}^2 = g^2 \left| \int \psi_f^* e^{i(\mathbf{k}+\mathbf{q})\cdot\mathbf{r}} \psi_i \, dv \right|^2 \tag{8.69}$$

Combining Eqs. (8.63) and (8.69) with Eq. (8.55), we obtain

$$N(p)\, dp = \frac{g^2|M|^2}{2\pi^3 c^3 \hbar^7} (E_{max} - E_\beta)^2 p_\beta^2 \, dp_\beta \tag{8.70}$$

where

$$M = \int \psi_f^* e^{i(\mathbf{k}+\mathbf{q})\cdot\mathbf{r}} \psi_i \, dv \tag{8.71}$$

Eq. (8.70) is the required distribution and is completely known except for the matrix element, M, defined by Eq. (8.71). Before we go into the discussion of the matrix element, M, it is worthwhile to say a few words about the constant g.

As we said before the constant g represents the weak interaction, and it has been found to be $g \simeq 1.4 \times 10^{-49}$ erg-cm^3. In order to get some idea of the order of magnitude of this interaction, it is convenient to compare this with other interactions by means of some equivalent quantities. For electromagnetic forces this quantity is $e^2/\hbar c = 1/137.04 \approx 10^{-2}$ and is known as the *coupling constant* for the electromagnetic interaction. The coupling constant for strong interactions (nuclear forces) is $f^2/\hbar c \approx 1$, and for the weak interactions the constant is $g^2/\hbar c \approx 10^{-13}$. For gravitational forces this constant is 10^{-39}.

A. ALLOWED TRANSITIONS.   Let us consider the exponential term $e^{i(\mathbf{k}+\mathbf{q})\cdot\mathbf{r}}$ and expand it in a power series

$$e^{i(\mathbf{k}+\mathbf{q})\cdot\mathbf{r}} = 1 + i(\mathbf{k}+\mathbf{q})\cdot\mathbf{r} - \frac{[(\mathbf{k}+\mathbf{q})\cdot\mathbf{r}]^2}{2!} + \cdots + \cdots \tag{8.72}$$

In many cases the momenta of the neutrino and the electron are small. The wave functions will have significance only over the nuclear dimensions, r, i.e., at the most, of the order of the nuclear radius. For a typical case of a few-Mev electron, the factor $(\mathbf{k}+\mathbf{q})\cdot\mathbf{r} \sim 1/10$. This term and the subsequent terms in the series may be neglected when compared with the first term. This implies that the matrix element, M, defined by Eq. (8.71), is independent of energy, i.e.,

$$M = \int \psi_f^* \psi_i \, dv \tag{8.73}$$

Under these circumstances the emission of the electron and neutrino does not depend upon their energies, and such transitions are called *allowed transitions*. We may write Eq. (8.70) in the form

$$[N(p)/p^2]^{1/2} = C(E_{max} - E_\beta) = C(K_{max} - K_\beta) \qquad (8.74)$$

where

$$C = g|M|/(2\pi^3 c^3 \hbar^7)^{1/2} \qquad (8.75)$$

and K_{max} is the maximum kinetic energy of the β-particles.

A plot of $[N(E)/p^2]^{1/2}$ versus K_β is known as a *Kurie plot*, or a *Fermi plot*, or a *Fermi-Kurie plot*. If the theory given above is correct, the Kurie plot obtained from the experimental values should be a straight line.

Before applying this theory to a test, it is necessary to apply a correction due to the coulomb field of the nucleus on the emitted negatrons and positrons. The coulomb interaction has the effect of distorting the wave function of the electron or positron, particularly if their energies are low. The coulomb force will retard the emission of negatrons and accelerate that of positrons. Thus there will be an excess of low-energy negatrons and a deficiency in low-energy positrons. This correction is applied[52] by multiplying Eq. (8.70) on the right side only by the *Fermi function*, $F(Z, E)$, which is given by

$$F(Z, E) = \frac{2(2pr)^{2s-2} e^{\pi \alpha ZE/p} |\Gamma(s + i\alpha ZE/p)|^2 (1 + s)}{[\Gamma(2s + 1)]^2} \qquad (8.76)$$

where

$$s = (1 - \alpha^2 Z^2)^{1/2}, \qquad (8.77)$$

where r is the nuclear radius, $\alpha\ (= 1/137)$ is the fine-structure constant, $\Gamma(\ )$ is the gamma function, and Z is the atomic number of the residual nucleus in the case of negatron emission (it is $-Z$ for the positron emission). Graphs of the modified Fermi function defined as $mcpF(Z, E)/E$ are available[52].

Thus after applying the coulomb correction, Eqs. (8.70) and (8.74) take the form

$$N(p)\, dp = \frac{g^2|M|^2}{2\pi^3 c^3 \hbar^7} F(Z, E)(E_{max} - E_\beta)^2 p_\beta^2\, dp_\beta \qquad (8.78)$$

and

$$[N(p)/F(Z, E)p^2]^{1/2} = C(K_{max} - K_\beta) \qquad (8.79)$$

respectively. This correction effects the distribution and is shown in Fig. 8.26. $[N(E)/F(Z, E)p^2]^{1/2}$ versus K_β has been plotted in many cases from the experimentally determined data for momentum distribution and are found to be straight lines, as we expect from the theory of allowed transitions. Figure (8.27a), Fig. (8.27b), and Fig. (8.27c) show the Kurie plots for β-decay of the neutron[53], tritium H^3,[54] and In^{114} [55], respectively. There are two advantages of drawing Kurie plots: It is easy to fit a straight line to the data,

3 cm and 7 cm can be calculated from the following empirical relationship:

$$\bar{R} = 0.318 \; E^{3/2} \tag{7.42}$$

where E is the energy in Mev and $\bar{R}$ is the mean range in cm in air at 15°C and 760 mm Hg.

Accurate range-energy curves have been drawn by the following procedure (see Fig. 7.17). The ranges and energies of the alpha particles from natural radioactive alpha emitters have been measured accurately[19]. This

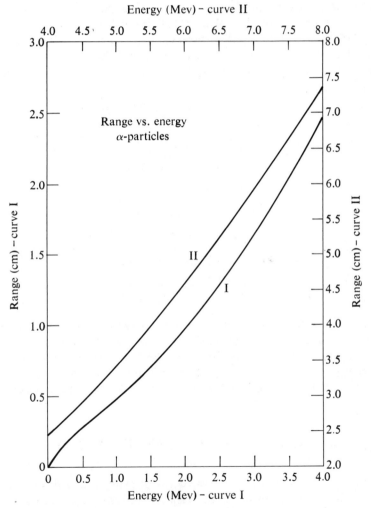

FIG. 7.17 Range-energy relation of slow alpha particles in air at 15°C and 760 mm. [Bethe, H. A., *Revs. Mod. Phys.*, **22**, 213, [1950].]

covers the energies from about 5 Mev to 10 Mev and ranges in air from 5 cm to 12 cm. The data for the points between these energies and data to extend the curves beyond 10 Mev are obtained by making use of the theoretical expression for the stopping power given in Sec. 5. These curves cannot be extended to lower energies by the use of alpha emitters because there are none with energies less than 5 Mev. The theoretical relation also does not hold for energies less than 5 Mev. The low energy alpha particles may be produced by slowing down fast alpha particles, but this method has not been found satisfactory[20].

The most satisfactory method for obtaining this information at low energies has been employed by Bethe[20]. This involves the measurement of energies and ranges of the alpha particles emitted in certain nuclear reactions. Two nuclear reactions that give out alpha particles have been found to be valuable for extending the range-energy curves to low energies. These reactions are:

$$(1) \quad {}_3\text{Li}^6 + {}_0\text{n}^1 \rightarrow {}_2\text{He}^4 + {}_1\text{H}^3 + Q$$

where[21,22]

$$Q = 4.788 \pm 0.023 \text{ Mev}$$
$$E_\alpha = 2.057 \pm 0.010 \text{ Mev}$$
$$\bar{R} = 1.04 \pm 0.02 \text{ cm}$$

$$(2) \quad {}_5\text{B}^{10} + {}_0\text{n}^1 \rightarrow {}_3\text{Li}^7 + {}_2\text{He}^4 + Q$$

where[23]

$$Q = 2.316 \pm 0.006 \text{ Mev}$$
$$E_\alpha = 1.474 \pm 0.004 \text{ Mev}$$
$$\bar{R} = 0.720 \pm 0.015 \text{ Mev}$$

There have been improvements in the knowledge of the relationship between ionization and energy loss[24]. Combining the results of theory, natural alpha emitters, and nuclear data, Bethe[20] has prepared accurate range-energy curves for alpha particles as shown in Fig. 7.17. Similar curves[25] have also been drawn for protons, extending to very high energies.

7. ALPHA DECAY SYSTEMATICS

The detailed investigation of the alpha decay of many radioactive nuclei has resulted in striking regularities in the variation of the total alpha disintegration energy ($E_0 = E_\alpha + E_{\text{recoil}}$) with the mass number, atomic number, and half-life. Empirical relations between R, E, $t_{1/2}$, λ, A, and Z have been useful in constructing and testing the theories of alpha decay. We shall discuss here two such systematics: (a) the relationship between *energy and half-life* which has been useful in investigating decay mechanism, and (b) the relationship between *energy and mass number* which has been helpful in obtaining information about nuclear stability.

A. ENERGY VERSUS HALF-LIFE. Rutherford[26] pointed out as early as 1907 that some systematic relationship seems to exist between the half-life and range of alpha particles. It was observed that the longer-lived nuclei emit the least energetic alpha particles, while the shorter-lived nuclei emit the most energetic alpha particles. The experimental results show that except for the long-range alpha particles, most of them have ranges varying from 2.5 cm to 9 cm, while their energies vary from 4 Mev to 9 Mev. A change of a factor of about 3.5 in the range comes from a change of energy by a factor of $\sim$2.5. Corresponding to this change in the energy, the half-life varies from $\sim 1.4 \times 10^{10}$ yr to $\sim 3 \times 10^{-7}$ sec while the decay constant changes from $\sim 1.6 \times 10^{-18}$ sec^{-1} to $\sim 2.3 \times 10^6$ sec^{-1}. We conclude from these observations that *a factor of 2 or 3 in the energy corresponds to a factor of 10^{24} in the half-life or decay constant.*

    These empirical facts were first correlated by H. Geiger and J. Nuttall[27,28] in 1911. When log λ was plotted against log R, members of the three naturally occurring radioactive series were found to fall along three straight lines, one for each family, as shown in Fig. 7.18. These straight lines are represented by the Geiger-Nuttall relation

$$\log \lambda = A \log R + B \tag{7.43}$$

where A and B are constant. The slope of A is the same for all three while the constant B is different for each of them. The range in air is related to the velocity by Geiger rule

$$R = \text{const.}\ v^3 \tag{7.44}$$

Therefore, Eq. (7.43) can be written as

$$\log \lambda = A_1 \log v + B_1 \tag{7.45}$$

Though the agreement between the experimental results and the Geiger-Nuttall Law is good, as is evident from Fig. 7.18, a more precise empirical correlation of the alpha energy and disintegration constant was given by I. Kaplan[29] in the following form

$$\log \lambda = (a/v) + b, \quad \text{for } Z \text{ constant} \tag{7.46}$$

This relation is predicted from the theory of alpha decay and the agreement with the experimental results is excellent as shown in Fig. 7.19, where log λ is plotted versus reciprocal alpha-velocity for a given value of Z.

A plot of log $t_{1/2}$ versus E in which all alpha emitters are included shows a considerable scatter about the general trends mentioned above. But if we consider only even–even alpha-emitter nuclei and join those that have the same Z, the plots result in smooth curves. Such plots have been drawn by

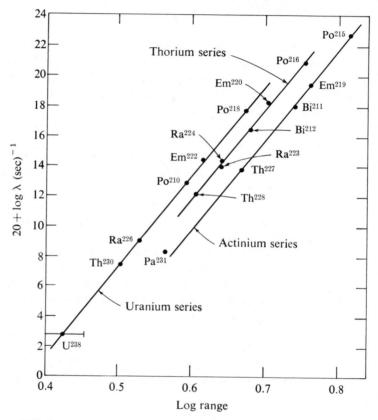

FIG. 7.18   Geiger–Nuttall law; the plot of log λ versus log R. [From: Geiger, H. and J. M. Nuttall, *Phil. Mag.*, **22**, 613, (1911).]

I. Perlman, *et al.*[31], and are shown in Fig. 7.20. For other types of alpha-emitters with even–odd, odd–even, and odd–odd nuclei, it is not possible to draw such smooth curves as for even–even nuclei; the odd–odd nuclei are the worst in this respect. Their periods are 2 to 1000 times longer than those for even–even types with the same Z and E. Figure 7.21 shows the case of even–odd nuclei.

B. ENERGY VERSUS MASS NUMBER.   The results of such systematics have been presented by I. Perlman, *et al.*[31], and R. Glass, *et al.*[32] Figure 7.22[33], which includes all the available data on heavy elements both artificially produced and naturally occurring, shows the regularities in the plot of total alpha-decay energies versus mass number. By drawing lines joining isotopes of each element, i.e., for each value of Z, the variation of alpha-decay energy, E, with mass number, A, becomes quite apparent. The indication is that lines for different values of Z are almost parallel. The following conclusions may be drawn from the observed regularities in Fig. 7.22.

(i) For a given A, E_α increases with Z.

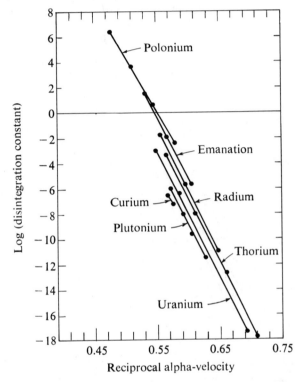

FIG. 7.19   Log λ versus $1/v$ for constant Z. The velocity of the alpha particles is expressed in units of 10^9 cm/sec. [From: Kaplan, I., *Phys. Rev.*, **81**, 962, (1951).]

(ii) For a given Z, E_α decreases as A increases. (This behavior was predicted by the liquid drop model also.)

(iii) If we continue decreasing A, over a limited range below $N = 128$, the variation in E_α with A reverses. The original trend is resumed if A is decreased still further.

(iv) There is a reversal of the behavior once again when $Z < 84$. This results in the alpha decay energies of bismuth ($Z = 83$) being much lower than

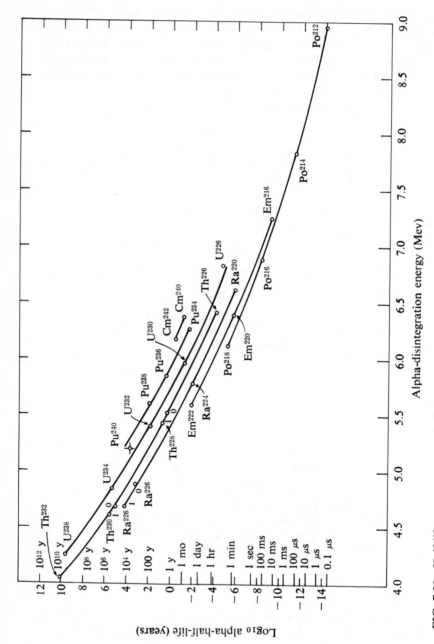

FIG. 7.20 Half-life versus energy relationship for even–even nuclides. [From: Perlman, I., A. Ghiorso, and G. T. Seaborg, *Phys. Rev.*, 77, 26, (1950).]

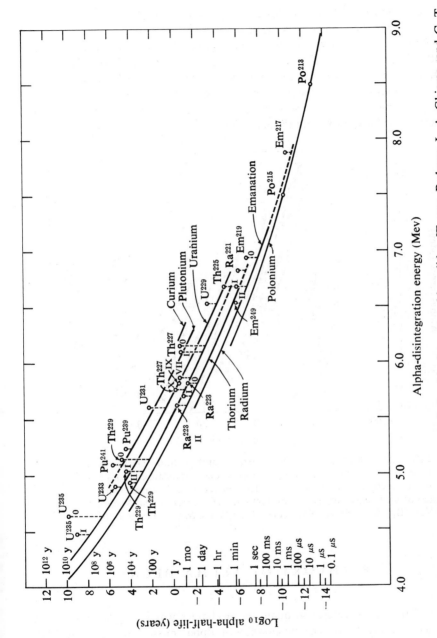

FIG. 7.21 Half-life versus energy relationship for even–odd nuclides. [From: Perlman, I., A. Ghiorso, and G. T. Seaborg, *Phys. Rev.*, **77**, 26, (1950).]

expected from the trend for $Z \geqslant 84$, while lead ($Z = 82$) and thallium ($Z = 81$) show no activity at all.

The effects (iii) and (iv) are due to the shell-model structure of the nucleus and will be explained later. The closure of the neutron shell at $N = 82$ also affects the energy release in the alpha-decay of the rare-earth elements.

The usefulness of these plots depends on how accurately they can predict the properties of the unobserved alpha emitters; for the case of even–even nuclei these have proved quite successful.

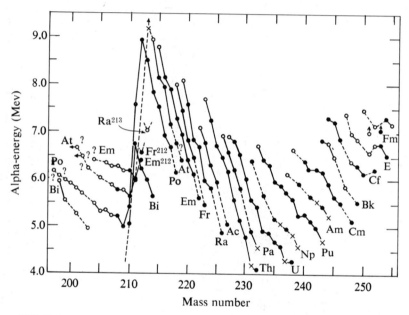

FIG. 7.22 Alpha-decay energy versus Z and A. Solid circles ● indicate mass certain, ○ indicate mass probable, while × indicate energies calculated from closed decay cycle, and ? denotes uncertain isotopes, while – – – – – denotes missing isotopes. [From: Hanna, G. C. *Experimental Nuclear Physics*, Vol. III, ed., E. Segre, New York: John Wiley & Sons, 1959, p. 65.]

8. THEORY OF ALPHA DECAY

One of the first successes of quantum mechanics was its application to the theory of alpha decay. The explanation of alpha emission was given in 1928 simultaneously by G. Gamow[34] and by R. Gurney and E. Condon[35]. The predictions of quantum theory are altogether different from the classical theory. The problem that we face in explaining alpha decay can be best understood from the following example. Po^{214} emits 7.68 Mev alpha particles. These alpha particles, when scattered from a foil of $_{92}U^{238}$, obey the Rutherford scattering law. No absorption seems to take place, because the Po-α particles do not have enough energy to cross the coulomb potential barrier as shown in Fig. 7.23. On the other hand, U^{238}, itself, emits alpha particles of kinetic energy equal to 4.20 Mev, even though this energy is not enough to cross the coulomb potential-barrier. Thus the paradox is that Po-α particles appear unable to cross the potential barrier, while the lower energy U^{238} alpha particles appear to cross.

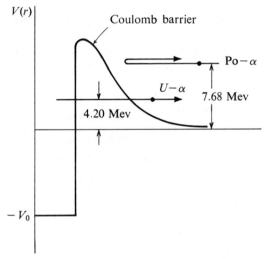

FIG. 7.23 Schematic representation of the nuclear-potential well and the coulomb barrier.

In order to resolve this paradox, it is necessary that we understand the problem of potential barrier from a quantum mechanical point of view.

A. ONE-DIMENSIONAL POTENTIAL BARRIER. Let a particle of rest mass m and kinetic energy E be incident on a potential barrier of height V_0 such that $E < V_0$ (Fig. 7.24) and

$$V(x) = \begin{cases} 0 & \text{for } x < 0 \\ V_0 & \text{for } 0 < x < a \\ 0 & \text{for } x > a \end{cases} \tag{7.47}$$

Because of the symmetrical nature of the problem, the particle may be incident either from the left or the right. We assume, in this case, that it is incident from the left.

Classically, a particle with kinetic energy $E < V_0$ can never penetrate the potential barrier. But quantum-mechanically we shall show that even

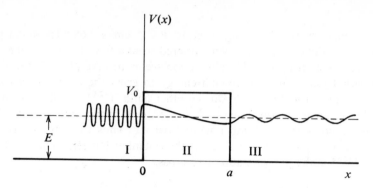

FIG. 7.24   One-dimensional rectangular potential barrier.

though $E < V_0$, the particle has some probability of crossing the potential barrier. This probability of penetration of the barrier, or *transparency*, is defined as

$$\text{transparency} = \frac{\text{transmitted intensity}}{\text{incident intensity}}$$

$$= \frac{(\text{transmitted amplitude})^2}{(\text{incident amplitude})^2} \qquad (7.48)$$

For regions I and III (Fig. 7.24), the time-independent Schrödinger wave equation is

$$\frac{d^2\psi}{dx^2} + \frac{2mE}{\hbar^2}\psi = 0 \qquad (7.49)$$

The solution of this equation is

$$\psi_I = I e^{ikx} + R e^{-ikx} \qquad (7.50)$$

$$\psi_{III} = T e^{ikx} \qquad (7.51)$$

where $k = \sqrt{2mE}/\hbar = p/\hbar$ and I, R, and T are the incident, reflected, and transmitted amplitudes, respectively.

In region II, the time-independent Schrödinger wave equation is

$$\frac{d^2\psi}{dx^2} - \frac{2m}{\hbar^2}(V_0 - E)\psi = 0 \qquad (7.52)$$

The solution of this equation is

$$\psi_{II} = A e^{k'x} + B e^{-k'x} \qquad (7.53)$$

where $k' = \sqrt{2m(V_0 - E)}/\hbar = q/\hbar$ and A and B are constants.

In terms of these constants, the transparency is defined as

$$\text{transparency} = \frac{|T|^2}{|I|^2} \qquad (7.54)$$

In order to calculate this we have to evaluate the constants, which can be accomplished by making use of the fact that the wave function must be well-behaved. Thus, applying the boundary conditions that ψ and $d\psi/dx$ (denoted by ψ') must be continuous at $x = 0$ and $x = a$, i.e.,

$$\psi_I(0) = \psi_{II}(0)$$

$$\psi_I'(0) = \psi_{II}'(0)$$

$$\psi_{II}(a) = \psi_{III}(a)$$

$$\psi_{II}'(a) = \psi_{III}'(a) \tag{7.55}$$

We get the following set of equations

$$I + R = A + B \tag{7.56a}$$

$$ik(I - R) = k'(A - B) \tag{7.56b}$$

$$Ae^{k'a} + Be^{-k'a} = Te^{ika} \tag{7.56c}$$

$$k'(Ae^{k'a} - Be^{-k'a}) = ikTe^{ika} \tag{7.56d}$$

Eliminating R from Eqs. (7.56a) and (7.56b), and evaluating A and B from Eqs. (7.56c) and (7.56d)

$$I = \frac{1}{2}\left(1 + \frac{k'}{ik}\right)A + \frac{1}{2}\left(1 - \frac{k'}{ik}\right)B \tag{7.57}$$

$$A = Te^{ika}\left(1 + \frac{ik}{k'}\right)\Big/2e^{k'a} \tag{7.58}$$

$$B = Te^{ika}\left(1 - \frac{ik}{k'}\right)\Big/2e^{-k'a} \tag{7.59}$$

Substituting the values of A and B in Eq. (7.57) and letting $k = p/\hbar$ and $k' = q/\hbar$, we get

$$I = \frac{T}{4}e^{ika}\left\{\left(1 + \frac{q}{ip}\right)\left(1 + \frac{ip}{q}\right)e^{-(qa/\hbar)} + \left(1 - \frac{q}{ip}\right)\left(1 - \frac{ip}{q}\right)e^{(qa/\hbar)}\right\} \tag{7.60}$$

Hence, the transparency $|T|^2/|I|^2$ can be calculated from this equation, and it is not zero as predicted by the classical theory.

The expression of Eq. (7.60) can be simplified if we assume

$$\frac{p}{q} = \frac{\sqrt{2mE}}{\sqrt{2m(V_0 - E)}} = \sqrt{\frac{E}{V_0 - E}} \sim 1$$

and also $qa/\hbar \gg 1$. This reduces Eq. (7.60) to

$$I \approx Te^{ika}e^{qa/\hbar} \tag{7.61}$$

Hence,

$$\text{transparency} = \frac{|T|^2}{|I|^2} \approx e^{-(2qa)/\hbar}$$

i.e.,

$$\text{transparency} \sim \exp\{-2\sqrt{2m(V_0 - E)}/\hbar^2 \, a\} \qquad (7.62)$$

For a barrier of arbitrary shape, the order of the magnitude of transparency is given by

$$\text{transparency} \sim \exp\left\{-2\int_a^b \sqrt{\frac{2m[V(x) - E]}{\hbar^2}} \, dx\right\} \qquad (7.63)$$

or

$$P = e^{-2\gamma} \qquad (7.64)$$

where P is the transparency and

$$\gamma = \int_a^b \sqrt{\frac{2m[V(x) - E]}{\hbar^2}} \, dx \qquad (7.65)$$

It is quite clear from Eq. (7.63) that P depends strongly on the mass of the particle and the width of the barrier.

B. ALPHA DECAY.   We are now in a position to understand most of the features of alpha decay in terms of the potential barrier problem[34,35]. The alpha particle is assumed to exist as a separate entity inside the parent nucleus. Due to the potential barrier of the daughter, the motion of the alpha particle is restricted to a spherical region. In its back-and-forth motion the alpha particle presents itself again and again to the potential barrier until the conditions are right for penetration of the barrier as shown in Fig. 7.25. Classically, the alpha particle does not have enough energy to climb the coulomb barrier. But quantum-mechanically, the wave associated with the alpha particle has some probability to leak through the barrier as if there were a hole in the barrier; this effect is called *tunneling*. This also accounts for the fact that the alpha-unstable nuclei do not decay immediately if their energies are less than the barrier potential.

The decay constant, which is defined as the probability of escape per second, is given by

$$\lambda = \text{frequency of hitting the barrier} \times \text{transparency}$$

or

$$\lambda = \omega P \qquad (7.66)$$

where

$$\omega = \frac{v_{in}}{2R} \approx \frac{10^9}{10^{-12}} \sim 10^{21} \qquad (7.67)$$

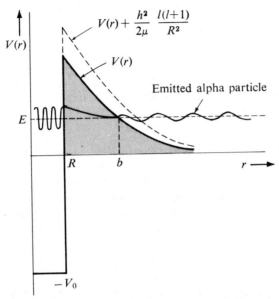

FIG. 7.25 Process of α-decay illustrated. Dotted line shows the sum of the coulomb and the centrifugal barrier.

v_{in} is the internal velocity of the alpha particle connected with the observed velocity, v (the velocity with which the α-particle leaves the nucleus), by the relation

$$\tfrac{1}{2}m_\alpha v_{in}^2 = \tfrac{1}{2}m_\alpha v^2 + V_0 = E_\alpha + V_0 \tag{7.68}$$

and P is given by

$$P = e^{-2\gamma} = \exp\left\{ -2 \int_R^b \sqrt{\frac{2m[V(r) - E_\alpha]}{\hbar^2}}\, dr \right\} \tag{7.69}$$

where $V(r) = zZe^2/r = 2Ze^2/r$, $z = 2$ for an alpha particle, and Z is the atomic number of the daughter nucleus.

Evaluating the integral in Eq. (7.69) and combining with Eq. (7.66), we get:

$$\lambda = 1/\tau \sim \frac{v_{in}}{R} e^{-2\gamma} \tag{7.70}$$

where

$$\gamma = \left[\left(\frac{2mzZe^2}{\hbar^2} \right)^{1/2} \left\{ \cos^{-1}\left(\frac{R}{b} \right)^{1/2} - \left(\frac{R}{b} - \frac{R^2}{b^2} \right)^{1/2} \right\} \right] \tag{7.71a}$$

or in terms of energies, because $R/b = E_\alpha/V(R) = E_\alpha R/zZe^2$, we get:

$$\gamma = \left[\left(\frac{2mzZe^2 b}{\hbar^2} \right)^{1/2} \left\{ \cos^{-1}\left(\frac{E_\alpha}{V(R)} \right)^{1/2} - \left(\frac{E_\alpha}{V(R)} - \frac{E_\alpha^2}{V(R)^2} \right)^{1/2} \right\} \right] \tag{7.71b}$$

The results of the theory given by Eq. (7.70) can be tested by comparing them with the experiments.

One of the main features of the alpha-decay systematics was that a change of a factor of 2 or 3 in the energy results in a change of 10^{24} in λ. This is true because of the exponential form of the relation $\lambda \sim$ const. $e^{-2\gamma}$, which can be written in the form

$$\log \lambda = \text{const.} - 2\gamma \qquad (7.72)$$

Although this is not the Geiger-Nuttal law, it gives the same shape-dependence of λ on E_α.

The agreement between the theory and the experimental results of even–even nuclei from the ground-state to ground-state transitions is excellent ($I = 0$ to $I = 0$). Let us assume that the barrier is very high and the potential well very narrow, i.e., $V(R) \to \infty$ and $R \to 0$, which from Eq. (7.71) leads to

$$\gamma \to 2\left(\frac{zZe^2}{\hbar v}\right)\frac{\pi}{2} \qquad (7.73)$$

When Eq. (7.73) is combined with Eq. (7.72), we get an equation of the form

$$\log \lambda = \frac{a}{v} + b \qquad (7.74)$$

or

$$\log t_{1/2} = \frac{a'}{E^{1/2}} + b' \qquad (7.75)$$

(a, b, a', and b' being constants), which predicts the plots given in Fig. 7.20 for different elements.

This theory can be used to calculate the nuclear radius from the data of $t_{\frac{1}{2}}$ and E for even–even nuclei. R will represent the sum of the radii of the daughter nucleus and the alpha particle. This was done in Chap. V, where we obtained the value of r_0 in $R = r_0 A^{1/3}$ to be $r_0 = 1.48 \times 10^{-13}$ cm, which is in agreement with the value of r_0 determined by other methods.

The theory just developed is for the case of a one-dimensional barrier. Deviation from one dimension results in the introduction of the angular momentum of the nucleus. This introduces a centrifugal barrier. The probability calculations can be made in this case[41,42] if we replace $V(r)$ by $V(r) + \frac{\hbar^2}{2\mu}\frac{l(l+1)}{R^2}$, as shown in Fig. 7.25, where μ is the reduced mass of the alpha particle and the daughter nucleus, and l is the angular momentum quantum number. The effect is almost negligible in the case of heavy nuclei because the ratio

$$\frac{\text{centrifugal barrier}}{\text{coulomb barrier at } R} \approx 0.002\, l(l+1) \qquad (7.76)$$

is very small. But for light nuclei the effect is large and may not be neglected.

For the case of odd–odd nuclei and for the transitions other than ground-state to ground-state, the theory does not agree with the experimental results. For odd–odd nuclei the transitions are much slower as compared to the theory. The ratio of the experimental half-life to the half-life predicted by the theory is called the *hindrance factor*. This measures the extent by which the transition is slowed down and may be as high as 10^4. Expected experimental values for the odd–odd nuclei may be predicted from the plots of even–even nuclei by interpolation.

The theory just described is mainly a one-body problem because of the assumption that the alpha particle exists as a separate entity before decay. Treating the decay as a many-body problem has not given favorable results. After the first derivation of one-body theory by Gamow in 1928, many more sophisticated alternative derivations have been given by different authors with various assumptions and approximations[36-44]. Recent modifications have been reported by H. J. Mang[45] that account for the decay properties of the rare-earth elements.

9. ALPHA-RAY SPECTRA

We shall divide the study of the alpha-ray spectra into the following three groups: (a) fine structure, (b) long-range alpha particles, and (c) rare-earth alpha emitters.

A. FINE STRUCTURE. Prior to 1930, it was assumed that all the alpha particles given out by an isotope have the same energy. By very careful ionization measurements, Bragg showed that there are four different energy groups of alpha particles emitted by a source of radium. That such is the case was confirmed by S. Rosenblum[46] in 1930, who demonstrated by the use of a magnetic spectrograph that many alpha emitters give out more than one alpha group with different energies. In such cases alpha emission is always followed by gamma emission. The observation of alpha-particle groups and the associated gamma radiation is a good demonstration of the existence of "discrete nuclear energy levels". Whenever some of the emitted alpha particles have less kinetic energy than the maximum available energy, the daughter nucleus is left in the excited state. The daughter nucleus decays to the ground state by the emission of one or more photons. The energies of these gamma rays have been measured and have been found to be equal to the differences in the kinetic energies of the alpha particles of different groups. For example, if E_0, E_1, and E_2 are the ground state and the excited energy levels of the daughter nucleus, respectively, then the energies of the gamma rays are given by

$$h\nu_1 = E_1 - E_0, \quad h\nu_2 = E_2 - E_0, \quad h\nu_3 = E_2 - E_1,$$

Figure 7.26[47] shows the decay of $_{90}Th^{228}$ to $_{88}Ra^{224}$ with the emission of five different groups of alpha particles. Note that the intensity of these groups (percent decay) decreases very rapidly with a slight decrease in energy as expected from the theory. Thus, from Fig. 7.26, the energy of the longest to the shortest alpha group is $5.421/5.137 = 1.055$, while the intensity changes by a factor of $71/0.03 \sim 2400$. There are some exceptions to this rule (α decay of Bi^{212} in Fig. 7.27) where the highest energy alpha group does not have the highest decay intensity. Such exceptions are explained by the hindrance factors, which may be very high in some cases of even–odd or odd–even nuclei.

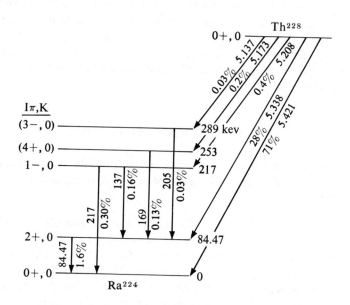

FIG. 7.26   Decay of $_{90}Th^{228} \xrightarrow{\alpha} {}_{88}Ra^{224}$. [From Stevens, F. S. Jr., F. Asaro, and I. Perlman, *Phys. Rev.*, **107**, 1091, (1957).]

B. LONG-RANGE ALPHA PARTICLES.   Figure 7.27[48] shows the decay

$$_{83}Bi^{212} \xrightarrow{\beta^-} {}_{84}Po^{212} \xrightarrow{\alpha} {}_{82}Pb^{208}$$

in which three groups of alpha particles have energies 9.522 Mev, 10.452 Mev, and 10.573 Mev. The intensities of these alpha particles are much smaller than the fourth group of 8.810 Mev which is a ground-state to ground-state transition. There is a decrease in intensity with the increase in energy contrary to the rule of the fine structure. The low intensities of these very long-range alpha particles (most of the alpha particles have energies between 5 and 9 Mev, as already mentioned) is because of the nature of their origin.

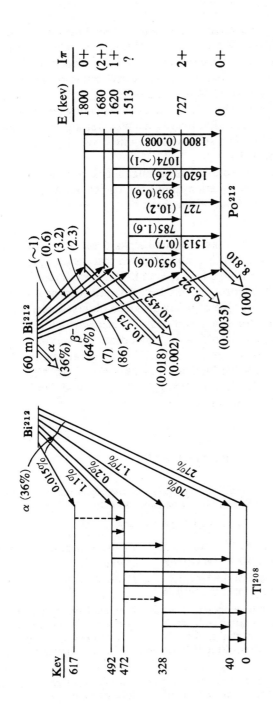

FIG. 7.27　Decay of $_{83}Bi^{212} \xrightarrow{\beta^-} {}_{84}Po^{212} \xrightarrow{\alpha} {}_{82}Pb^{208}$. [From: Emery, G. T. and W. R. Kane, *Phys. Rev.*, **118**, 755, (1960).]

The probability of beta decay is not such a strong function of energy as is alpha decay. Thus, the beta decay of $_{83}Bi^{212}$ leads not only to the ground state of $_{84}Po^{212}$, but also to the excited state of $_{84}Po^{212}$. The excited states of $_{84}Po^{212}$ have two choices in order to get de-excited, either by gamma emission to lower excited state (or to the ground state of $_{84}Po^{212}$) or directly to $_{82}Pb^{208}$ by alpha emission. Thus, there are two competing processes, alpha emission and gamma emission. But the gamma lifetimes are smaller than the alpha lifetimes by a factor of $\sim 10^{-5}$, which results in very low intensities for the long-range alpha particles.

The importance of the study of long-range alpha particles arises from the fact that these give information about the energy levels of the alpha emitter, itself, rather than about its daughter.

C. RARE-EARTH ALPHA EMITTERS. Natural alpha decay is mostly observed in the region of heavy elements. It is also observed that the energies available to alpha decay become very large near $A = 214$. This is explained by the fact that the presence of 126 neutrons forms a closed shell (just as do electrons around an atom). The same type of behavior is also observed near a neutron number of 82, which also forms a closed shell. The elements in this region are the rare earths. The energies available for alpha decay are very small (~ 2 to 4 Mev), but the coulomb barrier is also reduced to a great extent. Thus the alpha emitters have observable lifetimes. For example, $_{64}Gd^{148}(t_{1/2} \simeq 130$ yr), $_{63}Eu^{147}(t_{1/2} = 24$ days), $_{66}Dy^{152}(t_{1/2} = 2.3$ hr.), and also $_{60}Nd^{144}$, $_{62}Sm^{146}$, Gd^{149}, Tb^{149}, as well as others.

PROBLEMS

1. If we assume that the total binding energy of the alpha particle is 28 Mev, show that a nucleus will decay by alpha emission only if

$$(B_1A_2 - B_2A_1) < 4(7A_2 - B_2)$$

where A_1, A_2 are the mass numbers and B_1, B_2 the total binding energies of the parent and the daughter respectively.

2. Calculate the velocity and the kinetic energy of the daughter nucleus formed by the decay of the parent U^{238} nucleus.

3. If a heavy particle with velocity v collides with an electron at rest, show that the velocity of electron after collision is $2v$. Also calculate the energy transferred to the electron in this collision in terms of the energy of the incident particle E and the masses of the electron and the incident particles m_e and M respectively.

4. Prove that the maximum velocity imparted to a proton at rest by an alpha particle is 1.6 times the initial velocity of the alpha particle.

5. Calculate the value of v, Hr, and m/m_0 for 1 Mev, 2 Mev, 5 Mev and 10 Mev alpha particles.

6. Calculate the radius of curvature of a 5 Mev alpha particle in an air-filled cloud chamber under a magnetic field of 12,000 gauss.

7. Calculate the relative order of magnitude of the magnetic field which will produce the same curvature for 2 Mev electrons, protons, and alpha particles.

8. Starting from the equation

$$p_y = \int_{-\infty}^{\infty} e\, E_y\, dt$$

where E_y is the component of the electric intensity at $x = 0$, $y = b$, and making use of Gauss's theorem, and without actually integrating, derive Eq. (7.29).

9. Energy received by an electron from the passing alpha particle of 5 Mev is 32 ev. Calculate the momentum transferred to the electron (i) in the x-direction, and (ii) in the y-direction.

10. Compute $(-dE/dx)$ of air for 40 Mev alpha particles and for 10 Mev protons.

11. Compare the stopping power for alpha particles, protons, and electrons all moving with a speed of $0.25\,c$ in air at standard temperature and pressure.

12. Show that for particles of different masses but the same velocity, the ranges are proportional to their masses.

13. 15 Mev alpha particles and protons are incident on an Al foil 0.0030 inch thick. What are their energies after passing through the foil?

14. Calculate the thickness of an Al foil needed to reduce 50 Mev alpha particles to 20 Mev. What is the thickness in mg/in. needed to stop them completely?

15. Flux of 10^4 alpha particles of 40 Mev are passing through an Al foil 50 mg/cm^2 thick and 4 cm^2 area. Calculate the rate at which the temperature of Al is rising if the energy lost is completely used in heating the foil.

16. 14 Mev neutrons are incident on Li^6 target and produce H^3 and He^4. Calculate the range of He^3 and He^4 (a) in Al and (b) in air.

17. Derive Eq. (7.61) from Eq. (7.60) by making use of the following

$$p/q \sim 1 \quad \text{and} \quad qa/\hbar \gg 1$$

18. Outline a procedure for completing the integration in Eq. (7.69) and show how we arrive at Eqs. (7.70) and (7.71).

19. From a classical point of view what is the minimum energy needed by (a) an alpha particle, (b) a proton, to penetrate the coulomb barrier of Th^{232} nucleus?

20. Using Fig. 7.24, derive an expression for the amplitude of the reflected wave and show that the reflectivity of the barrier is $(1 - P)$, where P is the transparency.

21. Suppose that the kinetic energy of the alpha particle is $E_z = 0.5$ev. Let a be the thickness of the potential barrier and λ be the wave length associated with the alpha particle. For $a/\lambda = 0.1$, 0.2, 0.5, 1, 2, 5 make a plot of transparency versus a/λ.

22. A slowly moving (kinetic energy $\approx$ 0) car weighing 2 tons is incident on a square bump shown in the figure. What is the probability that the car will cross the bump?

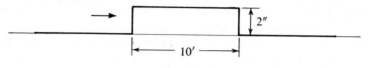

FIG. PR–7.22

23. A slowly moving (kinetic energy $\approx$ 0) car weighing 2 tons is incident on barrier of the form shown in the figure. Calculate the probability that the car will cross the barrier.

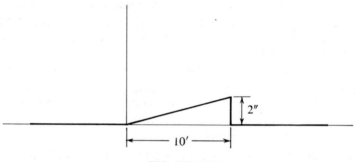

FIG. PR–7.23

24. Repeat the above problem for the potential barrier of the type shown in the figure.

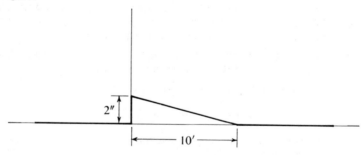

FIG. PR–7.24

25. U^{236} decays to Th^{232} with α-emission with 73% to the ground state and 27% to the excited state at 50 kev. The energy of the alpha group to the ground state is 4.5 Mev. Assuming that the ground state transition is unhindered, calculate the hindrance factor for the decay to the excited state.

26. U^{232} decays $(t_{1/2} = 74 \text{ yr})$ to Th^{228} by emission of three alpha groups with energies and intensities as 5.318 Mev (68%), 5.261 Mev (31.68%), and 5.134 Mev (0.32%). Compare these intensities with the theoretical values. Draw the energy level diagram and show the possible gamma rays accompanying the decay.

27. U^{236} decays with a half-life of 2.4 $\times$ 10^7 yr by emitting 4.5 Mev alpha particles and Po^{212} decays with a half-life of 3 $\times$ 10^{-7} sec by emitting 8.78 Mev alpha particles. What would be the half-life of an even–even radioactive nucleus if it decays by emitting 2 Mev alpha particles?

28. Show that the centrifugal potential barrier is given by

$$\frac{\hbar^2}{2\mu} \frac{l(l+1)}{R^2}$$

and also derive Eq. (7.76), i.e.,

$$\frac{\text{centrifugal barrier}}{\text{coulomb barrier at } R} \approx 0.002l(l+1)$$

29. In the decay of U^{236}, 27% of the alpha particles emitted take away 2 units of angular momentum. Calculate the centrifugal barrier and compare it with the coulomb barrier. What is the effect of the centrifugal barrier on the decay rate?

REFERENCES

1. Bethe, H. A. and J. Ashkin, *Experimental Nuclear Physics*, E. Segre, Vol. III, Part IX, New York: John Wiley & Sons, 1959.

2. Buechner, W. W., *Prog. Nucl. Phys.*, **5**, p. 1, (1955).

3. Rutherford, E., J. Chadwick, and C. D. Ellis, *Radiation From Radioactive Substances*. Chap. II, p. 56, New York: Cambridge University Press, 1930.

4. Robalt, J., *Prog. Nucl. Phys.*, **1**, p. 42, (1950)

5. Blankenship, J. L., and C. J. Borkowski, *I.R.E. Trans.* **NS-8**, p. 17, (1961).

6. Stephens, W. F., F. Asaro, and I. Perlman, *Phys. Rev.*, **96**, p. 1568, (1954).

7. Holloway, M. G., and M. S. Livingston, *Phys. Rev.*, **54**, p. 18, (1938).

8. Holloway, M. G., and M. S. Livingston, *Phys. Rev.*, **54**, p. 32, (1938).

9. Bethe, H. A., and J. Ashkin, *Experimental Nuclear Physics*, ed., E. Segre, pp. 166–357, New York: John Wiley & Sons, 1953.

10. Rutherford, E., J. Chadwick, and C. D. Ellis, *Radiation From Radioactive Substances*, Chap. III, p. 69, New York: Cambridge University Press, 1930.

11. Bohr, N., *Phil. Mag.*, **24**, p. 10, (1913); **30**, p. 581, (1915).

12. Bethe, H. A., *Ann. Physik*, **5**, p. 325, (1930).

13. Bethe, H. A., *Z. Physik*, **76**, p. 293, (1932).

14. Bloch, F., *Ann. Physik*, **16**, p. 285, (1933); *Lecture Series in Nuclear Physics MDDC* 1175, (1947), Lectures XI and XII.

15. Bethe, H. A., and J. Ashkin, *Experimental Nuclear Physics*, ed. E. Segre, Vol. **1**, p. 166, New York: John Wiley & Sons, 1953.

16. Livingston, M. S., and H. A. Bethe, *Revs. Mod. Phys.*, **9**, p. 263, (1937).

17. Kaplan, I., *Nuclear Physics*, p. 315. Reading, Mass.: Addison-Wesley Publishing Co., Inc., 1963.

18. Beiser, A., *Revs. Mod. Phys.*, **24**, p. 273, (1952).

19. Briggs, G. H., *Revs. Mod. Phys.*, **26**, p. 1, (1954).

20. Bethe, H. A., *Revs. Mod. Phys.*, **22**, p. 213, (1950).
21. Tollestrup, A. V., W. A. Fowler, and C. C. Lauritsen, *Phys. Rev.*, **76**, p. 428, (1949).
22. Boggild, J. K., and L. Minnhagen, *Phys. Rev.*, **75**, p. 782, (1949).
23. Bower, J. C., E. Bretscher, and C. W. Gilbert, *Proc. Camb. Phil. Soc.*, **34**, p. 290, (1938).
24. Jesse, W. P., and J. Sadauskis, *Phys. Rev.*, **75**, p. 1110, (1949); **78**, p. 1, (1950).
25. Bethe, H. A., and J. Ashkin, *Experimental Nuclear Physics*, ed. E. Segre, Vol. I, pp. 180–190, New York: John Wiley & Sons, 1953.
26. Rutherford, E., *Phil. Mag.*, **13**, p. 110, (1907).
27. Geiger, H., and J. M. Nuttall, *Phil. Mag.*, **22**, p. 613, (1911).
28. Geiger, H., *Z. Physik*, **8**, p. 45, (1921).
29. Kaplan, I., *Phys. Rev.*, **81**, p. 962, (1951).
30. Hanna, G. C., *Experimental Nuclear Physics*, ed. E. Segre, Vol. III, p. 94, New York: John Wiley & Sons, 1959.
31. Perlman, I., A. Ghiorso, and G. T. Seaborg, *Phys. Rev.*, **77**, p. 26, (1950).
32. Glass, R. A., S. G. Thompson, and G. T. Seaborg, *Inorg. Nucl. Chem.*, **1**, p. 3, (1955).
33. Hanna, G. C., *Experimental Nuclear Physics*, ed. E. Segre, Vol. III, p. 65, New York: John Wiley & Sons, 1959.
34. Gamow, G., *Z. Physik*, **51**, p. 204, (1928).
35. Gurney, R. W., and E. U. Condon, *Nature*, **122**, p. 439, (1928).
36. Hanna, G. C., *Experimental Nuclear Physics*, ed. E. Segre, Vol. III, p. 78, New York: John Wiley & Sons, 1959.
37. Rasetti, F., *Elements of Nuclear Physics*, p. 100, Englewood Cliffs, New Jersey: Prentice-Hall, 1936.
38. Bethe, H. A., *Revs. Mod. Phys.*, **9**, p. 161, (1937).
39. Preston, M. A., *Phys. Rev.*, **71**, p. 865, (1957).
40. Wilson, G. H., and O. C. Simpson, *ANL*, p. 4901, (1952).
41. Devaney, J. J., *Phys. Rev.*, **91**, p. 587, (1953).
42. Thomas, R. G., *Prog. Theoret. Phys.*, **12**, p. 253, (1954).
43. Wilson, G. H., *Phys. Rev.*, **96**, p. 1032, (1954).
44. Wilson, G. H., *ANL*, p. 5381, (1954).
45. Mang, H. J., *Phys. Rev.*, **119**, p. 1069, (1960).
46. Rosenblum, S., *J. Physics*, **1**, p. 438, (1930).
47. Stephens, F. S., Jr., F. Asaro, and I. Perlman, *Phys. Rev.*, **107**, p. 1091, (1957).
48. Emery, G. T., and W. R. Kane, *Phys. Rev.*, **118**, p. 755, (1960).

SUGGESTIONS FOR FURTHER READING

1. Hana, G. C., *Experimental Nuclear Physics*, ed. E. Segre, Vol. III, Part IX, New York: John Wiley & Sons, 1959.

2. Perlman, I., and J. O. Rasmussen, *Handbuch der Physik*, Vol. 42, pp. 109–204, Berlin: Springer Verlag, 1957.

3. Buechner, W. W., *Prog. Nucl. Phys.*, Vol. V, p. 1, (1955).

4. Bethe, H. A., and J. Ashkin, *Experimental Nuclear Physics*, ed. E. Segre, Vol. I, Part II, New York: John Wiley & Sons, 1953.

5. Evans, R. D., *The Atomic Nucleus*, Chaps. 16, 22. New York: McGraw-Hill Book Co., Inc., 1955.

6. Fermi, E., *Nuclear Physics*, Chaps. 2, 3. University of Chicago Press, 1950. Notes compiled by J. Orear, A. H. Rosenfeld, and R. A. Schluter.

7. Rutherford, Chadwick, Ellis, *Radiation from Radioactive Substances*, Chaps. 2, 3, 4, 5, 7. New York: Cambridge University Press, 1930.

8. Hyde, Seaborg, and Perlman, *The Nuclear Properties of the Heavy Elements*, Vol. I, Chaps. 1, 4. New York: Prentice-Hall, 1964.

VIII

BETA DECAY

1. INTRODUCTION

There are three types of processes that are called beta decay: (i) the nucleus decaying by electron emission, or *negaton emission*, denoted by β^-, (ii) the nucleus decaying by *positron emission*, denoted by β^+, and (iii) the capture of an extra-nuclear electron by the nucleus, called *electron capture*. These three types of disintegrations are often called *isobaric transformations* because they do not involve any change in the mass number A, i.e., $\Delta A = 0$, but there is always a change in the nuclear charge. Because the nucleus consists only of neutrons and protons, the conservation of electric charge requires, that in the process of β^--emission, a neutron must be converted into a proton, i.e., $\Delta Z = 1$. Similarly, the β^+-decay and electron capture involve a change of a proton into a neutron, i.e., $\Delta Z = -1$.

It was shown, in Chap. I, that the electrons (and the positrons, as well) cannot exist inside the nucleus. An important assumption is that the electron or the positron is created at the time the nucleus undergoes decay, while in the process of electron capture by the nucleus the electron disappears by converting its mass into energy.

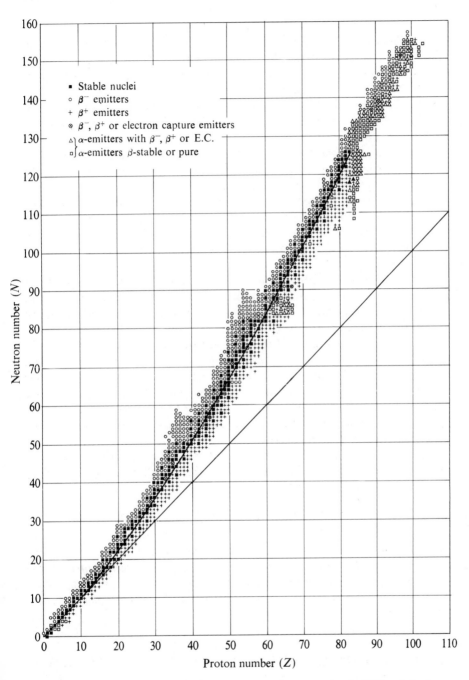

FIG. 8.1 The most stable nuclei lie on or around a curve that is $N/Z = 1$ for low Z and increases to $N/Z = 1.6$ as Z increases. The radioactive nuclei are on either side of the curve.

As shown in Fig. 8.1 the stable nuclei lie on a curve that deviates from the $N = Z$ line as Z increases. There are more than a thousand artificial radioactive isotopes that lie on each side of the stability curve. Many properties of these nuclei have been investigated and the conditions for their particular mode of decay have been found. It is evident from Fig. 8.1 that those radioactive nuclei that are located below the stability curve have too many protons and those above the stability curve have too many neutrons. A nucleus that has an excess of neutrons can become stable by increasing its charge, i.e., by having more protons. This is achieved through β^--emission in which the positive charge created will convert a neutron into a proton. On the other hand, if a nucleus has too many protons, the nuclear charge is decreased by β^+-emission, which is equivalent to converting a proton into a neutron. The charge on the nucleus is also decreased if the nucleus captures an orbital electron. In this sense, positron emission is a process competing with orbital-electron capture.

The process of electron capture takes place in the following manner. If the extra-nuclear electrons, in the process of their orbital motion, happen to come close to the nucleus, they may be captured. This is more likely to happen to the K-shell electrons of the atoms with high Z, because their orbits are very close to the nuclear surface. If an electron from the K-shell is captured, the process is called *K-capture*. Less probable processes are *L-capture, M-capture,* and so forth. The vacancy in the K-shell or L-shell is filled by the electrons from the outer shells. This results in the emission of K or L x-rays that are characteristic of the product nucleus. Because there is no charged particle emitted in the process of electron capture, the process is observed only through the emission of characteristic x-rays.

There is some probability that instead of x-ray emission, the excited K-shell will de-excite by giving its energy to the L-shell electron that will be emitted with kinetic energy K_e

$$K_e = h\nu_K - E_L = (E_K - E_L) - E_L$$
$$= E_K - 2E_L$$

where ν_K is the frequency of the K x-ray and E_K and E_L are the binding energies. Such a process is equivalent to an *internal photoelectric effect*. These electrons, which sometimes accompany the orbital-electron capture, are called *Auger electrons* after the name of the discoverer. Note that this is an extra-nuclear process.

2. CONDITIONS FOR SPONTANEOUS EMISSION

Beta decay will occur only if the energy available in the transition is sufficient to create an electron or positron. Whether or not an artificial radioactive nuclide will decay by electron emission, positron emission, or orbital electron capture can be discussed in terms of the energy available for the disintegration.

A. ELECTRON EMISSION. The process may be represented by the equation

$$_Z X^A \rightarrow _{Z+1} Y^A + _{-1}e^0 \tag{8.1}$$

Let the masses of the parent nucleus, X, and the daughter nucleus, Y, be M_p and M_d, respectively; m_e is the rest mass of the electron. Initially the parent nucleus is at rest, so its kinetic energy is zero. Let K_d and K_e be the kinetic energies of the daughter nucleus and the electron, respectively. From the conservation of energy principle

$$E_i = E_f \tag{8.2}$$

where E_i and E_f are the total initial and final energies of the system, respectively, or

$$M_p c^2 = M_d c^2 + K_d + m_e c^2 + K_e \tag{8.3}$$

Thus the Q-value of this decay process is

$$Q = K_d + K_e = (M_p - M_d - m_e)c^2 \tag{8.4}$$

Because for spontaneous decay the disintegration energy must be positive, we conclude from Eq. (8.4) that electron emission is possible only if the rest mass of the decaying nucleus is greater than the rest mass of the daughter nucleus plus the rest mass of an electron. If $M(Z)$ and $M(Z + 1)$ are the atomic masses of the parent and the daughter atoms, respectively, we have, after neglecting the very small binding energy of the electrons,

$$M(Z) = M_p + m_e Z$$
$$M(Z + 1) = M_d + m_e(Z + 1) \tag{8.5}$$

Substituting for M_p and M_d into Eq. (8.4), we get the condition for the decay in terms of the atomic masses, i.e.,

$$Q = [M(Z) - M(Z + 1)]c^2 \tag{8.6}$$

Equation (8.6) implies that β^--decay will occur whenever the mass of the parent atom is greater than that of the daughter atom, and the disintegration energy, Q, released as the kinetic energy is equal to the difference in their masses. Eq. (8.6) can be also interpreted as stating that an atom will decay by electron emission if it is heavier than another atom with Z greater by one, but with the same A (Fig. 8.2a).

B. POSITRON EMISSION. This process may be represented by the equation:

$$_Z X^A \rightarrow _{Z-1} Y^A + _1 e^0 \tag{8.7}$$

The disintegration energy for this process is given by

$$Q = K_d + K_e = (M_p - M_d - m_e)c^2 \tag{8.8}$$

Expressing Eq. (8.8) in terms of the atomic masses (and neglecting the binding energy of the electrons) we have

$$M(Z) = M_p + m_e Z$$
$$M(Z - 1) = M_d + m_e(Z - 1)$$

and we get

$$Q = [M(Z) - M(Z - 1) - 2m_e]c^2 \tag{8.9}$$

Because Q must be positive, the positron decay of an atom will take place only if its rest mass is greater than the sum of the rest masses of two electrons and an atom with the same A and with Z less by one (Fig. 8.2b).

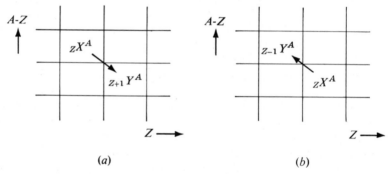

(a)   (b)

FIG. 8.2 Shifting the position of the radioisotopes on the N-Z diagram in the process of (a) β^--decay and (b) β^+ (or electron capture).

C. ELECTRON CAPTURE (E.C.). The process may be represented by the equation

$$_ZX^A + _{-1}e^0 \rightarrow {}_{Z-1}Y^A \tag{8.10}$$

The disintegration energy in this case is given by

$$Q = [M(Z) - M(Z - 1)]c^2 \tag{8.11}$$

i.e., for electron capture to happen, the mass of the parent atom must be greater than the mass of an atom with the same A and with Z less by one. This process fills up the energy gap that is left over by the other two beta decay processes (Fig. 8.2b).

The results of the above conditions for spontaneous decay may be stated in this way: No two adjacent isobars can both be stable. The heavier atom will always decay to the lighter atom, and by this process the unstable nuclei move back to the line of stability on the $A - Z$ versus Z plot. The way the transitions take place on this diagram are shown in Fig. 8.2a and 8.2b.

In this discussion we have assumed that the electrons take away all the maximum disintegration energy available. But as mentioned in Chap. II, the electrons coming out of radioactive nuclei have a continuous energy distribution. This means the electrons may have a kinetic energy anywhere from zero to a maximum value. As we shall see in Sec. 8.6, this necessitates the emission of another particle (neutrino or antineutrino) in the process of beta decay in order to remove the remainder of the energy. The rest mass of this particle is very small, almost zero, and hence the conditions for beta decay given above are still valid, provided the kinetic energy is taken to be the maximum energy, which is called the *end-point energy*, of the electron (or positron).

3. ENERGY MEASUREMENT OF BETA PARTICLES

The energy measurement in this case involves two types of electrons. First, the electrons emitted in the process of beta decay always have a continuous energy distribution which requires the measurement of the maximum energy, the end-point energy. Second, the conversion electrons, which are monoenergetic, are emitted by the following process: In the process of gamma decay, which usually follows beta decay, the nucleus often is de-excited by giving its energy to the orbital electron instead of emitting a gamma ray. These electrons are called *conversion electrons*. Conversion electrons show up as discrete lines superimposed on the continuous beta spectrum. Thus the measurement of energies requires scanning throughout the range of the whole spectrum.

An important point in connection with beta decay is the relativistic correction. Because the beta particles emitted from radioactive nuclei have velocities approaching that of the velocity of light, their motion must be described by the special theory of relativity instead of by classical mechanics.

The most precise measurements of the energies and the spectra of beta particles involve the use of magnetic spectrometers. For less accurate work many other methods have been designed that are much less cumbersome. In the following, we shall discuss magnetic spectrometers in some detail, while the other methods will be mentioned briefly.

A. MAGNETIC SPECTROMETERS.   The first analysis of the β-ray spectra of the natural radioactive elements was made by L. Baeyer and O. Hahn[1] in 1910. The electrons were deflected by a magnetic field and recorded by a photographic method. An improved form, the semicircular focusing magnetic spectrometer, was designed by J. Danysz[2] in 1911. Since then many precise magnetic spectrometers have been designed, and they constitute an important part of the instrumentation in the field of low-energy nuclear physics. The theory and design of some of these spectrometers are described by K. Siegbahn[3]. For our purpose we will give a brief design description and the first-order theory of some of the well-known and simpler β-ray spectrometers.

The performance of different types of spectrometers is compared by a *figure of merit*, which is defined by the ratio T/R. T is the *transmission coefficient*, defined as the fraction of the total number of particles of a given energy or momentum emitted by a source that are received by a detector. R is the *resolution*, defined as $\Delta E/E$ where ΔE is the width at half-maximum at energy E. The plots are usually made of the number of electrons versus Hr, where Hr is proportional to the momenta of the β-particles. We shall often use momentum resolution ($R_p = dp/p$) instead of energy resolution.

We shall describe the following three β-ray magnetic spectrometers[4,5]:

(1) semicircular focusing spectrometer
(2) magnetic lens spectrometer
(3) double focusing spectrometer.

(1) *Semicircular Focusing Spectrometer*[4,5,6]. This method is the same as that for alpha particles and uses the principle of $180°$, or semicircular focusing, but the details of the design differ considerably. Because β-particles are much lighter than α-particles, they do not need very high fields. A typical magnetic field used for β-particles is of the order of 1000 gauss as compared to 10,000 gauss for α-particles.

The source of β-particles is deposited on a wire a few millimeters long and a fraction of a millimeter in diameter, or on a long, narrow strip of thin foil, and placed in an evacuated chamber. A beam of electrons selected by the defining slit AB (Fig. 8.3) is brought to focus by the application of a magnetic field perpendicular to the plane of the motion of the particles. The motion is governed by the equation

$$Hev = \frac{mv^2}{\rho} \tag{8.12}$$

where m is the relativistic mass given by $\dfrac{m_0}{\sqrt{1 - v^2/c^2}}$ and ρ is the radius of curvature. Rewriting Eq. (8.12), we get

$$p = eH\rho \tag{8.13}$$

where p is the relativistic momentum. Once the momentum is known, the kinetic energy may be calculated.

$$K_e = mc^2 - m_0c^2 = E - E_0$$

where

$$E = \sqrt{p^2c^2 + E_0^2}$$

Hence

$$K_e = \sqrt{p^2c^2 + m_0^2c^4} - m_0c^2 \tag{8.14}$$

Either a photographic plate or a Geiger counter may be used for detection. The photographic plate has the advantage of recording the whole spectra in one exposure, but it suffers from the disadvantages of lower sensitivity and nonlinearity. For quantitative work the Geiger counter is best. The counter is placed in a fixed position while the magnetic field is varied. The number of β-particles reaching the counter, per unit time, is obtained for different values of H. Because ρ is fixed, each value of $H\rho$ corresponds to different values of p. The plot of number versus Hr gives the momentum distribution curve.

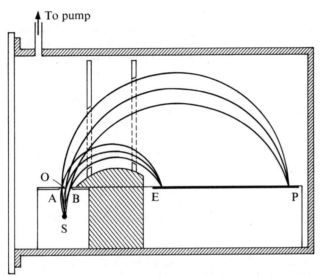

FIG. 8.3   Semicircular focusing spectrometer. [From Rutherford, Chadwick, and Ellis, *Radiation from Radioactive Substances*, New York: Cambridge University Press (1930).]

A complete theory of semicircular focusing has been worked out by K. T. Li[7] and is also presented by Siegbahn[3]. In most cases it is accurate enough to use simple first order theory, the results of which we shall summarize here. Let us assume that the source is a point source. A trajectory passing through the center of the defining slit PQ (the slit defines the acceptance angle 2α) has a diameter SA (Fig. 8.4). Any other trajectory making an angle α with the central trajectory intersects the diameter at B. The width of the image at the focus is $w_{i0} = AB$. Calculated from simple geometrical considerations

$$w_{i0} = 2\rho(1 - \cos \alpha) \simeq \rho\alpha^2 \qquad (8.15)$$

According to Eq. (8.15) the position of B is independent of the sign of α, and so the image shape is asymmetric. Eq. (8.15) also holds for electrons that make a small angle with the plane perpendicular to the magnetic field.

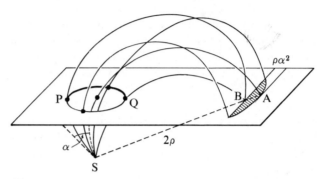

FIG. 8.4 Electron trajectories in the semicircular focusing spectrometer. [Reprinted with permission from Frisch, *Prog. Nucl. Phys.*, **1**, p. 140 (Cavanagh) Oxford: Pergamon Press Ltd. (1950).]

If the source is not a point source but has a width, s, the width of the image, w_i, is given by

$$w_i = s + w_{i0} = s + \rho\alpha^2 \tag{8.16}$$

Combining Eq. (8.16) and (8.13), for a fixed value of a magnetic field, the momentum resolution R_p is given by

$$R_p = dp/p = d\rho/\rho = w_i/\rho = (s/\rho + \alpha^2) \tag{8.17}$$

and the energy resolution (or the resolution of the instrument) is, therefore,

$$R = \tfrac{1}{2}(s/\rho + \alpha^2) \tag{8.18}$$

Eq. (8.18) is true only if a photographic plate is used as a detector. In the case of a Geiger counter, because the electrons to be detected must pass through the counter window, w_c, the resolution of the instrument takes the following form:

$$R = \frac{1}{2}\left(\frac{s + w_c}{\rho} + \alpha^2\right) \tag{8.19}$$

The transmission coefficient for a circular slit, PQ, which subtends a solid angle Ω, is

$$T = \Omega/4\pi = 2\pi(1 - \cos\alpha)/4\pi \simeq \alpha^2/4 \tag{8.20}$$

A typical resolution of this instrument is 1 percent, and the corresponding transmission is about 0.1 percent. The figure of merit, (T/R), therefore, is $\sim 1/10$.

(2) **Magnetic Lens Spectrometer.** Many beta-ray spectrometers[3,5] have been developed that make use of focusing in a uniform, longitudinal magnetic-field. This focusing property was first demonstrated by R. Tricker[8]. Beta spectrometers have been constructed by C. Witcher[9], J. DuMond[10], and many others who have developed and improved this method to a great

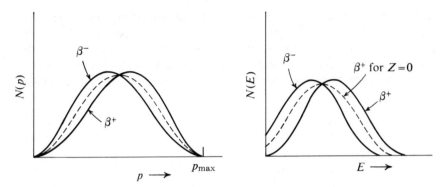

FIG. 8.26 The dotted curves are the distributions expected from the theory without coulomb correction due to nuclear field and are the same both for β^- and β^+. The solid curves are the coulomb-corrected curves and are different for β^- and β^+.

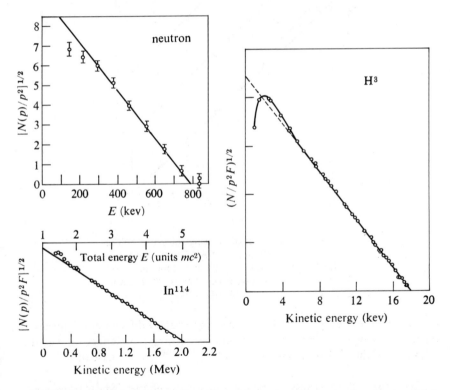

FIG. 8.27 Fermi–Kurie plots for allowed beta transitions in the decay of (a) neutron, (b) tritium (H^3), and (c) In^{114}. [From (a) Robson, J. M., *Phys. Rev.*, **83**, 349 (1951); (b) Langer, L. M., and R. D. Moffat, *Phys. Rev.*, **88**, 689 (1952); (c) Lawson, A. W., and J. M. Cork, *Phys. Rev.*, **57**, 982, (1940).]

and end-point energies can be measured more accurately because of the interception of the straight-line plot with the energy axis as compared with the parabolic plot of momentum distribution given by Eq. (8.78), in which the high-energy end approaches the energy axis asympototically. There are always some deviations from the straight line plots at the low-energy end. This is

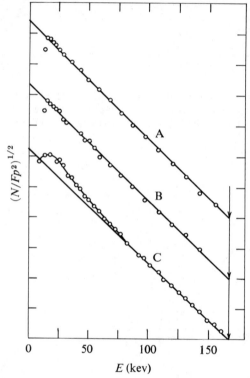

FIG. 8.28   The effect of backing thickness on the Fermi plot for beta decay of S^{35}. A, B, and C are for backing thickness of 1 mg/cm², 2 mg/cm², and 5 mg/cm², respectively. From Albert, R. D., and C. S. Wu, *Phys. Rev.*, **74**, 847, (1948).]

not due to the theory but rather to the experimental difficulties of measurement at low energies caused by the source backing. The effect of backing thickness of the beta source is shown in Fig. 8.28[56] for the case of S^{35}.

B. FORBIDDEN TRANSITIONS. There are many beta emitters whose transitions, unlike the allowed transitions, do not give straight lines for the Kurie plot. Their characteristic spectral shapes differ considerably from those determined only from the statistical factor and the coulomb factor. The reason for the deviation from the straight line is that the matrix element is not independent of energy. Such transitions have been classified as *forbidden transitions*. The spectrum of n-forbidden transitions may be written as[57]

$$N(p) \sim F(Z, E) \cdot pE(E_{max} - E)^2 S_n(E) \qquad (8.80)$$

where $S_n(E)$ is called the *shape factor* and depends on the type of interaction assumed, as we shall discuss in connection with selection rules. It is sufficient to say here that if $S_n(E)$ is included, the plot of $[N(E)/F(Z, E)p^2 S_n(E)]^{1/2}$ versus E, i.e., the Kurie plot, is a straight line. The detailed analysis of such plots is given by C. S. Wu[58].

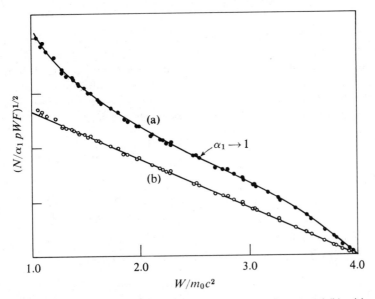

FIG. 8.29   The Kurie plot of Y^{91} (a) without shape factor and (b) with shape factor $S_1(E)$. [From Konopinski, E. J., and L. M. Langer, *Ann. Revs. of Nucl. Sci.*, **2**, 261, (1953).]

These forbidden transitions are actually the ones that provide the test of the Fermi theory because, unlike allowed transitions, their shape does depend on the matrix element, M. As an example, the Kurie plot of Y^{91} is definitely nonlinear as shown in Fig. 8.29(a), if one does not include the shape factor. But if one includes also a shape factor

$$S_1(E) = (E^2 - m_0^2 c^4) + (E_0 - E)^2 \qquad (8.81)$$

then the Kurie plot is a straight line as shown in Fig. 8.29(b)[59]. The decay of Y^{91} is, therefore, classified as a first forbidden transition.

Shape factors have also been evaluated for higher forbidden transitions. These shape factors modify the nonlinear Kurie plots to linear plots. For example, the shape factor for a second forbidden transition is

$$S_2(E) = (E^2 - m_0^2 c^4)^2 + (E_0 - E)^4 + (10/3)(E^2 - m_0^2 c^4)(E_0 - E)^2 \quad \textbf{(8.82)}$$

Note that these shape factors are for unique first forbidden transitions only.

C. BETA DECAY RATE AND COMPARATIVE LIFETIME.   Eq. (8.70) with the Fermi function $F(Z, E)$ included is

$$N(p)\,dp = \frac{g^2 |M|^2}{2\pi^3 c^3 \hbar^7} F(Z, E)(K_{max} - K)^2 p^2\,dp \quad \textbf{(8.83)}$$

and represents the probability per second for emission of an electron with momentum between p and $(p + dp)$. The probability per second that an electron will be emitted with momentum between 0 and p_{max} may be obtained by integrating Eq. (8.83) from 0 to p_{max}. This total probability is nothing but the disintegration constant, λ. Thus, rearranging and expressing momentum and energy in units of mc and mc^2, respectively, we get

$$\lambda = \frac{1}{\tau} = \frac{ln2}{t_{1/2}} = \frac{g^2 |M|^2 m^5 c^4}{2\pi^3 \hbar^7} f(Z, K_{max}) \quad \textbf{(8.84)}$$

where

$$f(Z, K_{max}) = \int_0^{p_{max}/mc} F(Z, E) \left(\frac{K_{max} - K}{mc^2}\right)^2 \left(\frac{p}{mc}\right)^2 \frac{dp}{mc} \quad \textbf{(8.85)}$$

Let us consider a special case in which $p_{max}/mc \gg 1$, or $K_{max}/mc^2 \gg 1$ and $F(Z, E) \approx 1$, then we can show from Eq. (8.85) that

$$f(Z, K_{max}) \approx \text{constant} \times K_{max}^{\ 5} \quad \textbf{(8.86)}$$

Combining Eq. (8.85) with Eq. (8.84) we get

$$\lambda = 1/\tau \propto K_{max}^{\ 5} \quad \textbf{(8.87)}$$

This is the same relation as the one discussed in Sec. 8.8 known as the fifth-power law. The straight line resulting from the plot of $\log_{10} \lambda$ versus $\log_{10} K_{max}$ has a slope of 5 as expected, and this is particularly true for the allowed positron decay of light nuclei.

Returning to Eqs. (8.84) and (8.86), we may write

$$ft = \frac{2\pi^3 \hbar^7 |ln2|}{g^2 m^5 c^4 |M|^2} = \frac{\text{constant}}{|M|^2}$$

or

$$ft = \text{constant}\ |M|^{-2} \quad \textbf{(8.88)}$$

where f is the function given by Eq. (8.85) and the subscript, 1/2, in t has been dropped. The product ft is called the *comparative life-time* of the nucleus and it represents the half life corrected for Z and E. It provides a simple way of comparing lifetimes of different beta emitters on the basis of the same Z and E_{max}. This also provides a simple method of getting information about the matrix element, M. It is more convenient to discuss beta emission in terms of $\log_{10} ft$ value instead of the ft value. The evaluation of $\log_{10} ft$ involves the calculation of the function f from Eq. (8.85), which is not so simple. Graphs have been drawn by S. Moszkowski[60], from which the $\log_{10} ft$ may be calculated easily if $t_{1/2}$ and E_{max} are known. Such graphs are shown in Fig. 8.30 and Fig. 8.31 (a), (b), (c). The $\log_{10} ft$ value is written as the sum of two terms

$$\log ft = \log (f_0 t) + \log C \qquad (8.89)$$

where $\log (f_0 t)$ is obtained from Fig. 8.30 and $\log C$ from Fig. 8.31.

In an effort to define clearly the degree of forbidden transitions and to gain some information about the nuclear matrix element, M, a compilation of the $\log_{10} ft$ values has been made for all known beta emitters. It is found that different beta emitters have $\log_{10} ft$ values anywhere from 3 to 20, though most of them lie in the range 3 to 10. The results of such a compilation are illustrated in the form of a histogram as shown in Fig. 8.32[61]. As is evident, there is no significant grouping of the $\log_{10} ft$ values. But with the additional information obtained from shell-model considerations or the spin determination of the parent and the daughter nuclei involved in the disintegration, it is possible to classify these transitions. The transitions with $\log ft$ of 3 to 6 are classified as allowed transitions, those which lie between ~ 6 and ~ 9 as first forbidden. For second forbidden transitions $\log_{10} ft$ is greater than 9, and so forth.

In Fig. 8.32 the portion that is dotted represents those nuclei for which $\log ft$ is less than 4. These transitions are called *super-allowed transitions* and include all the mirror nuclei. The reason the mirror nuclei have super-allowed transitions is easily understood in terms of the matrix element, M, that contains the wave functions of the initial and the final state of the nucleus. The magnitude of the matrix element depends on the degree of overlap of the initial and final wave functions. For example, consider the mirror pair $_9F^{17}$ and $_8O^{17}$, in which $_8O^{17}$ is formed by the β^+-decay of $_9F^{17}$. The odd nucleons in both cases are in $d_{5/2}$ state. This means that the wave functions of the initial and final state are identical, and they completely overlap, resulting in a very large matrix element, M, and producing a very small $\log_{10} ft$ value. For the allowed and the forbidden transitions the overlapping of the wave functions becomes less, resulting in smaller values of M and larger values of $\log_{10} ft$. A further discussion of this will appear in Sec. 8.11.

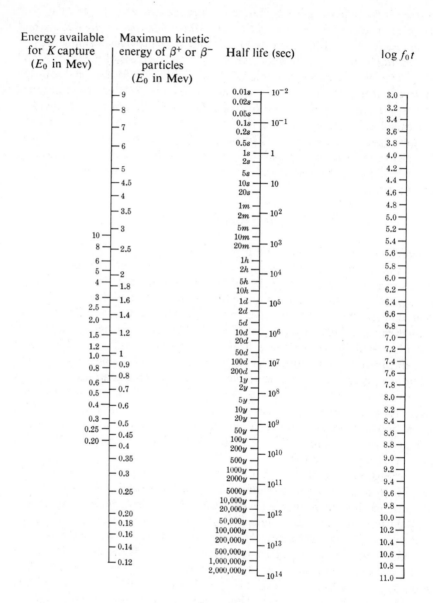

FIG. 8.30 Log $f_0 t$ as a function of E_0 and t. [From Moszkowski, S. A., Phys. Rev., **82**, 35, (1951).]

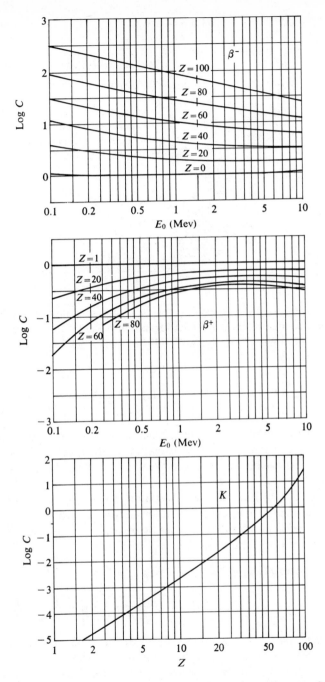

FIG. 8.31 Shows (a) log C versus E_0 for various Z in case of β^--emission, (b) log C versus E_0 for various Z in case of β^+-emission, and (c) log C versus Z for K electron-capture. [From Moszkowski, S. A., *Phys. Rev.*, **82**, 35, (1951).]

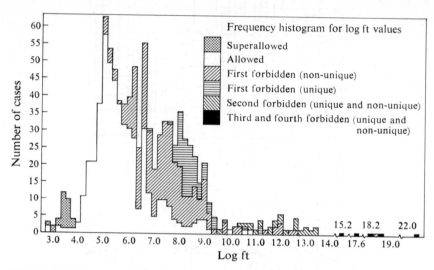

FIG. 8.32 Histogram of the number of cases of nuclides for different log *ft* values. The cross-hatched area is for mirror nuclei transitions, and the dotted areas are the unique-shape transitions. [From Nuclear Data Sheets: 5-5-140 (Nov. 1963).]

10. NEUTRINO REST-MASS

The results of the neutrino mass determination were given in Sec. 8.7. One method mentioned there was the investigation of the spectral shapes of the beta particles near the high-energy end. We shall now describe this method in some detail.

The derivation of Eq. (8.83) was based on the assumption that the neutrino rest-mass is zero. If we assume that the rest-mass of the neutrino is very small, but not zero, and denote this mass by m_{v0}, the following equation will result for the electron distribution[62].

$$N(p)\, dp = \text{constant } F(Z, p)p^2(K_{max} - K)[(K_{max} - K)^2 - m_{v0}^2 c^4]^{1/2}$$

$$\times \left[1 \pm \frac{(m_0 c^2)(m_{v0} c^2)}{(K + mc^2)(K_{max} - K)} \right] dp \quad (8.90)$$

Of course, if $m_{v0} = 0$, this equation reduces to Eq. (8.83). As already mentioned, the Fermi plots (or Kurie plots) are linear for allowed transitions if the neutrino mass is zero. Because the neutrino rest-mass, if any, is very small, it will effect the linearity of the Fermi plot only near the end-point energy K_{max} as shown in Fig. 8.33. The reason is that $(K_{max} - K)$ becomes smaller near the end-point energy, and the distribution becomes more sensitive to the neutrino rest-mass. The effect of the neutrino rest-mass will be still

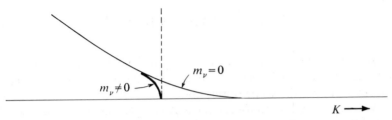

FIG. 8.33 The end portion of the Fermi plot with and without neutrino rest-mass. [From Langer, L. M., and R. D. Moffat, *Phys. Rev.*, **88**, 689, (1952).]

more pronounced (the departure from the linear Fermi plot) if we consider a beta decay in which K_{max} itself is very small.

L. Langer and R. Moffat[62] have studied the electron distribution resulting from the disintegration

$$H^3 \rightarrow He^3 + \beta^- + \bar{\nu} \qquad (8.91)$$

which has $K_{max} = 18$ kev. Such a low energy does produce many problems in the accurate determination of the energies of the emitted electrons. Langer and Moffat have been successful in this respect, and their results are shown in Fig. 8.34. A comparison between the theoretical and the experimental plots has been made for different neutrino rest-masses. Their results show that the neutrino rest-mass is less than 0.05 percent of the electron rest-mass, and may very well be zero.

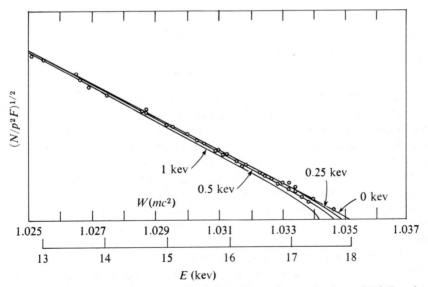

FIG. 8.34 Comparison of the end portion of experimental points of H^3 Fermi plot with curves for different neutrino rest-masses. [From Langer, L. M., and R. D. Moffat, *Revs. Mod. Phys.*, **23**, 10, (1951).]

11. SELECTION RULES[63]

The particles emitted in beta decay have very high velocities, and the derivation of selection rules requires a relativistic treatment of the theory. Such a treatment is beyond the scope of this book. We shall only outline the results and give a brief justification for the same. A complete matrix element will be obtained by writing the expectation value H_{if} from Eq. (8.54) in the form

$$H_{if} = g \int \psi_f^*(\mathbf{r})\phi_\beta^*(\mathbf{r})Oo\phi_\nu(\mathbf{r})\psi_i(\mathbf{r})dv \qquad (8.92)$$

where O and o are the operators operating on the heavy and light particles, respectively. The various choices of these operators lead to different selection rules. Because the beta decay interactions do not depend on the velocities of the particles, the operators do not contain space derivatives. The operators O and o are only spin operators. Relativistic conditions require that these operators must be invariant under a proper Lorentz transformation, i.e., under rotation in the four-dimensional space-time continuum. This results in certain invariant quantities that are scalar products and leads to the following five different types of interactions:

S—scalar interaction

V—polar vector interaction

A—axial vector interaction

T—tensor interaction

P—pseudoscalar interaction

The names of these interactions come from their transformation properties.

The matrix element depends on the nuclear wave-functions and the relative direction of emission of the electron and the neutrino. The electron and the neutrino, each with a spin 1/2, can be emitted with their spins antiparallel or parallel. If they are emitted antiparallel, the total spin is zero and we call them *Fermi-transitions*. Similarly, if they are emitted with spins parallel, resulting in a total spin of 1, we called them *Gamow-Teller transitions*. Furthermore, Fermi-type transitions assume scalar and/or polar vector-type interactions while Gamow-Teller-type transitions assume axial vector and/or tensor-type interactions.

As already explained, allowed transitions are those in which the light particles are emitted as a S-wave and, therefore, do not remove any orbital angular momentum. Because the parity of a state with $l = 0$ is even, the transforming nucleus does not change its parity. From the conservation of angular momentum and parity the following selection rules may be obtained for the allowed transitions:

$$\Delta I = 0, \qquad \text{no parity change} \quad \text{pure Fermi}$$

$$\left.\begin{array}{l} \Delta I = 0 \text{ or } \pm 1 \\ \quad \text{except} \\ \quad 0 \to 0 \end{array}\right\} \quad \text{no parity change} \quad \text{pure Gamow-Teller}$$

The absence of $0 \to 0$ transitions is because $\Delta I = I_f - I_i = S = 1$ (for $G - T$) cannot be satisfied if $I_i = I_f = 0$. Examples of pure Fermi and pure Gamow-Teller transitions are

$$O^{14} \to N^{14*} + \beta^+ + \nu$$

and

$$He^6 \to Li^6 + \beta^- + \bar{\nu}$$

respectively.

It has also been confirmed that there are certain beta decays in which the mixing of the antiparallel (Fermi) and parallel (Gamow-Teller) spin states takes place in definite proportions.

The selection rules for first-forbidden transitions may be arrived at by considering the expansion of the lepton wave-functions. This brings in a factor of **r**, and the particle cannot be emitted as a S-wave. This, in turn, leads to the P-wave emission of the particle, thereby resulting in $l = 1$ and a change in parity. The selection rules derived for the first and higher forbidden transitions are summarized in Table 8.1.

The forbiddenness of the transitions is not only due to increasing ΔI but also arises from relativistic correction that may utilize the pseudoscalar interaction.

TABLE 8.1

SELECTION RULES FOR BETA DECAY[63]

Transition	ΔI	Parity Change	Log ft Value	Name of Rules
1. Super-allowed	0	no	3	
2. Allowed	0	no	3–6	Fermi
	0, ± 1 (No $0 \to 0$)	no	3–6	Gamow-Teller
3. First Forbidden	0, ± 1 (No $0 \to 0$)	yes	6–10	Fermi
	0, ± 1, ± 2 *(No $0 \to 0$)	yes	6–10	Gamow-Teller
4. Second Forbidden	± 1, ± 2 *(No $1 \to 0$)	no	10–14	Fermi
	± 2, ± 3	no	10–14	Gamow-Teller

---

* There are other cases of ΔI for which the transitions are not allowed.

12. THEORY OF ELECTRON CAPTURE[64,65]

All through this chapter we had many occasions to talk about electron capture, especially in connection with the establishment of the existence of the neutrino. One essential feature of the electron-capture decay is that it does not have a continuous spectrum. The neutrinos emitted are mono-energetic. The process of orbital electron-capture takes place when the density of the orbital electrons is high. The nucleus captures an electron and transforms itself into the daughter nucleus. The probability of such a transition is given by

$$\lambda = \frac{1}{\tau} = \frac{ln2}{t_{1/2}} = \frac{2\pi}{\hbar} \left| \int \Psi_f^* H_{op} \Psi_i \, dv \right|^2 \frac{dn}{dE} \tag{8.93}$$

As before, $H_{op} = g\phi_\beta\phi_v$ is the interaction energy as given by the Fermi theory. We can still use the same neutrino wave-function as given in the Fermi theory of beta decay, i.e. $\phi_v = e^{i\mathbf{q}\cdot\mathbf{r}}$ and $E_v = cp_v$. Because the electron is now in a bound state, we cannot use the free particle wave-function. The nearest orbital electron is in the 1s state and the wave functions for this and other orbital electrons are given by H. White[66]. For the case of 1s electron, the wave function is

$$\phi_{1s} = \frac{1}{\pi^{1/2}} \left(\frac{Z}{a_B} \right)^{3/2} e^{-Zr/a_B} \tag{8.94}$$

where a_B is the Bohr radius. Thus if we know the wave functions of the different orbital electrons, we can calculate their probability of capture by the nucleus. Because only the neutrino is emitted in the decay process, the factor dn/dE is given by

$$\frac{dn}{dE_v} = \frac{dn}{dp} \cdot \frac{dp}{dE_v} = \frac{E_v^2}{2\pi^2\hbar^3 c^3} \tag{8.95}$$

Combining Eqs. (8.94) and (8.95) with Eq. (8.93), the decay constant for the K-capture is given by [67]

$$\lambda_k = (g^2 m^3/\pi^2\hbar^7)(Z/137)^3 |M|^2 E_v^2$$

where $e^2/\hbar c = 1/137$. The transition probability for the L-capture may be calculated in a similar manner.

The process that competes the most with E.C. is the decay by positron emission, and the ratio of the two is given by

$$\frac{N_k}{N_\beta^+} = \frac{\lambda_k}{\lambda_\beta^+} \approx \frac{1}{2\pi} \left(\frac{Z}{137} \right)^3 \frac{E_v^2}{m^2 c^4} \frac{1}{f(Z, K_{max})} \tag{8.96}$$

Plots of such ratios for different Z have been drawn by Feenberg[67].

13. SYMMETRY LAWS AND PARITY NONCONSERVATION IN BETA DECAY[68]

For a long time it has been well accepted that symmetry or invariance principles generate conservation laws. These invariance principles have proved to be powerful in establishing conservation laws. Take, for example, the conservation of linear momentum, which is a consequence of the invariance of physical laws under displacement. Similarly the conservation of angular momentum is a consequence of invariance under a rotation in space. Development of quantum mechanics led to the extension of symmetry principles to atomic physics with great consequences[69], such as the "invariance of the Schrödinger equation for an n-electron atom under symmetric group of order n." The most amazing application of the symmetry principles was in the prediction of antiparticles[70]. For example, the invariance under the Lorentz transformation of a relativistic wave equation for an electron (the Dirac equation) led to the prediction of the positron[71].

Another important invariance principle is that of left-right symmetry, or symmetry under reflection. According to this principle a mirror image of an object is also an object that exists in nature. The mirror image of any motion is also a motion permitted by physical laws and so on. The left-right symmetry led to the establishment of the *law of conservation of parity*. According to this principle, the parity of a system does not change. In any transformation, the parity of individual nucleons or the parity of a part of the system may change, but the parity of the whole system remains constant. The parity of the whole system is the product of parities of the individual parts of the system.

Until 1956, it was taken for granted that the principle of conservation of parity is valid in all interactions. The principle of conservation of parity had been verified in the case of strong and medium interactions but not for weak interactions. The validity of the conservation of parity in the case of weak interactions was first questioned by T. Lee and C. Yang[72] in 1956. They suggested that the parity might not be conserved in weak interactions such as β-decay. What we mean by the nonconservation of parity may be understood from the following explanation.

Consider a change of the coordinates of a system from (x, y, z) to $(-x, -y, -z)$. This will reverse the direction of all the components of a linear momentum vector $\mathbf{p}$. The angular momentum vector $\mathbf{L}$, which is a product of the linear momentum vector $\mathbf{p}$ and position vector $\mathbf{r}$, will not reverse its direction because both $\mathbf{p}$ and $\mathbf{r}$ change signs.

Consider a β^--decaying nucleus with spin angular momentum vector $\mathbf{I}$. Suppose the beta particles are emitted in the direction parallel to the spin of the nucleus. Reversing the signs of all the coordinates will not change the direction of the spin vector **I**, but the beta particles will be emitted in the direction opposite to the spin vector of the nucleus. The system, after the change of the sign of the coordinates, is not the same as before, and we state this by saying that the parity is not conserved in beta decay. In order for the parity to be conserved, as many particles should be emitted in the direction parallel to the spin direction as in the opposite direction, so that the reversal

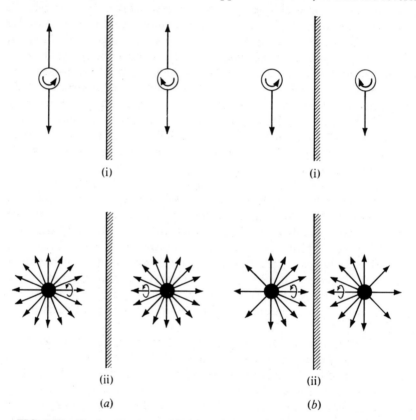

(i)   (i)

(ii)   (ii)

(a)   (b)

FIG. 8.35 Nuclear systems with (a) parity conservation and (b) parity non-conservation.

of sign will not change the system. This is depicted in Fig. 8.35. In order to test this hypothesis of nonconservation of parity, Lee and Yang[72] suggested the experiments that were performed by C. Wu, E. Ambler, R. Hayward, D. Hoppes, and R. Hudson[73], as described below, and showed that β^- decay of Co^{60} is an anisotropic process and thus does not conserve parity.

The apparatus shown in Fig. 8.36(a) was used by Wu, et al.[73]. The decay scheme of Co^{60} in Fig. 8.36(b) shows that it emits negatrons of energy 0.312 Mev and two gamma rays of energies 1.19 Mev and 1.32. A source, about 0.002

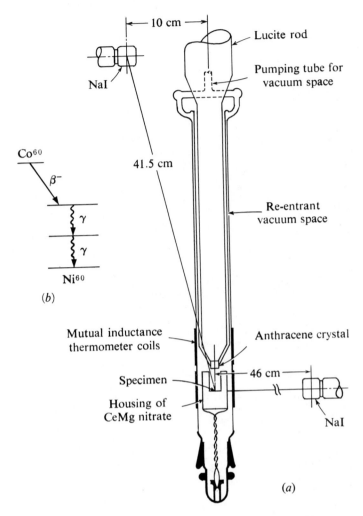

FIG. 8.36 The experimental setup used by Wu, *et al.* for measuring asymmetry in electron distribution from polarized Co⁶⁰ nuclei. [From Wu, C. S., E. Ambler, R. W. Hayward, D. P. Hoppes, and R. P. Hudson, *Phys. Rev.*, **105**, 1413, (1957).]

in. thick and having a several-microcurie disintegration rate, was deposited in a crystal of cerium magnesium nitrate (which possesses a strong internal magnetic field). In order to reduce the thermal motion to a minimum, the crystal was cooled to $0.01°K$ by the method of adiabatic demagnetization. By applying an external magnetic field, the Co⁶⁰ nuclei were polarized (i.e., they were aligned along the direction of the applied field). The degree of polarization was measured by observing the anisotropy of gamma emission. The

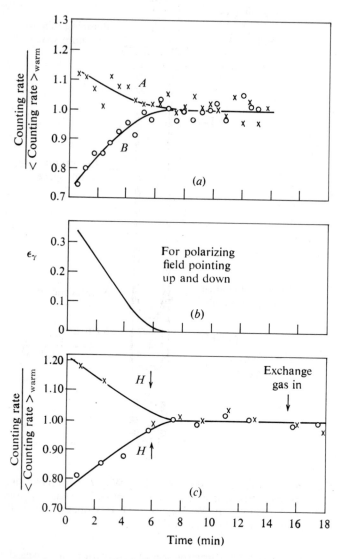

FIG. 8.37   The results obtained by Wu, *et al.* by using the
apparatus shown in Fig. 8.36. [From Wu., *et al.*, *Phys. Rev.*,
105, 1413, (1957).] (a) gamma-anisotropy obtained by equa-
torial counter (*A*) and polar counter (*B*). (b) gamma-anisotropy
calculated from (a). (c) beta-asymmetry.

NaI(Tl) crystals, as shown in Fig. 8.36, were used for gamma detection. For beta detection an anthracene scintillation crystal ($\frac{3}{8}$ in. diameter and $\frac{1}{16}$ in. thick) was placed inside the cryostat, and light was conveyed to the photomultiplier by means of a light pipe. After the material was cooled to 0.01°K, the magnetic field was shut off, coils were raised, and the counting rate started within 20 seconds. The results of beta intensity measurements are shown in Fig. 8.37. As time passes, the temperature rises and thermal motion reduces the polarization to zero, and the β^- intensity distribution becomes isotropic.

Fig. 8.37 clearly indicates that there is asymmetry in the counting rate as large as 20 percent. This proves the hypothesis that the parity is not conserved in beta decay and also that the effect is large.

As a consequence it was pointed out by many[74,75,47] that if parity is violated, the emission of beta particles from nonaligned nuclei should be longitudinally polarized, i.e., the direction of motion of the electron should be the same as of its spin. This implies that it should have a helicity of $+1$. (Remember that helicity was defined as the cosine of the angle between the direction of spin and the direction of motion.) Many helicity measurements have been made on samples such as Sc^{46}, Eu^{152m}, Co^{60}, and on others, confirming the predictions[76,77]. It has also been shown[77] that the neutrinos emitted in K-capture have negative helicity.

We may add here that the first indications that the parity may not be conserved in some reactions did not come from beta decay, but from the decay of two heavy mesons. They are called the θ-meson and the τ-meson. They are similar in all respects—mass, charge, spin—except one decays by emitting two pions and the other, by three pions. These and other problems of weak interactions will be taken up in the last chapter of the book.

PROBLEMS

1. Derive Eq. (8.11).
2. Rederive Eq. (8.4) taking into consideration the binding energies of the atomic electrons as well.
3. Which of the following nuclei will decay by (i) β^- emission, (ii) β^+ emission or (iii) electron capture:

$$Co^{60}, O^{15}, Na^{22}, P^{32}, A^{37}, Cu^{64}$$

4. O^{15} decays by positron emission to its mirror pair N^{15} with a half-life of 124 s. What energy would you expect for the end point of the positron spectrum?
5. The following reaction is endothermic with $Q = -2.9$ Mev.

$$_{13}Al^{27} + \alpha \rightarrow {}_{15}P^{30} + n$$

The nucleus $_{15}P^{30}$ produced in this reaction decays by positron emission. Calculate the disintegration energy for the decay.

6. The mass of a neutron is 1.30 Mev greater than the mass of the proton. A free neutron is unstable and decays into a proton by β^- emission. Calculate the kinetic energy of the β^- particles and the maximum kinetic energy of the recoil protons.

7. Show that for an electron in a magnetic field of strength H gauss the kinetic energy of the electron may be expressed in the following form

$$K = [m_0{}^2 + A(Hr)^2]^{1/2} - m_0$$

where m_0 is the rest mass energy of the electron (0.511 Mev), r is the radius of curvature in cm, and A is a constant equal to 8.989×10^{-8} (Mev/gauss-cm)^2.

8. Outline briefly a method for deriving Eq. (8.19) assuming the image line shape is roughly triangular.

9. In a 180° semi-circular focusing spectrometer show that there is approximate focusing of a slightly divergent monoenergetic beam.

10. In a 180° semi-circular focusing spectrometer, the uncertainty in the position of the slit image may be calculated in terms of a ratio of slit image width to mean distance between slit and image. Assuming that the source slit is a geometrical line, calculate the percentage uncertainty for beam divergence of half-angles 1°, 6° and 10°.

11. Show that in the case of semi-circular focusing, the length of the source is limited to $2\rho\alpha$ which then leads to the optimum source area of $2\rho^2\alpha^2$.

12. Show that for best results the counter window should have the same width as the source in beta-ray spectrometers.

13. Calculate the order of the error that will be introduced by treating a problem non-relativistically if the kinetic energy of a particle is (a) 10%, (b) 20% and (c) 50% of the rest-mass energy.

14. Show that the distance r of the electron from the source (Fig. 8.5b) is given by

$$R = 2R_0 \operatorname{Sin}\left(\frac{\pi z}{L}\right).$$

15. The ranges of three different groups of beta (β^-) particles in aluminum are 320 mg/cm^2, 755 mg/cm^2 and 932 mg/cm^2 respectively. From the empirical relations given in the text calculate the energies of the three beta groups.

16. Derive Eq. (8.35) from Eq. (8.34).

17. For $Z = 10$, 20, 30, 40, 50, 60, 70, 80, 90 what are the values of electron energies for which the $(dE/dx)_{\text{rad}} = (dE/dx)_{\text{coll}}$? Plot E versus Z for this case.

18. What will be the percentage error in the range, if for 5-Mev electrons we calculate the range from Eq. (8.41) instead of Eq. (8.42)? Also calculate the percentage error in the range if we use Eq. (8.42) for 1-Mev electrons instead of Eq. (8.41).

19. Express the recoil energy of an atom due to the emission of a conversion electron in terms of the mass of the atom and the kinetic energy of the conversion electron.

20. A^{37} decays by K capture to Cl^{37} with a half-life of 35 days. Assuming that the rest-mass of neutrino is zero, calculate the recoil velocity of the Cl^{37} nucleus.

21. The Q value for the electron capture decay of Be^7 is 0.863 Mev. If the maximum recoil energy was found to be 55 ev, what is the kinetic energy taken away by a neutrino which has zero rest-mass.

22. In a calorimetric experiment what is the rate at which heat is produced from a 50 mg sample of RaE? Assume that all the beta particles are absorbed and their average energy is 0.34 Mev. The half-life of the sample is 5 days.

23. A radioactive sample decays by the three processes β^-, β^+ and electron capture. The process of beta decay is followed by γ-emission, electron conversion and internal pair conversion. Outline the experimental procedures for measuring the intensities and the energies of the different particles.

24. Using the Fermi formula for energy distribution, show that the average energy of the β-particles is one-third of the end point energy. Assume that $E_0 \ll m_0 c^2$.

25. Cs^{137} decays by β^--emission with a half-life of 27 years. 92% of the nuclei decay to the first excited state of Ba^{137} and the remaining 8% decays to the ground state. The end point energies of the two beta groups are 0.52 Mev and 1.2 Mev. Calculate the rate at which 1 gm of radioactive Cs^{137} will produce heat if the beta particles are completely absorbed in water surrounding the source.

26. Assume that the neutrino rest-mass, m_v is finite, though very small but not zero, and derive the expression for the statistical factor dn/dE_β. How does this modify the Fermi plots?

27. P^{32} decays by β^--emission to the ground state of S^{32} with a half-life of 14.3 days. The maximum beta end-point energy is 1.71 Mev. Using the graphs given in the text make a rough estimate of the comparative life. Classify this transition as an allowed or first forbidden.

28. Cs^{135} decays by β^--emission to the ground state of Ba^{135} with a half-life of 3×10^6 years. The end point energy of the β^- is 0.21 Mev. Make an estimate of the comparative life-time. What spin change is predicted by this estimated log ft value and how does it compare with the measured spins of $\frac{7}{2}+$ and $\frac{3}{2}+$ for the ground state of Cs^{135} and Ba^{135} respectively?

29. Figure 8.14 shows the beta spectrum of RaE. From this data, plot the Fermi-Kurie plot of RaE. Calculate (i) end-point energy from this plot, (ii) estimate the comparative lifetime and (iii) classify the transition as allowed or forbidden ($t_{1/2} = 1600$ yr).

30. Repeat problem for C_s^{137} whose beta spectrum is shown in Fig. 8.16. [Plot up to 2.0 on current scale.]

31. By drawing Fermi-Kurie plots of β^- for Cl^{38} from the data of Fig. 8.17, make an estimate of the comparative lifetime for the three different energy beta groups and classify the transitions ($t_{1/2} = 37$ m).

32. Tritium decays to the ground state of helium with a half-life of 12.4 years

$$_1H^3 \rightarrow {}_2He^3 + \beta^- + \bar{\nu}$$

The maximum end point energy is 18 kev. Calculate the log ft value and classify the transition as allowed or first forbidden. If the ground state spin of $_1H^3$ is $\frac{1}{2}+$, what is the spin of ground state of $_2He^3$ according to different selection rules (Fermi or Gamow-Teller).

33. $_{43}Te^{99}$ decays by electron capture to Ru ^{99} with a half-life of 2.1×10^5 years and disintegration energy equal to 0.293 Mev. Calculate the log ft value and classify the transition. If the ground state spin of Ru^{99} is $\frac{5}{2}+$ what is the spin and parity of the ground state of $_{43}Tc^{99}$?

34. $_{40}Zr^{93}$ decays with a half-life of 1.1×10^6 years by emitting two groups of beta particles. One group with a 96% intensity goes to the ground state of $_{41}Nb^{93}$ while the other with a 4% intensity goes to the excited state and is followed by a 0.03 Mev gamma ray. The end point energy of the first group is 0.056 Mev. Calculate the log ft values for the two groups and classify the transitions. If the spins and the parities of the ground and the first excited state of Nb^{93} are $\frac{9}{2}+$ and $\frac{1}{2}-$ respectively, what are the spin and parity of Zr^{93}?

REFERENCES

1.   Baeyer, L. V., and O. Hahn, *Physik*, **11**, p. 488, (1910).

2.   Danysz, J., *C. R. Acad. Sci.* (Paris), **153**, p. 339, (1911).

3.   Siegbahn, K., ed., *Beta- and Gamma-Ray Spectroscopy*, pp. 79–176, New York: Interscience Publishers, Inc., 1965.

4.   Frisch, *Prog. Nucl. Phys.*, **1**, (Cavanagh), p. 140, (1950).

5.   Frisch, *Prog. Nucl. Phys.*, **2**, (Verster), p. 1, (1952).

6.   Rutherford, E., and H. Robinson, *Phil. Mag.*, **26**, p. 717, (1913).

7.   Li, K. T., *Proc. Camb. Phil. Soc.*, **33**, p. 164, (1937).

8.   Tricker, R. A., R., *Proc. Camb. Phil. Soc.*, **22**, p. 454, (1924).

9.   Witcher, C. M., *Phys. Rev.*, **60**, p. 32, (1941).

10.   DuMond, J. W. M., *Rev. Sci. Instr.*, **20**, p. 160, (1949).

11.   Klemperer, O., *Phil. Mag.*, **20**, p. 545, (1935).

12.   Deutsch, M., L. G. Elliott, and R. D. Evans, *Rev. Sci. Instr.*, **15**, p. 178, (1944),

13.   Svartholm, N., and K. Siegbahn, *Ark. Mat. Ast. Fys.*, **A33**, No. 21, (1946).

14.   Siegbahn, K., and N. Svartholm, *Nature*, **157**, p. 872, (1946).

15.   Kurie, F. N. D., J. S. Osoba, and L. Slack, *Rev. Sci. Instr.*, **19**, p. 771, (1948).

16.   Shull, F. B., *Phys. Rev.*, **74**, p. 917, (1948).

17.   Kerst, D. W., and R. Serber, *Phys. Rev.*, **60**, p. 53, (1941).

18.   Halliday, D., *Introductory Nuclear Physics*, p. 482, New York: John Wiley & Sons, Inc., 1955.

19.   Purcell, E., *Phys. Rev.*, **54**, p. 918, (1938).

20.   Rogers, F. Jr., *Rev. Sci., Instr.*, **8**, p. 22, (1937); **11**, p. 19, (1939); **14**, p. 216, (1943); **22**, p. 723, (1951).

21.   Kobayashi, Y., *Jour. Phys. Soc.* (Japan), **8**, 1953.

22.   Bethe, H. A., and J. Ashkin, *Experimental Nuclear Physics*, ed. E. Segre, Vol. I., p. 252, (1953), New York: John Wiley & Sons. Part II.

23.   Bethe, H. A., *Handbuch der Physik*, Vol. 24, p. 273, Berlin: Julius Springer, 1933.

24.   Bethe, H. A., and W. Heitler, *Proc. Roy. Soc.*, **A146**, p. 83, (1934).

25.   Heitler, W., *The Quantum Theory of Radiation*, Ch. 5, p. 222. Oxford University Press, 1944.

26. Katz, L., and A. S. Penfold, *Revs. Mod. Phys.*, **24**, p. 28, (1952).

27. Glendenin, L. E., *Nucleonics*, **2**, p. 12, (1948).

28. *N. B. S. Circular* 499, "Nuclear Data," U. S. Dept. of Commerce.

29. Neary, G. J., *Proc. Roy. Soc.* (London), **A175**, p. 71, (1940).

30. Fan, C. Y., *Phys. Rev.*, **87**, p. 258, (1952).

31. Langer, L. M., *Phys. Rev.*, **77**, p. 50, (1950).

32. Reitz, J. R., *Phys. Rev.*, **77**, p. 10, (1950).

33. Ellis, C. D., and W. A. Wooster, *Proc. Roy. Soc.* (London), **A117**, p. 109, (1927).

34. Meitner, L., and W. Orthmann, *Z. Physik*, **60**, p. 143, (1930).

35. Zlotowski, I., *Phys. Rev.*, **60**, p. 483, (1941).

36. Fermi, E., *Z. Physik*, **88**, p. 161, (1934).

37. Robson, J. M., *Phys. Rev.*, **83**, p. 349, (1951).

38. Rodeback, G. W., and J. S. Allen, *Phys. Rev.*, **86**, p. 446, (1952).

39. Kofoed-Hansen, O., *Phys. Rev.*, **96**, p. 1045, (1954).

40. Snell, A. H., and F. Pleasonton, *Phys. Rev.*, **97**, p. 246, (1955); **100**, p. 1396, (1955).

41. Deutsch, M., and O. Kofoed-Hansen, *Experimental Nuclear Physics*, ed. E. Segre, Vol. III, p. 571, (1959), New York: John Wiley & Sons, 1959.

42. Reines, F., and C. L. Cowan, Jr., *Phys. Rev.*, **90**, p. 492, (1953); **113**, p. 273, (1959).

43. Reines, F., C. L. Cowan, Jr., F. B. Harrison, H. W. Kruse, and A. D. McGuire, *Phys. Rev.*, **117**, p. 159, (1960).

44. Davis, R., *Phys. Rev.*, **97**, p. 766, (1955).

45. Sargent, B. W., *Proc. Roy. Soc.* (London), **A139**, p. 659, (1933).

46. Feather, N., *Nuclear Stability Rules*, Chap. 3. Cambridge: University Press, 1952.

47. Lee, T. D., and C. N. Yang, *Phys. Rev.*, **105**, p. 1671, (1957).

48. Fermi, E., *Nuclear Physics*, Chap. IV. Chicago: University of Chicago Press, 1950. (Notes compiled by J. Orear, A. H. Rosenfeld, and R. A. Schluter.)

49. Konopinski, E. J., *Revs. Mod. Phys.*, **15**, p. 209, (1943).

50. Wu, C. S., *Revs. Mod. Phys.*, **22**, p. 386, (1950).

51. Schiff, L. I., *Quantum Mechanics*, p. 153. New York: McGraw-Hill Book Co., 1955.

52. Rose, M. E., N. M. Dismuke, C. L. Perry, and P. R. Bell, *Oak Ridge National Laboratory Report No. 1222*.

53. Robson, J. M., *Phys. Rev.* **83**, p. 349, (1951).

54. Langer, L. M., and R. D. Moffat, *Phys. Rev.*, **88**, p. 689, (1952).

55. Lawson, A. W., and J. M. Cork, *Phys. Rev.*, **57**, p. 982, (1940).

56. Albert, R. D., and C. S. Wu, *Phys. Rev.*, **74**, p. 847, (1948).

57. Ridley, B. W., *Prog. Nucl. Phys.*, **5**, p. 196, (1956).

58. Wu, C. S., *Revs. Mod. Phys.*, **22**, p. 386, (1950).

59. Langer, L. M., and H. C. Prince, *Phys. Rev.*, **75**, p. 1109, (1949).

60. Moszkowski, S. A., *Phys. Rev.*, **82**, p. 35, (1951).
61. Nuclear Data Sheets: 5-5-140 (Nov. 1963).
62. Langer, L. M., and R. J. D. Moffat, *Phys. Rev.*, **88**, p. 689, (1952).
63. Konopinski, E. J., *Revs. Mod. Phys.*, **15**, p. 209, (1943).
64. Marshak, R. E., *Phys. Rev.*, **61**, p. 431, (1942).
65. Bouchez, R., *Physica*, **18**, p. 1171, (1952).
66. White, H. E., *Introduction to Atomic Spectra*, p. 70. New York: McGraw-Hill Book Co., Inc., 1934.
67. Feenberg, E., and G. Trigg, *Revs. Mod. Phys.*, **22**, p. 399, (1950).
68. Yang, C. N., *Science*, **127**, p. 565, (1958).
69. Wigner, E. P., *Group Theory and Its Application to Quantum Mechanics of Atomic Spectra*, Chaps. 17, 18. New York: Academic Press, 1959.
70. Shapiro, A. M., *Revs. Mod. Phys.*, **28**, p. 164, (1956).
71. Dirac, P. A. M., *The Principles of Quantum Mechanics*, 4th ed., Chap. 12. Oxford: Clarendon Press, 1958.
72. Lee, T. D., and C. N. Yang, *Phys. Rev.*, **104**, p. 254, (1956).
73. Wu, C. S., E. Ambler, R. W. Hayward, D. P. Hoppes, and R. P. Hudson, *Phys. Rev.*, **105**, p. 1413, (1957).
74. Curtis, R. B., and R. R. Lewis, *Phys. Rev.*, **107**, p. 543, (1957).
75. Landu, L., *Nucl. Phys.*, **3**, p. 127, (1957).
76. DeWaard, H., and O. J. Poppeina, *Physica*, **23**, p. 597, (1957).
77. Goldhaber, M., L. Grodzins, and A. W. Singar, *Phys. Rev.*, **109**, p. 1015, (1958).

SUGGESTIONS FOR FURTHER READING

1. Frisch, *Prog. Nucl. Phys.*, Vol. I, (Cavanagh), p. 140, (1950).
2. Frisch, *Prog. Nucl. Phys.*, Vol. II, (Verster), p. 1, (1952).
3. Siegbahn, K., ed., Beta- and Gamma-Ray Spectroscopy, pp. 79–176. New York: Interscience Publishing, 1965.
4. Deutsch, M., and O. Kofoed-Hansen, *Experimental Nuclear Physics*, ed. E. Segre, Vol. III, Part XI, (1959). New York: John Wiley & Sons.
5. Rutherford, Chadwick, and Ellis, *Radiation From Radioactive Substances*, Chaps. 12, 13, 14. New York: Macmillan Co., 1930.
6. Fermi, E., *Nuclear Physics*, Chaps. 2, 4, Chicago: University of Chicago Press, 1950. (Notes compiled by J. Orear, A. H. Rosenfeld, and R. A. Schluter.)
7. Evans, R. D., *The Atomic Nucleus*, Chap. 6, pp. 17–21. New York: McGraw-Hill Book Co., 1955.
8. Allen, J. S., *The Neutrino*, Princeton: Princeton University Press, 1958.

IX

GAMMA RADIATION

1. GAMMA DECAY

The decay of a nucleus by emission of a particle, such as an alpha or a beta particle, usually leaves the nucleus in an excited state. The energy available for further decay to a lower energy or ground state is either not enough to cause an emission of another particle, or the decay by particle emission is so slow that emission by electromagnetic interaction becomes effective. The nucleus makes the transition from the higher energy state, E_i, to the lower energy state, E_f, and gives out the excess energy $\Delta E = E_i - E_f$ by means of one of the following three processes: (a) gamma-ray emission, (b) internal conversion, or (c) internal pair-creation. Of these, gamma emission takes place more often than do the other two processes. We shall start with the discussion of gamma emission in some detail, while the discussion of internal conversion and internal pair-creation will be taken up near the end of the chapter.

As in the case of atomic spectra, the gamma spectra of nuclei consist of sharp lines, showing, thereby, that the nucleus has discrete energy levels. The energy of a gamma ray emitted is given by the relation.

$$hv = \Delta E = E_i - E_f \qquad (9.1)$$

If E_f corresponds to the ground state, no further emission of photons will be possible, otherwise the nucleus will emit one or more photons before going to the ground state. (See Fig. 9.1.)

Unlike alpha and beta decay, the gamma decay does not cause a change in the atomic number or mass number of the nucleus. As compared to the

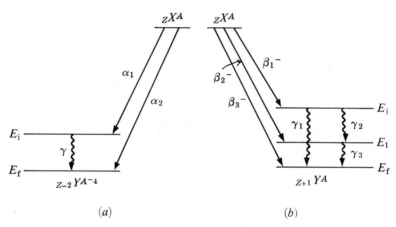

(a)   (b)

FIG. 9.1 Emission of gamma rays following (a) α-decay where $hv = E_i - E_f$, and (b) beta decay where $hv_1 = E_i - E_f$, $hv_2 = E_i - E_1$, and $hv_3 = E_1 - E_f$.

half-lives of alpha- and beta-emitters, the gamma emitters have very short half-lives. As stated in Chap. II, Sec. 2.2, gamma rays are electro-magnetic waves of very high penetrating power. They do not cause much ionization and are not deflected by the electric or magnetic fields. In fact, the interaction of gamma rays with matter differs considerably from that of the charged particles. Therefore, it is essential to understand these interactions before we can proceed to the measurement of photon energies and other characteristics relating to gamma emission.

2. ABSORPTION COEFFICIENT OF PHOTONS

The intensity of a beam of x-rays or γ-rays passing through a material follows the exponential law of absorption, because the change in intensity is directly proportional to the incident intensity and the thickness of the material. Let us consider a beam of photons with intensity I falling perpendicular to a material of thickness Δx. Then the change in intensity, ΔI, is given by

$$\Delta I = -\mu I \Delta x \qquad (9.2)$$

where μ is the proportionality constant and is known as the *absorption coefficient*. For a given material, μ is different for photons of different energies. The negative sign in Eq. (9.2) indicates that the intensity decreases with increasing thickness. Thus for a homogeneous radiation, μ is constant and from Eq. (9.2) we get

$$I = I_0 e^{-\mu x} \tag{9.3}$$

where I is the intensity of the beam after the beam of initial intensity, I_0, has crossed a thickness x of the material.

Due to the exponential nature of their absorption, gamma rays do not have a definite range as do alpha and beta particles but are characterized by the attenuation absorption-coefficient, μ. Also, we may write

$$I = h\nu\phi \tag{9.4}$$

where $h\nu$ is the energy of each photon, and ϕ is the number of photons crossing a unit area in a unit time and is called the flux. Combining Eqs. (9.3) and (9.4), we get

$$\phi = \phi_0 e^{-\mu x} \tag{9.5}$$

where ϕ_0 is the initial flux. Note that I denotes the energy flux (or intensity), and ϕ is the number flux. μ is sometimes called the *linear absorption coefficient*.

Besides the linear absorption coefficient, μ, the other coefficients that are commonly used are *mass absorption coefficient*, μ_m, *atomic absorption coefficient* $_a\mu$ and *electronic absorption coefficient* $_e\mu$. These four coefficients are related to each other in the following way:

$$_a\mu = Z_e\mu$$

$$\mu = \frac{\rho N_A}{A} \,_a\mu = \frac{\rho N_A Z}{A} \,_e\mu$$

$$\mu_m = \frac{\mu}{\rho} = \frac{N_A \,_a\mu}{A} = \frac{N_A Z}{A} \,_e\mu \tag{9.6}$$

where Z is the atomic number, A is the atomic weight, ρ is the density in g/cm^3, and N_A is Avogadro's number. Because μx is a dimensionless quantity, if x is expressed in cm, μ will be in cm^{-1}. Accordingly, for the mass absorption coefficient, μ_m, x is expressed in gm/cm^2 and μ_m in cm^2/gm. Similarly if x is expressed in atom/cm^2 or electron/cm^2, $_a\mu$ and $_e\mu$ are expressed as cm^2/atom and cm^2/electron, respectively.

Because Z/A changes very slowly with increasing Z, and $_e\mu$ is the same for all elements in a certain energy range, this leads to the conclusion that μ_m does not vary much for all elements in this energy range.

The half-thickness, $x_{1/2}$, is the characteristic of the absorber as the half-life is of the decaying nucleus. $x_{1/2}$ is defined as the thickness that reduces the incident beam intensity to one-half of its initial intensity, i.e.,

$$I/I_0 = 1/2 = e^{-\mu x_{1/2}}$$

or

$$x_{1/2} = 0.693/\mu = 0.693/\rho\mu_m \qquad (9.7)$$

If the incident beam consists of photons of different energies, Eq. (9.5) is replaced by the following equation

$$\phi = \phi_{01}e^{-\mu_1 x} + \phi_{02}e^{-\mu_2 x} + \phi_{03}e^{-\mu_3 x} + \cdots \qquad (9.8)$$

where $\phi_{01}, \phi_{02}, \phi_{03}, \ldots$ and $\mu_1, \mu_2, \mu_3, \ldots$ are the initial fluxes and absorption coefficients, respectively, of photons with energies $h\nu_1, h\nu_2, h\nu_3, \ldots$.

The coefficient, μ, used above is actually the sum of two processes: (i) the process in which the photon loses its energy in whole or in part to a particle, which in turn is easily absorbed. The energy, therefore, is deposited inside the material, and (ii) the process in which photons are scattered outside the beam with no absorption of energy in the material. We may write μ, therefore, as the sum of two terms,

$$\mu = \mu_a + \mu_s \qquad (9.9)$$

where μ_a corresponds to absorption and μ_s to scattering.

3. INTERACTION OF GAMMA RADIATION WITH MATTER[1]

There are numerous processes by which gamma rays interact with matter and lose their energy. Fortunately, all these processes do not contribute to the same extent for different energy photons. The gamma rays emitted in nuclear decay usually have energies ranging from a fraction of a Mev to a few Mev. In this range, the three main processes by which photons lose their energies by interaction with matter are: (a) photoelectric effect (P.E.), (b) Compton effect (C.E.) or Compton scattering, and (c) pair production (P.P.).

These three processes are dominant in different ranges of the photon energy: the photoelectric effect from ~0.01 Mev to ~0.5 Mev, the Compton scattering from ~0.1 Mev to ~10 Mev, and pair production starts at 1.02 Mev and increases with increasing gamma energy. All three processes are independent of each other and by analogy with Eq. (9.2), we may write

$$(\Delta I)_{P.E.} = -\mu_\tau I \Delta x \qquad (9.10a)$$

$$(\Delta I)_{C.E.} = -\mu_\sigma I \Delta x \qquad (9.10b)$$

$$(\Delta I)_{P.P.} = -\mu_\kappa I \Delta x \qquad (9.10c)$$

where μ_τ, μ_σ, and μ_κ are the absorption coefficients for the photoelectric effect, the Compton effect, and pair production, respectively. Adding all three together, we may write

$$\Delta I = (\Delta I)_{\text{P.E.}} + (\Delta I)_{\text{C.E.}} + (\Delta I)_{\text{P.P.}}$$

$$= -(\mu_\tau + \mu_\sigma + \mu_\kappa)I\Delta x \qquad (9.11)$$

and comparing with Eq. (9.2), we get

$$\mu = \mu_\tau + \mu_\sigma + \mu_\kappa \qquad (9.12)$$

Our purpose is to investigate the variation of μ_τ, μ_σ, and μ_κ as a function of photon energy and the atomic number of the absorber. Before we go into the details of these interactions, we shall mention briefly the other processes, although they do not contribute much to the absorption coefficient in this energy range of the gamma rays.

(i) *Rayleigh scattering*[2]: This is the famous classical coherent-scattering (elastic scattering), and it takes place whenever the incident photons fall on bound electrons, provided the electrons do not get enough energy to be ejected from the atom. Thus, it will be more prominent at low photon energies and absorbers with high Z.

(ii) *Thomson scattering:* This may also be called nuclear Compton-scattering and takes place between the incident photon and a nucleus instead of a free electron. Because of the large mass of the nucleus, the effect is very small.

(iii) *Nuclear photoelectric effect:* In this process the high-energy photon may be absorbed by the nucleus, resulting in the ejection of a nucleon. This is the so-called *photodisintegration*, and it is more prevalent for high Z.

(iv) *Nuclear-resonance scattering:* In this process the nucleus is excited by the absorption of an incident photon having an energy equal to the difference between two nuclear energy levels. This is followed by the de-excitation of the nucleus. We shall discuss this process in some detail in this chapter.

(v) *Elastic nuclear-potential scattering (or Delbruck scattering):* The scattering of a photon may also be caused by the electromagnetic field of the nucleus.

All these processes, (i) to (v), contribute very little to the three main processes. Except for (iv), nuclear resonance scattering, we shall not discuss these minor contributions but will take up in detail the investigation of the other principal absorption processes.

A. PHOTOELECTRIC EFFECT.   This effect is more prominent at low energies of the incident photon. The incident photon is absorbed by one of the electrons of the atom. In the process the photon disappears and the electron is ejected (Fig. 9.2) with a kinetic energy K_e, given by

$$K_e = h\nu - I_B \qquad (9.13)$$

where $h\nu$ is the energy of the incident photon, and I_B is the binding energy of the orbital electron.

It is impossible for a free electron to absorb a photon because it will not conserve both momentum and energy. But in the case of a bound electron, the atom recoils and, therefore, conserves the momentum. Because the mass of the atom is very large, its recoil energy is very small, and it has been neglected in Eq. (9.13).

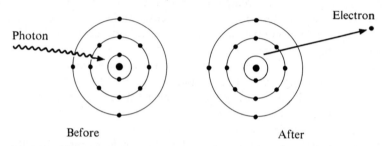

FIG. 9.2   The photoelectric effect; absorption of a photon results in the emission of K-electron.

The theoretical calculations for the cross section of the photoelectric effect involve the use of Dirac's relativistic equation for a bound electron. This makes evaluation difficult. For different regions of energy of the photons, the cross sections have been evaluated by different authors[3,4,5]. The calculations become somewhat simpler if the energy of the photon is small enough to neglect the relativistic effects and large enough to neglect the binding energy of the orbital electron. Neglecting the binding energy of the K-electron, W. Heitler[5] obtained the following expression for the photo-electric absorption cross-section (in the range 0.1 Mev to 0.35 Mev).

$$_a\tau_K = \varphi_0 Z^5 (1/137)^4 \, 4\sqrt{2}(n)^{7/2} \qquad (9.14)$$

where

$$\varphi_0 = (8\pi/3)(e^2/m_0 c^2)^2 = 6.651 \times 10^{-25} \text{ cm}^2 \qquad (9.15)$$

and

$$n = m_0 c^2/h\nu \qquad (9.16)$$

Z is the atomic number of the absorber, e is the charge of the electron, c is the velocity of light, and m_0 is the rest mass of an electron.

Eq. (9.14) applies only to the ejection of electrons from the K-shell of the atom, which usually accounts for about 80 per cent of the photoelectric absorption. In general, $_a\tau$ depends on Z and $h\nu$ in the following fashion

$$_a\tau \propto Z^5 \qquad (9.17a)$$

$$\propto 1/(h\nu)^{7/2} \qquad (9.17b)$$

As the energy of the photon becomes lower, it is not possible to neglect the binding energy of the K-electron. This correction has been applied by M. Stobbe[6].

The calculated photoelectric absorption coefficients for different hv and Z are plotted in the form μ_{at}/Z^5n versus Z for different n, as shown in Fig. 9.3. These curves have been obtained by C. Davisson and R. Evans[1] by joining the theoretical curves that hold for different regions of photon energies.

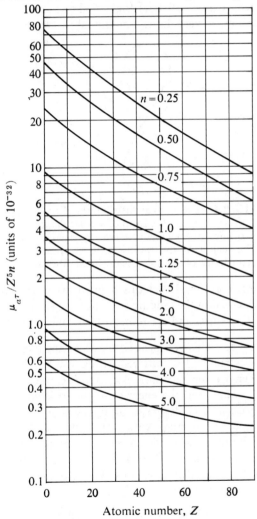

FIG 9.3   The plots of photoelectric cross-section, in the form of μ_{at}/Z^5n versus Z for different values of $n\left(=\dfrac{m_0c^2}{hv}\right)$.   [From Davisson, C. M., and R. D. Evans, *Revs. Mod. Phys.*, **24**, 79, (1952).]

The photoelectrons produced by the gamma rays are not emitted isotropically. As a matter of fact they are emitted preferentially in the direction of the electric vector of the incident gamma ray. This is shown in Fig. 9.4, and it indicates that the distribution depends on the velocity of the emitted electrons. The length of the line from the origin to the curve indicates the probability of photoelectron emission at any angle θ.

Lastly, we shall note that when the energy of the incoming photon becomes very small (say, $\gtrsim 20$ kev) Fig. 9.5 shows that the absorption coefficient increases by a very large amount at some definite energies for

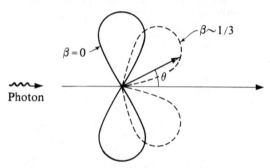

FIG. 9.4   The angular distribution of photoelectrons is shown in the form of a polar diagram for two different velocities $\beta = (v/c) = 0$ and $\beta = 1/3$. The length of the radius vector represents the probability of photoemission in the direction θ.

different materials. It is found that this happens when the energy of the incoming photons is equal to the binding energy of the K-electrons. These peaks are the K-absorption edges and are indicative of some sort of resonances.

B. COMPTON EFFECT.   This is a process by which the incident photon interacts with a free electron and is scattered with a lower energy, the rest of the energy being taken by the recoiling electron. Because the electrons in an atom are loosely bound and the energies of the incident photons are comparatively high, we may include the scattering of photons by the electrons of the atom as Compton scattering. An incident photon of energy $h\nu$ strikes a free electron with a rest mass m_0. The interaction results in a scattered photon of energy $h\nu'$ ($< h\nu$) at an angle θ and a recoiling electron with kinetic energy K_e at an angle ϕ (Fig. 9.6). From the conservation of momentum and energy, using the relativistic expressions, we obtain

$$h\nu/c = (h\nu'/c) \cos \theta + m_0\beta c(1 - \beta^2)^{-\frac{1}{2}} \cos \phi \qquad \textbf{(9.18a)}$$

$$(h\nu'/c) \sin \theta = m_0\beta c(1 - \beta^2)^{-\frac{1}{2}} \sin \phi \qquad \textbf{(9.18b)}$$

and

$$h\nu = h\nu' + m_0c^2[(1 - \beta^2)^{-\frac{1}{2}} - 1] \qquad \textbf{(9.18c)}$$

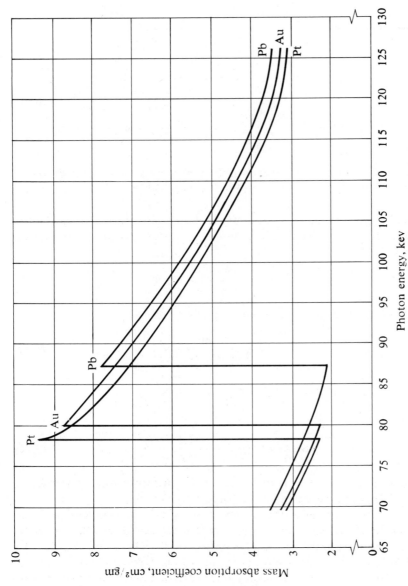

FIG. 9.5 Absorption coefficient versus photon energy for different elements, for which K-absorption edges are shown.

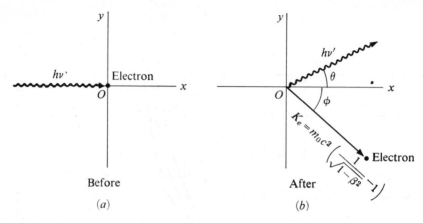

FIG. 9.6 Compton scattering; the incident photon energy is shared between the scattered photon of energy hv' where $(v' < v)$ and an electron.

where $\beta = v/c$, v being the velocity of the electron after the collision. Eliminating ϕ and β from the above equations, we get the change in wave length given by

$$\lambda' - \lambda = \left(\frac{h}{m_0 c}\right)(1 - \cos\theta) \qquad (9.19)$$

We can establish the following relations by using Eqs. (9.18a, b, and c).

$$hv' = \frac{hv}{1 + \alpha(1 - \cos\theta)} \qquad (9.20)$$

$$K_e = hv - hv' = hv\left(1 - \frac{1}{1 + \alpha(1 - \cos\theta)}\right) \qquad (9.21)$$

and

$$\cos\theta = 1 - \frac{2}{(1 + \alpha)^2 \tan^2\phi + 1} \qquad (9.22)$$

where $\alpha = hv/m_0 c^2$, i.e., α is the energy of the incident photon expressed in units of the rest-mass energy of the electron.

In order to calculate the Compton scattering cross-section, and the attenuation coefficient due to the Compton effect, the problem is to be treated quantum-mechanically, making use of the Dirac equation for the electron. Such calculations have been carried out theoretically by O. Klein and Y. Nishina[7]. There are many quantities of interest that may be calculated[1]. Some of these are:

(1) $_e\sigma$ = total Compton cross-section for the number of
            photons scattered,

(2) $_e\sigma_s$ = Compton cross-section for the energy of the photons scattered,

(3) $_e\sigma_a$ = Compton cross-section for the energy absorbed by the electrons,

(4) $_e\sigma^{\theta_0}$ = cross-section for the number of photons scattered between 0 and θ_0,

(5) $_e\sigma_s^{\theta_0}$ = cross-section for energy scattered between 0 and θ_0, and

(6) $_e\sigma_f$ = cross section for the number of photons scattered forward.

These and many other cross sections have been calculated and compiled in the form of graphs[8]. We shall state the calculated cross-sections for the first three of them, which are related by the following equation

$$_e\sigma = {}_e\sigma_s + {}_e\sigma_a \qquad (9.23)$$

The theoretical values of $_e\sigma$ and $_e\sigma_s$ are[1,7]

$$_e\sigma = \tfrac{3}{4}\varphi_0 \left\{ \frac{1+\alpha}{\alpha^2} \left[\frac{2(1+\alpha)}{1+2\alpha} - \frac{1}{\alpha} \ln{(1+2\alpha)} \right] + \frac{1}{2\alpha} \ln{(1+2\alpha)} - \frac{1+3\alpha}{(1+2\alpha)^2} \right\} \qquad (9.24)$$

and

$$_e\sigma_s = \tfrac{3}{8}\varphi_0 \left\{ \frac{1}{\alpha^3} \ln{(1+2\alpha)} + \frac{2(1+\alpha)(2\alpha^2 - 2\alpha - 1)}{\alpha^2(1+2\alpha)^2} + \frac{8\alpha^2}{3(1+2\alpha)^3} \right. \qquad (9.25)$$

where, as already stated, $\varphi_0 = (8\pi/3)(e^2/m_0c^2)^2 = 6.651 \times 10^{-25}$ cm^2 and $\alpha = h\nu/m_0c^2$.

The corresponding absorption coefficients μ_σ, μ_{σ_s}, and μ_{σ_a} are related to $_e\sigma$, $_e\sigma_s$, and $_e\sigma_a$ in the following manner

$$\sigma = \frac{\rho N_A Z}{A} \,{}_e\sigma, \; \sigma_s = \frac{\rho N_A Z}{A} \,{}_e\sigma_s, \; \sigma_a = \frac{\rho N_A Z}{A} \,{}_e\sigma_a \qquad (9.26)$$

The plots of $_e\sigma$, $_e\sigma_s$, and $_e\sigma_a$ versus photon energy are shown in Fig. 9.7[1].

The following observations are made from Eqs. (9.24), (9.25), and (9.26):

(i) $_e\sigma$, $_e\sigma_s$, and $_e\sigma_a$ (cm^2/electron) are independent of the properties of the absorber while μ_σ, μ_{σ_s}, and μ_{σ_a} are functions of the atomic number of the material, i.e., the scattering is proportional to Z.

(ii) The mass absorption coefficient μ_σ/ρ is given by

$$\sigma/\rho = N_A(Z/A)_e\sigma \qquad (9.27)$$

Because for light elements $Z/A \approx \tfrac{1}{2}$, Eq. (9.27) implies that the mass-absorption coefficient for a given photon energy is practically constant for light elements.

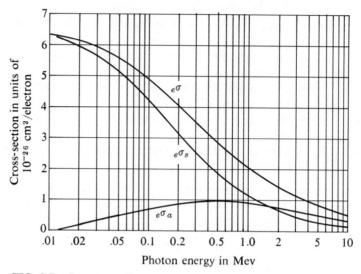

Photon energy in Mev

FIG. 9.7   Compton effect. Cross-section versus energy. $_e\sigma$ — the cross-section for the number of photons scattered; $_e\sigma_s$ the cross-section for the energy of the photons scattered; and $_e\sigma_a$ — the cross-section for the energy absorbed by the electrons. [From Davisson, C. M., and R. D. Evans, *Revs. Mod. Phys.*, **24**, 79, (1952).]

(iii) The decrease of the total scattering-coefficient per electron, $_e\sigma$, is slow for photon energies up to 0.5 Mev, but beyond that the decrease is roughly proportional to $1/h\nu$.

(iv) Fig. (9.8) shows the plots, for different photon energies, of differential cross-sections per unit solid angle for the number of photons scattered at the angle θ, i.e., $d_e\sigma/d\Omega$. Fig. 9.9 shows the differential cross-sections per unit angle for the number of photons scattered in the direction of θ, i.e., $d_e\sigma/d\theta$. Note the marked difference in the two plots. Similar plots have been drawn[1] for the energies of the scattered photon.

C. PAIR PRODUCTION.   The third most important process by which photons lose their energy is electron-positron pair formation. The threshold energy for this process is $2m_0c^2$. It is found that if a photon of energy greater than 1.02 Mev strikes a foil of high Z, the photon disappears and in its place an electron-positron pair is formed, (Fig. 9.10a). If a pair is produced in a cloud chamber and a magnetic field is applied, the electrons and the positrons are deflected in the opposite direction with equal curvature as shown in Fig. 9.10(b).

The conservation of momentum requires the presence of a heavy body. Actually the pair formation takes place in the field of the nucleus and the conservation of energy gives

$$h\nu = 2m_0c^2 + E_+ + E_- + E_{nuc} \tag{9.28}$$

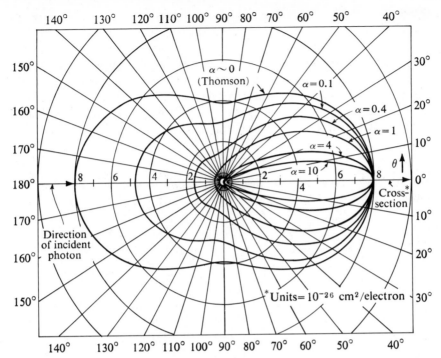

FIG. 9.8 Compton scattering; plots of differential cross-section per unit solid angle for photon energy scattered at the angle θ, i.e., $d_e\sigma/d\Omega$. [From Davisson, C. M., and R. D. Evans, *Revs. Mod. Phys.*, **24**, 79, (1952).]

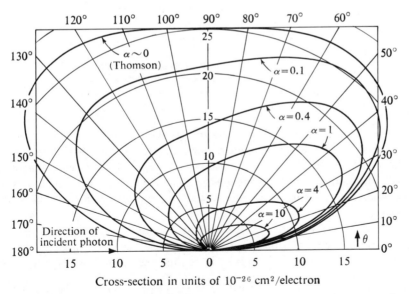

Cross-section in units of 10^{-26} cm²/electron

FIG. 9.9 Compton scattering; plots of differential cross-section per unit angle for the photon energy scattered in the direction θ, i.e., $d_e\sigma/d\theta$. [From Davisson, C. M., and R. D. Evans, *Revs. Mod. Phys.*, **24**, 79 (1952).]

where $h\nu$ is the energy of the incident photon, $2m_0c^2$ is the energy equivalent to the rest mass of the electron and the positron; E_+, E_-, and E_{nuc} are the kinetic energies of the positron, electron, and the recoiling nucleus, respectively. Because the mass of the nucleus is very large, it takes away a very small amount of kinetic energy, and so E_{nuc} may be neglected. Thus Eq. (9.28) takes the form

$$h\nu = 2m_0c^2 + E_+ + E_- \tag{9.29}$$

which clearly shows that the threshold for pair formation is $2m_0c^2$ or 1.02 Mev.

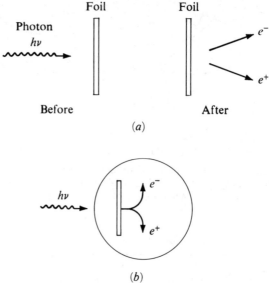

FIG. 9.10   (a) Electron-positron pair formation, and (b) Pair formation in a cloud chamber where the magnetic field is applied at right angles to the plane of the paper.

Pair formation is also possible in the fields of light particles, but the thresholds in such cases are higher. For example, the pair production in the field of an electron[9] has a threshold of $4m_0c^2$, i.e., it will take place only if the gamma rays have energies greater than 2.04 Mev. In the following discussion, we are interested only in the pair formation in the field of the nucleus.

In the case of pair production the theoretical calculations for the cross section are much more difficult. This has been accomplished by H. Bethe and W. Heitler[10] and their results are shown in Fig. 9.11. In Fig. 9.11 $\dfrac{{}^a\kappa E_+}{\bar{\phi}} (h\nu - 2m_0c^2)$ where $\bar{\phi} = \dfrac{Z^2e^4}{m_0^2c^4}\left(\dfrac{1}{137}\right)$ has been plotted versus $(E_+ - m_0c^2)/(h\nu - 2m_0c^2)$. This is done because the area under each curve now gives the total absorption cross-section for different photon energies. Fig. 9.12 shows the plot of total cross-section versus energy as calculated from Fig. 9.11. The absorption coefficient $_a\kappa$ per atom increases with increasing energy of the photon and also increases with Z^2.

At photon energies greater than ~ 10 Mev, the effect of screening due to the orbital electrons becomes important. At these energies pair production

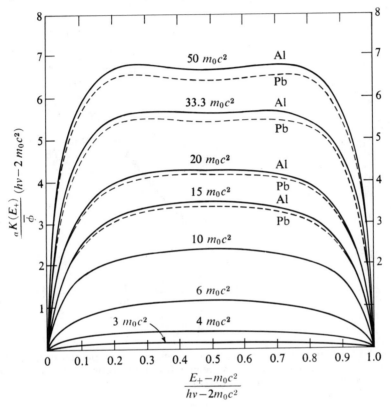

FIG. 9.11   Pair production; differential cross-section per unit positron energy for the production of positrons in the pair for different photon energies in Al and Pb. [From Davisson, C. M., and R. D. Evans, *Revs. Mod. Phys.*, **24**, 79, (1952).]

takes place some distance away from the nucleus, even outside some electron shells, and this reduces the probability of pair production to the extent that at higher energies the value of $_a\kappa/\bar{\phi}$ is somewhat smaller for lead than for air or aluminum as shown in Fig. 9.11.

One question that we have avoided so far in connection with pair-production is, "what happens to the positron?" We do not find positrons in free space as we do electrons. The process by which positrons are removed from circulation is called *pair annihilation*.

When a positron is created, it has some kinetic energy that it loses by collisions with the atoms in its surroundings. After it has slowed down considerably, it may form a kind of atom with one of the electrons of the medium. The so-called *positronium atom* is shown in Fig. 9.13(a), and is like a hydrogen atom, except a positron has replaced the proton. If the positronium atom

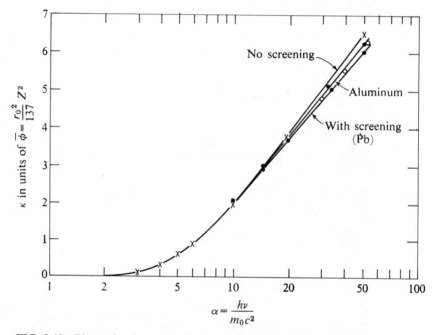

FIG. 9.12   Plots of pair production cross-sections versus photon energy. The upper curve is calculated without screening. [From Davisson, C. M., and R. D. Evans, *Revs. Mod. Phys.*, **24**, 79, (1952).]

formed is such that the spins of the electron and the positron are antiparallel, the atom disappears in a very short time ($\sim 10^{-10}$ sec), and it results in the creation of two photons, as shown in Fig. 9.13(b). The following equations for conservation of energy and momentum

$$2m_0c^2 = h\nu_1 + h\nu_2 \qquad\qquad (9.30)$$

$$\frac{h\nu_1}{c} = \frac{h\nu_2}{c} \qquad\qquad (9.31)$$

imply

$$h\nu_1 = h\nu_2 = m_0c^2 = 0.511 \text{ Mev} \qquad\qquad (9.32)$$

Thus wherever there are positrons, the 0.511 Mev photons will be created in pairs and emitted in the opposite directions. If the spins of the electron and positron in the positronium atom are parallel, there will be three or more photons emitted in order to conserve angular momentum. The probability of such a process is low, as the positronium is not often formed with parallel spins.

The positron was discovered by Anderson[11] in 1932 in the cloud-chamber photographs of cosmic radiation. High energy photons accompanying cosmic radiation produced electron-positron pairs that were detected

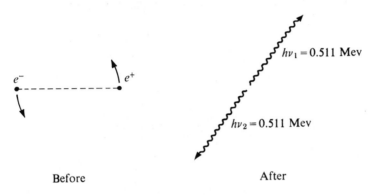

Before   After

FIG. 9.13 (*a*) Formation of positronium atom and (*b*) Annihilation of positronium atom.

in a cloud chamber by the application of a magnetic field as shown in Fig. 9.10(b). The positron had already been predicted theoretically by P. Dirac[12], who used a complicated set of relativistic quantum-mechanical equations for the electron. Pair production follows as a consequence of the solution of these equations. The explanation is based on the so-called "hole theory."

D. HOLE THEORY.   This is a crude picture to explain pair production. The total energy, E, of a particle of rest mass m_0 and momentum p is given by

$$E^2 = m_0^2 c^4 + p^2 c^2 \tag{9.33}$$

Thus for any particle

$$E = \pm\sqrt{m_0^2 c^4 + p^2 c^2} \tag{9.34}$$

If we assume that the positive square root is the only one that has any significance, E is always $\geqslant m_0 c^2$. But according to Dirac

$$E \geqslant m_0 c^2 \tag{9.35a}$$

or

$$E \leqslant -m_0 c^2 \tag{9.35b}$$

which means that an electron may have a total positive energy from $+m_0c^2$ to $+\infty$ or a negative energy from $-m_0c^2$ to $-\infty$. The reason we see electrons in the positive energy states only, with no transition to the negative energy state, is because the negative energy states are completely filled with electrons, and the Pauli exclusion principle forbids any further dropping of electrons from the positive energy states. But a photon with energy greater than $2m_0c^2$ has enough energy to raise an electron from a negative energy-state to a positive energy-state. This results in a "hole" in the negative energy-state and an observable electron in the positive-energy state, as shown in Fig. 9.14. This hole is supposed to behave like a positron.

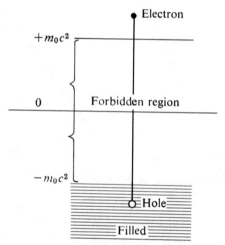

FIG. 9.14   The formation of an electron-positron pair according to hole theory. It corresponds to a lift of an electron from the completely filled region.

Another picture of this process that does not involve the concept of densely filled negative-energy states was suggested by E. Stueckelberg[13] and has been developed by R. Feynman[14]. Stating it according to this theory, "a positron is an electron moving backward in time."

E. SUMMARY.   The values of the atomic absorption cross-sections $_a\tau$, $_a\sigma$, and $_a\kappa$ depend on the atomic number Z and the photon energy $h\nu$, approximately in the following way:

$$_a\tau \propto Z^5/(h\nu)^{7/2}$$

$$_a\sigma \propto Z/(h\nu)^a$$

$$_a\kappa \propto Z^2(h\nu)^b$$

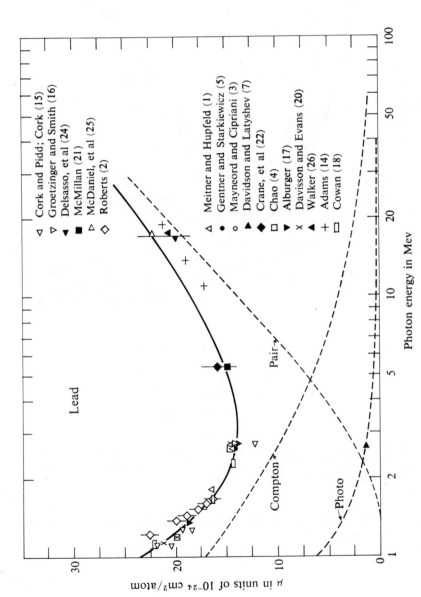

FIG. 9.15 Total absorption coefficient per centimeter versus gamma ray energy for lead. The dotted curves show the individual contributions from photoelectric, Compton, and pair for lead. [From Davisson, C. M., and R. D. Evans, *Revs. Mod. Phys.*, **24**, 79, (1952).]

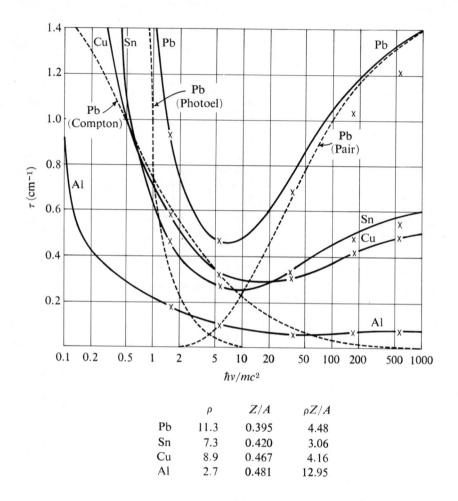

	ρ	Z/A	$\rho Z/A$
Pb	11.3	0.395	4.48
Sn	7.3	0.420	3.06
Cu	8.9	0.467	4.16
Al	2.7	0.481	12.95

FIG. 9.16 Total absorption coefficient per centimeter versus gamma ray energy for Pb, Sn, Cu, and Al. [From W. Heitler, *The Quantum Theory of Radiation*, Clarendon Press, Oxford (1954).]

where a and b are positive numbers and have different values in different regions of photon energy.

The total absorption coefficient per atom, $_a\mu$, is given by

$$_a\mu = {_a\tau} + {_a\sigma} + {_a\kappa} \qquad (9.36)$$

The linear absorption coefficient is given by

$$\mu = (\rho N_A/A)[_a\tau + {_a\sigma} + {_a\kappa}] \qquad (9.37)$$

and the mass absorption coefficient is given by

$$\mu/\rho = (N_A/A)[_a\tau + {_a}\sigma + {_a}\kappa]$$ (9.38)

The values of different absorption coefficients are listed in many sources[1,15]. To get some idea of their variations, Fig. 9.15 shows the plots of individual absorption coefficients and their total, in the case of lead, and Fig. 9.16 shows the total absorption coefficient for different absorbers.

4. MEASUREMENT OF ABSORPTION COEFFICIENT[1,16]

The absorption coefficient is used in the sense of attenuation. Its measurement imposes many problems on the source, absorber, and the geometrical setup for the source and the detector.

If the source emits photons of a single energy, the calculation of μ is very simple. But, if the photons emitted have different energies, then the expected transmission is given by

$$I/I_0 = \sum_n \epsilon_n f_n e^{-\mu_n x} \Big/ \sum \epsilon_n f_n$$ (9.39)

where f_n is the fraction of photons of nth energy with μ_n linear absorption coefficient and ϵ_n is the detector efficiency for this photon. The source, however, must be thin so that there is negligible self absorption.

The absorber thickness should be known accurately. It, also, should be very thin so as to avoid multiple scattering inside the absorber. If it is not a pure material, its composition must be known.

The problem of good geometry arises from two factors: the beam must be well collimated, and the scattered photon should not reach the detector after additional scattering. Good geometry has been achieved in two different ways. (a) The arrangement used by Davisson and Evans[1] shown in Fig. 9.17 has proved to be very satisfactory. (b) The alternative arrangement is that of Cowan[16]. The source, the detector, and the absorber are supported vertically in the air away from the ground by means of a 1/4" steel cable tied between the third floor window of the laboratory and a tree 130 ft away from the window. The source was 25 ft above the ground and 60 ft away from the window. The detector used was a Geiger counter about $27\frac{1}{2}$ ft above the ground and in line with the source.

The agreement between the measured values of the absorption coefficients and the theoretical prediction is excellent. This is obvious from Fig. 9.18 where the solid points are the measured values of the absorption coefficient by C. Cowan[16] and the continuous curve is a theoretical plot.

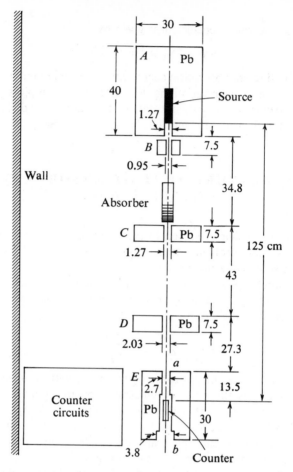

FIG. 9.17 A good geometry absorption-arrangement used by Davisson and Evans. Dimensions shown are in centimeters. [From Davisson, C. M., and R. D. Evans, *Revs. Mod. Phys.*, **24**, 79, (1952).]

5. MEASUREMENT OF GAMMA-RAY ENERGIES

Depending on the energy of the gamma rays, the strength of the source of gamma rays, and the accuracy required, one of the following may be used for the measurement of gamma ray energies: (a) absorption method, (b) crystal-diffraction spectrometer, (c) magnetic spectrometer, (d) pair spectrometer, (e) scintillation method, or (f) other methods. We shall discuss these methods in some detail.

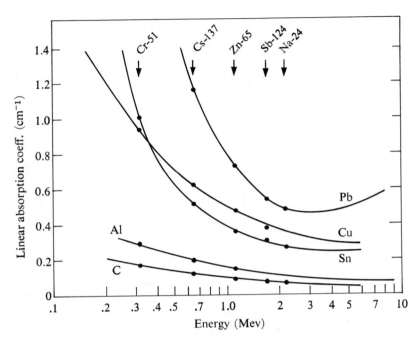

FIG. 9.18   The agreement between the measured values (dots) of absorption coefficients and the theoretical values (lines). Experimental points are due to Cowan. [From Cowan, C. L., *Phys. Rev.*, **74**, 1841, (1948).]

A. ABSORPTION METHOD.   This is the earliest, simplest, and quickest method for the determination of γ-ray energies. It is based on the measurement of the absorption coefficient of an absorber by plotting intensity (count rate) versus thickness of the absorber. The measured absorption coefficient is compared with the theoretical values, as shown in Sec. 4, from which the energy of the γ-ray may be interpreted. Though this method is convenient only for the monoenergetic (homogeneous) γ-rays, it can be extended to include cases in which γ-rays of two or more widely separated energies are present. It involves the plot of intensity versus thickness on semilog paper. Different energy components may be separated by a method similar to that given in Sec. 2.8. The slopes of the straight lines give the absorption coefficients for different energy components of the γ-rays.

For very weak sources with energies up to ~400 kev, the use of any kind of geometry gives a fairly accurate value of the γ-ray energies. This is because the secondaries produced are very soft and are easily absorbed. A convenient way to measure the γ-ray energy is to measure the half-thickness in an absorber such as Al and compare it with the plot of energy versus half-thickness shown in Fig. 9.19[17]. For high-energy gamma rays, say ~4 Mev, we definitely need a good geometry similar to the one shown in Fig. 9.17, but this imposes a condition that the source must have a very high disintegration rate in order to get an appreciable count-rate. Absorption measurements do not give accurate results at higher energies because of the minimum in the absorption curve that may correspond to more than one energy.

For very low energies, say 1 kev to 100 kev, the method of critical absorption may be employed for accurate energy determination. By making absorption measurements in materials of different atomic number, it is

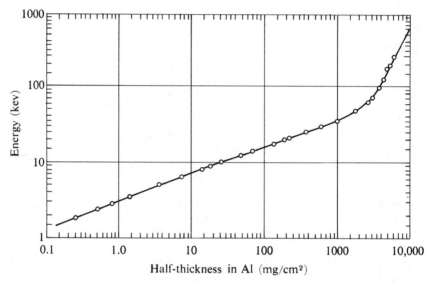

FIG. 9.19   Relation between half-thickness $X_{1/2}$ in Al (mg/cm²) to photon energy. [From Glendenin, L. E., *Nucleonics*, **2**, No. 1, 12, (1948).]

possible to bracket the γ-ray energy within the K-absorption edges of two absorbers of adjacent atomic numbers. Further interpolation can give an accurate energy of the γ-ray.

B. CRYSTAL-DIFFRACTION SPECTROMETER. Unlike other methods, this method gives a direct measurement of the wave length. Because gamma rays are electromagnetic waves, it should be possible to diffract them. Knowing the diffraction angle, θ, the wave length, λ, of the gamma ray may be calculated from Bragg's condition,

$$2d \sin \theta = n\lambda \qquad (9.40)$$

where d is the grating spacing, and n is the order of diffraction. Thus from λ, one can calculate the photon energy.

For the purpose of gamma-spectroscopy, crystal diffraction spectro-meters of very high precision have been developed by J. DuMond and collab-orators[18,19]. The instrument used is a transmission-type spectrometer using a curved crystal-diffraction grating in the following manner.

A flat piece of crystalline quartz is bent into an arc in such a way that the diffracting planes meet at a distance 2R from the center of the crystal

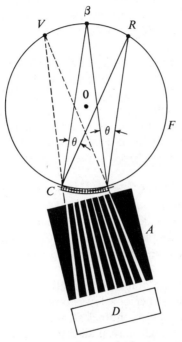

FIG. 9.20 Geometrical arrange-ment of DuMond's crystal spec-trometer for the measurement of photon energies. [From Du-Mond, J. W. M., *Rev. Sci. Inst.*, **18**, 626, (1947).]

in a line at β (Fig. 9.20). The radius of curvature of the crystal is equal to the diameter of the focusing circle F. The source of gamma rays is placed at R. If Bragg's condition is satisfied, the gamma rays reflected from the crystal, C, seem to diverge from a point, V, on the circle, F. This divergent beam (or diffracted beam) is received by a detector, D, (usually a scintillation detector). The system of baffles, A, shown in Fig. 9.20 serves to collimate the beam as well as to shield the detector from radiation coming directly from the source. A mechanical arrangement is made to move the source accurately along the focusing circle, F, which automatically rotates the crystal as well.

This eliminates the movement of the detector and collimator (both of which are heavy) to find the diffraction peaks at different angles corresponding to different wave lengths. A typical crystal grating is about 1 mm thick, 50 mm wide, and 70 mm high. The radius of curvature is 2.0 in.

This method of gamma-energy determination is the most accurate and precise and is used for providing standard calibration sources. The resolution of this instrument is approximately 1 percent, the accuracy ~ 0.04 percent, and the efficiency $\sim 10^{-9}$ per photon. For example, the energy of a Cs^{137} gamma ray is $hv = (0.66160 \pm 0.00014)$ Mev and that of Au^{198} is $hv = (0.411770 \pm 0.000036)$ Mev.

There are two limitations on the use of this method:– Very high activity sources are required (a few curies), which are difficult to produce and handle, and this method is good only up to gamma energies of 1 Mev because of the limitation on the lattice-spacing, which becomes too large to cause diffraction of high-energy γ-rays through a measurable angle. By means of certain improvements, this method has been extended up to 2 Mev by the use of a two-crystal spectrometer developed at the Chalk River Laboratory.

C. MAGNETIC SPECTROMETERS.   When one or several groups of gamma rays of moderate energies (from ~ 1 Mev to ~ 3 Mev) are present, their accurate energy-determination is made by using a magnetic spectrometer. Gamma rays are made to produce photoelectrons or Compton-recoil electrons, and the energies of these electrons are measured by means of a spectrometer. The procedure is as follows:–

To make use of the Compton-recoil electrons, the source of gamma rays is enclosed in an absorber of a low atomic number, such as aluminum, so as to keep the production of photoelectrons to a minimum. The thickness of the absorber is just enough to stop all primary electrons coming from the source and accompanying the gamma rays. The Compton electrons ejected from the absorber are focused in the spectrometer (Fig. 9.21). The Compton electrons form a continuous spectrum with a fairly sharp, well-defined upper energy-limit. If the intensity of the lower-energy gamma rays is not very low, their end points also can be separated with a sufficient accuracy. Knowing the maximum energy of the Compton electrons, the gamma-ray energies may be calculated by making use of Eq. (9.21). The maximum kinetic energy, K_m, is obtained from Eq. (9.21) by substituting $\theta = 180°$ (or $\phi = 0°$), i.e., in the head-on collision,

$$K_m = hv/(1 + m_0c^2/2hv) \qquad (9.41)$$

or

$$hv = \tfrac{1}{2}[K_m + (K_m^2 + 2K_m m_0 c^2)^{1/2}] \qquad (9.42)$$

In order to make use of the photoelectric effect, a radiator of a medium or high atomic number is placed in front of the box absorber as shown in

Fig. 9.21. The photoelectrons show up as spectral lines superimposed on the continuous Compton spectrum (Fig. 9.22). Lines corresponding to the K-shell and L-shell electrons show up in most cases. If spectrometers of very high resolutions are used, lines corresponding to the M-shell electrons are also resolved. Energies of these electrons can be calculated from the $H\rho$ values. After correcting for the thickness of the radiator and adding the

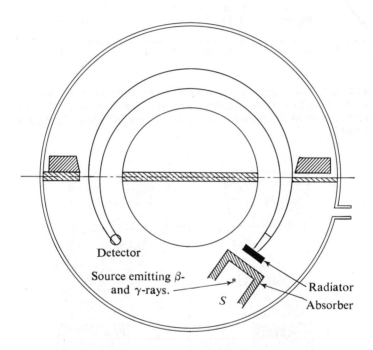

Detector

Source emitting β-
and γ-rays.

S

Radiator

Absorber

FIG. 9.21 An outline sketch of a magnetic spectrometer for measuring energies of the gamma rays using Compton recoils and photoelectrons.

binding energies of their respective shells, the energy of the gamma ray is given by

$$h\nu = K_e + I_B \tag{9.43}$$

As an example, using lens spectrometer, spectra of photoelectrons and Compton-recoil electrons due to gamma rays of Mn^{52} are shown in Fig. 9.22.

D. PAIR SPECTROMETER[20,21]. As the energy of the gamma rays increases, the Compton and photoelectron cross-sections continuously decrease while the pair-production cross-section increases rapidly. Thus, for measurement

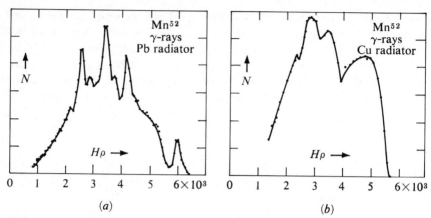

FIG. 9.22 (a) Photoelectrons and Compton recoil-electrons due to the gamma rays of Mn^{52} (peaks are due to photoelectrons). (b) Compton recoil electrons due to gamma rays of Mn^{52}. [From Peacock, W. C., and M. Deutsch, *Phys. Rev.*, **69**, 306, (1946).]

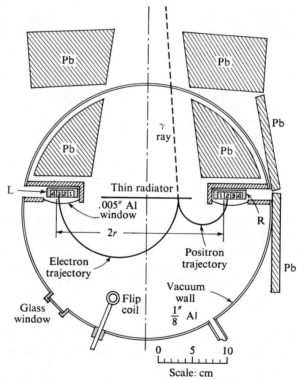

FIG. 9.23 Sketch of a pair spectrometer. [From Walker, R. L., and B. D. McDaniel, *Phys. Rev.*, **74**, 315, (1948).]

of gamma-ray energies greater than 3 Mev, use may be made of pair-pro-duction. The instrument used is called a pair spectrometer shown in Fig. 9.23 and described below.

A parallel beam of γ-rays falls on a thin absorber and produces electron-positron pairs. For energies greater than 3 Mev, the pairs are produced almost in the forward direction. A uniform magnetic field is applied perpendicular to the plane of the figure. The electrons and the positrons are focused on one of a number of Geiger counters placed on each side of the radiator. Geiger counters in pairs, one from each side, are connected to a coincidence circuit. The function of the coincidence circuit is to record a count if an electron received by one counter and a positron by the other counter come from the same gamma ray, independent of where the pair was produced in the radiator. Knowing the energies of the electron and the positron and adding their rest-mass energies gives the energy of the incident photon. We shall show here that for a high-energy gamma ray the sum of the radii of curvatures of the electron and the positron is constant. The energy of the gamma ray is

$$E_\gamma = E_+ + E_- = (p_+^2 c^2 + m_0^2 c^4)^{1/2} + (p_-^2 c^2 + m_0^2 c^4)^{1/2} \qquad (9.44)$$

Neglecting $(m_0 c^2)^2$ as compared to $p_+^2 c^2$ or $p_-^2 c^2$ we may write

$$E_\gamma = p_+ c + p_- c$$
$$= He\rho^+ c + He\rho^- c$$
$$= Hec(\rho^+ + \rho^-)$$
$$= kH \qquad (9.45)$$

where $k = ec\,(\rho^+ + \rho^-)$. Thus ρ^+ and ρ^- may be fixed, and by changing H, E_γ can be determined.

E. SCINTILLATION METHOD.   The use of a NaI (Tl) crystal has been discussed in detail in Chap. 3. This is one of the simplest and most reliable methods for energy, as well as intensity, measurements of gamma rays from 50 kev to several Mev. Though the resolution is not high, it has a very high efficiency. The pulses produced are directly proportional to the energy deposited inside the crystal. Compton distribution and photoelectric peaks also show up and are easily recognized.

At high energies a three-crystal pair spectrometer[22] may be used. An incident γ-ray is indicated by the central scintillator. When a γ-ray produces a pair, and the positron annihilates itself by producing two 0.511 Mev γ-rays, these are detected by the scintillators placed on either side of the central scintillator. Pulses from the three scintillators are correlated by means of a triple coincidence counter.

F. OTHER METHODS. (i) Proportional and high pressured ionization chambers are used for very low-energy γ-rays (<50 kev). (ii) A cloud chamber may be used for energy determination of γ-rays by measuring the ranges of the Compton, photo- and pair electrons. The results obtained, however, are not very accurate. (iii) The Bothe method measures the range of Compton electrons. The arrangement is shown in the Fig. 9.24. Compton electrons pass through two thin-walled Geiger counters connected to a coincidence circuit. The coincidence counting rate is measured as a function of the thickness of the absorber placed between the two counters. The thickness of the absorber that results in a zero coincidence-rate corresponds to the range

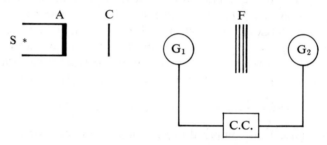

FIG. 9.24 The Bothe method for measuring the range of Compton electrons. S: source, A: absorber for electrons, C: produces Compton electrons, $G_1 G_2$: Geiger counters, F: foils of various thicknesses and C.C.: coincidence counter. The coincidence counter registers counts only if an electron passes through both the counters G_1, G_2.

of Compton electrons from which the energy of the incident photon may be calculated. (iv) At high energies a photon may cause the distintegration of a deuteron (photodisintegration), resulting in a proton and a neutron. From the measurement of the range of the proton, (in a high-pressured chamber) the photon energy can be deduced. (v) For better resolution, a Li-drifted Ge crystal is being used at present. The use of the solid-state detector was described in Chap. III; see Fig. 3.15.

6. MULTIPOLE MOMENTS

From our knowledge of electromagnetic theory[23], we know that the periodic motions of the electric charges result in the emission of electromagnetic waves. Similarly, the time-varying currents of a system and the motion of a magnetic dipole generate an electromagnetic wave. The emission is the result of an electromagnetic interaction between the charges and the magnetic poles.

Because gamma rays are electromagnetic waves, one would expect to extend the classical treatment to the nucleus for the calculation of the probability of gamma emission. This can be done with certain limitations, because the structure of the nucleus is not known very well. Before we make use of this classical analogy, it is necessary to understand the meaning of electric and magnetic multipole moments and the extension of their definitions to the nucleus. We shall show that it is possible to express any arbitrary static-charge distribution in terms of the standard distributions, the multipole moments.

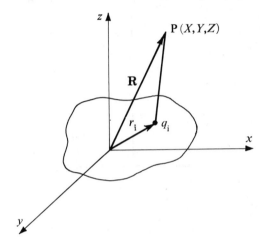

FIG. 9.25   An arbitrarily-charged distribution.

Let us consider an arbitrary static-charge distribution within a small volume near the origin as shown in Fig. 9.25. Let the charge q_i be located at the point r_i (x_i, y_i, z_i). In terms of the charges, q_i, and their distances, r_i, from the origin, we can define different multipoles. The *dipole moment*, p_d, is a vector quantity whose components are

$$p_x = \sum_i q_i x_i, \qquad p_y = \sum_i q_i y_i, \qquad p_z = \sum_i q_i z_i \qquad (9.46)$$

The *quadrupole moment* p_Q, is a tensor with the following six components:

$$p_{xx} = \sum_i q_i x_i^2; \qquad p_{yy} = \sum_i q_i y_i^2; \qquad p_{zz} = \sum_i q_i z_i^2;$$

$$p_{xy} = \sum_i q_i x_i y_i; \qquad p_{xz} = \sum_i q_i x_i z_i; \qquad p_{yz} = \sum_i q_i y_i z_i \qquad (9.47)$$

Similarly, we can define *octupole moment*, p_O, as a product of three displacements which has nine components. These multipoles are usually indicated by $2^1, 2^2, 2^3, ..., 2^L$ representing the dipole, quadrupole, octupole,

..., 2^L-pole, respectively. The electric multipoles are denoted by EL and the magnetic multipoles by ML. A few examples of electric multipoles are shown in Fig. 9.26.

Referring to Fig. 9.25, the potential at a point P at a distance $\mathbf{R} \gg \mathbf{r}_i$

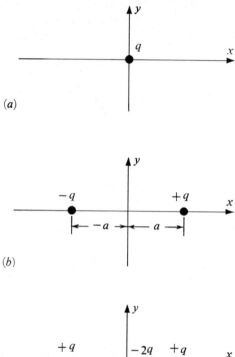

(a)

(b)

(c)

FIG. 9.26 Different charge distributions produce different radiation: (a) monopole, (b) dipole, and (c) quadrupole.

may be expressed in terms of the multipole moments. The electrostatic potential at P is given by

$$\phi(\mathbf{R}) = \sum_i \frac{q_i}{|\mathbf{R} - \mathbf{r}|} = \sum_i q_i D_i \tag{9.48}$$

where, expressing $\mathbf{R}$ and $\mathbf{r}_i$ in rectangular coordinates, $D_i = [(X - x_i)^2 + (Y - y_i)^2 + (Z - z_i)^2]^{-\frac{1}{2}}$. Because we have assumed that X, Y and $Z \gg x_i$

y_i and z_i we can expand D_i in terms of a Taylor Series with respect to x, y and z, i.e.,

$$D_i(X, Y, Z) = [D_i]_0 + \left[\left(\frac{\partial D_i}{\partial x}\right)_0 x_i + \left(\frac{\partial D_i}{\partial y}\right)_0 y_i + \left(\frac{\partial D_i}{\partial z}\right)_0 z_i\right]$$

$$+ \left[\frac{1}{2}\left(\frac{\partial^2 D_i}{\partial x^2}\right)_0 x_i^2 + \frac{1}{2}\left(\frac{\partial^2 D_i}{\partial y^2}\right)_0 y_i^2 + \frac{1}{2}\left(\frac{\partial^2 D_i}{\partial z^2}\right)_0 z_i^2\right.$$

$$\left. + \left(\frac{\partial^2 D_i}{\partial x \partial y}\right)_0 x_i y_i + \left(\frac{\partial^2 D_i}{\partial x \partial z}\right)_0 x_i z_i + \left(\frac{\partial^2 D_i}{\partial y \partial z}\right)_0 y_i z_i\right] + \cdots \quad \textbf{(9.49)}$$

The subscript $_0$ means that the derivatives have to be evaluated at the origin. Combining Eqs. (9.46) to (9.49) with the definition of the directional cosines $l = X/R$, $m = Y/R$, and $n = Z/R$, we obtain the following expression for the electrostatic potential at P:

$$\phi(X, Y, Z) = (1/R) \sum_i q_i + (1/R^2)[l p_x + m p_y + n p_z]$$

$$+ (1/R^3)[\tfrac{1}{2}(3l^2 - 1)p_{xx} + \tfrac{1}{2}(3m^2 - 1)p_{yy}$$

$$+ 1/2(3n^2 - 1)p_{zz} + 3lm p_{xy} + 3ln p_{xz} + 3mn p_{yz}] + \cdots \quad \textbf{(9.50)}$$

Note that $\sum_i q_i = p_0$ is called the *monopole moment*, i.e., the 2^0-pole.

It is clear from Eq. (9.50) that any charge distribution can be expressed in terms of standard multipoles. The same is true for the case of the magnetic potential. It can be expressed in terms of magnetic dipole, quadrupole, and other multipole moments. Note that there can be no magnetic monopole, equivalent to the electric monopole $\sum_i q_i = p_0$, because magnetic poles exist only in pairs.

Our next step is to extend the definition of dipole and quadrupole moments given by Eqs. (9.46) and (9.47) to the nucleus. First, let us assume that the charge distribution inside the nucleus is continuous and not discrete. If $\rho(\mathbf{r})$ is the charge density inside the nucleus, the components of the dipole moment are

$$p_x = \int \rho(\mathbf{r}) x \, dv, \qquad p_y = \int \rho(\mathbf{r}) y \, dv, \qquad p_z = \int \rho(\mathbf{r}) z \, dv \quad \textbf{(9.51)}$$

and for the quadrupole moment

$$p_{xx} = \int \rho(\mathbf{r}) x^2 \, dv, \qquad p_{yy} = \int \rho(\mathbf{r}) y^2 \, dv, \qquad p_{zz} = \int \rho(\mathbf{r}) z^2 \, dv$$

$$p_{xy} = \int \rho(\mathbf{r}) xy \, dv, \qquad p_{yz} = \int \rho(\mathbf{r}) yz \, dv, \qquad p_{xz} = \int \rho(\mathbf{r}) xz \, dv \quad \textbf{(9.52)}$$

where dv is a small volume inside the nucleus. This definition is still classical.

To make it quantum mechanical, we express $\rho(\mathbf{r})$ in terms of the wave function of the state, i.e.,

$$\rho(\mathbf{r}) = e\psi^*(\mathbf{r})\psi(\mathbf{r}) \tag{9.53}$$

Because it is the motion of the charges that leads to the emission of multipole radiation, we must include the wave functions not only for the initial state but for the final state of the nucleus as well. Thus Eq. (9.53) is modified to

$$\rho(\mathbf{r}) = e\psi_f^*(\mathbf{r})\psi_i(\mathbf{r}) \tag{9.54}$$

The lack of knowledge of these wave functions for different states limits the exact calculation of the transition probability for gamma emission.

The second assumption involves the shape of the charge distribution of the nucleus. If the charge distribution has spherical symmetry, all the components of the moments vanish. Another important case is that in which the nucleus is an ellipsoid of revolution with the Z-axis as symmetry axis. If the center of charge is the origin, we get from Eq. (9.51) $p_x = p_y = p_z = 0$, i.e., all dipole components are zero, and also $p_{xy} = p_{yz} = p_{zx} = 0$. The only non-zero moments are the three components p_{xx}, p_{yy} $(=p_{xx})$, and p_{zz} of the quadrupole moment.

Note that if the components of the dipole moment are zero, it does not mean that there will be no dipole radiation. The motion of the static-charge distribution can always cause redistribution in such a way to emit dipole radiation.

Lastly, let us consider the effect of an external field on the charge distribution. This is important because the nucleus is immersed in the external field of the electrons. Let the external field produce a potential $V(\mathbf{r}_i)$ at $\mathbf{r}_i$ where the charge is q_i. The energy of the system is given by

$$E = \sum_i q_i V(x_i, y_i, z_i) \tag{9.55}$$

Expanding $V(\mathbf{r})$ in a Taylor series and using the definition of moments, we get

$$\begin{aligned}
E = [V_0 p_0] &+ \left[\left(\frac{\partial V}{\partial x}\right)_0 p_x + \left(\frac{\partial V}{\partial y}\right)_0 p_y + \left(\frac{\partial V}{\partial z}\right)_0 p_z \right] \\
&+ \left[\frac{1}{2}\left(\frac{\partial^2 V}{\partial x^2}\right)_0 p_{xx} + \frac{1}{2}\left(\frac{\partial^2 V}{\partial y^2}\right)_0 p_{yy} + \frac{1}{2}\left(\frac{\partial^2 V}{\partial z^2}\right)_0 p_{zz} \right. \\
&+ \left. \left(\frac{\partial^2 V}{\partial x \partial y}\right)_0 p_{xy} + \left(\frac{\partial^2 V}{\partial x \partial z}\right)_0 p_{xz} + \left(\frac{\partial^2 V}{\partial y \partial z}\right) p_{yz} \right] + \cdots
\end{aligned} \tag{9.56}$$

Once again we assume that there is an axial symmetry about the z-axis, i.e., the components $p_x = p_y = p_z = 0$, $p_{xy} = p_{yz} = p_{xz} = 0$, and p_{xx}, p_{yy} $(=p_{xx})$ and p_{zz} are nonzero. Also from Laplace's theorem:

$$\left(\frac{\partial^2 V}{\partial x^2}\right)_0 + \left(\frac{\partial^2 V}{\partial y^2}\right)_0 + \left(\frac{\partial^2 V}{\partial z^2}\right)_0 = 0, \tag{9.57}$$

we get for the quadrupole energy

$$E_Q = \tfrac{1}{2}(p_{zz} - p_{xx})\left(\frac{\partial^2 V}{\partial z^2}\right)_0 = \tfrac{1}{4}Q\left(\frac{\partial^2 V}{\partial z^2}\right)_0 \tag{9.58}$$

where

$$Q = 2(p_{zz} - p_{xx}) \tag{9.59}$$

is called the quadrupole moment, and may be expressed as

$$Q = 2p_{zz} - p_{xx} - p_{yy}$$
$$= \Sigma q_i(2z_i^2 - x_i^2 - y_i^2)$$
$$= \Sigma q_i(3z_i^2 - r_i^2)$$

or for a continuous charge distribution

$$Q = \int \rho(3z^2 - r^2)\, dv \tag{9.60}$$

In order to remove the dimensions of charge, we redefine Eq. (9.60) as

$$Q = 1/e \int \rho(3z^2 - r^2)\, dv \tag{9.61}$$

where Q is expressed in units of cm^2 or in barns.

Note that if Q is positive, i.e., $p_{zz} > p_{xx}$, the charge distribution is prolate (cucumber- or cigar-shaped) about the Z-axis, as shown in Fig. 9.27(a). If Q is negative that is, if $p_{zz} < p_{xx}$, the charge distribution is oblate (door-knob shape) as shown in Fig. 9.27(b).

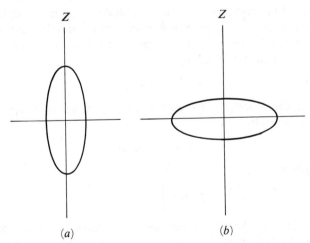

FIG. 9.27 (a) The prolate charge distribution, which results in a positive value of electric quadrupole moment Q. (b) The oblate charge distribution, which results in a negative value of Q.

7. THEORY OF GAMMA EMISSION[24]

In the previous section we have shown that the charge distribution of the nucleus may be expressed in terms of standard multipoles. In analogy with the classical electromagnetic theory, the motion of these multipoles results in the emission of electromagnetic waves, i.e., gamma rays, from the nucleus. The motion of the electric and the magnetic multipoles give out electric and magnetic multipole radiation, respectively. It has been shown by W. Heitler[25] that a photon emitted by either the electric or magnetic 2^L multipole carries away an angular momentum equal to $L\hbar$. Because the initial and final states of the nucleus have definite spins and parities, the photon should carry away a definite amount of angular momentum. The theory should express the transition rate in terms of spin (I), parity (π), and angular momentum (L). Unlike classical situations, the structure of the nuclei, and their wave functions are not known; but by assuming a certain model of the nucleus, it is possible to estimate the transition probabilities. A quantum-mechanical treatment of this problem has been given by V. Weisskopf[26]. Before stating his results, we shall see how far we may go with the help of a classical treatment.

Let us consider an oscillating electric dipole of the form in which $p_x = p_y = 0$, and $p_z \neq 0$. The rate at which this oscillating dipole radiates energy is given by[23]

$$dE/dt = (64/3)(\pi^4 v^4/c^3)p_z^2 \qquad (9.62)$$

where v is the frequency and p_z is the amplitude of the time-varying electric dipole moment. Because a photon emitted from a dipole carries away an amount of energy hv, the probability per unit time, λ, of photon emission is obtained by dividing Eq. (9.62) by hv,

$$\lambda = (32/3)(\pi^3 v^3/c^3 h)p_z^2 \qquad (9.63)$$

According to the definition of the electric dipole moment, as applied to the nucleus, p_z is given by

$$p_z = \int \rho(r)z \, dv \qquad (9.64a)$$

or from wave mechanics

$$p_z = e \int \psi_f^* z \psi_i \, dv \qquad (9.64b)$$

where ψ_i and ψ_f are the wave functions of the initial and final states of the nucleus, and $\int \psi_f^* z \psi_i \, dv$ is the matrix element of z. The evaluation of this matrix element is not possible because the wave functions ψ_i and ψ_f are not known. Some rough estimates for the dipole, quadrupole, and higher multipole matrix-elements can be made. For example, the maximum value expected for a quadrupole matrix-element is eR^2 from Eq. (9.60), where R is the nuclear radius, or R^2 from Eq. (9.61).

Detailed classical calculations give the following result[24] for the transition probability, $\lambda(L)$, for a gamma ray of energy E_γ and multipolarity L:

$$\lambda(L) = \frac{8\pi(L+1)}{L[(2L+1)!!]^2} \frac{1}{\hbar}\left(\frac{E_\gamma}{\hbar c}\right)^{2L+1} B_{eg}(L) \, \sec^{-1} \qquad (9.65)$$

The double factorial, !!, stands for the product of odd numbers, i.e.,

$$(2L+1)!! = 1 \cdot 3 \cdot 5 \cdots \cdot (2L+1)$$

and $B_{eg}(L)$ is known as the *reduced transition probability*, the subscripts indicate that the transition is from the excited to the ground state (or to a lower excited-state). Theoretical evaluation of B_{eg} involves nuclear quantities and may be calculated only for specific models of the nucleus. The two models that have proved successful for such calculations are a single particle model and a collective model.

A. SINGLE PARTICLE MODEL.   By making the assumptions that the nucleus is spherical, that the γ-emission is the result of a transition of a single proton from one state to another, and that the final state has zero orbital angular-momentum, Weisskopf[26] has derived the following rough estimates for the reduced transition probabilities:

For electric radiation

$$B(EL) = \frac{e^2}{4\pi}\left(\frac{3}{L+3}\right)^2 R^{2L} \qquad (9.66)$$

and for magnetic radiation

$$B(ML) = 10\left(\frac{\hbar}{m_p c}\right)^2 \frac{1}{R^2} B(EL) \qquad (9.67)$$

where m_p is the mass of a proton and $R(=r_0 A^{1/3})$ is the radius of the nucleus. Combining Eqs. (9.66) and (9.67) with Eq. (9.65), we obtain the following expressions for the electric and the magnetic transition probabilities

$$\lambda_{EL} = \frac{1}{\tau_{EL}} \approx \frac{4.4 \times 10^{21}(L+1)}{L[(2L+1)!!]^2}\left(\frac{3}{L+3}\right)^2\left(\frac{E_\gamma}{197}\right)^{2L+1}(R^{2L}) \sec^{-1} \quad (9.68)$$

$$\lambda_{ML} = \frac{1}{\tau_{ML}} \approx \frac{1.9 \times 10^{21}(L+1)}{L[(2L+1)!!]^2}\left(\frac{3}{L+3}\right)^2\left(\frac{E_\gamma}{197}\right)^{2L+1}(R^{2L-2}) \sec^{-1} \quad (9.69)$$

where R is in fermis ($1f = 10^{-13}$cm) and E_γ is in Mev. For quick estimates, the decay constants λ_{EL} and λ_{ML} versus gamma-ray energies for different values of L have been drawn[27] and are shown in Fig. 9.28. These plots indicate that the half-life decreases with increasing gamma ray energies and increases very rapidly with increasing L; also the electric transitions are faster than the magnetic transitions. This is one of the reasons that E2 transitions (i.e., electric quadrupoles) compete with M1 transitions (i.e., magnetic dipoles). The primary reason is explained in the section on the collective model.

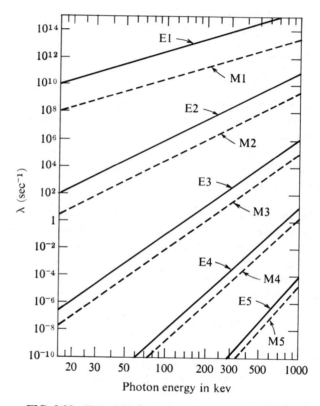

FIG. 9.28   Transition probability for pure electric and magnetic multipole radiations for excited nuclei calculated from Weisskopf formula. [Seigbahn, K. (ed.,) *Alpha-Beta- and Gamma-Ray Spectroscopy*, p. 882, New York: Interscience Publishers (1965).]

From the foregoing equations we can show that after rearranging, the functions $\tau_{EL}A^{2L/3} E_\gamma^{2L+1}$, and $\tau_{ML}A^{(2L-2)/3} E_\gamma^{2L+1}$ are independent of gamma energies and mass number A. In order to compare the theoretical values with experimentally measured half-lives of nuclear states, plots of these functions (reduced lifetimes) versus neutron number are drawn in the form shown in Fig. 9.29(a) and Fig. 9.29(b)[28]. The success of a single particle model is quite obvious and shows the grouping of different types of transitions.

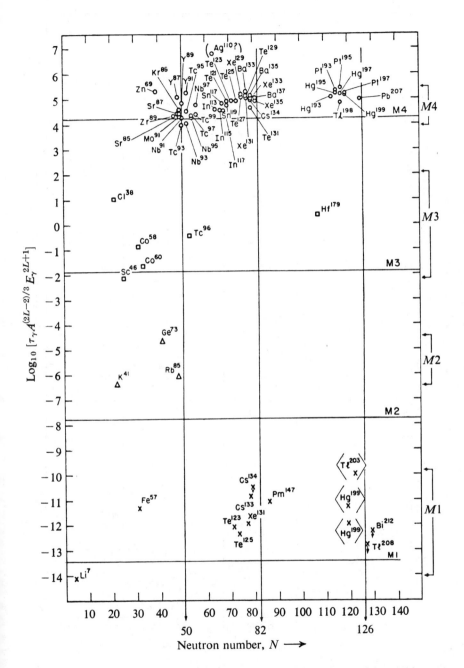

FIG. 9.29(a)   Comparison of the theoretical reduced lifetimes with experimental values. [From Goldhaber, M., and J. Weneser, *Ann. Revs. of Nucl. Sci.*, 5, (1955).]

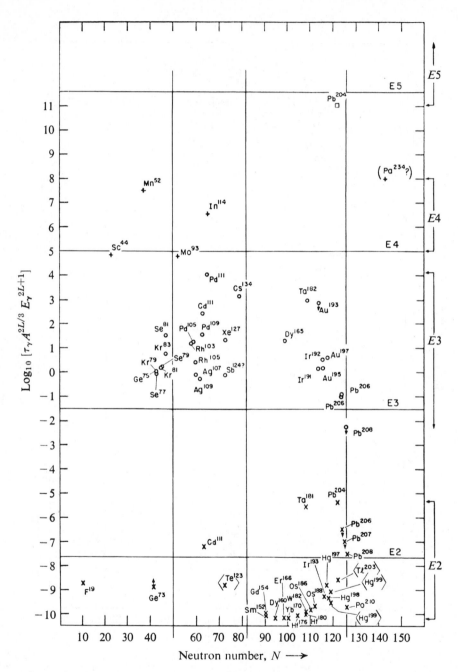

FIG. 9.29(b) Comparison of the theoretical reduced lifetimes with experimental values. [From Goldhaber, M., and J. Weneser, *Ann. Revs. of Nucl. Sci.*, 5, (1955).]

B. COLLECTIVE MODEL. Looking carefully at Fig. 9.29(a) and Fig. 9.29(b), one finds that in all groups, except E2, the experimental reduced lifetimes are usually longer than the theoretical values. In the case of E2 transitions, it is just the reverse, i.e., the E2 transitions are much faster than theoretically predicted by the single-particle model. These E2 transitions are better explained by the collective model.

According to this model, the excitation energy is stored in the collective, in-phase motion of several protons resulting in an increased decay constant and a shorter lifetime. For electric quadrupole radiation, (E2), from the state with spin $(I + 2)$ to state I the reduced transition probability is given by[29]

$$B(E2) = \frac{15}{32\pi} e^2 Q_0^2 \frac{(I + 1)(I + 2)}{(2I + 3)(2I + 5)} \qquad (9.70)$$

where Q_0 is the static nuclear quadrupole-moment that has a much larger value for deformed nuclei than the single-particle moments. There are many examples of such transitions in the high mass-number nuclei.

8. SELECTION RULES

The selection rules may be derived by the application of different conservation laws to a given system. The two most important conservation laws applicable in the present situation are those of angular momentum and parity.

A. ANGULAR MOMENTUM. The conservation of angular momentum requires that the total angular momentum of the initial system be equal to that of the final system. If $L\hbar$ is the angular momentum carried away by a photon and $\mathbf{I}_i$ and $\mathbf{I}_f$ are the spins of the initial and the final states, respectively, of the nuclei

$$\mathbf{I}_i - \mathbf{I}_f = \mathbf{L}$$

or

$$(I_i + I_f) \geqslant L \geqslant |I_i - I_f| \qquad (9.71)$$

For example, $I_i = 3$, $I_f = 2$, then $L = 5, 4, 3, 2, 1$. According to this, the emitted photon may carry any amount of angular momentum: $1\hbar$, $2\hbar$, $3\hbar$, $4\hbar$, $5\hbar$. Usually the photons will be emitted with only the lowest allowed angular momentum ($1\hbar$ in this example), because the transition probability for higher multipole radiation falls off very rapidly (see Fig. 9.28). Similarly if $I_i = 7/2$ and $I_f = 3/2$, most of the γ-rays will be carrying angular momentum equal to $2\hbar$. The higher-multipole radiations ($3\hbar$, $4\hbar$, $5\hbar$) have very low transition probabilities. The exception to this rule is the E2 transition that is much faster than the M1 transition, particularly in the excited states of heavy elements.

Transitions in which $L = 0$ are completely forbidden, i.e., no monopole radiation exists because it would require a spherically symmetric charge-distribution. Such a distribution is not able to account for the transverse electric-field characteristics of the electromagnetic radiation. Thus photons must carry at least $1\hbar$ angular momentum.

Also there can be no γ-emission between the states for which $I_i = I_f = 0$, i.e., $0 \to 0$ transitions are always forbidden, because there is no way in which a photon may have an angular momentum $1\hbar$.† For a nucleus with a zero spin there is a spherically symmetric charge-distribution, the pulsation of which results in an oscillating monopole. Such motion does not produce varying electric and magnetic fields outside the nucleus, and no gamma emission takes place. The number of nucleons is the same before and after the transition, and, therefore, the gamma transitions take place between the states with either integral spins or half-integral spins.

B. PARITY. The law of conservation of parity as applied to electromagnetic interactions requires that parity be conserved, i.e., the parity of the initial system be the same as the final system. Even-parity states are denoted by $+$ and odd parity by $-$. In gamma emission the system involves the parity of the initial state wave function ψ_i, the parity of the final state wave function ψ_f, and the parity of the multipole radiation field. We shall denote the parities of these three by π_i, π_f, and π_L. Thus if the parity of π_L is even $(+)$, the parities of π_i and π_f both should be odd or both even, so that

$$\pi_i(+) = \pi_L(+)\,\pi_f(+)$$

or

$$\pi_i(-) = \pi_L(+)\,\pi_f(-)$$

If π_L is odd, $(-)$, then π_i and π_f should have opposite parity, i.e.,

$$\pi_i(+) = \pi_L(-)\,\pi_f(-)$$
$$\pi_i(-) = \pi_L(-)\,\pi_f(+)$$

It can be shown from quantum mechanics that the parity change required by the wave functions $\psi_i\psi_f$ are given by $(-1)^L$ for the pure electric multipole transitions and by $-(-1)^L$ for the pure magnetic multipole transitions (-1 means a change in parity, $+1$ no change.)

For example, for the E1 transition there is a change in parity, i.e., π_i and π_f have opposite parity, while for M1 they have the same parity. Table 9.1 summarizes the selection rules for both angular momentum and parity change.

† Emission of two photons should be possible between $0 \to 0$, but no such transition has ever been observed.

TABLE 9.1
SELECTION RULES FOR RADIATIVE TRANSITIONS

Type	Notation	Angular Momentum L (or Spin Change ΔI)	Parity Change
Electric dipole	E1	$1\hbar$	Yes -1
Magnetic dipole	M1	$1\hbar$	No $+1$
Electric quadrupole	E2	$2\hbar$	No $+1$
Magnetic quadrupole	M2	$2\hbar$	Yes -1
Electric octupole	E3	$3\hbar$	Yes -1
Magnetic octupole	M3	$3\hbar$	No $+1$
Electric 2^L-pole	EL	$L\hbar$	$(-1)^L$
Magnetic 2^L-pole	ML	$L\hbar$	$-(-1)^L$

9. INTERNAL CONVERSION

We mentioned, in the discussion of beta decay, that there generally is a line spectrum superimposed on the continuous beta spectrum, as was shown in Fig. 8.15 and Fig. 8.16. These monoenergetic electrons are called conversion electrons, and the process by which they are emitted is called internal conversion. The kinetic energy, K_e, of the conversion electrons is given by the formula

$$K_e = E_\gamma - I_B \tag{9.72}$$

I_B represents the corresponding binding energy of the electron, and E_γ is the available energy for gamma emission by the nucleus. Because the relation of Eq. (9.72) is well satisfied and is similar to the photoelectric effect, it led C. Ellis[30] to state that the internal conversion is a two-step process. In the first step a γ-ray is emitted, and in the second step it interacts with an orbital electron, which is ejected with a kinetic energy given by Eq. (9.72). Later on, it was shown by S. Rosseland[31] that this is not the true nature of the process and the explanation given is incorrect. According to Rosseland the emission of a conversion electron is a one-step process and is an alternative to the gamma emission. Classically, an orbital electron cannot penetrate into the nucleus, but according to quantum mechanics there is some probability that the wave function of the orbital electron will for a certain fraction of the time. There is a probability, therefore, that the unstable nucleus will de-excite by giving its energy directly to the orbital electron instead of by gamma emission. The strongest argument that suggests that internal conversion is a one-step process comes from zero–zero transitions.

According to the gamma selection rules, the $0 \rightarrow 0$ transition is completely forbidden because the emitted γ-ray must carry away at least a unit angular momentum, $1\hbar$, which is clearly not available in such transitions. If the wave function of the orbital electron penetrates the nuclear volume, the nucleus will de-excite by giving its energy to the orbital electron. There are some examples of such transitions in which only conversion electrons are emitted.[32-34] Some of these are $_{84}Po^{214}$, $_{58}Ce^{140}$, and $_{32}Ge^{70}$.

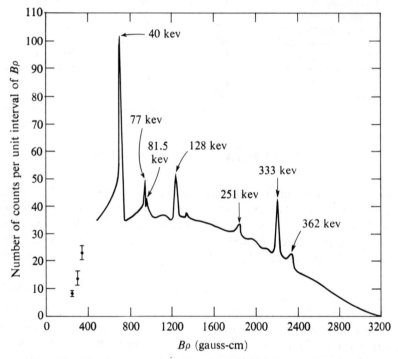

FIG. 9.30 The continuous-electron momentum spectrum of I^{131} with conversion lines superimposed on it. [From Owen, G. E., D. Moe, and C. S. Cook, *Phys. Rev.* **74**, 1879, (1948).]

Fig. 9.30[35] shows as many as 7 lines superimposed on the continuous beta spectrum. In some cases, if the lifetime of the gamma decay is long, (see Sec. 10) it can be separated from the rest of the beta-emitting nuclei, and the line spectra of the conversion electrons will be free from the continuous β-spectrum. An example of this is shown in Fig. 9.31[36]. The intensities of K, L_I, L_{II}, and M_I conversion electrons depend upon the probabilities of finding these electrons inside the nuclear volume. By using hydrogen-like wave functions for these electrons, E. Church and J. Weneser[37] have calculated the probabilities for different orbital electrons to exist inside the nuclear volume. Their results show that the probability for K-electrons is the maximum, next in decreasing order are L_I and M_I electrons, while for $L_{II,III}$ the probability is much smaller. The reason for this is that the M-orbit electrons penetrate deeper into the nucleus than the $L_{II,III}$ electron-shell orbits. In many cases, therefore, the intensity of the M-conversion electrons will be measurable with some accuracy, while that for $L_{II,III}$ conversion electrons may be almost zero. These predictions agree with the experimentally observed

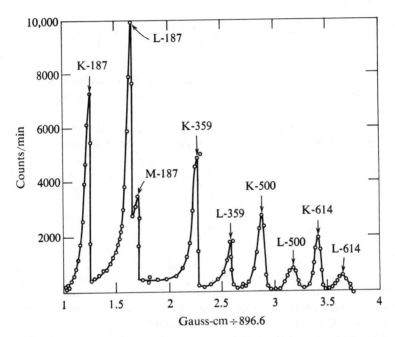

FIG. 9.31 Internal-conversion electron spectrum of Os^{190m}. The beta activity that results in a continuous spectrum has been removed. [From Scharff-Goldhaber, G., D. E. Alburger, G. Harbottle, and M. McKeown, *Phys. Rev.*, **111**, 913, (1958).]

values. Note that both gamma transitions and internal conversion are due to electromagnetic interaction.

Because internal conversion and γ-emission are competing processes, the total transition probability, λ, for a given state will be the sum of the transition probabilities for γ-emission, λ_γ, and conversion electron emission, λ_e, i.e.,

$$\lambda = \lambda_\gamma + \lambda_e \tag{9.73}$$

and

$$\lambda_e = \lambda_K + \lambda_L + \lambda_M + \cdots \tag{9.74}$$

where λ_K, λ_L, and λ_M are the transition probabilities, respectively, for the K, L, and M conversion-electron emission. If a given radioactive sample emits N_γ gamma rays, in a given time and N_e conversion electrons in the same time, the ratio N_e/N_γ is called the *conversion coefficient*, α, i.e.,

$$\alpha = N_e/N_\gamma = \lambda_e/\lambda_\gamma \tag{9.75}$$

where α may have any value between 0 and ∞. Because $N_e = N_K + N_L + N_M + \cdots$ we may write Eq. (9.75) as

$$\alpha = \frac{N_K + N_L + N_M + \cdots}{N_\gamma} = \frac{N_K}{N_\gamma} + \frac{N_L}{N_\gamma} + \frac{N_M}{N_\gamma} + \cdots = \alpha_K + \alpha_L + \alpha_M + \cdots \tag{9.76}$$

where α_K, α_L, and α_M are called the K, L, and M conversion coefficients, respectively. The total conversion coefficient, α, therefore, is the sum of the individual-conversion coefficients.

Combining Eqs. (9.74) and (9.76), we may relate the mean life τ of the total transition and τ_γ for the gamma transition in the following way:

$$\tau = \frac{1}{\lambda} = \frac{1}{\lambda_\gamma + \lambda_e} = \frac{1/\lambda_\gamma}{1 + \lambda_e/\lambda_\gamma}$$

or

$$\tau = \frac{\tau_\gamma}{1 + \alpha}$$

i.e.,

$$\tau_\gamma = \tau(1 + \alpha) \tag{9.77}$$

Equation (9.77) implies that the mean lives predicted by the theory that assumes a single particle model (a point nucleus) must be corrected for the mean lives of the conversion electron transitions.

Theoretical evaluation of the K-, L-, and M- shell conversion-coefficients involves the use of relativistic equations. Basically their values depend upon four factors: (a) the energy available in the transition, (b) the atomic number, (c) the spin change, and (d) the parity change. By making use of high-speed computers, the calculations of the conversion coefficients have been carried out by M. Rose[38], and L. Sliv and I. Band[39]. The values obtained by them agree for the most part; Fig. 9.32 shows such a plot. A comparison of the theoretical value with the experimentally observed value of conversion coefficients makes it possible to make some predictions about the multipolarities of the emitted gamma rays and the spin and parity changes in the nucleus.

Sometimes, it is more convenient to know the ratio of N_K/N_L, called the K/L conversion ratio, given by

$$\frac{K}{L} = \frac{N_K}{N_L} = \frac{\lambda_K}{\lambda_L} = \frac{\lambda_K}{\lambda_{L_I} + \lambda_{L_{II}} + \lambda_{L_{III}}} \tag{9.78}$$

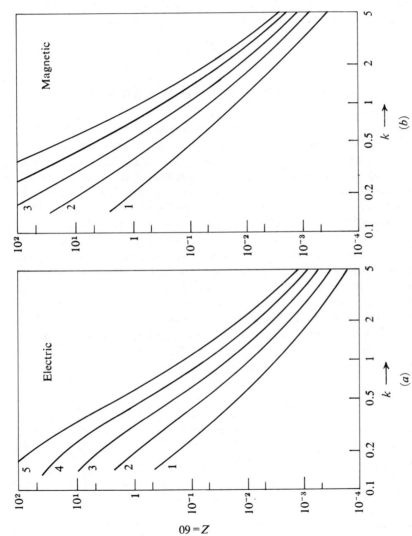

FIG. 9.32 Plot of K-conversion coefficient versus gamma ray energy (expressed in terms of the rest-mass of the electrons, i.e. $\alpha = h\nu/m_0c^2$) for $Z = 60$, (a) for electric multipole transitions, and (b) for magnetic multipole transitions. [From Vegors, Heath and Hammer, *Plots of K-conversion coefficients.*]

Similarly, L_I/L_{II}, L_{II}/L_{III} and L/M conversion ratios may be measured. This eliminates the measurement of γ-ray intensity that cannot be as accurately determined as the electron intensities measured by the use of a magnetic spectrometer. Experimental values of such ratios are obtained by dividing the areas under the individual conversion peaks. The theoretical value of the K/L conversion ratio may also be obtained from α_K and α_L. Because $\alpha_K = N_K/N_\gamma$ and $\alpha_L = N_L/N_\gamma$, dividing one by the other, we obtain

$$K/L = \alpha_K/\alpha_L \tag{9.79}$$

10. NUCLEAR ISOMERISM

In most cases the nuclei decaying by gamma emission have very high transition probabilities and very short half-lives ($<< 10^{-8}$ sec); but quite a few cases have been discovered (~ 100) in which the nucleus in an excited state decaying by gamma emission to a lower excited state, or, more commonly, to the ground state, has a very small transition probability. The measured half-lives have been found to be in the range of $\sim 10^{-8}$ sec to several years. The states with half-lives in this range are called *isomeric states* and the transitions are called *isomeric transitions*. There is no essential difference between the isomeric states and the states with much shorter half-lives. The range of half-lives that defines isomeric states is fixed arbitrarily. The existence of an isomeric transition (or a delayed transition) results in a pair of nuclei that have the same mass number and atomic number, but one has more energy than the other and, therefore, has different radioactive properties. A pair of such nuclei are *nuclear isomers* and the phenomena is *nuclear isomerism*. An isomeric state is also called a *metastable state* and the member of the nuclear isomer with higher energy is denoted by m, e.g., Se^{81m} in Fig. 9.33.

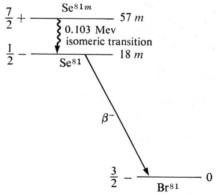

FIG. 9.33 Nuclear isomerism in Se^{81m}.

There are two factors that are primarily responsible for a very low transition probability of gamma emission: A large difference in the total angular momentum, (I), between the excited state and the lower excited state or the ground state, and a small energy difference between the two states. The small transition probabilities for gamma rays of higher multipolaries and low energies are in accordance with the predictions of the single-particle model (or the shell model) as seen from Fig. 9.28. We shall discuss this in a little more detail in Chap. 10.

If the energy of the excited state is large enough to make a β-decay energetically possible, the γ-transition (or radiative transition) is very slow, and it may be negligible. On the other hand, if the excited state is β-stable, the isomeric state of the nucleus is highly favorable for internal-conversion. This competing process of internal conversion reduces the observed lifetime of the nuclear isomeric transition. The partial lifetime, τ_γ, for gamma transition from the isomeric state is given by Eq. (9.77), i.e.,

$$\tau_\gamma = \tau_{\text{Expt.}}(1 + \alpha) \qquad (9.77)$$

where $\tau_{\text{Expt.}}$ is the experimentally observed lifetime of the isomeric state and α is the conversion coefficient equal to N_e/N_γ.

11. THE AUGER EFFECT[40,41]

The Auger effect is the emission of low-energy orbital electrons as an alternative to the emission of x-rays. There is always a vacancy created in the electronic shells by internal conversion, photoelectric effect, electron capture, or some other transitions. This vacancy is filled by the transition of an electron from an outer orbit to the inner orbit, and the excited inner orbit gets rid of its energy either by emission of x-rays or by transferring its energy to the electron in a lower-energy shell. The electrons emitted by such a process are *Auger electrons*, after the name of its discoverer, Pierre Auger. This process is analogous to internal conversion except that it is an atomic process in contrast to internal conversion, which is a nuclear process. The energies of the Auger electrons are usually lower than those of the conversion electrons.

For example, if there is a vacancy in the K-shell, the transition of an electron from L-shell to K-shell will result in the excitation of the K-shell with energy equal to the difference in the binding energies of the K- and L-shells, i.e., $\Delta E = I_K - I_L$. The excited K-shell gets rid of its energy either by emitting a photon of energy $h\nu_K$ given by $h\nu_K = I_K - I_L$, where ν_K is the frequency of the K-x-ray or by emitting an L-Auger-electron with a kinetic energy K_L given by

$$K_L = \Delta E - I_L = I_K - 2I_L \qquad (9.80)$$

The vacancy created in the L-shell results in further emission of L-x-rays or M-Auger-electrons. It must be clearly understood that the Auger effect is an alternative process to x-ray emission and is not an internal photoelectric effect.

There is competition between the Auger-electron emission and the emission of x-rays. The relative probability for x-ray emission and Auger-electron emission is measured by the *fluorescence yield*, which is defined as

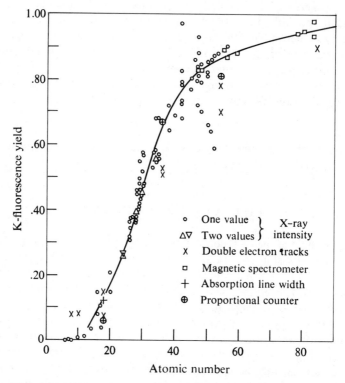

FIG. 9.34   The variation of the K-fluorescence yield with atomic number. [From Broyles, C. D., D. A. Thomas, and S. K. Hayes, *Phys. Rev.* **89**, 715, (1953).]

the number of x-rays emitted per shell vacancy. For example, in the case of the K-shell we define the K-fluorescence yield Y_K as

$$Y_K = \frac{\text{number of K-x-rays}}{\text{number of K-shell vacancies}} \qquad (9.81)$$

The variation of the K-fluorescence yield with atomic number has been calculated by C. Broyles, et. al.[40] and is shown in graphical form in Fig.

9.34. In general the trend is that the relative probability of x-ray emission is almost unity for high atomic-number elements and zero for low atomic-number elements. Thus, Auger-electron emission takes place predominantly for low atomic-number elements.

12. INTERNAL PAIR CONVERSION

In addition to gamma emission and conversion-electron emission, there is another competing process—internal pair-conversion—for the de-excitation of the nucleus. We have already discussed the fact that whenever gamma rays of energies greater than 1.02 Mev interact with an absorber, electron-positron pairs are ·produced in the coulomb field of the nucleus. It has been shown that an excited nucleus with energy $>2m_0c^2$ may de-excite by a creation of an electron-positron pair somewhere in its own coulomb field. Such a process is called *internal pair-conversion* and is an alternative to the γ-emission and conversion-electron emission. Again the process, just like γ-decay and conversion-electron processes, is due to an electromagnetic interaction. The total available energy, E_0, for the transition is distributed as

$$E_0 = 2m_0c^2 + K_+ + K_- \tag{9.82}$$

where K_+ and K_- are the kinetic energies of the positron and electron, respectively, and $2m_0c^2$ is the sum of the rest masses of the positron and the electron.

A theory has been worked out for the calculation of the probability of internal pair-conversion and the results are shown by means of plots in Fig. 9.35[(42)]. The results of the theoretical predictions, which agree with the experiments, indicate the following:

(a) The internal pair-conversion rate increases with increasing energy, but decreases with an increase in L, which is the multipolarity of the transition.

(b) The internal pair-conversion is almost independent of Z, or it decreases very slowly with increasing Z.

(c) As the energy E_0 increases ($\gtrsim 10$ Mev) the internal pair-conversion coefficients become insensitive to L.

It is quite obvious that the dependence of the internal pair-conversion rate is altogether opposite to that of the internal conversion. This difference arises from the nature of their processes. The process of internal pair-conversion involves the transfer of an electron in the negative-energy state to the positive-energy state. There are an infinite number of electrons available for this process. On the contrary, in the process of internal conversion, the only electrons available are those in the electronic orbits of the atom. Because for light elements, the internal conversion coefficient is very small, the internal pair-conversion study becomes useful for the determination of the spin, parity, and multipolarities of different states. Actually, internal conversion and internal pair-conversion supplement each other, and they both compete with γ-emission. The most useful method for investigating the spin and parity of the excited state and the multipolarities of the γ-rays in the case of

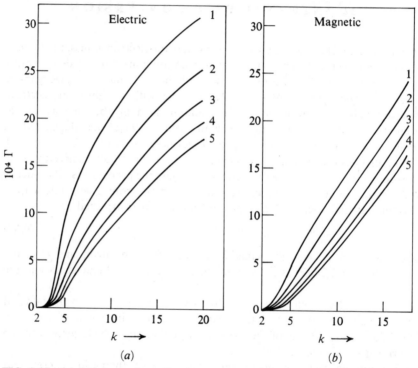

FIG. 9.35 (a) Total number of pairs per quantum for electric multipoles. The curves are for different values of L, and (b) the same as (a) for magnetic multipoles.

light elements is to measure the $(e^+ - e^-)$ angular correlations. The usefulness of this is illustrated in Fig. 9.36 and one can conclude that the 2.86 Mev transition in B^{10} is M1 or E2.

Internal pair-conversion probabilities are small and, therefore, are difficult to measure. H. Slatus and K. Siegbahn[43] have measured the internal pair-conversion coefficients for some standard γ-ray transitions and have found them to be of the order of 5×10^{-4} or less.

One may ask what happens to the electron created in the pair. Usually the electron goes into the continuum because all the low-energy states are filled. However, the most interesting case is the one in which internal pair-conversion follows electron capture. There will be short intervals of time

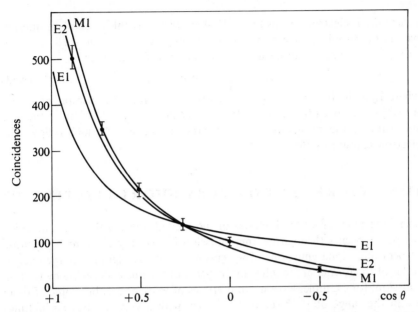

FIG. 9.36 Internal pair conversion, e^--e^+, angular correlation for the 2.86 Mev transition in B^{10}. It is obvious that M1 or E2 is the most likely transition. [From Gorodetzky, S., P. Chevallier, R. Armbruster, G. Shutt, *Nucl. Phys.* **12**, 354, (1959).]

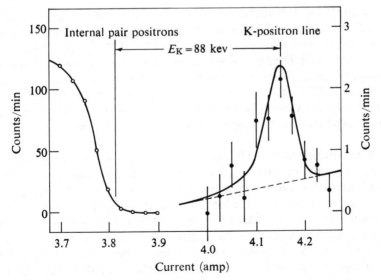

FIG. 9.37 The line spectra of the positrons emitted by Pb^{206} that follows the electron capture decay of Bi^{206}. E_K is the binding energy of K electron. [From Brunner, *et al., Phys. Rev. Letters* **2**, p. 207, (1959).]

before the L-electron jumps to the K-shell. If during this interval an internal pair is produced, the electron produced may occupy the K-shell. In such cases, the positrons will be monoenergetic with K_+ given by

$$K_+ = E_0 - 2m_0c^2 + I_B \qquad (9.83)$$

where I_B is the binding energy of the orbital electron. An example of such a transition has been found by J. Brunner, et al.[44]. Fig. 9.37 shows the line spectrum of the positrons emitted by the excited Pb^{206} which follows the electron capture of Bi^{206}.

13. MEASUREMENT OF VERY SHORT LIFETIMES[45]

The determination of the lifetimes of the excited states of the nuclei in which the decay occurs through gamma emission is basically different from those of beta and alpha emissions. The reason is that the lifetimes of the excited states of the former are much shorter. Most of the nuclei decaying by gamma emission, for example, have mean lifetimes of $< 10^{-11}$ sec, but some of them are in the range of 10^{-6} sec to 10^{-11} sec, with a very few having lifetimes greater than 10^{-6} sec. From the uncertainty principle, the relation between the lifetime, τ, and the level width Γ (Γ is the uncertainty in the energy of the level) is given by the following:

$$\Gamma \cdot \tau = \hbar \qquad (9.84)$$

For $\tau \approx 10^{-12}$ sec, Γ is of the order of 7×10^{-4} ev. Such narrow level widths are hard to measure, and special techniques have been developed. At present the shortest measureable lifetime is of the order of 10^{-14} sec. The different methods that have been developed up to the present day are the following: (a) delayed-coincidence method ($\tau \sim 10^{-6} - 10^{-11}$ sec), (b) nuclear-resonance methods ($\tau \sim 10^{-13}$ sec), (c) nuclear- and doppler-recoil methods ($\tau \sim 10^{-7} - 10^{-14}$ sec), (d) Coulomb-excitation method ($\tau \sim 10^{-6} - 10^{-14}$ sec), and (e) alternative-transitions comparison method ($\tau \leqslant 10^{-6}$ sec).

A. DELAYED COINCIDENCE METHOD.   This method is possible whenever the gamma emission is preceeded by another transition; for example, a beta decay may be followed by gamma emission. A simplified sketch of the experimental setup is shown in Fig. 9.38. The beta particles are detected in one detector and the gamma rays in the other. The beta detector is also provided with a variable delay box, so that the pulses from this may be delayed for different lengths of time. A coincidence rate is observed between the beta and the gamma rays as a function of the delay time of the beta pulses. The maximum coincidence counting-rate corresponds to the lifetime of the excited state. As shown in Fig. 9.39, the lifetime of Sn^{117m} is 3.1×10^{-10} sec. This method has been used frequently in nuclear spectroscopy as well as with accelerators.

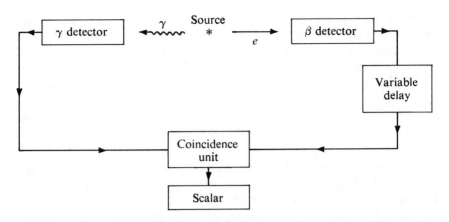

FIG. 9.38 A simplified sketch of the experimental setup for the delayed-coincidence method.

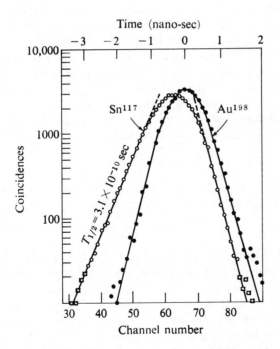

FIG. 9.39 Time spectrum of e-γ coincidences in the decay of Sn^{117m}. A prompt time distribution from β-γ coincidences in Au^{198} decay is also shown. [From Schmorak, M., A. C. Li, and A. Schwarzschild, *Phys. Rev.* **130**, 727, (1963).]

B. NUCLEAR-RESONANCE METHODS. In this method the levels are directly excited by means of incident radiation, and after measuring the scattering cross-sections, one may calculate the level widths and the lifetime in the following manner.

As we shall see in Chap. XI, the resonant cross-section, σ is given by

$$\sigma = \pi \lambda^2 g \frac{\Gamma_a \Gamma}{(E - E_0)^2 + \Gamma^2/4} \qquad (9.85)$$

where g is the statistical weight factor, Γ is the total width of the level, and Γ_a is the partial-width of the level for a particular type of reaction, λ is the wave length of the incident radiation of energy E, and E_0 is the energy of the level above the ground state. If the incident radiation consists of photons of energy $E = E_0$ and $\Gamma_a = \Gamma_\gamma$, the absorption cross-section for the photons will be given by

$$\sigma_a = 4\pi \lambda^2 g(\Gamma_\gamma/\Gamma) \qquad (9.86)$$

By measuring the resonance cross-sections it is possible to obtain the relative width of the levels for gamma emission; but to obtain the resonance cross-sections we need photons of energies exactly equal to the energies of the excited states. Sources of monoenergetic photons are hard to obtain. One may suggest that the photons emitted by a nucleus may be used to excite the same type of nuclei as the source. However, as we shall see, the energy of the photon emitted is not equal to the energy of the transition, and it cannot be used for resonance excitation of the same level.

When a gamma ray is emitted from a nucleus, the conservation of momentum requires that the nucleus recoil according to the relation

$$MV = E_\gamma/c \qquad (9.87)$$

where M and V are the mass and velocity of the nucleus, and E_γ is the photon energy. The kinetic energy, E_n, of the nucleus is

$$E_n = \tfrac{1}{2}MV^2 = \tfrac{1}{2}E_\gamma^2/Mc^2 \qquad (9.88)$$

The emitted photon, therefore, has energy $(\tfrac{1}{2})E_\gamma^2/Mc^2$ less than the transition energy E_0. Similarly, if the level of energy E_0 is to be excited by photons, an additional energy, E_n, is required for the recoil of the nucleus in order to conserve momentum. Thus if the photons of energy E_γ are used to excite the level E_0, the energy of the photons will be less than the energy required to cause resonance excitation by an amount ΔE given by

$$\Delta E = E_\gamma^2/Mc^2 \qquad (9.89)$$

This difficulty has been overcome by restoring the recoil energy by means of either the Doppler effect or the Mössbauer effect.

C. THE DOPPLER EFFECT[46,47,48]. In this method the source is placed on the tip of a high-speed rotor. The Doppler effect will increase the frequency of the emitted radiation. If the speed of the rotor is such that the condition

$$E_\gamma(v/c) = E_\gamma^2/Mc^2 \qquad (9.90)$$

is satisfied, it will be possible to observe resonance scattering with photons of energy E_γ. This method has been demonstrated by P. Moon and W. Davey[46,47].

Doppler broadening[48] has also been achieved by heating the radioactive source to temperatures of the order of 1200°C.

D. THE MÖSSBAUER EFFECT[49,50]. In this method the need to supply the recoil energy is eliminated by using the technique developed by R. Mössbauer. The gamma-emitting nucleus is made a part of a crystal lattice and the recoil energy is shared by the whole lattice, not only by the nucleus. Such a condition is usually achieved by placing the source, which forms a part of the crystal, at low temperature. Under such circumstances, the energy loss by the recoil is negligible. Similarly, the target is made a part of the lattice at low temperature, and resonance scattering is easily obtained by using the emitted gamma rays. A resonance curve may be obtained by using a very small variable-velocity of the source.

The apparatus used by Mössbauer[51] and the results obtained for Ir^{191} (129 kev gamma rays) are shown in Fig. 9.40. The Mössbauer effect is used more commonly in the study of hyperfine structure and in the solid state.

14. GAMMA-GAMMA ANGULAR CORRELATIONS

In the last fifteen years work on gamma–gamma angular correlations has become popular. It has proved to be a valuable means of (1) determining the spins of the excited states, (2) confirming the spin assignments determined by other methods, and (3) determining the character of the transition between the states.

The theory of angular correlation as applied to the successive emission of any nuclear radiation was first given by D. Hamilton[52]. It was shown that the theoretical specification of angular correlation requires two kinds of information: (a) the angular momentum of the nuclear states and the emitted radiation, and (b) the Hamiltonian interaction between the outgoing particles and the nucleus. In the case of gamma rays emitted in cascade as in Fig. 9.41(a), the correlation $W(\theta)$, where θ is the angle between the successive gamma rays, as in Fig. 9.41(b), is a function of the spins of the initial, intermediate, and final states, J_1, J, and J_2, respectively, and the multipolarities

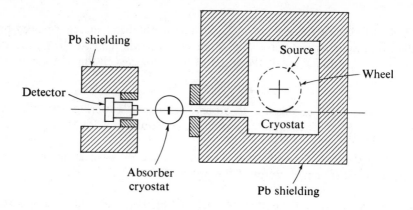

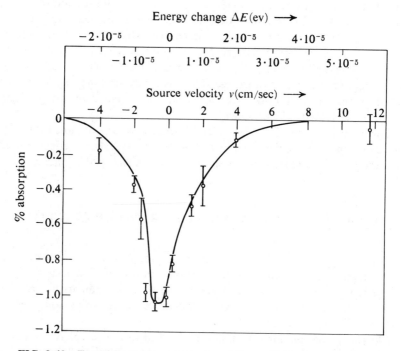

FIG. 9.40 Experimental demonstration of recoilless resonance-absorption of 129-kev gamma radiation of Ir^{191}. [From Mössbauer, R. L., *Natur Wiss*, **45**, 538, (1958).] (*a*) An outline of the experimental arrangement used by Mössbauer. Both the source and the absorber are inside the cryostat. The source is mounted on the wheel, which may be rotated in either direction with variable velocity. (*b*) The effect of the motion of the source on resonant absorption at 88 K. The half-width at half-maximum absorption is

$$2\Gamma = (9.2 \pm 1.2)10^{-6} \text{ ev.}$$

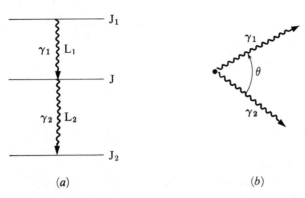

FIG. 9.41 (a) Successive emission of two gamma rays. L_1 and L_2 are the multipolarities of γ_1, and γ_2, respectively. J_1, J, and, J_2 are the spins of the initial, intermediate, and final states, respectively. (b) The angle between the directions of emission of two successive gamma rays is given by θ.

L_1 and L_2 of the two gamma rays respectively. In the original form the correlation function was expressed by Hamilton as

$$W(\theta) = 1 + a_2 \cos^2 \theta + a_4 \cos^4 \theta + \cdots \qquad (9.91)$$

The more convenient and general form of the angular correlation was developed independently by S. Lloyd[53], L. Falkoff, and G. Uhlenbeck, D. Ling[54,55] and G. Racah[56] in the form of a Legendre series in the cosine of the angle, θ, between the successive gamma rays, or

$$W(\theta) = 1 + A_2 P_2(\cos \theta) + A_4 P_4(\cos \theta) + \cdots$$
$$= 1 + \sum_k A_k P_k(\cos \theta) \qquad (9.92)$$

which is normalized to unit average at 90°. An easier and more explicit calculation of the coefficients, A_k, is greatly facilitated by the fact that they can be broken up into two factors, each depending on only one transition of the cascade, i.e.,

$$W(\theta) = 1 + A_2^{(1)} A_2^{(2)} P_2(\cos \theta) + A_4^{(1)} A_4^{(2)} P_4(\cos \theta) + \cdots$$
$$= 1 + \sum_k A_k^{(1)} A_k^{(2)} P_k(\cos \theta) \qquad (9.93)$$

where the sum is taken over even values of k given by

$$0 \leqslant \text{even } K \leqslant \min (2J, 2L_1, 2L_2)$$

and

$$L_1 = 1 \text{ if } J_1 = J \text{ or } L_1 = |J_1 - J| \text{ if } J_1 \neq J$$
$$L_2 = 1 \text{ if } J_2 = J \text{ or } L_2 = |J_2 - J| \text{ if } J_2 \neq J$$

If both the transitions in the cascade are pure multipoles of order L_1 and L_2 respectively, the A coefficients are given by

$$A_k^{(1)} = F_k(L_1, L_1, J_1, J)$$

and

$$A_k^{(2)} = F_k(L_2, L_2, J_2, J) \tag{9.94}$$

where the F coefficients are the combinations of the Clebsch-Gordan C and the Racah coefficient, W, and are tabulated by M. Ferentz and N. Rosenzweig[57] for different combinations of L's and J's. Equation (9.94) takes a more complicated form if the transitions are not of pure multipolarities.

The experimental work is limited to the use of the first two coefficients only, and the correlation is expressed as

$$W(\theta) = 1 + A_2 P_2(\cos \theta) + A_4 P_4(\cos \theta) \tag{9.95}$$

The theoretical values of A_2 and A_4 are compared with the experimental values of these coefficients and the predictions about the spins and the

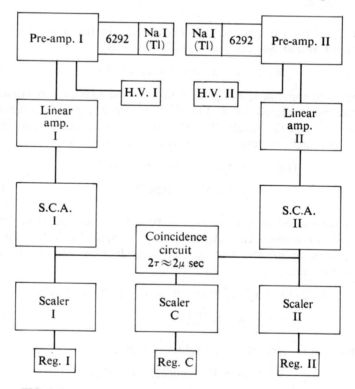

FIG. 9.42 An experimental arrangement for investigation of gamma-gamma angular correlations. [From Arya, A. P., *Phys. Rev.*, **122**, 1226, (1961).]

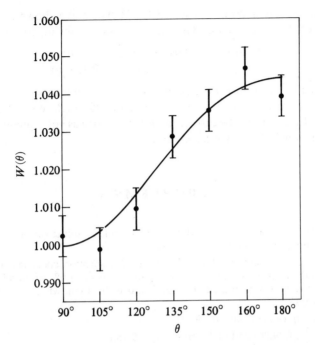

FIG. 9.43   Angular correlation of the 356–82 kev gamma cascade in Cs^{133}. The points with flags are the experimental points, the flags indicating the standard deviation. The continuous curve is the least-square fit of the experimental points. [From Arya, A. P., *Phys. Rev.*, **122**, 549, (1961).]

multipolarities can be made. The experimental values of A_2 and A_4 are evaluated from the experimentally determined values of $W(\theta)$. An experimental arrangement (Fig. 9.42) used by the author[58] is described in the following.

Two NaI(Tl) detectors, shown in Fig. 9.42, are used for the detection of gamma rays. The signals are amplified by means of linear amplifiers, and the energy selection of the two gamma rays in the cascade is made by means of single-channel analyzers (or discriminators). The two signals from the analyzers are fed to the coincidence circuit that produces counts only if the two signals correspond to the two gamma rays emitted from a nucleus in cascade (within a time interval of $<2\tau$ sec, the resolving time of the coincidence circuit). One NaI(Tl) detector is fixed, while the other is moved to find the coincidence rates at different angles. We can then find $W(\theta) = N(\theta)/N(90°)$, where $N(\theta)$ and $N(90°)$ are the coincidence-count rates at angle θ and $90°$, respectively. Knowing $W(\theta)$ for different θ, the coefficients A_2 and A_4 in Eq. (9.95) may be calculated by making a least-square fit. As an example, Fig. 9.43[59] shows the experimentally measured directional correlation of the 356 and 82 kev gamma cascade in Cs^{133}. The curve shown is the least-square fit of the experimental data and gives the following correlation:

$$W(\theta) = 1 + (0.042 \pm 0.005)P_2(\cos \theta)$$
$$+ (0.0041 \pm 0.0038)P_4(\cos \theta)$$

This angular correlation is consistent with spin assignments of $\frac{7}{2}^+$, $\frac{5}{2}^+$, and $\frac{1}{2}^+$ for the level at ground state, 82 kev and 438 kev levels in Cs^{133}. The correlation functions can be further modified for the case of alpha-gamma[60] and beta-gamma[61] angular correlations.

PROBLEMS

1. Calculate the thickness of lead needed to reduce the intensity to one-half of (a) 1 Mev γ-rays, and (b) 2 Mev γ-rays.

2. Calculate the thickness of lead in terms of absorption coefficient needed to reduce the intensity of monoenergetic gamma rays to 1.0% of initial intensity. If the thickness of lead used above is found to be 4 cm, what is the energy of the γ-rays?

3. Derive Eq. (9.19) from Eq. (9.18).

4. Derive Eqs. (9.20) and (9.22) from Eqs. (9.18).

5. What is the range of energies for which the Compton effect predominates over the photoelectric effect and pair production for absorption of photons by (a) lead, (b) copper and (c) aluminum. Compare the Compton absorption coefficients at some particular energies.

6. Show that in the process of pair production the presence of a nucleus (or some other body) is necessary in order to conserve momentum and energy.

7. Show that in the process of pair production from a given energy photon the maximum momentum will be carried away if the momenta of the two particles are equal.

8. Show that it is not possible for a photon to transfer all its energy to an electron.

9. Show that Bremsstrahlung cannot occur in free space.

10. Gamma rays of different energies are allowed to fall on a lead radiator. The use of a magnetic spectrometer shows that there are four groups of electrons corresponding to Hr values of 1020-, 1530-, 2150- and 2430-gauss-cm respectively. What are the energies of the gamma rays if the K shell binding energy of lead is 89.1 kev?

11. Calculate the energies of the gamma rays from the following data. Gamma rays are incident on aluminum foil and the Compton electrons emitted are analyzed by means of a magnetic spectrometer. The electrons fall into four groups with maxima at 2750, 3890, 4890 and 5575 gauss-cm respectively.

12. Electrons are ejected by radiating lead with monoenergetic gamma rays. The electrons are incident on two electron counters in coincidence. Energy of the gamma rays is measured by placing thin foils between the two counters. If the window of each counter is 10 mg/cm² and a sheet of 200 mg/cm² of Al reduces the coincidence counting rate to zero, what is the energy of the gamma ray?

13. In a quartz crystal the inter-planar spacing is 1.1776×10^{-8} cm. A grating made out of this crystal is used in a diffraction spectrometer. Calculate the angle corresponding to a first order Bragg reflection for a 661.77 kev gamma ray.

14. Cs^{137} decays by β^- emission as shown in the diagram. Calculate the energies of the K and L shell conversion lines. The K and L shell binding energies for barium are 37.44 and 5.99 kev respectively.

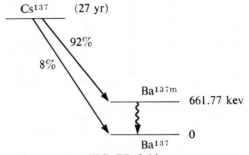

FIG. PR–9.14

15. Corresponding to Fig. 9.26, for electric dipole, quadrupole and octupole, construct the corresponding static magnetic multipoles by using current loops.

16. Consider a cube of length l with charge $-q$ placed at each of the corners. Calculate the components of dipole and quadrupole moments with respect to the center of the cube.

17. At what distance from the center of the nucleus should a photon of 1.5 Mev be created so that it carries away an angular momentum of $2\hbar$?

18. What are the most probable multipole gamma transitions expected between the following states?
(a) $2^+ \to 0^+$, (b) $3^- \to 1^+$, (c) $2^+ \to 4^+$
(d) $2^+ \to 4^-$, (e) $2^+ \to 1^-$, (f) $2^+ \to 1^+$
(g) $4^+ \to 1^+$, (h) $1^- \to 4^+$

19. What are the most probable multipole gamma transitions expected between the following states?
(a) $\frac{11^-}{2} \to \frac{3^+}{2}$, (b) $\frac{11^-}{2} \to \frac{5^+}{2}$, (c) $\frac{5^-}{2} \to \frac{1^-}{2}$
(d) $\frac{5^-}{2} \to \frac{1^+}{2}$, (e) $\frac{9^+}{2} \to \frac{3^-}{2}$, (f) $\frac{5^+}{2} \to \frac{1^+}{2}$

20. Consider a portion of the decay scheme of Xe^{128} shown in the figure. (a) Will the level 0.98 Mev decay mainly to 0^+ or 2^+? (b) What are the relative intensities of these two transitions as predicted by the theory?

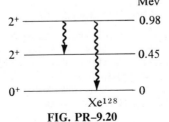

FIG. PR–9.20

21. Nuclei in the excited state at 0.680 Mev (see fig.) can decay to all three lower states. To which state will they mostly decay? Calculate theoretically the relative transition probabilities of these three transitions.

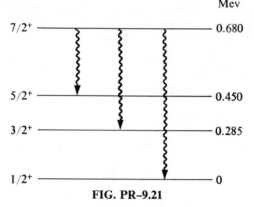

FIG. PR–9.21

22. One of the excited states of Co^{59} at 1.289 Mev decays by emission of two gamma rays as shown. The 1.289 Mev gamma ray is about 15 times more intense than 0.191 Mev gamma ray. (a) What are the multipolarities of these two gamma rays? (b) Compare the experimentally determined relative intensities of these two gamma rays with the theoretically predicted values and explain any discrepancy.

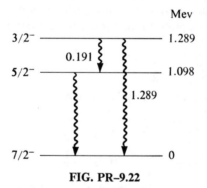

FIG. PR–9.22

23. A nucleus in an excited state decays by emission of three gamma rays as shown. The 0.41 Mev gamma ray is a M1 transition, 2.51 Mev is an E2 transition, while 1.31 Mev is an E1 transition. The ground state of the nucleus is $\frac{3}{2}^{+}$. (a) What are the spins and parities of the different excited states? (b) If the relative intensities of these gamma rays are as shown in the figure, how do these compare with the theoretical values? (c) If 0.41 Mev and 1.31 Mev were not pure dipole transitions, what higher multipole mixtures would be expected in these two transitions? (d) What are the energies, intensities and multipolarities of other gamma rays that will accompany the decay?

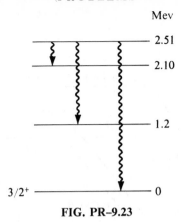

FIG. PR–9.23

24. The ground state of Pm^{147} has a spin of $\frac{5^+}{2}$ while the excited state at 92 kev has $\frac{7^+}{2}$. The gamma transition from the excited state to the ground state is a mixture of 95% M1 + 5% E2. (a) What is the theoretical conversion coefficient for this transition? (b) What is the partial lifetime of the 92 kev level?

25. If the lifetime of the first excited state of I^{129} at 27 kev is 2×10^{-9} second, what is the width of this level? The state at 27 kev decays by 20% electron capture and 80% by gamma emission. From theory calculate the partial lifetime of this level. If the gamma transition is a mixture of M1 and E2, calculate their percentage mixture.

26. Au^{197} has a metastable state at 0.409 Mev. This metastable state decays with the emission of two gamma rays as shown. The spins of the different states are also shown. (a) What are the multipolarities of the two gamma rays? (b) Calculate the partial lifetimes for the two gamma rays from theory. (c) What are their relative intensities if the mean lifetime of the 0.409 Mev gamma ray as measured experimentally is 7.2 seconds?

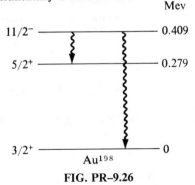

FIG. PR–9.26

27. A partial decay scheme of Tc^{93m} is shown in Fig. PR–9.27. (a) What is the nature of the isomeric transition? (b) If 31% of the isomeric transition takes place through electron capture, what is the theoretical lifetime of the metastable state? How does this compare with the experimental value?

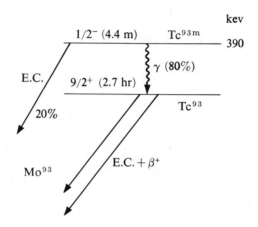

FIG. PR–9.27

28. According to the measurement made by Mössbauer, the width at half maximum of absorption of 129 kev level in Ir^{191} in terms of the velocity spread of the source is 1.51 cm/sec. (a) Calculate the level width in ev. (b) Calculate the half-life of the excited state.

29. Calculate the recoil energy of the Nb^{94} nucleus after it emits a 42 kev gamma ray. If the 42 kev gamma ray is to be reabsorbed in Nb^{94}, what should be the relative velocity between the source and the absorber?

30. What is the form of the correlation function for the two gamma rays in cascade if the spin of the intermediate level is (a) 0, (b) $\frac{1}{2}$, (c) 1, (d) $\frac{3}{2}$, (e) 2?

31. In order to obtain a true angular correlation (undisturbed) between two gamma rays in cascade, the resolving time of the coincidence circuit must be longer than the mean lifetime of the intermediate level. Explain.

32. Show that in order to measure a true angular correlation experimentally the maximum source strength is limited by the relation

$$S < \frac{1}{2\tau}$$

where S is the disintegration rate of the radioactive sample and 2τ resolving time of the coincidence circuit.

33. How will a very strong source affect the measurement of the angular correlation function?

REFERENCES

1. Davisson, C. M., and R. D. Evans, *Revs. Mod. Phys.*, **24**, p. 79, (1952).

2. Fano, U., *Nucleonics*, **11**, No. 9, p. 55, (1953).

3. Hall, H., *Phys. Rev.*, **45**, p. 620, (1935); **84**, p. 167, (1951).

4. Hulme, H. R., J. McDougall, R. A. Buckingham, and R. H. Fowler, *Proc. Roy Soc.*, (London), **149A**, p. 131, (1935).
5. Heitler, W., *The Quantum Theory of Radiation*, Chapter 3, p. 119. (London): Oxford University Press, 1936.
6. Stobbe, M., *Ann. Physik*, **7**, p. 661, (1930).
7. Klein, O., and Y. Nishina, *Z. Physik*, **52**, p. 853, (1928).
8. "Graphs of the Compton Energy-Angle Relationship and the Klein-Nishina Formula." *NBS Circular* 542.
9. Perrin, F., *Compt. Rend.*, **197**, p. 1100, (1933). Watson, K. M., *Phys. Rev.*, **72**, p. 1060, (1947).
10. Bethe, H., and W. Heitler, *Proc. Roy. Soc.*, (London), **146A**, p. 83, (1954).
11. Anderson, Carl D., *Phys. Rev.*, **43**, p. 491, (1933).
12. Dirac, P. A. M., *Proc. Roy. Soc.*, **126**, p. 360, (1930); **133**, p. 61, (1931).
13. Stueckelberg, E. C. G., *Helv. Phys. Acta.*, **14**, p. 588, (1941); **15**, p. 23, (1942).
14. Feynman, R. P., *Phys. Rev.*, **76**, p. 749, (1949).
15. *N.B.S. Circular 583*; *N.B.S. Report 1003* (1952).
16. Cowan, C. L., *Phys. Rev.*, **74**, p. 1841, (1948).
17. Glendenin, L. E., *Nucleonics*, **2**, No. 1, p. 12, (1948).
18. DuMond, J. W. M., *Rev. Sci. Inst.*, **18**, p. 626, (1947); *Ann. Revs. Nucl. Sci.*, **8**, p. 163, (1958).
19. Muller, D. E., H. C. Hoyt, D. J. Klein, and J. W. M. DuMond, *Phys. Rev.*, **88**, p. 775, (1952).
20. Walker, R. L., and B. D. McDaniel, *Phys. Rev.*, **74**, p. 315, (1948).
21. Frisch, O. R., *Prog. Nucl. Phys.*, **1**, (Cavanagh), p. 152, (1950).
22. Bair, J. K., and F. C. Maienschein, *Rev. Sci. Inst.*, **22**, p. 343, (1951).
23. Slater, J. C., and N. H. Frank, *Electromagnetism*, p. 227. New York: McGraw-Hill Book Co., 1947.
24. Blatt, J. M., and V. F. Weisskopf, *Theoretical Nuclear Physics*, p. 627. New York: John Wiley & Sons, 1952.
25. Heitler, W., *Proc. Camb. Phil. Soc.*, **32**, p. 112, (1936).
26. Weisskopf, V. F., *Phys. Rev.*, **83**, p. 1073L, (1951).
27. Seigbahn, K., ed., *Alpha-, Beta- and Gamma-Ray Spectroscopy*, p. 882, New York: Interscience Publishers, (1965).
28. Goldhaber, M., and J. Weneser, *Ann. Revs. of Nucl. Sci.*, p. 5, (1955).
29. Rainwater, J., *Phys. Rev.*, **79**, p. 432 (1950).
30. Ellis, C. D., *Z. Physik*, **10**, p. 303, (1922).
31. Rosseland, S., *Z. Physik*, **14**, p. 173, (1923).
32. Ellis, C. D., and G. H. Aston, *Proc. Roy. Soc.*, **A129**, p. 180, (1930); Alburger, D. E., and A. Hedgran, *Ark. Fys.*, **7**, p. 423, (1953–54).
33. Dzelepow, B. S., Yu V. Kholnov, and V. P. Prikhodtseva, *Nuc. Phys.*, **9**, p. 665, (1958–59).
34. Alburger, D. E., *Phys. Rev.*, **109**, p. 1222, (1958).
35. Owen, G. E., D. Moe, and C. S. Cook, *Phys. Rev.*, **74**, p. 1879, (1948).

36. Scharff-Goldhaber, G., D. E. Alburger, G. Harbottle, and M. McKeown, *Phys. Rev.*, **111**, p. 913, (1958).

37. Church, E. L., and J. Weneser, *Phys. Rev.*, **103**, p. 1035, (1956); *Ann. Revs. Nucl. Sci.*, **10**, p. 193, (1960).

38. Rose, M. E., *Internal Conversion Coefficients*. Amsterdam: North Holland Publishing Co., 1958; New York: Interscience Publishing Inc., 1958.

39. Sliv, L. A., and I. M. Band, *Tables of Internal Conversion Coefficients of Gamma Radiation*. Moscow–Leningrad: USSR Academy of Sciences Publishing House, 1956.

40. Broyles, C. D., D. A. Thomas, and S. K. Haynes, *Phys. Rev.*, **89**, p. 715, (1953).

41. Burhop, E. H. S., *The Auger Effect and Other Radiationless Transitions*. London: Cambridge University Press, 1952.

42. Rose, M. E., *Phys. Rev.*, **78**, p. 184L, (1950).

43. Slätis, H. and K. Siegbahn, *Ark. Fys.*, paper 32, **4**, p. 485, (1952).

44. Brunner, J. H., H. J. Leisi, C. F. Perdrisat, and P. Scherner, *Phys. Rev. Letters*, **2**, p. 207, (1959).

45. Devons, S., "The Measurement of Very Short Lifetimes," *Nuclear Spectroscopy*, Part A, ed. F. Ajzenberg-Selove, Academic Press, 1960.

46. Moon, P. B., *Proc. Phys. Soc.*, **A-64**, 76, (1951).

47. Davey W. G., and P. B. Moon, *Proc. Phys. Soc.*, **A-66**, p. 956, (1953).

48. Frisch, O. R., *Prog. Nucl. Phys.*, **7**, (Metzger), (1959).

49. Mössbauer, R. L., *Z. Physik*, **151**, p. 124, (1958).

50. Boyle, A. J. F., and H. E. Hall, *Rep. Prog. Phys.*, **25**, p. 441, (1962).

51. Mössbauer, R. L., *Naturwiss*, **45**, p. 538, (1958); *Z. Naturforsch*, **14a**, p. 211, (1959); *Z. Phys.* **151**, p. 124, (1958).

52. Hamilton, D. R., *Phys. Rev.*, **58**, p. 122, (1940).

53. Lloyd, S. P., *Phys. Rev.*, **81**, p. 307, (1951).

54. Falkoff, D. L., and G. E. Uhlenbeck, *Phys. Rev.*, **79**, p. 323, (1950).

55. Ling, D. S., and D. L. Falkoff, *Phys. Rev.*, **76**, p. 1639, (1949).

56. Racah, G., *Phys. Rev.*, **82**, p. 309, (1961).

57. Ferentz, M. and N. Rosenzweig, *ANL-5324*, (1954).

58. Arya, A. P., *Phys. Rev.*, **122**, p. 1226, (1961).

59. Arya, A. P., *Phys. Rev.*, **122**, p. 549, (1961).

60. Siegbahn, Kai, ed.; *Alpha-, Beta- and Gamma-Ray Spectroscopy*, p. 1051. North Holland Publishing Co., Amsterdam, (1965).

61. Siegbahn, Kai, ed.; *Alpha-, Beta- and Gamma-Ray Spectroscopy*, p. 1055. North Holland Publishing Co., Amsterdam, (1965).

SUGGESTIONS FOR FURTHER READING

1. Bethe, H. A. and J. Ashkin, *Experimental Nuclear Physics*, ed. E. Segre, Vol. I, Part II, (1953). New York: John Wiley & Sons.

2. Davisson, C. M., and R. D. Evans, *Revs. Mod. Phys.*, **24**, p. 79, (1952).

3. Siegbahn, K., ed., *Alpha-, Beta- and Gamma-Ray Spectroscopy*. New York: Interscience Publishing, 1965, and Amsterdam: North Holland Publishing.

4. Fermi, E., *Experimental Nuclear Physics*, Chaps. 2 and 5. Chicago: University of Chicago Press, 1950. Notes compiled by J. Orear, A. H. Rosenfeld, and R. A. Schluter.

5. Rutherford, Chadwick, and Ellis, *Radiation From Radioactive Substances*, Chaps. 12 and 15. New York: Cambridge University Press, 1930.

6. Deutsch, M., and O. Kofoed-Hansen, *Experimental Nuclear Physics*, ed. E. Segre, Vol. III, Part X, (1959). New York: John Wiley & Sons.

7. Evans, R. D., *The Atomic Nucleus*, Chaps. 5, 23, 24, and 25. New York: McGraw-Hill Book Co., 1955.

8. Ajzenberg, F., *Nuclear Spectroscopy*, ed. Selove, Parts A and B. New York: Academic Press, 1960.

X

NUCLEAR
MODELS

1. INTRODUCTION

It would be an ideal situation if we could find a single model of the nucleus that would explain all the nuclear properties. Unlike atomic models, where the law of force is known and the models are on firm footing, no such definiteness exists in the nuclear models because of a lack of knowledge of nuclear forces. Nuclear forces have been investigated in detail for the two-body problem as we shall see in Chap. XII, but their extension to the many-body problem is formidable because of the mathematical complexity involved.

The development of nuclear models has taken place along two lines. There are those in which the constituents of the nucleus are treated on a statistical basis, as in the case of a liquid drop or a volume of gas. Statistical models provide excellent agreement with the experiments when the number of particles in the system is very large. Although the nucleus does not contain a very large number of nucleons, statistical models have been developed for heavy nuclei and have proved to be successful. The second type of models are constructed in analogy with the shell model of the atom. The nucleons are treated as individual particles in this system.

It has been necessary to develop more models in order to explain nuclear reactions and the properties of the excited states in different energy ranges. Once the true nature of the law of force is discovered, however, these several models may not give a true description of the nuclei. At present, however, they are helpful in explaining certain properties of the nuclei. Some of the models are the following: (1) shell model, (2) collective model, (3) Fermi gas-model, (4) liquid-drop model, (5) compound-nucleus model, (6) direct-interaction model, and (7) optical model.

We shall discuss the first three models in some detail. The discussion of the last four models, which are very useful in explaining nuclear reactions, will be postponed until Chap. XI and Chap. XIII.

2. THE SHELL MODEL

It has been long established that the electrons in an atom tend to occupy distinct shells. Such a shell structure is evident from Fig. 10.1, where ionization potential has been plotted against atomic number, Z. Five inert gases He, Ne, Ar, Kr, and Xe, corresponding to atomic numbers 2, 10, 18, 36, and 54 respectively, have very high ionization potentials and, therefore, do not enter easily into chemical combination with other elements. These numbers 2, 10, 18, 36, and 54, that correspond to these extra-stable elements may be called

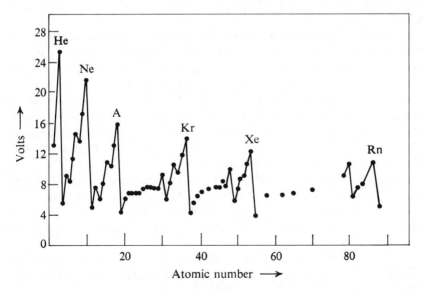

FIG. 10.1 A plot of the ionization potential versus atomic number, Z. The atomic shell structure is evident from this figure.

the *magic numbers* of the periodic table and correspond to the closed shells in the atomic structure.

As a result of the investigation of static and dynamic properties of the nuclei, it becomes obvious that the periodicities in the properties of the nuclei might be due to a shell structure similar to the atomic shell structure. The first such indications were pointed out by G. Gamow[1] and W. Elsasser[2]. The evidence given here implies that the numbers, 2, 8, 20, 28, 50, 82, and 126 corresponding to the number of protons or neutrons in the nucleus, may be the magic numbers of the nucleus. These magic numbers are not as strong as in the case of the atomic structure.

A. EVIDENCE FOR THE SHELL STRUCTURE.

(1) *Number of Stable Isotopes.* An element whose atomic number is one of the magic numbers has many more stable isotopes[3] than its neighbor. For example, $_{20}$Ca has six stable isotopes, while $_{19}$K has three, and $_{21}$Sc has only one. Similarly, $_{50}$Sn has ten stable isotopes (the maximum in the periodic table), while $_{49}$In and $_{51}$Sb each have only 2. $_{82}$Pb, as another example, has four stable isotopes, while $_{81}$Tl has two, and $_{83}$Bi has one.

(2) *Number of Stable Isotones.* As in the case of isotopes, an element whose neutron number is one of the magic numbers has many more stable isotones[3] than its neighbors. For example, for $N = 20$ there are 5 stable isotones, while for $N = 19$ there are none, and $N = 21$ has only one. For $N = 50$ there are six isotones, while corresponding to $N = 49$ and $N = 51$ there is only one for each. Similar behavior is also found for other magic numbers.

(3) *Natural Isotopic Abundances of the Nuclides.* The natural abundance of those isotopes for which the number of neutrons or protons is equal to one of the magic numbers is much larger than expected from the general distribution. For example, there are only three isotopes with even A whose abundances are greater than 60 percent and their neutron numbers match the magic numbers. These are $_{38}$Sr^{88} ($N = 50$) 82.6 percent, $_{56}$Ba^{138} ($N = 82$) 71.7 per cent, and $_{58}$Ce^{140} ($N = 82$) 88.5 percent. The isotopic abundance of $_{82}$Pb^{208}, which is doubly magic, ($Z = 82$, $N = 126$) is 52.3 percent and is much higher than other even-even nuclei.

The abundances of the lighter isotopes of elements with $Z > 32$, except for five isotopes, are less than 2 percent. The other five isotopes are Zr^{90} ($N = 50$) 51.5 percent, Mo^{92} ($N = 50$) 15.9 percent, Ru^{96} ($N = 52$) 5.5 percent, Nd^{142} ($N = 82$) 27.1 percent, and Sm^{144} ($N = 82$) 3.2 percent. Except for Ru^{96}, the other four have magic numbers of neutrons.

(4) *Decay Product of Radioactive Series.* The end products of the radioactive series—thorium series, uranium series, and actinium series, are $_{82}$Pb^{208}, $_{82}$Pb^{206}, and $_{82}$Pb^{207}, respectively. They all have a magic number of protons $Z = 82$), and the most abundant isotope of lead $_{82}$Pb^{208} also has $N = 126$,

a magic number. The final end-product of the fourth series, i.e., the neptunium chain, is Bi^{209} which also has $N = 126$.

(5) *Neutron Capture Cross-Sections.*   Fig. 10.2[4] shows the plot of the neutron capture cross-section versus neutron number. At the magic numbers, the cross-sections are very low indicating that the shells are closed and do not absorb the incoming neutrons. This is especially evident from the doubly magic isotopes $_{20}Ca^{40}$ and $_{82}Pb^{208}$ which have very low neutron capture cross-sections.

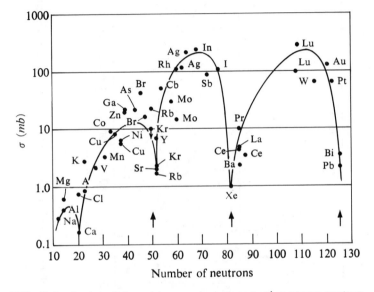

FIG. 10.2   A plot of the neutron capture cross-section versus neutron number. [From: Hughes D. J., and D. Sherman, *Phys. Rev.*, **78**, 632, (1950).]

On the other hand, if the shell is completely filled at the magic number, the isotopes with the number of neutrons one less than the magic number should have a very high cross-section for neutron absorption. This is clearly evident from Fig. 10.2 especially in the case of Xe^{135} and V^{50}.

(6) *Binding Energy of the Last Neutron or Proton.*   If the shells close at the magic numbers, the isotopes corresponding to these numbers should be very stable. This implies that the binding energies of the last added neutron or proton (to close the shell) should be very large. That such is the case is evident from Fig. 10.3[5] where the binding energy for the last added neutron has been plotted versus neutrons $N + 1$. High binding energy peaks are clearly visible.

(7) *Spontaneous Neutron Emitters.*   We should expect from the shell model that in the case of elements having one neutron in excess of the magic

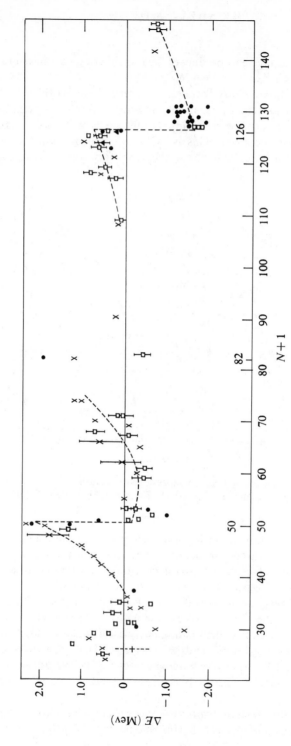

FIG. 10.3 A shell structure is evident from the plot of the difference in the binding energy versus neutron number. [From: Harvey, J. A., *Phys. Rev.*, **81**, 353, (1951).]

number, (i.e., a neutron in excess of the closed neutron shell), this last neutron should have a very small binding energy. This in fact is true and of the four known spontaneous neutron emitters, O^{17}, Kr^{87} and Xe^{137} have one neutron outside the closed shell while Kr^{89} has three neutrons outside a closed shell.

(8) *The Electric Quadrupole Moments.* From the definition of the electric quadrupole moment given in Chap. IX, we know that if a nucleus is spherically symmetric, it has no electric quadrupole-moment. The more it departs from a spherically symmetric charge distribution the larger will be its electric quadrupole-moment. This, in terms of the shell structure, means that for closed-shell isotopes the electric quadrupole-moment should be almost zero (or very small), while in between it should be very large. This is illustrated in Fig. 10.4[6] which confirms this prediction.

Thus, all the evidence proves that there are closed shells for neutrons and protons (separately) corresponding to the magic numbers 2, 8, 20, 28, 50, 82, and 126 for neutrons and 2, 8, 20, 28, 50, and 82 for protons, and the nuclei with one or both of the magic numbers show much greater stability than the other nuclei.

B. NUCLEAR SHELL MODEL.   We shall attempt to derive the magic numbers by considering the solution of a Schrödinger wave equation (S.W.E.) for a particle moving in a spherically symmetric field. A potential function of the form $V(r)$, where $V(r)$ is a function of r only, is assumed. Calculations of this type lead to the shell model of the nucleus. In the case of the atomic shell model, the form of the potential $V(r)$ was known exactly, and exact solutions of the S.W.E. were obtained. This is not so in nuclear physics. Different forms of $V(r)$ must be tried in order to obtain the required magic numbers.

The shell model calculations are based on the following two assumptions: (i) Each nucleon is assumed to move freely in a force field described by a potential that is a function only of the radial distance from the center of the system. This potential function represents its interaction with other nucleons. Each nucleon experiences the same potential. (ii) We assign definite states to single nucleons. Different levels are filled up according to Pauli's exclusion principle.

$$\Psi_{\text{antisymmetric}} = \phi(1)\phi(2)\phi(3) \dots \phi(n)$$

i.e., the total wave-function may be written as the product of the individual nucleon wave-functions.

Thus the S.W.E. to be solved for a nucleon of mass M and angular momentum $l\hbar$ moving in a potential $V(r)$ is given by (See Appendix A)

$$\frac{d^2}{dr^2}(rR) + \frac{2M}{\hbar^2}\left[E - V(r) - \frac{l(l+1)\hbar^2}{2Mr^2}\right](rR) = 0 \qquad \textbf{(10.1)}$$

where the radial wave-function, R, and the energy eigenvalue, E, are both functions of the total quantum number, n, and the angular-momentum quantum-number, *l*. Regardless of the form of $V(r)$, as long as it is a function of radial distance, *r*, the same quantum numbers result both in atomic as well as nuclear shell models, i.e., n, l, j, m_j.

In order to solve Eq. (10.1) we must know the exact shape of the potential

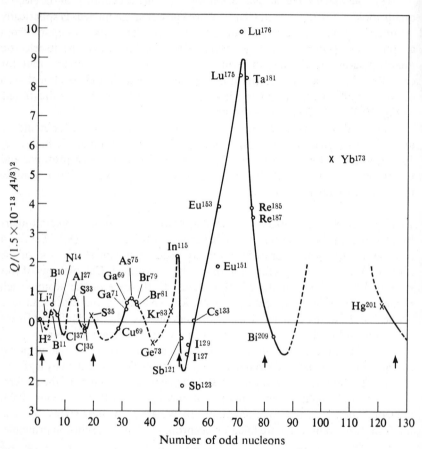

FIG. 10.4 Plot of quadrupole moments versus the number of odd nucleons; $\times$ and $\bigcirc$ indicate the nuclei with an odd number of neutrons and protons, respectively. The arrows correspond to the magic numbers. [From Townes, C. H., H. M. Foley, and W. Low, *Phys. Rev.*, **L76**, 1415, (1949).]

function, $V(r)$. The radial shape of the nuclear field is well known from scattering experiments, but its use in Eq. (10.1) makes it very complicated to solve the S.W.E. Because we are not interested in finding the exact binding energies, we can use simpler potentials that will give us the order of the levels corresponding to different states of the motion of the nucleon. Also we know that the binding energy per nucleon is constant and that the nuclear forces are short range. This means that the nucleons experience a large force inside the nucleus, and the potential falls sharply to zero at the nuclear surface. Two simple potentials commonly used are the square-well potential and the harmonic-oscillator potential. These two potential functions are shown in Fig. 10.5.

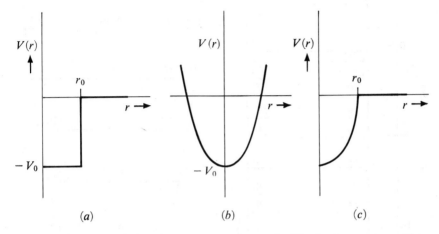

FIG. 10.5 Plots of (a) the square-well potential, (b) the harmonic-oscillator potential, and (c) the combined square-well and oscillator potential.

(1) *The Square-Well Potential.* The square well-potential[7] is given by

$$V(r) = \begin{cases} -V_0 & \text{for } r < r_0 \\ 0 & \text{for } r > r_0 \end{cases} \tag{10.2}$$

The problem is made mathematically simpler if we assume a potential well with infinite walls of the form

$$V(r) = \begin{cases} -V_0 & r < r_0 \\ \infty & r > r_0 \end{cases} \tag{10.3}$$

Use of the infinite potential changes the energy by a very small amount, but the order of the levels is unaffected. The solution of Eq. (10.1), (S.W.E.), for the infinite-potential well given by Eq. (10.3) gives the levels from the bottom of the well in the following order (as shown in Fig. 10.6a).

$$1s\ 1p\ 1d\ 2s\ 1f\ 2p\ 1g\ 2d\ 1h\ 3s\ 2f\ 1i\ 3p \cdots\cdots$$

where s, p, d, f, g, h, ... stand for the usual spectroscopic notation $l = 0, 1, 2, 3, 4, 5, \ldots$, respectively. Because the total number of protons or neutrons in a given l state is given by $2(2l + 1)$, it will predict the shell closure at 2, 8, 18, 20, 34, 40, 58, which do not correspond to the nuclear magic-numbers mentioned earlier.

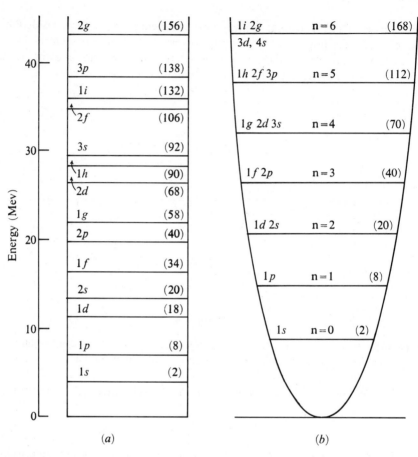

FIG. 10.6 Nuclear energy levels due to (a) an infinite square-well potential and (b) an oscillator potential. The levels in the oscillator potential are equally spaced. Parity of a level is even or odd as n is even or odd.

(2) The Harmonic-Oscillator Potential. In this case the potential is given by[7]

$$V(r) = -V_0 + \tfrac{1}{2}Kr^2 \qquad (10.4)$$

which has a parabolic form shown in Fig. 10.5(b). Solution of the S.W.E., Eq. (10.1), for the three-dimensional harmonic-oscillator potential of Eq. (10.4), gives the following discrete energy-eigenvalues, measured from the bottom of the well,

$$E = (n_1 + n_2 + n_3 + 3/2)\hbar\omega$$

or

$$E = (n_0 + 3/2)\hbar\omega \qquad (10.5)$$

where n_1, n_2, n_3 are the integers and $n_0(= n_1 + n_2 + n_3 \geqslant 0)$ is the total number of finite nodes in the wave function. If n_0 is even, $l = n_0, n_0 - 2, ...,$ 0, and if n_0 is odd, $l = n_0, n_0 - 2, ..., 1$. The degeneracy of the level n_0 is given by $[(n_0 + 1)(n_0 + 2)]$ or $2(2l + 1)$. This leads to the following level scheme (shown in Fig. 10.6b):

$$1s\ 1p\ 1d\ 2s\ 1f\ 2p\ \cdots$$

The shell closure occurs at numbers 2, 8, 20, 40, 70, and 112, which are not identical to the nuclear magic numbers.

Another scheme using a combination of the square-well and the harmonic oscillator potential was employed by L. Nordheim[8]. In this case the potential takes the form (shown in Fig. 10.5c)

$$V(r) = \begin{cases} -V_0(1 - r^2/r_0^2) & \text{for } r < r_0 \\ 0 & \text{for } r > r_0 \end{cases} \tag{10.6}$$

The results obtained give all the magic numbers except 28.

C. THE SPIN-ORBIT COUPLING MODEL. A different and successful model was suggested independently by M. Mayer[9], and O. Haxel, J. Jensen and H. Suess[10]. Until recently the only part played by l-s coupling was to give two levels corresponding to $j = l - \frac{1}{2}$ and $j = l + \frac{1}{2}$. According to Mayer, and Haxel, et al., in addition to the potential $V(r)$ there is a strong spin-orbit interaction proportional to $\mathbf{S \cdot L}$ acting on a nucleon in the nucleus. The spin-orbit interaction results in a noncentral component of force, and the magnitude of this interaction depends on, in addition to the magnitude of $\mathbf{L}$, the relative orientation of the spin and the orbital angular-momentum vectors. The spin-orbit interaction in this case is inverted, which means that the energy of the nucleon decreases when $\mathbf{S \cdot L}$ is positive and increases when $\mathbf{S \cdot L}$ is negative. This implies that the state $j = l + \frac{1}{2}$ has less energy and lies lower than the state $j = l - \frac{1}{2}$. This is just opposite of what happens in the case of the atomic electron. Thus by using a potential of the form $V(\mathbf{r})\ \mathbf{S \cdot L}$ where $V(\mathbf{r})$ is the central component of the force given by Eq. (10.6) (a combination of square-well and oscillator-potential), the resulting levels are given by [due to central potential term plus spin-orbit term]

$$1s_{1/2},\ 1p_{3/2},\ 1p_{1/2},\ 1d_{5/2},\ 1d_{3/2},\ 2s_{1/2},\ \cdots\cdots$$

measured from the bottom of the well. These levels are shown in Fig. 10.7[11]. It is important to note that because the spin-orbit interaction increases with increasing l, and the interaction is inverted, it may cause the depression of a state with high l. For example, in the $n_0 = 3$ oscillator level, the state $f_{7/2}$, which has $l = 3$ may be depressed enough to come close to the $n_0 = 2$ oscillator-level. The rearrangement of the levels, therefore, takes place and the closure of the shells occurs at

$$2, 8, 20, 28, 50, 82, 126,$$

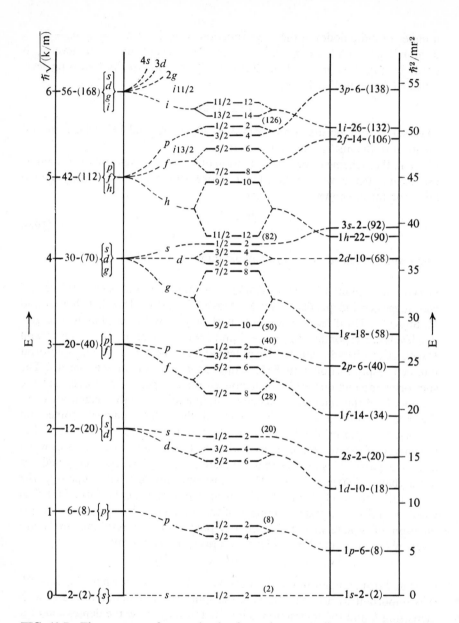

FIG. 10.7 The sequence of energy levels of a nucleon according to the shell model. On the right are the levels due to a square-well potential, and on the left are the levels due to an oscillator potential. In between are the levels obtained by using the mean of the two potentials and the effect of spin-orbit coupling. [From Haxel, O., J. H. D. Hensen and H. Suess, *Z. Phys.*, **128**, 298, (1950).]

which are exactly the required magic numbers. The quantum numbers which we use in the presence of spin-orbit coupling are n, l, j, and m_j. The total capacity of any level is $(2j + 1)$ protons or neutrons.

The spin-orbit interaction is not of an electromagnetic origin but is the result of nuclear force, and is much stronger than the magnetic interaction in the case of atomic electrons. The existence of the spin-orbit interaction has been verified by neutron-polarization scattering experiments. The sign of polarization is the same as required by the shell model and the amount of polarization is proportional to the strength of the spin-orbit coupling.

Another effect that we have not discussed so far is the coulomb inter-action of the protons. As a matter of fact this does effect the potential function in the case of protons, but it does not for neutrons. Thus, for a given quantum number, the proton-energy levels will be slightly different than those of the neutrons. Figure 10.8[12] shows the different levels of Fig. 10.7 after taking into account (i) the coulomb effect, and (ii) the pairing effect (Chap. V). Note that this is not an energy-level diagram for any particular nucleus, it is merely the order of levels in the shell model. For low quantum numbers the levels appear in the following order:

$$1s_{1/2}, \ 1p_{3/2}, \ 1p_{1/2}, \ 1d_{5/2}, \ 2s_{1/2}, \ 1d_{3/2}, \ 1f_{7/2}, \ \ldots\ldots .$$

D. APPLICATIONS. The existence of the shell model is established by its applications, which we shall discuss here. Quite a good agreement has been found between the experimental values and the shell-model predictions. We shall assume that the order of filling the energy levels is given by the shell model.

(1) *Nuclear Spins and Parities.* We may predict the spins and parities of the nuclei in the ground states if we consider the following: (1) In a complete-ly filled level (sub-shell or shell), the orbital angular momenta and spins of the nucleons add in such a way as to give a zero-resultant total angular-momentum. (2) In the levels that are not completely filled, the nucleons form pairs (proton pairs and neutron pairs, but no proton-neutron pairs: "pairing effect"). These two assumptions lead to the following coupling rules:

Rule 1: The ground states of even-even nuclei have zero angular mo-menta and even parity regardless of the number of protons and neutrons, i.e.,

$$\sum J_N = 0, \quad \text{and} \quad \sum J_P = 0$$

where J_N and J_P are the total angular momenta of the neutrons and the protons, respectively.

Rule 2: In a nucleus with an even numbers of neutrons and an odd number of protons, the ground-state properties are determined by the protons only, i.e., because $\Sigma J_N = 0$, the spin of the nucleus is determined by the last odd proton. In a nucleus with an even number of protons and an odd number

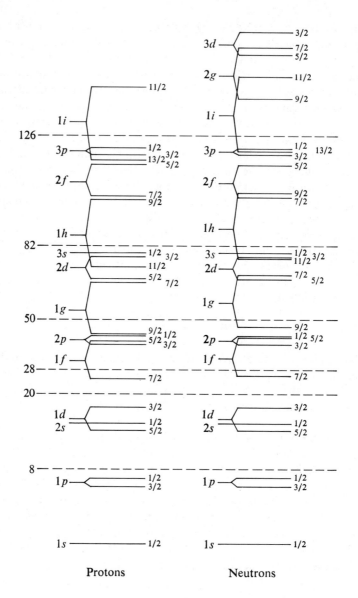

FIG. 10.8 The neutron- and the proton-level scheme and the shell structure. The proton-energy levels have been corrected for the proton's coulomb energy. [From: Klinkenberg, P. F. A., *Revs. Mod. Phys.*, **24**, 63, (1952).]

of neutrons, the ground-state properties are determined by the neutrons only, i.e., because $\Sigma J_p = 0$, the spin of the nucleus is determined by the last odd neutron.

These rules, however, do not predict the spins of the nuclei with an odd number of protons and an odd number of neutrons. Suppose the spin of the odd proton is j_1, and that of the odd neutron is j_2, then the nuclear spin may have any value between $|j_1 - j_2|$ and $|j_1 + j_2|$. Only the exact calculations may indicate which spin gives the most stable state.

TABLE 10.1

MEASURED AND PREDICTED SPINS OF SOME ODD NUCLIDES

Nuclide	Predicted Spin and Parity	Measured Spin and Parity
neutron	$1s_{1/2}$	$\frac{1}{2}+$
proton	$1s_{1/2}$	$\frac{1}{2}+$
$_1\mathrm{H}^3$	$1s_{1/2}$	$\frac{1}{2}+$
$_2\mathrm{He}^3$	$1s_{1/2}$	$\frac{1}{2}+$
$_3\mathrm{Li}^7$	$1p_{3/2}$	$\frac{3}{2}-$
$_4\mathrm{Be}^9$	$1p_{3/2}$	$\frac{3}{2}$
$_5\mathrm{Be}^{11}$	$1p_{3/2}$	$\frac{3}{2}$
$_6\mathrm{C}^{13}$	$1p_{1/2}$	$\frac{1}{2}$
$_8\mathrm{O}^{17}$	$1d_{5/2}$	$\frac{5}{2}$
$_9\mathrm{F}^{17}$	$1d_{5/2}$	$\frac{5}{2}$
$_9\mathrm{F}^{19}$	$1d_{5/2}$	$\frac{1}{2}$†
$_{11}\mathrm{Na}^{23}$	$1d_{5/2}$	$\frac{3}{2}$†
$_{20}\mathrm{Ca}^{43}$	$1f_{7/2}$	$\frac{7}{2}$
$_{23}\mathrm{V}^{51}$	$1f_{7/2}$	$\frac{7}{2}-$
$_{53}\mathrm{I}^{129}$	$1g_{7/2}$	$\frac{7}{2}+$

† The discrepancies are explained in the text.

Let us consider a few examples in which the above rules are applicable and some deviations from these rules. Table 10.1 lists the spin configurations predicted by the shell model as well as the experimental values. Some of the reasons for the discrepancies will be explained. (The level scheme for one of them, $_8\mathrm{O}^{17}$, is shown in Fig. 10.9.)

The first discrepancy occurs at $A = 19$ for $_9\mathrm{F}^{19}$, which according to the shell model, should have a spin of $d_{5/2}$, but the experimental value is 1/2. This discrepancy may be easily explained. Because $1d_{5/2}$ and $2s_{1/2}$ lie very close, the last-added proton goes to the $2s_{1/2}$ state rather than to the $1d_{5/2}$ state. This may also be explained as the result of coupling between the nucleons outside the closed shell, i.e., the two neutrons each having a spin of $\frac{5}{2}$ and a

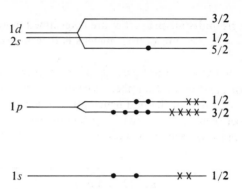

FIG. 10.9 Configuration of $_8O^{17}$. The last-odd particle is a neutron in the $d_{5/2}$ state; $\times$ indicates protons and ● indicates neutrons.

proton with a spin of $\frac{5}{2}$. Many examples of this type are found, such as Na^{23} which has a spin of $\frac{3}{2}$, while the one predicted by the shell model is $d_{5/2}$.

Another discrepancy occurs for very high orbital angular-momentum states. For example, one will expect that for a high atomic-mass number, A, there will be many stable nuclei with spin $\frac{11}{2}$ corresponding to an odd nucleon in the $1h_{11/2}$-state, but not even a single nucleus has ever been observed. The reason for this is that the shell model does not take into consideration the extra binding energy of the pairing of nucleons because interaction between individual nucleons has been neglected. As the orbital angular-momentum increases, the binding energy of pair formation also increases. The higher angular-momentum states are usually formed in pairs, and the odd nucleon goes to the higher energy level, which has a lower spin and greater stability. Thus a level $1h_{11/2}$ may be filled in pairs while the odd nucleon goes to $3s_{1/2}$ or $2d_{3/2}$. In other words, this means that the level $1h_{11/2}$ may be depressed below $3s_{1/2}$ or $2d_{3/2}$. For example, the measured spin of $_{56}Ba^{137}$ is $d_{3/2}$ while the one predicted by the shell model is $1h_{11/2}$. The rearranged levels are shown in Fig. 10.8.

The parity of the system is given by $(-1)^l$, where l is the orbital quantum number of the last-odd nucleon. For a nucleon in a state, $s, d, g, \ldots$ corresponding to $l = 0, 2, 4, \ldots$ the parity is even $(+)$; while for the states $p, f, h, \ldots$, corresponding to $l = 1, 3, 5, \ldots$, the parity is odd $(-)$.

(2) *Magnetic Moment.* Again, on the basis of the one particle theory, i.e., the properties of the nuclei are determined by the last-single-odd nucleon, we can calculate the magnetic moment. For the case of even-even nuclei, because the spin (total angular momentum) is zero, the magnetic moment is also zero. For an odd-A nucleus the magnetic moment is given by

$$\boldsymbol{\mu} = g_l a_l \mathbf{j} + g_s a_s \mathbf{j} \qquad (10.7)$$

where $g_l = 1$ for a proton and $g_l = 0$ for a neutron; while $g_s = 5.5854$ for a proton and -3.8262 for a neutron. The coefficients a_l and a_s are defined as the projections of $\mathbf{l}$ and $\mathbf{s}$ on $\mathbf{j}$, i.e.,

$$a_l = \frac{\mathbf{l} \cdot \mathbf{j}}{|\mathbf{j}|^2} = \frac{j(j+1) + l(l+1) - s(s+1)}{2j(j+1)} \tag{10.8}$$

and

$$a_s = \frac{\mathbf{s} \cdot \mathbf{j}}{|\mathbf{j}|^2} = \frac{j(j+1) + s(s+1) - l(l+1)}{2j(j+1)} \tag{10.9}$$

Also replacing s and l by $s = \frac{1}{2}$ and $j = l + \frac{1}{2}$ or $j = l - \frac{1}{2}$; and combining the above equations, we get

$$\mu_I = (j - \tfrac{1}{2})g_l + \tfrac{1}{2}g_s \quad \text{for } I = j = l + \tfrac{1}{2} \text{ or } l = j - \tfrac{1}{2} \tag{10.10}$$

and

$$\mu_I = \frac{j}{j+1}\left[\left(j + \frac{3}{2}\right)g_l - \tfrac{1}{2}g_s\right] \text{for } I = j = l - \tfrac{1}{2} \text{ or } l = j + \tfrac{1}{2} \tag{10.11}$$

The values of μ were put in this form by T. Schmidt[13,14,15] and are known as *Schmidt's limits*. In Fig. 10.10(a) are shown the plots of the measured

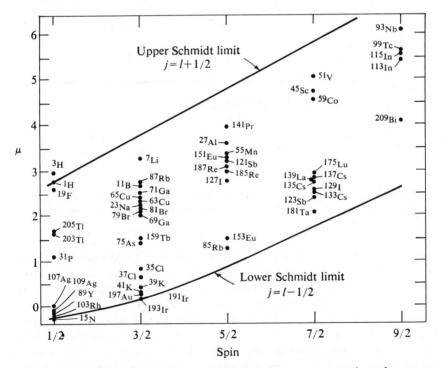

FIG. 10.10 (a) Magnetic moments of nuclei having an even number of neutrons and an odd number of protons. Continuous lines show the Schmidt limits.

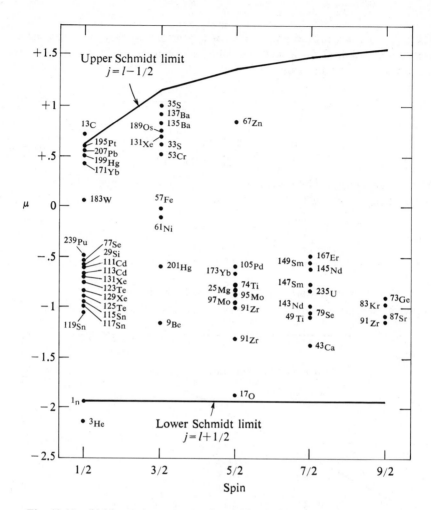

Fig. 10.10 (b) Magnetic moments of nuclei having an even number of protons and an odd number of neutrons. [From Bin-Stoyle, R. J., *Revs. Mod. Phys.*, **24**, 63, (1952).]

magnetic moments versus the spin $I(=j$ of the single-odd nucleon) for the odd-A nuclei having Z odd and N even. Fig. 10.10(b) shows the same plots of N-odd and Z-even. Schmidt's limits are also shown. It is clear that the magnetic moments lie within these limits, and most of them are near to one or the other limit. The deviation from the limits may be explained by the fact that the magnetic moment is the resultant of a mixture of states. (Note that it cannot be a mixture of two limiting states with $j = l - \frac{1}{2}$ and $j = l + \frac{1}{2}$ because they have opposite parity.) One may ask why this did not happen in the case of spin prediction by the shell model. The explanation is that the spin is

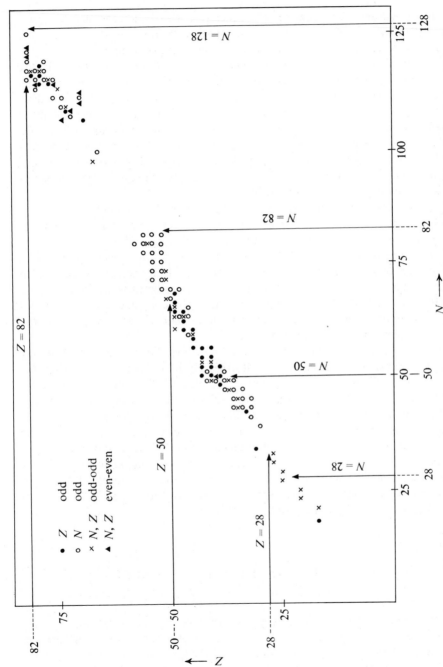

FIG. 10.11 Number of isomeric states of odd-mass-number nuclides versus number of odd nucleons. As is evident, these occur in the regions of isomerism as predicted from the shell model.

quantized, and has a definite value; therefore, the shell model has to give a right or wrong answer, but nothing in between. In most cases it does give the right answer. This is not so in the case of magnetic moments.

(3) *Electric Quadrupole-Moments.* The assumption that the nuclei are spherical in shape is true when the number of neutrons and protons are equal to or near (1 or 2, more or less) the magic numbers. Any further deviation from these magic numbers should result in the deviation from the spherical shape (into spheroidal shape), thereby increasing the electric quadrupole-moments. This was shown in Fig. 10.4. The quadrupole moments are found to be very large in the region of the rare-earth elements, for which Z is roughly between 50 and 82, and N is between 82 and 126. The measured quadrupole moments are much higher than predicted by the shell model.

(4) *Nuclear Isomerism.* In Sec. 9.10, we explained nuclear isomerism and concluded that a very long half-life is the result of a large spin change $\Delta I \geqslant 3$ between the two excited states and the energy difference between the two states being very small. Fig. 10.11 shows a plot of isomeric pairs versus number of nucleons. It is clear that most of the isomeric pairs occur for an odd number of neutrons or protons in the regions between nucleon numbers 19 to 27, 33 to 49, 63 to 81, and 107 to 127. These regions are called *islands of isomerism*. The number of isomeric states reduces very sharply near the magic numbers 50, 82, and 128.

The reason for the small transition probability and long half-life for isomeric states can be explained with the help of a single-particle model for odd A nuclides. As a shell approaches closure, the single-particle levels lie very close, and, therefore, the transitions will have very small energies. Usually a level from the higher oscillator state falls down (this is depression due to spin-orbit coupling of higher l) to the lower oscillator level near the close of the shell. This availability of high spin difference and low energies makes the transitions very slow. Because the levels belong to two different oscillator states, there is a change in parity in such transitions. E3 and M4 transitions, therefore, are common in isomeric transitions in the regions $1f_{7/2} \rightarrow 2s_{1/2}$, $1g_{9/2} \rightarrow 2p_{1/2}$, $1h_{11/2} \rightarrow 2d_{3/2}$, etc.

3. THE COLLECTIVE MODEL

The shell model has been very successful in predicting many properties and regularities observed in several nuclides. But there are certain aspects which it cannot explain. According to the shell model, the excited states are formed whenever one or more nucleons are raised from the ground state to the predicted excited states. There are many known cases in which the excited states are formed in altogether different manners and are not predicted by the shell model. The measured magnetic and quadrupole moments deviate considerably from the ones calculated using the single-particle shell model in which the closed shells forming the nuclear "core" play no part. It may be possible to explain these moments by assuming that they result from a mixture of many states, but such calculations will be difficult and even impossible.

A simpler explanation was given on the basis of another model, called the collective model, first suggested by J. Rainwater[16], and a quantitative development of the model was given by A. Bohr[17,18] and B. Mottelson[17]. According to them, the shape and the angular momentum of the core plays an important part. The excited states and the magnetic and quadrupole moments are the result of collective motion of many nucleons, not just of those nucleons that are outside the closed shell. The collective model incorporates the properties of the shell model, and the liquid-drop model, which was discussed in Section 5.10.

According to the collective model, as in the case of the shell model, the nucleons in a nucleus move independently in a real potential $V(r)$. But, unlike the shell-model potential, in the collective model the spherically symmetric potential, $V(r)$, is capable of undergoing a deformation in its shape as a result of the motion of the nucleon or nucleons around the core. This causes the core to lose its spherical symmetry, and it becomes elongated in the direction of the orbital nucleon. The shape of the core is determined by the shape of the potential. The collective motion of the nucleons may be described as a vibrational motion about the equilibrium position and a rotational motion that maintains the deformed shape of the nucleus. Although some transitions observed correspond to the vibrational motion, it is the rotational motion that is more important and will be discussed below. The collective rotation of nucleons around the surface of a nucleus may also be thought of as a "tidal wave" circulating around the surface of the core, similar to a ripple traveling around the surface of the liquid drop, causing a stable deformation of the core. The properties of the nucleus are now determined not only by the odd nucleon outside the closed shell, but also by the core itself. For example, even though the angular momentum is not changed, it is now shared between the odd nucleon and the core.

If the deformation is such that the nucleus takes an elliptical shape, symmetrical about the body axis Oz', as shown in Fig. 10.12, the deformation parameter β is defined as

$$\beta = \Delta R / R_0 \qquad (10.12)$$

where R_0, is the mean radius of the nucleus, and ΔR is the difference between the semimajor axis and the semiminor axis of the ellipse. The deformation depends on the number of nucleons outside the closed shell and will be maximum for the nuclei in between the magic numbers. K. Alder et al.[19] have calculated the potential energy as a function of deformation, while the deformation parameter, β, has been calculated as a function of the neutron number, N, by G. Temmer[20], and is shown in Fig. 10.13, where β^2 has been plotted versus the neutron number, N. The initial sudden rise at $N \sim 90$ is due to the vibrational states.

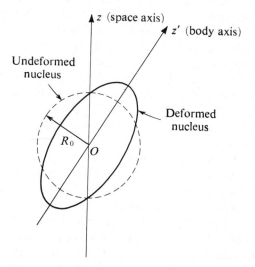

FIG. 10.12   Deformation of a nucleus about the body's Oz' axis.

It may be noted that the energy of the rotational levels E_{rot} is usually small as compared to the energy of intrinsic (single-particle) levels E_{int}, i.e.,

$$E_{int} \gg E_{rot}$$

Our next step now will be to explain the rotational levels and the observed magnetic and electric moments. The single-particle levels are related to the rotational levels in the same way as the electronic level is related to rotational levels of molecules.

A. ROTATIONAL LEVELS.   Energy due to the rotational motion is quantized, and it requires the introduction of another quantum number. The total angular momentum, I, of the nucleus is no longer just equal to the j of the nucleons outside the closed shell, but is $\mathbf{I} = \mathbf{j} + \mathbf{R}$ where R is due to the rotational motion. If we denote the angular momentum due to the collective motion by $R\hbar$ as shown in Fig. 10.14,

$$|R|^2\hbar^2 = [I(I+1) - |K|^2]\hbar^2 \qquad (10.13)$$

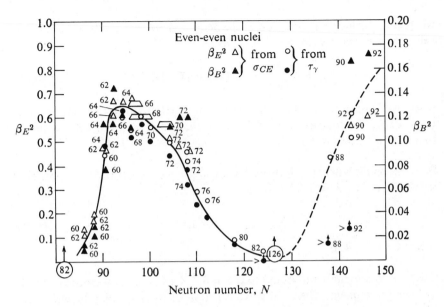

FIG. 10.13 Variation of the square of the deformation parameter, β^2, versus neutron number N. [From Temmer, G. M., *Revs. Mod. Phys.*, **30**, 498, (1958).]

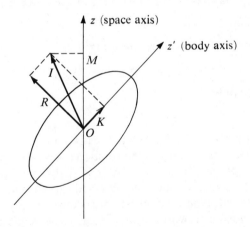

FIG. 10.14 Coupling scheme of a deformed nucleus.

where $K\hbar$ is the component along the body Z'-axis of the angular momentum of the nucleons outside the closed shell. The component of $I\hbar$ along the space Z-axis is $M\hbar$, as usual.

The rotational kinetic energy of the system may be defined as

$$E_{\text{rot}} = \tfrac{1}{2}\mathscr{I}\omega^2 \qquad (10.14)$$

where $\mathscr{I}$ is the moment of inertia of the deformed nucleus, and ω is the angular velocity. We may rewrite Eq. (10.14) as

$$E_{rot} = \frac{(\mathscr{I}\omega)^2}{2\mathscr{I}} = \frac{1}{2\mathscr{I}}[I(I+1) - |K|^2]\hbar^2 \qquad (10.15)$$

where we have substituted for the angular momentum $\mathscr{I}\omega = |R|\hbar$. For a given value of K, the rotational band is obtained, which we shall discuss under two separate headings.

B. EVEN–EVEN NUCLEI. As is well known, for even–even nuclei the intrinsic spin is zero, i.e., $K = 0$. Therefore,

$$E_{rot} = \frac{1}{2\mathscr{I}} I(I+1)\hbar^2 \qquad (10.16)$$

where $I = 0, 2, 4, 6, \ldots$.

That the rotational band should have $I = 0, 2, 4, 6, \ldots$ can be deduced from the following argument. The total wave function of the state may be written as

$$\Psi = \rho_{rot}\psi_{int\ nucl.} \qquad (10.17)$$

where ρ_{rot} is the rotational wave function. For even-even nuclei

$$P\Psi = +\ \Psi \qquad (10.18)$$

where P is the parity operator, we must have

$$P\rho_{rot} = +\rho_{rot} = (-1)^I \rho_{rot} \qquad (10.19)$$

which is possible only if

$$I = 0, 2, 4, 6, \ldots$$

Note that an increase in the deformation causes an increase in the moment of inertia, and hence the energy of the rotational levels E_{rot} becomes smaller. Another feature of these rotational levels is that the ratios E4/E2 = 3.33, E6/E4 = 2.1, E8/E6 = 1.71 should be observed experimentally for all nuclei. Rotational levels of even-even nuclei are shown in Fig. 10.15, and the experimental ratios agree with the theoretical value very well. The ratio of E4/E2 obtained for some nuclei are $_{72}Hf^{176}$ ($= 3.30$), $_{72}Hf^{180}$ ($= 3.33$), $_{90}Th^{228}$ ($= 3.26$), and $_{92}Cf^{250}$ ($= 3.39$), etc. Almost all even-even nuclei have the first excited state 2^+. The low-lying states are easily excited by coulomb excitation by incident charged particles.

In the case of odd-A nuclei, the intrinsic spin K is not zero but has a half-integral value. The allowed spins in this case are

$$I = K, K + 1, K + 2,$$

and are half integral.

C. MAGNETIC AND ELECTRIC MOMENTS.   As we mentioned before, the core is not inert but contributes to the angular momentum, which in this case is in the form of a wave motion circulating on the surface of the core. This circulating deformation is just like a current and contributes to the magnetic moment. The contribution to the angular momentum is due both to the neutrons and protons, while the contribution to the magnetic moment is due

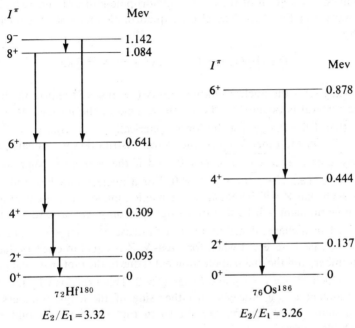

FIG. 10.15   Rotational levels of even–even nuclei: $_{72}Hf^{180}$ and $_{76}Os^{186}$. [From Stromminger *et al.*, *Revs. Mod. Phys.*, **30**, (1958).]

to the protons alone. This implies that if the angular momentum of the core is L_{core}, the core contribution to the magnetic moment is of the order of $\left(\dfrac{Z}{A}\right) L_{core}$. This change in the magnetic moment is enough to explain the discrepancy between the Schmidt lines and the measured magnetic moments.

It is now easy to understand why the measured electric quadrupole moments are much larger than the single-particle predictions of the shell model. A small deformation of the core will result in a very large quadrupole moment because many protons are taking part. As the number of particles outside the shell increases, the deformation also increases, and hence the quadrupole moment increases. Because the deformation is maximum in between the magic numbers, the quadrupole moment is also maximum. The deformation may be caused either by an odd proton or an odd neutron, therefore, very large quadrupole moments are observed not only for odd-Z nuclei but also for odd-N nuclei. The protons in the core will contribute in both cases. In order to get some idea as to how many protons contribute, the measured quadrupole moment may be divided by the quadrupole moment due to a single proton. A value of as high as 40 is found in some cases.

Another remarkable success of the collective model is the explanation of the oscillatory variation of the electric quadrupole-moment versus odd-Z or odd-N shown in Fig. 10.4. The electric quadrupole-moment of a nucleus is given by

$$Q = \int \rho(x, y, z)[3z^2 - (x^2 + y^2 + z^2)] \, dv \qquad (10.20)$$

where $\rho(x, y, z)$ is the nuclear charge density (because of the proton charge), and the integral is taken over the whole volume of the nucleus. It is quite evident that if the charge distribution is spherically symmetric, $\overline{x^2} = \overline{y^2} = \overline{z^2}$, and $Q = 0$. On the other hand, if the charge distribution is elongated along the body Z-axis, $\overline{z^2} > \overline{x^2}(=\overline{y^2})$, $Q > 0$, and if the charge distribution is an oblate shape, i.e., $\overline{z^2} < \overline{x^2}(=\overline{y^2})$, $Q < 0$. For a nucleus that has odd Z and even N such that Z will be equal to the magic number plus one proton, the quadrupole moment will be due to a single proton going around a symmetrical closed-shell charge distribution. For this case $\overline{z^2} < \overline{x^2}(=\overline{y^2})$, and hence $Q < 0$. The case is reversed when for even-N, Z is equal to one less than the magic number, and the quadrupole moment is due to the motion of the proton hole for which $\overline{z^2} > \overline{x^2}(=\overline{y^2})$, and hence $Q > 0$. This explains why the quadrupole moment of the nucleus on either side of the magic numbers have opposite signs. These features are shown in Fig. 10.4 both for odd-Z and odd-N stable nuclei.

4. THE FERMI GAS MODEL

The Fermi gas model finds its applications not only in atomic physics, especially in connection with the theory of conduction electrons in metals, but also in nuclear physics. The Fermi gas model, as applied to the nucleus, explains some terms in the empirical mass formula and the very long mean-free-path of the nucleon scattering at extremely high energies. Some predictions about the depth of the potential well are also made.

According to the Fermi gas model of the nucleus, the neutrons and the protons are assumed to be moving freely in an attractive potential well of nuclear dimensions. The forces between the pairs of nucleons are neglected altogether, even though these forces are responsible for the very existence of the potential well. All the nucleons are assumed to be contained in a small spherical volume, equal to the volume of the nucleus, and the nucleus is then treated from a statistical point of view just as the statistical treatment of a gas in the kinetic theory of gases. In the present case, the volume is a mixture of two gases, the neutron Fermi gas and the proton Fermi gas, and these two gases are treated separately. The statistical treatment does not allow us to calculate exact numerical values for different properties of the individual levels, but gives sufficient information to draw a good qualitative picture of the nucleus.

Neutrons and protons, both being Fermi particles (each has a spin 1/2) obey the Pauli exclusion-principle. In the ground state, the nucleons in the

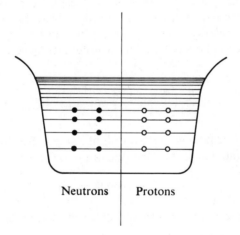

Neutrons   Protons

FIG. 10.16 Schematic energy-level diagram according to the Fermi gas model.

nucleus fill up the energy levels according to the Pauli exclusion principle and keep the energy of the nucleus to a minimum. Thus each neutron level contains two neutrons, and each proton level contains two protons. Unlike a classical gas, all the lowest available energy states are completely filled as shown in Fig. 10.16. The spacing between the levels is of the order of a few Mev, and because the lowest energy states are completely filled, the nucleus, even in the first few excited states, finds itself completely degenerate. In a classical gas, as the temperature is lowered (keeping the pressure constant), the rate of collisions between the particles increases, and hence the mean free-path decreases, as compared to the dimensions of the volume of the gas. The same is not true of the Fermi gas. The lowest energy states are already occupied and the only transfer of energy and momentum that is possible is between the two nucleons of the same state. But this seems as if there were no collision, because the two nucleons in the same state are indistinguishable. Transfer to the other states is not possible because these states are already occupied. Thus in a degenerate gas the mean free-path of a particle is very long compared with the dimensions of the volume of the Fermi gas, i.e., in this case the volume of the nucleus. This accounts for the long mean-free-path at high energies (where the shell model is not of much use) and for neglecting the interaction between the particles.

We shall now proceed to calculate the depth of the potential well for the ground state of the nucleus according to the Fermi model. We assume that each Fermi particle moves in a constant potential inside a certain region, which we consider to be a cubical box instead of a spherical volume. This does not make much difference, because we are just interested in the order of magnitude. Because the nucleon is confined to this volume, we assume the potential at the boundaries to be very large or infinite so as to make the wave function vanish at the boundaries. The Schrödinger wave equation for the nucleon is

$$-\frac{\hbar^2}{2M}\left(\frac{\partial^2\psi}{\partial x^2} + \frac{\partial^2\psi}{\partial y^2} + \frac{\partial^2\psi}{\partial z^2}\right) = E\psi \qquad (10.21)$$

The solution of this equation must vanish at $x = y = z = 0$ and at $x = y = z = L$, where L is the side of the cube. We can write for ψ,

$$\psi(x, y, z) = X(x)\,Y(y)Z(z),$$

and by using separation of variables we get for the x-component of the wave equation

$$-\frac{\hbar^2}{2M}\frac{d^2X(x)}{dx^2} = E_x X(x)$$

which has the solution

$$X(x) = A' \sin\frac{\sqrt{2ME_x}}{\hbar}x$$

where

$$\frac{\sqrt{2ME_x}}{\hbar}L = n_x\pi \quad \text{and} \quad n_x = 1, 2, 3, 4, \ldots$$

or

$$E_x = \frac{n_x^2\pi^2\hbar^2}{2ML^2}$$

Similar expressions may be obtained for $Y(y)$, $Z(z)$, and E_y, E_z. Hence

$$\psi(x, y, z) = A \sin \frac{\sqrt{2ME_x}}{\hbar} x \sin \frac{\sqrt{2ME_y}}{\hbar} y \sin \frac{\sqrt{2ME_z}}{\hbar} z \qquad (10.22)$$

and

$$E = E_x + E_y + E_z = \frac{\pi^2 \hbar^2}{2ML^2} (n_x^2 + n_y^2 + n_z^2) \qquad (10.23)$$

where $n_x = 1, 2, 3, 4, ..., n_y = 1, 2, 3, 4, ..., n_z = 1, 2, 3, 4, ...$ Because $E = p^2/2M = (1/2M)(p_x^2 + p_y^2 + p_z^2)$, we get

$$p^2 = p_x^2 + p_y^2 + p_z^2 = \frac{\pi^2 \hbar^2}{L^2} (n_x^2 + n_y^2 + n_z^2) = \frac{\pi^2 \hbar^2}{L^2} n^2 \qquad (10.24)$$

where $n^2 = n_x^2 + n_y^2 + n_z^2$. Thus the number of states with momentum from 0 up to p is given by

$$n^2 (= n_x^2 + n_y^2 + n_z^2) \leqslant \frac{p^2 L^2}{\pi^2 \hbar^2} \qquad (10.25)$$

The number of different possible states with momentum from 0 up to p may be calculated from the number of unit lattice-points (in quantum number space) constructed in one octant (since n_x, n_y and n_z must all be positive) of a sphere of radius $pL/\pi\hbar$ in such a way that three coordinates of each point of the lattice are equal to a possible set of quantum numbers n_x, n_y, n_z (each being greater than zero). Keeping in mind that each state can have two particles, we get

$$n = 2 \times (1/8) \times (4\pi/3)(pL/\pi\hbar)^3$$

or

$$n = (1/3) \times (p^3 V/\pi^2 \hbar^3) \qquad (10.26)$$

where $V = L^3$, and the number of states between the momentum p and $(p + dp)$ is

$$dn = \frac{V p^2}{\pi^2 \hbar^3} dp \qquad (10.27)$$

We are now in a position to calculate the maximum energy of the nucleons, i.e., the Fermi energy, and the average energy of the nucleons inside the nucleus. When the nucleus is in the ground state, $n = N$ or Z and $V = (4\pi/3)(R^3)$, where $R = r_0 A^{1/3}$, the maximum value of the momentum is from Eq. (10.26)

$$p_{max}^p = C'(Z/A)^{1/3}, \quad \text{and} \quad p_{max}^n = C'(N/A)^{1/3} \qquad (10.28)$$

where the superscripts "p" and "n" stand for the proton and neutron and $C' = (9\pi/4)^{1/3}(\hbar/r_0)$. The Fermi energy is given by ($E_f = p_{max}^2/2M$)

$$E_f^p = C(Z/A)^{2/3} \qquad \text{for proton}$$
$$E_f^n = C(N/A)^{2/3} \qquad \text{for neutron} \qquad (10.29)$$

where $C = (1/2M)(9\pi/4)^{2/3} (\hbar^2/r_0^2)$. Thus E_f^p and E_f^n may be calculated if r_0 is known. Thus if we take $r_0 \simeq 1.2 \times 10^{-13}$ cm and $N \approx Z \approx A/2$, we obtain for the Fermi energy (for a neutron or a proton)

$$E_f \simeq 32 \text{ Mev}$$

If the binding energy of each nucleon is about 8 Mev, the potential V_0 is given by

$$V_0 = E_f + E_b \simeq 40 \text{ Mev}$$

The relation between V_0, E_f, and E_b are shown in Fig. 10.17.

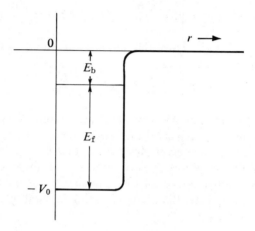

FIG. 10.17 Schematic diagram showing the relation between the binding energy, E_b, the Fermi energy, E_f, and the depth of the potential well, V_0.

The total kinetic energies of all the protons E_Z and of the neutrons E_N in their respective Fermi gases may be calculated from the relations

$$E_Z = \int_0^Z E \, dn$$

$$E_N = \int_0^N E \, dn \tag{10.30}$$

E_Z and E_N are evaluated by using Eq. (10.27) for dn, substituting $E = p^2/2M$ and evaluating the integral after changing the limits. Thus using Eq. (10.29), we obtain

$$E_Z = (3/5)(ZE_f^p)$$

$$E_N = (3/5)(NE_f^n) \tag{10.31}$$

The energy of the nucleus is thus given by

$$E(Z, A) = E_Z + E_N = (3/5)CA^{-2/3}(Z^{5/3} + N^{5/3}) \qquad (10.32)$$

Because

$$Z + N = A \qquad (10.33)$$

the energy $E(Z, A)$ is a function only of Z and A. For a typical nucleus, the average kinetic energy per nucleon is about 20 Mev.

We can now calculate the effect of pairing of nucleons on the semi-empirical mass formula. The minimum energy $E(Z, A)$ obtained from Eqs. (10.32) and (10.33) is given by $N = Z = A/2$. The departure from the minimum energy may be written as

$$f(Z, A) \propto E(Z, A) - E(Z, A)_{min}$$
$$= (3/5)CA^{-2/3}[N^{5/3} + Z^{5/3} - 2(A/2)^{5/3}]$$

If we substitute

$$d = N - Z = N - (A/2) = (A/2) - Z$$

we get

$$f(Z, A) = \frac{3}{5}C(A)^{-2/3}\left[\left(\frac{A}{2} + d\right)^{5/3} + \left(\frac{A}{2} - d\right)^{5/3} - 2\left(\frac{A}{2}\right)^{5/3}\right] \qquad (10.34)$$

Expanding $\left(\frac{A}{2} + d\right)^{5/3}$ and $\left(\frac{A}{2} - d\right)^{5/3}$ in terms of a Taylor series, and keeping only the terms up to d^2, we obtain

$$f(Z, A) \propto d^2/A = \frac{\left(\frac{A}{2} - Z\right)^2}{A} \qquad (10.35a)$$

or

$$f(Z, A) = a_4 \frac{\left(\frac{A}{2} - Z\right)^2}{A} \qquad (10.35b)$$

where a_4 is a constant. Thus $f(Z, A)$ has the form used in the semiempirical mass formula.

Finally, we shall explain why in stable nuclei there are more neutrons than protons. In the previous discussion we have neglected the Coulomb interaction between the protons. If V is the electrostatic potential inside the nucleus, the bottom of the proton well will be raised by an amount eV as compared to the neutron well shown in Fig. 10.18. But the highest filled levels both for protons and neutrons have almost the same energy. Thus, as is clear from Fig. 10.18 for a given energy, a nucleus has more neutron levels than proton levels and, hence, more neutrons than protons in a stable state.

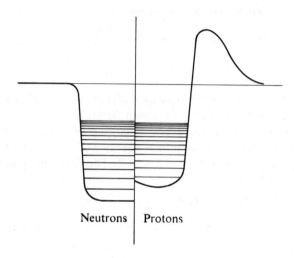

FIG. 10.18   Energy-level diagram for neutrons and protons. The proton levels have been corrected for the coulomb effect.

5. OTHER MODELS

The nuclear models discussed so far, the shell model, the collective model, and the Fermi gas model, are mostly concerned with the properties of the nuclei in the ground state. In addition to these, the liquid-drop model, which has already been discussed in Chap. V, has also proved to be successful in many respects. As we saw in Sec. 5.10, the liquid-drop model has been used in deriving the semiempirical mass formula. It has also been successfully applied in explaining many aspects of fission, which we shall discuss in Chap. XIII.

The other three models, compound nucleus, direct interaction, and optical are applicable only in explaining the properties of the nuclei in the exicted states and some characteristics of nuclear reactions. We introduced the optical model in Sec. 6.4 in connection with scattering of fast neutrons. The further details of the optical model and the other models for nuclear reactions will be discussed in Chap. XI.

PROBLEMS

1.   Calculate the energies of the lowest energy levels for a particle of mass M moving in (a) a square well potential, and (b) harmonic oscillator potential. What is the fundamental difference in the order of spacing between the levels in the two cases?

2. How do you justify the fact that the spin-orbit coupling term $\mathbf{L}\cdot\mathbf{S}$ represents a potential?

3. Starting with the relation
$$|\mathbf{j}|^2 = |\mathbf{l}|^2 + |\mathbf{s}|^2 + 2\mathbf{l}\cdot\mathbf{s}$$
show that
$$\mathbf{l}\cdot\mathbf{s} = l \quad \text{if} \quad j = l + \tfrac{1}{2}$$
and
$$\mathbf{l}\cdot\mathbf{s} = (l+1) \quad \text{if} \quad j = l - \tfrac{1}{2}$$

4. What are the ground state spins and parities of the following nuclei according to the shell model?
$$_{21}Sc^{45}, \ _{44}Ru^{101}, \ _{48}Cd^{113}, \ _{17}Cl^{35}$$

5. What do you expect for the spins and parities of the first excited state of the following nuclei, from shell model considerations: $_{53}I^{127}$, $_{52}Te^{125}$, $_{42}Mo^{95}$, $_{15}P^{31}$, $_{20}Ca^{43}$?

6. Draw schematic shell model diagrams for the following nuclei showing the filling up of the levels by neutrons and protons
$$_{3}Li^{7}, \ _{13}Al^{27} \text{ and } _{20}Ca^{43}$$

7. The ground state spin of $_{9}F^{19}$ as predicted by the shell model is $1d_{5/2}$ while the experimentally measured value is 1/2. How can this discrepancy be explained by taking into consideration the order of the shell model levels?

8. The measured value of the spin of $_{11}Na^{23}$ nucleus is 3/2 while the shell model predicts a value of $d_{5/2}$. Is it possible to account for this experimental value by combining some of the most probable shell model states of more than one nucleon?

9. The experimentally measured spin of $_{5}B^{10}$ is 3. Is it possible to account for this value by combining different neutron, proton shell model states?

10. The ground state and the first three excited states of $_{47}Ag^{109}$ are $\tfrac{1}{2}^-$, $\tfrac{7}{2}^+$, $\tfrac{3}{2}^-$ and $\tfrac{5}{2}^-$. What different shell model states are responsible for these assignments?

11. The ground state and the two excited states of $_{56}Ba^{137}$ are $\tfrac{3}{2}^+$, $\tfrac{1}{2}^+$ and $\tfrac{11}{2}^-$. What different shell model states are responsible for these values?

12. $_{14}Si^{27}$ decays by beta emission to $_{13}Al^{27}$ with a half-life of 4.2 sec. The end point energy of the beta group is 3.84 Mev and has a log ft value of 3.65. The ground state of $_{13}Al^{27}$ has been found to be $d_{5/2}$. What is the spin and parity of the ground state of $_{14}Si^{27}$? Does this value agree with the value predicted by the shell model?

13. $_{26}Fe^{59}$ decays by beta emission to $_{27}Co^{59}$. The log ft value of the beta group from ground state to ground state is 10.9. If the measured value of the ground state spin of $_{27}Co^{59}$ is $f_{7/2}$, what is the spin of $_{29}Fe^{59}$, and how does this value compare with the shell model?

14. For what values of A and Z will the ground state spins of the nuclei predicted by the shell model, without taking into account the coulomb repulsion, be different from the ones predicted by taking into account the coulomb repulsion? Give a few examples.

15. What are the spin and magnetic moment of $_{3}Li^{7}$ according to the shell model? How does this value of magnetic moment compare with the experimental value of 3.2563 nm?

386 NUCLEAR MODELS CH. X

16. What are the spin and magnetic moment of $_4\text{Be}^9$ according to the shell model? How does this value of magnetic moment compare with the experimental value of -1.777 nm?

17. What are the spin and magnetic moment of $_7\text{N}^{14}$ according to the shell model? How do these values compare with the experimental values of 1 for the spin and 0.404 nm for the magnetic moment?

18. Looking at Fig. 10.10 for Schmidt's limits, pick up a group of nuclei for which the experimental values for magnetic moment lie (a) very close to Schmidt's limits, (b) far away from the Schmidt's limit. Can you explain the apparent agreement in one case and the disagreement in the other?

19. From problem No. 18, calculate the percentage deviation of the experimental values from the theoretical values. By plotting $\dfrac{\Delta\mu\%}{\text{theo}}$ versus Z, N and A, find out if there is any correlation (or general trend).

20. Why does isomerism tend to occur for odd-A nuclei with nearly filled neutron and proton shells?

21. If the energy of the first excited rotational level of an even–even nucleus is 0.32 Mev and its spin 2^+, what are the energies of the 4^+, 6^+, and 8^+ rotational states?

22. For $_{90}\text{Th}^{228}$ the first excited rotational level is at 0.057 Mev. Some of the other excited levels are at 0.186 Mev, 0.328 Mev, 0.393 Mev, 0.965 Mev. Which level or levels belong to a rotational band?

23. On the basis of the Fermi gas model, calculate the raising of the proton well due to the coulomb effect.

REFERENCES

1. Gamow, G., *Z. Physik.*, **89**, p. 592, (1934).
2. Elsasser, W., *J. Phys. Rad.*, **5**, p. 635, (1934).
3. *Chart of the Nuclides*, General Electric Co.
4. Hughes, D. J., and D. Sherman, *Phys. Rev.*, **78**, p. 632, L (1950).
5. Harvey, J. A., *Phys. Rev.*, **81**, p. 353, (1951).
6. Townes, C. H., H. M. Foley, and W. Low, *Phys. Rev.*, **76**, p. 1415, L (1949).
7. Schiff, L. I., *Quantum Mechanics*, Chap. IV, New York: McGraw-Hill Book Co. Inc., (1955).
8. Nordheim, L. W., *Phys. Rev.*, **75**, p. 1894, (1949).
9. Mayer, M. G., *Phys. Rev.*, **74**, p. 235, (1948); **75**, p. 1969, (1949); **78**, p. 16, (1950).
10. Haxel, O., J. H. D. Jensen, and H. E. Suess, *Phys. Rev.*, **75**, p. 1766, L (1949).
11. Haxel, O., J. H. D. Jenson, and H. Suess, *Z. Physik*, **128**, p. 295, (1950).
12. Klinkenberg, P. F. A., *Revs. Mod. Phys.*, **24**, p. 63, (1952).
13. Schmidt, T., *Z. Physik*, **106**, p. 358, (1937).

14. Blin-Stoyle, R. J., *Revs. Mod. Phys.*, **28**, p. 75, (1956).
15. Kopfermann, H., *Nuclear Moments*, New York: Academic Press, 1958.
16. Rainwater, J., *Phys. Rev.*, **79**, p. 432, (1950).
17. Bohr, A., *Phys. Rev.*, **81**, p. 134, (1951).
18. Bohr, A., and B. R. Mottelson, *Dan. Mat. Fys. Medd.*, **27**, No. 16, (1953).
19. Alder, K., and A. Bohr, T. Huss, B. Mottelson, and A. Winther, *Revs. Mod. Phys.*, **28**, p. 432, (1956).
20. Temmer, G. M., *Revs. Mod. Phys.*, **30**, p. 498, (1958).

SUGGESTIONS FOR FURTHER READING

1. Mayer, M. G., and J. H. D. Jensen, *Elementary Theory of Nuclear Shell Structure.* New York: John Wiley & Sons, Inc., 1955.
2. Feenburg, E., *Shell Theory of Nucleus.* Princeton: Princeton University Press, 1955.
3. Elton, L. R. B., *Introductory Nuclear Theory*, Chap. 5. New York: Interscience Publishers, Inc., 1959.
4. Preston, M. A., *Physics of the Nucleus*, Chaps. 7 and 8. Massachusetts: Addison-Wesley Publishing Co., Inc., 1962.

XI

NUCLEAR
REACTIONS II

1. INTRODUCTION

This chapter will investigate several different mechanisms of nuclear reactions in some detail. Keeping in view the limitations of this text and the background knowledge of the student, it will not be possible to present all the theories of nuclear reactions. To start with, we shall present a wave-mechanical treatment of the collision problem which in addition to some other aspects sets limits on the scattering and reaction cross-sections. Next, we shall discuss the compound-nucleus model which is useful in explaining nuclear reactions at low energies ($\lesssim 30$ Mev) of the incident particles. This will be followed by the direct-interaction model of nuclear reactions at high energies of incident particles. Our next step will be to discuss briefly the optical model which is an attempt to fuse together the other two models and has been successful to a certain extent. Finally, a brief mention of nuclear reactions at very high energies will be made. Whenever possible, within limits, the experimental results will be explained with the help of the theories of wave mechanics. Before we go into the discussion, we shall summarize the usual notation used in nuclear reactions.

A nuclear reaction may be represented, as given in Sec. 4.1, by an equation of the form

$$x + X \to Y + y + Q \tag{11.1}$$

where x and y stand for the incident and outgoing particles, respectively; X and Y are the target and recoil nucleus, respectively, and Q is the distintegration energy, or the Q-value, of the nuclear reaction. The system $(x + X)$ defines the *incident, or entrance, channel* and $(Y + y)$, the *exit, or reaction, channel*. We shall denote the incident channel by α and the exit channel by β. Furthermore, the reactions may be classified as elastic or inelastic reactions.

(i) Elastic reactions are those in which $Q=0$, i.e., the energy of the particle before or after the reaction (or collision) is the same; only the direction is changed. The final products are the same as the initial. Hence, Eq. (11.1) takes the form

$$x + X \to X + x \tag{11.2}$$

(ii) Inelastic reactions are those in which $Q \neq 0$. The inelastic collisions may proceed through one of the many available channels, i.e.,

$$x + X \to Y_1 + y_1 + Q_1$$
$$\to Y_2 + y_2 + Q_2$$
$$\to Y_3 + y_3 + Q_3 \tag{11.3}$$

It is also possible that the outgoing particle may be the same as the incident particle, but with different kinetic energy. The recoil nucleus is usually left in the excited state. The reaction is then represented by

$$x + X \to X^* + x' + Q \tag{11.4}$$

In any inelastic reaction the recoil nucleus may be left in the excited state.

Unless specified, the discussion of nuclear reactions will be taken, throughout this chapter, in the center-of-mass coordinate system, with a restriction that the target nucleus is at rest in the laboratory-coordinate system.

The total cross section, σ_T, is given as the sum of the two parts

$$\sigma_T = \sigma_s + \sigma_r \tag{11.5a}$$

where σ_s is the scattering cross section for the elastic collisions represented by Eq. (11.2), and σ_r is the reaction or absorption cross section for the inelastic collisions (inelastic scattering). If more than one type of inelastic collision takes place, then σ_r is the sum of the individual cross sections

$$\sigma_r = \sigma_{r1} + \sigma_{r2} + \sigma_{r3} + \dots \tag{11.5b}$$

Finally, only the stable or ground states (or the stationary states) of the nuclei can have sharp, well-defined energies. All the excited states, according to the uncertainty principle, must have an uncertainty in energy E_c by an amount Γ, called the *level width*, which is related to the decay time, τ, of the excited level by the relation

$$\Gamma\tau = \hbar \tag{11.6}$$

where $\Gamma/\hbar = 1/\tau (=\lambda)$ is the decay probability of the excited level.

2. WAVE-MECHANICAL TREATMENT OF SCATTERING[1–5]

Scattering experiments constitute one of the most important methods for obtaining information about the nucleus, and the interpretation of the results is made with the help of theories that are based primarily on wave-mechanical treatments. *Partial wave analysis*, one of the most important methods, gives the exact solution of the scattering problem at all energies. Its greatest use, however, is at low and medium energies.

In the following, we shall treat the scattering of particles by a short-range central potential, i.e., the potential is angle-independent so that $V(\mathbf{r}) = V(r)$, which implies that we are dealing with a radial-wave function. For the sake of simplicity let us further assume that the incident particle has no charge and that the incident particle and the target have no spin.

Consider a beam of particles moving along the z-direction with velocity v that is incident on a target at 0; see Fig. 11.1(a). Let there be one particle per unit volume in the incident beam, so that there will be v particles crossing

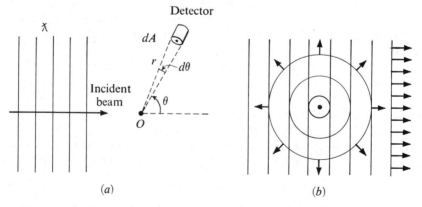

FIG. 11.1   (a) Schematic diagram of scattering. (b) Incident and scattered beams as viewed at large distances from the scattering center.

a unit area per second. Thus, the incident wave associated with the particle has a unit amplitude; it is given by the wave function

$$\psi_{inc} = e^{ikz} \tag{11.7}$$

where k is the wave number with respect to the center-of-mass coordinate system, i.e., $k = 1/\lambda = p/\hbar = \sqrt{2ME}/\hbar$. The result of the scattering of the incident wave by the potential $V(r)$ is an outgoing spherical wave with axial symmetry, which may be represented by

$$\psi_{scatt} = f(\theta)(e^{ikr}/r) \tag{11.8}$$

where $f(\theta)$ is the amplitude of the scattered wave and is a function of θ. Because of the symmetry of the scattering potential, there can be no ϕ dependence of $f(\theta)$. The factor $(1/r)$ gives the decrease in the intensity of the scattered wave according to the inverse-square law.

If we look at the incident and scattered waves that are very close to the scattering potential $V(r)$, we see they are very much distorted and difficult to distinguish from one another. But, if we look at these waves at very great distances, where the potential will approach zero, the situation is much simpler, as is shown in Fig. 11.1(b). The wave function, ψ, of the system may be written as the sum of ψ_{inc} and ψ_{scatt}, i.e.,

$$\psi \sim \psi_{inc} + \psi_{scatt}$$
$$= e^{ikz} + f(\theta)(e^{ikr}/r)$$
$$\text{as } r \to \infty \tag{11.9}$$

The number of particles in the incident wave that cross a unit area in unit time is given to be v and may be written as

$$I = v|\psi_{inc}|^2 = v(e^{ikz})(e^{ikz})^* = v \tag{11.10}$$

Similarly, the number of scattered particles per unit time reaching an area dA after being scattered at an angle between θ and $(\theta + d\theta)$, as shown in Fig. 11.1(a), is given by

$$v|\psi_{scatt}|^2 \, dA = v|f(\theta)(e^{ikr}/r)|^2 \, dA$$
$$= v|f(\theta)|^2 dA/r^2$$

But dA/r^2 is the solid angle, $d\Omega$, shown in Fig. 11.1(a), and the number of particles scattered per unit solid angle per second $S(\theta)$ is given by

$$S(\theta) = v|f(\theta)|^2 \tag{11.11}$$

By definition, therefore, the differential scattering cross section, $d\sigma/d\Omega$, is given by

$$\frac{d\sigma(\theta)}{d\Omega} = \frac{S(\theta)}{I} = |f(\theta)|^2 = f^*(\theta)f(\theta) \tag{11.12}$$

while the scattering cross section is given by

$$\sigma = \int \frac{d\sigma(\theta)}{d\Omega}\, d\Omega = 2\pi \int |f(\theta)|^2 \sin\theta \, d\theta \tag{11.13}$$

The evaluation of the cross section, σ, involves finding an expression for $f(\theta)$, and this may be accomplished in the following manner.

The incident particle that has a definite linear momentum, $k\hbar$, may have any value of angular momentum, $l\hbar$, about the nucleus because the impact parameter has no definite value. It is, therefore, convenient to replace the plane wave, e^{ikz}, of the incident particle by a series of spherical waves, each representing a particle with a definite orbital angular momentum about the nucleus. e^{ikz}, the wave function of a free particle, is a solution with axial symmetry of the Schrödinger wave equation

$$\nabla^2 \psi + k^2 \psi = 0 \tag{11.14}$$

Because of the axial symmetry, there is no ϕ-dependence ($m = 0$), and the solution is of the form

$$\psi_l = j_l(r) P_l(\cos\theta) \tag{11.15}$$

where l (an integer) $= 0, 1, 2, 3, \ldots$; $P_l(\cos\theta)$ is a Legendre polynomial; and $j_l(r)$ is the solution of the radial-wave equation

$$\frac{1}{r^2}\frac{d}{dr}\left(r^2\frac{dj}{dr}\right) + \left[k^2 - \frac{l(l+1)}{r^2}\right]j = 0 \tag{11.16}$$

where $j_l(r)$ are the spherical Bessel functions of order l related to the ordinary Bessel function of order $(l + \tfrac{1}{2})$ by the equation

$$j_l(r) = \left(\frac{\pi}{2r}\right)^{1/2} J_{l+\frac{1}{2}}(r) \tag{11.17}$$

For axial symmetry, therefore, the most general solution of Eq. 11.14 is

$$\psi = \sum_{l=0}^{\infty} a_l j_l(r) P_l(\cos\theta) \tag{11.18}$$

Identifying ψ with the plane wave function of the free particle, we get

$$e^{ikz} = e^{ikr\cos\theta} = \sum_{l'=0}^{\infty} a_{l'} j_{l'}(r) P_{l'}(\cos\theta) \tag{11.19}$$

The constant coefficients, a_l, may be evaluated by multiplying both sides of Eq. (11.19) by $P_l(\cos\theta)$ and integrating from 0 to π; we obtain (after substituting $\mu = \cos\theta$)

$$\int_{-1}^{1} e^{ikr\mu} P_l(\mu)\, d\mu = \left(\frac{2}{2l+1}\right) a_l j_l(r) \tag{11.20}$$

where we have used Eq. (A.41 of Appendix A) for the normalization of the Legendre polynomial. In order to evaluate the left-hand side of Eq. (11.20), we integrate it by parts twice, and in the limit $(r \to \infty)$, we neglect the terms in r^{-2} as compared to the r^{-1} term. Making use of the property that $P_l(\cos \theta) = 1$ for $\cos \theta = 1$, and $P_l(\cos \theta) = (-1)^l = e^{il\pi}$ for $\cos \theta = -1$, we obtain

$$\left(\frac{2}{2l+1}\right) a_l j_l(r) \sim \frac{1}{ikr}\left[e^{ikr} - e^{il\pi}e^{-ikr}\right]$$

$$= \frac{1}{ikr} e^{\frac{1}{2}il\pi}\left[e^{i(kr - \frac{1}{2}l\pi)} - e^{-i(kr - \frac{1}{2}l\pi)}\right]$$

$$= \left(\frac{2i^l}{kr}\right) \sin(kr - \tfrac{1}{2}l\pi)$$

or

$$a_l j_l(r) \sim (2l+1)i^l \frac{\sin[kr - (l\pi/2)]}{kr}$$

and we identify the constants, a_l, by

$$a_l = (2l+1)i^l \qquad (11.21a)$$

and the function $j_l(r)$ or $j_l(kr)$ by

$$j_l(kr) \sim \frac{\sin[kr - (l\pi/2)]}{kr} \qquad (11.21b)$$

Thus the complete asymptotic solution $(r \to \infty)$ is of the form

$$e^{ikr \cos \theta} \triangleq \sum_{l=0}^{\infty} (2l+1)i^l \left\{ \frac{\sin[kr - (l\pi/2)]}{kr} \right\} P_l(\cos \theta) \qquad (11.22)$$

We now proceed to the solution of S.W.E. inside the potential range, i.e.,

$$\nabla^2 \psi + [k^2 - (2M/\hbar^2)V(r)]\psi = 0 \qquad (11.23)$$

(M is the reduced mass) which must be satisfied by the wave function of the system given by Eq. (11.9), i.e.,

$$\psi(r, \theta) \sim e^{ikz} + f(\theta)(e^{ikr}/r) \qquad (11.9)$$

$$\text{for } r \to \infty$$

Actually, the effect of the central potential $V(r)$ may be either to change the phase (elastic scattering) or to change both the phase and amplitude (inelastic scattering). For the time being, we shall restrict ourselves to elastic scattering only.

As before, the most general solution with axial symmetry for Eq. (11.23) is

$$\psi = \sum_{l=0}^{\infty} A_l R_l(kr) P_l(\cos \theta) \tag{11.24}$$

which has the same angular dependence as before while $R_l(kr)$ is the radial-wave function of the equation

$$\frac{1}{r^2} \frac{d}{dr}\left(r^2 \frac{dR}{dr}\right) + \left[k^2 - \frac{2M}{\hbar^2} V(r) - \frac{l(l+1)}{r^2}\right] R = 0 \tag{11.25}$$

A critical look at the functions $R_l(kr)$ and $j_l(kr)$ reveals that they are essentially the same everywhere except at small values of r for which $V(r) \neq 0$. Thus, if we do not look too closely, for $r \to \infty$, $V(r) = 0$ and $R_l(kr)$ is the same as $j_l(r)$ except for a small phase shift δ_l that results because R_l has a different r-dependence in the region where $V(r) \neq 0$. This statement will always be true so long as $V(r)$ approaches zero faster than r^{-1}. Thus

$$R_l(kr) \doteq \frac{\sin\left(kr - \dfrac{l\pi}{2} + \delta_l\right)}{kr} \qquad \text{as } r \to \infty \tag{11.26}$$

and

$$\psi \overset{\Delta}{=} \sum_{l=0}^{\infty} A_l \frac{\sin\left(kr - \dfrac{l\pi}{2} + \delta_l\right)}{kr} P_l(\cos \theta) \tag{11.27}$$

Substituting for e^{ikz} and ψ from Eqs. (11.22) and (11.27), respectively, into Eq. (11.9) and then equating the coefficients of e^{ikr} and e^{-ikr}, we obtain

$$A_l = i^l(2l+1)e^{i\delta_l} \tag{11.28}$$

which gives

$$\psi = \sum_{l=0}^{\infty} (2l+1)i^l e^{i\delta_l} R_l(kr) P_l(\cos \theta) \tag{11.29}$$

and

$$f(\theta) = \frac{1}{2ik} \sum_{l=0}^{\infty} (2l+1)(e^{2i\delta_l} - 1)P_l(\cos \theta) \tag{11.30}$$

Thus the total cross section may be obtained from Eq. (11.13), i.e.,

$$\sigma = \int \frac{d\sigma}{d\Omega} \, d\Omega = 2\pi \int |f(\theta)|^2 \sin \theta \, d\theta \tag{11.13}$$

Substituting for $f(\theta)$ from Eq. (11.30) into Eq. (11.13) and integrating (and ignoring the cross terms of the types $P_l(\cos \theta)P_{l'}(\cos \theta)$ because these vanish) we obtain

$$\sigma = \frac{\pi}{2k^2} \int_0^\pi \sum_{l=0}^{\infty} (2l+1)^2(2 - 2\cos 2\delta_l)[P_l(\cos \theta)]^2 \sin \theta \, d\theta$$

or

$$\sigma = (4\pi/k^2) \sum_{l=0}^{\infty} (2l + 1)\sin^2 \delta_l \qquad (11.31)$$

Thus the total scattering cross section (elastic) is a function of k and the phase shift, δ_l.

We can now show by a semiclassical treatment that if the range of the scattering potential is finite, only a finite number of δ_l contribute to the sum in Eq. (11.31). We shall first give the classical interpretation of the partial waves, and then extend the problem of scattering to include inelastic scattering (absorption) as well.

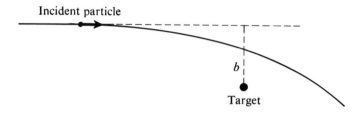

FIG. 11.2   Interaction between the incident particle and the target nucleus; b is the impact parameter.

Let a particle in the incident beam have a linear momentum $p = mv$ and an impact parameter b as shown in Fig. 11.2. The angular momentum of the particle is given by $L = mvb$. This must be equal to the quantum-mechanical value of the angular momentum $L = [l(l + 1)]^{1/2}\hbar$, i.e.,

$$mvb = [l(l + 1)]^{1/2}\hbar \qquad (11.32)$$

Eq. (11.32) puts a limit on the number of terms in Eq. (11.31). The scattering will take place only if the impact parameter b is less than the range R_0 of the potential. This says that for scattering to take place

$$[l(l +1)]^{1/2} < kR_0 \qquad (11.33)$$

For a given energy particle, that is for a given k, only those partial waves are affected for which Eq. (11.33) holds and for values of l in which $[l(l + 1)]^{1/2} > kR_0$, the δ_l are negligible.

The S.W.E. for inside and outside the potential range are given by Eqs. (11.23) and (11.14), respectively. Asymptotically, their solutions are given by Eqs. (11.26) and (11.21b) (radial-wave functions), respectively.

$$j_l(kr) \approx (1/kr)\sin(kr - \tfrac{1}{2}l\pi) \qquad (11.21b)$$

and

$$R_l(kr) \approx (1/kr)\sin(kr - \tfrac{1}{2}l\pi + \delta_l) \qquad (11.26)$$

As is evident from these equations, the scattered wave, Eq. (11.26), differs from the undisturbed wave, Eq. (11.21b), only in the phase change of δ_l. Within the range of potential the wave length changes from $\lambda = 2\pi/k$ to $\lambda' = 2\pi/\sqrt{k^2 - 2MV/\hbar^2}$. Thus if $V(r) < 0, \lambda' < \lambda$, the wave is pulled in, and the phase shift δ_l, is positive for an attractive potential. For $V(r) > 0, \lambda' > \lambda$, the

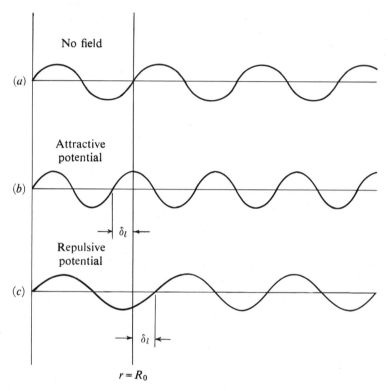

FIG. 11.3 The radial wave functions for three different cases: (a) $V(r) = 0$; no field, (b) $V(r) < 0$, attractive potential, and (c) $V(r) > 0$, repulsive potential.

wave is pushed out, and the phase shift, δ_l, is negative for a repulsive potential. Outside the potential range the wave function is undisturbed. The phase shifts for the three cases are shown in Fig. 11.3.

Until now we have been considering only elastic scattering. Frequently in nuclear reactions particles may be absorbed. In the following we shall calculate the absorption cross-section for different l-values. It must be made clear that the term absorption or reaction cross-section includes also the particles scattered inelastically, i.e., with loss of energy in the CMCS, while scattering implies only elastic scattering in CMCS. The total absorption cross-section can again be expressed as the sum of the partial cross-sections corresponding to different values of l, i.e.,

$$\sigma_r = \sum_l \sigma_{r,l} \tag{11.34}$$

and

$$\sigma_s = \sum_l \sigma_{s,l} \tag{11.35}$$

Thus, we need only calculate $\sigma_{r,l}$ and $\sigma_{s,l}$.

As before, the wave function of the incident particle may be written as

$$\psi_{\text{inc}} = e^{ikr\cos\theta} \sim \frac{1}{kr} \sum_{l=0}^{\infty} (2l+1)i^l \sin(kr - \tfrac{1}{2}l\pi)P_l(\cos\theta)$$

$$= \frac{1}{2ikr} \sum_{l=0}^{\infty} (2l+1)i^l\{e^{i[kr-(l\pi/2)]} - e^{-i[kr-(l\pi/2)]}\}P_l(\cos\theta) \tag{11.36}$$

where $e^{-i[kr-(l\pi/2)]}$ are a series of spherical waves converging towards 0 and $e^{i[kr-(l\pi/2)]}$ are diverging from 0. The presence of a potential field will effect only the outgoing wave. Thus if η_l is a factor that represents the change in phase or the change in phase and amplitude both, the wave function $\psi = \psi_{\text{inc}} + \psi_{\text{scatt}}$ may be written as

$$\psi = \frac{1}{2ikr} \sum_{l=0}^{\infty} (2l+1)i^l(\eta_l e^{i[kr-(l\pi/2)]} - e^{-i[kr-(l\pi/2)]})P_l(\cos\theta) \tag{11.37}$$

We may proceed as before or write from Eq. (11.30)

$$f(\theta) = \frac{1}{2ik} \sum_{l=0}^{\infty} (2l+1)(\eta_l - 1)P_l(\cos\theta) \tag{11.38}$$

where η_l is no longer equal to $e^{2i\delta_l}$ but is given by

$$\eta_l = A_l e^{2i\delta_l} \tag{11.39}$$

where $0 \leqslant A_l \leqslant 1$.

For pure scattering, and no absorption, $A_l = 1$ and $\eta_l = e^{2i\delta_l}$, while in the case of absorption A_l will be less than 1. Note that if $A_l = 1$ and $\eta_l = e^{i2\delta_l} = 1$, the scattered wave becomes just the incident wave, i.e., with no interaction. Thus, for scattering $\eta_l = e^{2i\delta_l} \neq 1$, while for absorption $A_l \neq 1$, and the amplitude of the scattered wave is less than the incident wave. The scattering cross-section may be calculated as before and we obtain

$$\sigma_s = \frac{\pi}{k^2} \sum_{l=0}^{\infty} (2l+1)|1 - \eta_l|^2$$

$$= \pi\lambda^2 \sum_{l=0}^{\infty} (2l+1)|1 - \eta_l|^2 \tag{11.40}$$

while the absorption cross-section is equal to the number of particles taken out of the beam per unit incident particle, i.e.

$$\sigma_r = \frac{\text{Number of particles taken out of the beam per sec}}{\text{Incident flux}} \quad \textbf{(11.41a)}$$

As shown before, the incident flux is equal to v, while the numerator is the absorbed flux given by

$$N_a = \text{Absorbed flux} = \text{Net number of particles}$$
$$\text{per second crossing a sphere of radius } R$$
$$\text{surrounding the target nucleus.}$$

or

$$N_a = \int_s I\, ds = \int_s I R^2 \sin\theta\, d\theta\, d\phi \quad \textbf{(11.41b)}$$

where I is the probability current density defined as

$$I = \frac{\hbar}{2iM}\left(\psi^* \frac{\partial\psi}{\partial r} - \frac{\partial\psi^*}{\partial r}\psi\right) \quad \textbf{(11.41c)}$$

M is the reduced mass and ψ is given by Eq. (11.37). The calculations yield the following expression for the absorption cross-section.

$$\sigma_r = \pi \lambdabar^2 \sum_{l=0}^{\infty}(2l+1)(1-|\eta_l|^2) \quad \textbf{(11.42)}$$

Thus we have

$$\sigma_{s,l} = \pi\lambdabar^2(2l+1)|1-\eta_l|^2 \quad \textbf{(11.43)}$$

$$\sigma_{r,l} = \pi\lambdabar^2(2l+1)(1-|\eta_l|^2) \quad \textbf{(11.44)}$$

and

$$\eta_l = A_l e^{2i\delta_l} = U_l + iW_l \quad \textbf{(11.45)}$$

where the real part of η_l relates to the change in amplitude and the imaginary part to change in phase. These equations also indicate that absorption and scattering are not independent. It may be shown that whenever there is absorption, there must be scattering also, but the reverse is not always true. It is possible to have scattering without absorption. For example, if there is no scattering, from Eq. (11.43) we must have $\eta_l^* = \eta_l = 1$, which in turn from Eq. (11.44) implies that there can be no absorption. However, it is possible to have $|\eta_l|^2 = 1$ and $\eta_l^* \neq 1$, $\eta_l \neq 1$, i.e., there can be scattering without absorption. Because $|\eta_l| \leqslant 1$, it is possible to say

$$\sigma_{s,l} \leqslant 4\pi\lambdabar^2(2l+1)$$
$$\sigma_{r,l} \leqslant \pi\lambdabar^2(2l+1)$$
$$\sigma_{t,l} \leqslant 4\pi\lambdabar^2(2l+1) \quad \textbf{(11.46)}$$

The relation between $\sigma_{s,l}$ and $\sigma_{r,l}$ is shown in Fig. 11.4.

An important and simple application is the scattering of very high-energy particles. In this case λ of the incident particle is very, very small as compared to the radius, R, of the nucleus. This is the case of the so-called *black sphere* or *black nucleus*, or the perfectly absorbing sphere. Classically, for a particle

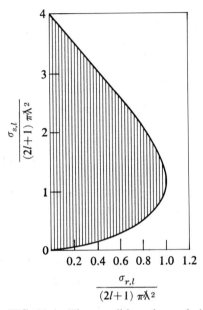

FIG. 11.4 The possible values of the partial scattering cross-sections for different partial absorption cross-sections. The cross-hatched area represents the permissible values for the two cross sections. [From Blatt, J. M., and V. F. Weisskopf, *Theoretical Nuclear Physics*, p. 322, New York: John Wiley & Sons, (1958).]

of linear momentum p, $pb = l\hbar (= \sqrt{l(l+1)}\hbar$ by quantum mechanics), where b is the impact parameter, or

$$l = bp/\hbar = b/\lambda$$

or

$$b = l\lambda$$

The reaction will take place only if

$$b = l\lambda \leqslant R$$

or

$$l \leqslant R/\lambda (= Rk)$$

If $l \leqslant R/\lambda$, the reaction takes place everytime, and in this case, where $\eta_l = 0$, the reaction cross-section is maximum. If $l > R/\lambda$, $\eta_l = 1$, and no reaction takes place.

Thus we need consider only the first l-partial cross-sections for $l < R/\lambda$ ($= Rk$) and we get

$$\sigma_s = \sum_{l=0}^{R/\lambda} \sigma_{s,l} = \pi\lambda^2 \sum_{l=0}^{R/\lambda} (2l + 1) \approx \pi R^2 \qquad \text{(11.47a)}$$

$$\sigma_r = \sum_{l=0}^{R/\lambda} \sigma_{r,l} = \pi\lambda^2 \sum_{l=0}^{R/\lambda} (2l + 1) \approx \pi R^2 \qquad \text{(11.47b)}$$

i.e.,

$$\sigma_s = \sigma_r = \pi R^2$$

and

$$\sigma_t = \sigma_s + \sigma_r = 2\pi R^2 = 2 \times \textit{geometrical} \text{ cross-section} \qquad \text{(11.47c)}$$

These results have been verified experimentally. One would expect that at very high energies, $\lambda \ll R$, the cross-section should be equal to the reaction cross-section only, with no scattering at all, i.e., equal to the geometrical cross-section πR^2. But this is not true; diffraction still takes place contributing $\sigma_s (= \pi R^2)$ to the total cross-section.

3. THE RECIPROCITY THEOREM FOR NUCLEAR REACTIONS

This theorem states the relation between the cross-section $\sigma(\alpha \to \beta)$ of the reaction with the entrance channel, α, and the exit channel, β, and the cross-section $\sigma(\beta \to \alpha)$ that is just the reverse of the first. The relation may be stated for the spinless particles, the target, and the recoil nucleus as

$$k_\alpha^2 \sigma(\alpha \to \beta) = k_\beta^2 \sigma(\beta \to \alpha) \qquad \text{(11.48a)}$$

or

$$\frac{\sigma(\alpha \to \beta)}{\lambda_\alpha^2} = \frac{\sigma(\beta \to \alpha)}{\lambda_\beta^2} \qquad \text{(11.48b)}$$

where k_α, k_β; and λ_α, and λ_β are the wave numbers and the wave lengths, respectively, of the entrance and the exit channels. We shall derive these relations in the following manner.

Consider a box of large volume, V, containing an arbitrary number of particles x, X, Y, and y. Assume that the two reactions $x + X \rightleftharpoons Y + y$ are in dynamic equilibrium, i.e., the number of transitions $\alpha \to \beta$ are equal to the number of transitions $\beta \to \alpha$ in the same energy range. Now, the number of states of the particle with momentum between p_α and $(p_\alpha + dp_\alpha)$ is

$$N_\alpha = \frac{4\pi p_\alpha^2 \, dp_\alpha}{h^3} V = \frac{4\pi p_\alpha^2 V}{h^3 v_\alpha} \, dE \qquad \text{(11.49)}$$

where $v_\alpha dp = dE$. The probability of formation of the reaction $(\alpha \to \beta)$ is the product of $P(\alpha \to \beta)$ and the number of possible states of motion given by Eq. (11.49), where $P(\alpha \to \beta)$ is the probability that the nucleus X is contained within the small volume $\sigma(\alpha \to \beta)v_\alpha$ swept out by the effective collision area per second, i.e., $P(\alpha \to \beta) = \dfrac{\sigma(\alpha \to \beta)v_\alpha}{V}$ = number of particles scattered into a unit area per unit time. Thus the probability of the reaction in the volume V per second in the given energy range is

$$N_\alpha P(\alpha \to \beta) = \frac{4\pi p_\alpha^2 V \, dE}{h^3 v_\alpha} \frac{\sigma(\alpha \to \beta)v_\alpha}{V} \tag{11.50}$$

and similarly

$$N_\beta P(\beta \to \alpha) = \frac{4\pi p_\beta^2 V \, dE}{h^3 v_\beta} \frac{\sigma(\beta \to \alpha)v_\beta}{V} \tag{11.51}$$

For dynamic equilibrium,

$$N_\alpha P(\alpha \to \beta) = N_\beta P(\beta \to \alpha)$$

or

$$p_\alpha^2 \sigma(\alpha \to \beta) = p_\beta^2 \sigma(\beta \to \alpha)$$

or using the relation $k = p/\hbar$, we obtain

$$k_\alpha^2 \sigma(\alpha \to \beta) = k_\beta^2 \sigma(\beta \to \alpha) \tag{11.48a}$$

or

$$\frac{\sigma(\alpha \to \beta)}{\lambda_\alpha^2} = \frac{\sigma(\beta \to \alpha)}{\lambda_\beta^2}, \tag{11.48b}$$

which is the relation stated above.

If the spins of different states are also taken into consideration, the above equations must be modified by multiplying the density of the states by the statistical factor $(2 \times \text{spin} + 1)$, i.e., we obtain

$$(2I_x + 1)(2I_X + 1)k_\alpha^2 \sigma(\alpha \to \beta) = (2I_Y + 1)(2I_y + 1)k_\beta^2 \sigma(\beta \to \alpha) \tag{11.52}$$

where the I's are the respective spins.

4. THE COMPOUND-NUCLEUS MODEL

Before 1936 the only known mechanism for nuclear reactions was that of a direct interaction in which the incident particle interacts only with a limited number of nucleons. The picture was more or less like a single-particle shell-model. The cross section decreased with increasing incident particle energy, and resonances were observed whenever the energy was equal to a virtual single-particle state. These levels are about 10 Mev apart and 1 Mev wide. The discovery of very sharp resonances at very low neutron energies altogether changed the picture. These resonance levels are only a few electron volts apart and their widths are of the order of a few tenths of an electron volt. In order to explain these resonances and some other features of nuclear reactions at low energies, N. Bohr[6] in 1936 proposed the *compound-nucleus hypothesis*.

According to Bohr, the compound-nucleus hypothesis implies that a nuclear reaction takes place in two stages. First, the incident particle interacts very strongly with the target nucleus, giving away all its energy in collisions to the nucleons of the target nucleus. Once this has happened, the incident particle loses its identity and becomes a part of the target nucleus. The nucleus thus formed is called the compound nucleus and is in a highly excited state. Second, if in due course of time, by statistical fluctuations, one or more nucleons happen to be at the surface of the compound nucleus with enough energy to escape, the decay of the compound nucleus will take place. We may represent the decay process by the following equations:

incident particle + target nucleus → compound nucleus

compound nucleus → recoil nucleus + outgoing particle, or

$$x + X \rightarrow C \rightarrow Y + y \tag{11.53}$$

The formation of the compound nucleus as an intermediate state of the nuclear reaction implies that there is a strong interaction between the incident particle and the nucleons of the target. The compound nucleus hypothesis also implies that the decay of the compound nucleus is independent of the way it was formed. This will be true only if the decay time of the compound nucleus is much longer than the natural *nuclear time*, i.e., time for the incident particle to go across the diameter of the nucleus. In a typical case of 1-Mev neutrons the velocity is $\sim 10^9$ cm/sec and the nuclear size $\sim 10^{-12}$ cm. Thus the nuclear time $\sim 10^{-12}/10^9 = 10^{-21}$ sec is much shorter than the decay time of the compound nucleus $\sim 10^{-14}$ sec. In other words, the mean free path, Λ, of the nucleon is very small compared to the nuclear diameter, i.e., $\Lambda \langle\langle d$. The compound nucleus may be said to exist in a *quasi-stationary state* or a *virtual state*, which means that although it exists for a long interval compared to the natural nuclear time, it can still disintegrate. The compound-nucleus decay, therefore, is independent of the way it was formed; we may say that the compound nucleus "forgets" the mode of its formation. Of course, its decay depends on its energy, angular momentum, and parity. The compound nucleus may decay through more than one channel. As an example, consider $_{13}Al^{27} + _1H^1 \rightarrow (_{14}Si^{28})^*$, where ( )* indicates the formation of a compound nucleus, which decays by the following different processes:

$$(_{14}Si^{28})^* \rightarrow {}_{12}Mg^{24} + {}_2He^4$$
$$\rightarrow {}_{14}Si^{27} + {}_0n^1$$
$$\rightarrow {}_{14}Si^{28} + \gamma$$
$$\rightarrow {}_{11}Na^{24} + 3_1H^1 + {}_0n^1 \tag{11.54}$$

Because there is no coulomb barrier for the neutrons, the emission of neutrons is easier than the emission of protons. The energy level diagram for the formation and the decay of the compound nucleus is shown in Fig. 11.5.

The *excitation energy*, E_c, of the compound nucleus is given by

$$E_c = E_x'\left(= \frac{E_x M_X}{M_X + m_x} \right) + E_B \qquad (11.55)$$

where E_B is the binding energy of the particle x when the compound nucleus is in the ground state and E_x' is the fraction of the incident particle energy that is used in excitation of the nucleus. E_x' may be calculated as follows:

If the target nucleus is at rest, from the conservation of angular momentum,

$$m_x v_x = M_{CN} V$$

or

$$V = (m_x/M_{CN})v_x$$

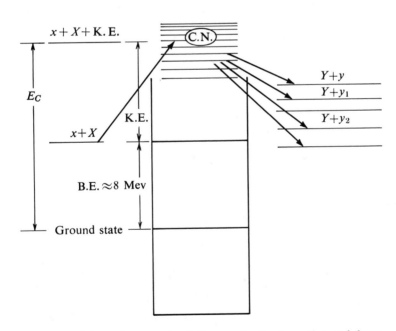

FIG. 11.5 Schematic energy-level diagram for the formation and decay of the compound nucleus.

where M_{CN} and V are the mass and velocity of the compound nucleus, respectively. The fraction of the incident energy that goes into the excitation is

$$E'_x = \tfrac{1}{2}m_x v_x^2 - \tfrac{1}{2}M_{CN}V^2$$

$$= \tfrac{1}{2}m_x v_x^2\left(1 - \frac{m_x}{M_{CN}}\right) = E_x\left(1 - \frac{m_x}{M_{CN}}\right)$$

Substituting $M_{CN} = m_x + M_X$, we get

$$E'_x = E_x\left(\frac{M_X}{M_X + m_x}\right) \tag{11.56}$$

which is the required result.

Thus the following two conditions must be satisfied for the compound nucleus model:

(a) $\Lambda \ll d$, and

(b) $E_c \ll (A - 1)S$, where S is the average separation energy of a nucleon. Both these conditions are satisfied if we are dealing with nuclei of $A > 10$ and also if the incident energies are such that $E_c < 50$ Mev.

The best test of the hypothesis that the decay of the compound nucleus is independent of its mode of formation is given by the experiments of S. Ghoshal[7] shown in Fig. 11.6. The compound nucleus $(_{30}Zn^{64})^*$ may be produced by two different methods as shown (with its decay products).

$$_1H^1 + {_{29}}Cu^{63} \rightarrow (_{30}Zn^{64})^* \rightarrow {_{30}}Zn^{63} + {_0}n^1$$

$$\rightarrow {_{30}}Zn^{62} + {_0}n^1 + {_0}n^1$$

$$\rightarrow {_{29}}Cu^{62} + {_0}n^1 + {_1}H^1 \tag{11.57}$$

and also

$$_2He^4 + {_{28}}Ni^{60} \rightarrow (_{30}Zn^{64})^* \rightarrow {_{30}}Zn^{63} + {_0}n^1$$

$$\rightarrow {_{30}}Zn^{62} + {_0}n^1 + {_0}n^1$$

$$\rightarrow {_{29}}Cu^{62} + {_0}n^1 + {_1}H^1 \tag{11.58}$$

If the decay of the compound nucleus is independent of the mode of its formation, the cross sections obtained for different modes of decay from Eq. (11.57) should be the same as that from Eq. (11.58), i.e.,

$$\sigma(p, n): \quad \sigma(p, 2n): \quad \sigma(p, pn) = \sigma(\alpha, n): \quad \sigma(\alpha, nn): \quad \sigma(\alpha, np)$$

That this is the case is clearly shown in Fig. 11.6. Our predictions of the compound nucleus are, therefore, experimentally verified.

Using the strong-coupling model, and the help of the compound-nucleus hypothesis, it is possible to write the cross section for a nuclear reaction $\sigma(\alpha \rightarrow \beta)$, i.e.,

$$\sigma(\alpha \rightarrow \beta) = \sigma_c(\alpha)G_c(\beta) \tag{11.59}$$

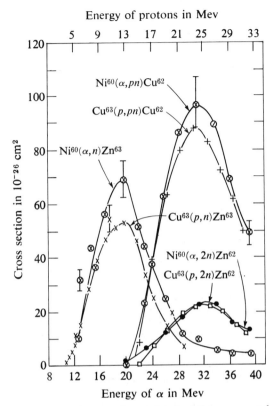

Energy of protons in Mev

Ni$^{60}(\alpha, pn)$Cu^{62}

Cu$^{63}(p, pn)$Cu^{62}

Ni$^{60}(\alpha, n)$Zn^{63}

Cu$^{63}(p, n)$Zn^{63}

Ni$^{60}(\alpha, 2n)$Zn^{62}

Cu$^{63}(p, 2n)$Zn^{62}

Cross section in 10^{-26} cm^2

Energy of α in Mev

FIG. 11.6   The experimental test of the compound-nucleus hypothesis. A comparison of the (p, n), $(p, 2n)$, and (p, pn) cross sections with those of (α, n), $(\alpha, 2n)$, and (α, pn) reaction cross-sections. [From Ghoshal, S. N., *Phys. Rev.*, **80**, 939, (1950).]

where $\sigma_c(\alpha)$ is the cross section for the formation of the compound nucleus through channel α, and $G_c(\beta)$ is the probability of the decay of the compound nucleus through channel β. Our aim is to derive an expression for $G_c(\beta)$, which is assumed to be a function of the excitation energy E_c. The width of the level at E_c for the reaction through channel β is given by

$$\Gamma_\beta \tau_\beta = \hbar \tag{11.60}$$

where $\Gamma_\beta / \hbar = (1/\tau_\beta) = \lambda_\beta$ is the decay probability through channel β. The total width of the level for decay through different processes is given by

$$\Gamma = \sum_\beta \Gamma_\beta \tag{11.61}$$

and hence

$$G_c(\beta) = \Gamma_\beta / \Gamma \tag{11.62}$$

Combining Eq. (11.59) and Eq. (11.62) with Eq. (11.48a)

$$k_\alpha^2 \sigma(\alpha \to \beta) = k_\beta^2 \sigma(\beta \to \alpha) \qquad (11.48a)$$

we obtain

$$\frac{k_\alpha^2 \sigma_c(\alpha) \Gamma_\beta}{\Gamma} = \frac{k_\beta^2 \sigma_c(\beta) \Gamma_\alpha}{\Gamma}$$

or

$$\frac{k_\alpha^2 \sigma_c(\alpha)}{\Gamma_\alpha} = \frac{k_\beta^2 \sigma_c(\beta)}{\Gamma_\beta} = U(E_c) \qquad (11.63)$$

where U is a function of energy E_c only. Combining Eqs. (11.62) and (11.63), we may write

$$G_c(\beta) = \frac{\sigma_c(\beta) k_\beta^2}{\sum_\eta \sigma_c(\eta) k_\eta^2} \qquad (11.64)$$

where the sum is taken over all possible channels through which the compound nucleus may be formed. If the only reaction that takes place is $X(x, y) Y$, then $G_c(\beta) = 1$. We shall now proceed to the application of the compound-nucleus model to different nuclear reactions. To start with, at low excitation energies the level widths, Γ, are very small as compared to the separation, D, between the levels. But as the excitation energy increases, the level width also increases, and the separation D between the levels decreases, so much so that at high energies the levels overlap. Our discussion will be divided into two parts (a) $\Gamma/D \ll 1$, the resonance region, and (b) $\Gamma/D \gg 1$, the continuum region. Before going into these we shall discuss the problem of a nucleus with a well-defined surface.

5. NUCLEAR REACTIONS WITH A NUCLEUS OF WELL-DEFINED SURFACE

A simplified quantitative treatment of nuclear reactions may be obtained by making the following assumptions:

(a) If the incident particle has low energy, its wave length will be very large as compared to the radius R_x of the target nucleus, and under such circumstances we may say that the target nucleus has a well-defined surface. There will be no interaction between the incident particle and the target if the distance between them is greater than R_x.

(b) The incident particle is a neutron with $l = 0$. This simplifies the problem in two respects. First, because the neutron has no charge, there is no coulomb barrier. Second, because $l = 0$, there is no centrifugal barrier, $l(l + 1)\hbar^2/2\mu r^2$.

(c) The spin of the target nucleus is zero.

For $l = 0$, and $r > R_x$, there is no interaction and the wave function is the radial-wave function $u(r) = r\psi$, which satisfies the Schrödinger wave equation

$$\frac{d^2u}{dr^2} + k^2u = 0 \qquad \begin{cases} \text{for } l = 0 \\ \text{and } r > R_x \end{cases} \tag{11.65}$$

and the wave function is given by

$$u(r) = C \sin (kr + \delta_0) \qquad \text{for } r > R_x \tag{11.66}$$

where δ_0 is the phase shift that is completely determined by the boundary condition at the surface. The boundary condition is the continuity of the logarithmic derivative of $u(r)$ at the boundary and we define it as

$$f_l(r) = R_x\left(\frac{du/dr}{u}\right) = R_x\left(\frac{d}{dr}(\ln u)\right) \tag{11.67}$$
$$r = R_x$$

which for $l = 0$ and $r = R_x$ takes the form

$$f_0 = kR_x \cot (kR_x + \delta_0) \tag{11.68}$$

This equation may be rewritten in the form

$$f_0 = -ikR_x\left\{\frac{e^{-2ikR_x} + \eta_0}{e^{-2ik}R_x - \eta_0}\right\}$$

where $\eta_0 = e^{2i\delta_0}$,

or rearranging we may write

$$\eta_0 = e^{2i\delta_0} = \frac{f_0 + ikR_x}{f_0 - ikR_x}e^{-2ikR_x} \tag{11.69}$$

We are now in a position to calculate the scattering and reaction cross-sections with the help of Eqs. (11.43) and (11.44) which, for $l = 0$ take the following forms:

$$\sigma_{s,0} = \pi\lambda^2(|1 - \eta_0|^2) \tag{11.70}$$

and

$$\sigma_{r,0} = \pi\lambda^2(1 - |\eta_0|^2) \tag{11.71}$$

Thus if we know f_0 from the boundary condition, we can calculate η_0 from Eq. (11.69) and hence $\sigma_{s,0}$ and $\sigma_{r,0}$ from Eqs. (11.70) and (11.71). Thus

$$|1 - \eta_0|^2 = \left| 1 - \frac{f_0 + ikR_x}{f_0 - ikR_x} e^{-2ikR_x} \right|^2$$

$$= \left| e^{2ikR_x} - \frac{f_0 + ikR_x}{f_0 - ikR_x} \right|^2$$

$$= \left| e^{2ikR_x} - 1 - \frac{f_0 + ikR_x}{f_0 - ikR_x} + 1 \right|^2$$

$$= \left| e^{2ikR_x} - 1 + \frac{-2ikR_x}{f_0 - ikR_x} \right|^2$$

The scattering cross-section, therefore, is given by

$$\sigma_{s,0} = \pi\lambda^2 \left| \frac{-2ikR_x}{f_0 - ikR_x} + e^{2ikR_x} - 1 \right|^2$$

$$= \pi\lambda^2 |A_{res} + A_{pot}|^2 \tag{11.72}$$

where

$$A_{res} = \frac{-2ikR_x}{f_0 - ikR_x} \tag{11.73}$$

and

$$A_{pot} = e^{2ikR_x} - 1 \tag{11.74}$$

A_{res} is called the *resonance scattering-amplitude*, and A_{pot} is called the *hard-sphere potential scattering-amplitude*. The total scattering cross-section is due to these two amplitudes. The hard-sphere potential scattering, or shape-elastic scattering, comes from the reasoning that at the surface $u(r) = 0$ and $f_0 = \infty$, i.e., the sphere is impenetrable. At any energy there will always be some potential scattering, but the contribution due to A_{res} will be mainly at the resonance energies that may be calculated from Eq. (11.73).

Similarly we may calculate the reaction cross-section, which turns out to be

$$\sigma_{r,0} = \pi\lambda^2 \frac{-4kR_x \operatorname{Img} f_0}{(\operatorname{Re} f_0)^2 + (\operatorname{Img} f_0 - kR_x)^2} \tag{11.75}$$

Note that if f_0 is real, δ_0 will be real, and there will be only scattering and no reaction. On the other hand, if $\sigma_{r,0} \neq 0$, f_0 must have an imaginary part. And we may conclude

only if
$$\left. \begin{array}{c} \sigma_{r,0} \geqslant 0 \\[2mm] \operatorname{Img} f_0 \leqslant 0 \end{array} \right\} \tag{11.76}$$

6. THEORY OF RESONANCE SCATTERING

To start with let us assume that the incident particles are neutrons with very low energy. This simplifies the problem in two respects. First, the neutron energy being low, only $l = 0$ neutrons are affected by the target nucleus. Second, the only channel open for the decay of the compound nucleus is the entrance channel, α. Thus we are dealing with elastic scattering only. The outgoing wave-function will differ from the incident wave-function only in a phase shift. Thus the total wave function in channel α may be written as

$$u \sim e^{-iKr} + e^{i(Kr+2\zeta)}$$

$$\text{for } r < R_x \qquad (11.77)$$

where K is the wave number of the system in channel α. Using the definition given in Eq. (11.67), i.e.,

$$f_l = R_x \left(\frac{u'(r)}{u(r)} \right)_{r=R_x}$$

we obtain

$$f_0(E) = -KR_x \tan(KR_x + \zeta) \qquad (11.78)$$

or

$$f_0(E) = -KR_x \tan Z(E) \qquad (11.79a)$$

where

$$Z(E) = (KR_x + \zeta) \qquad (11.79b)$$

As the energy of the incident particle increases, according to Eq. (11.79) the function $f_0(E)$ will pass through successive zeros and infinities. From Eq. (11.73) we note that the amplitude of resonance scattering A_{res} will be maximum if f_0 is zero. We call E_n the *resonance energies* defined as

$$f_0(E_n) = 0, \qquad n = 0, 1, 2, 3, \qquad (11.80a)$$

or

$$Z(E_n) = n\pi \qquad (11.80b)$$

We shall expand $f_0(E)$ near its zero value or near the resonance energy, E_n,

$$f_0(E) = \left(\frac{\partial f}{\partial E} \right)_{E=E_n} (E - E_n) + \cdots \qquad (11.81)$$

Thus near the resonances, substituting for f_0 in Eq. (11.73),

$$A_{res} = \frac{-2ikR_x}{\left(\dfrac{df_0}{dE} \right)_{E_n} (E - E_n) - ikR_x} \qquad (11.82)$$

We may define a quantity Γ_n (half-width) as

$$\Gamma_n = \frac{-2kR_x}{(df_0/dE)_{E_n}} \tag{11.83}$$

which gives

$$A_{res} = \frac{i\Gamma_n}{(E - E_n) + (i/2)\Gamma_n} \tag{11.84}$$

or

$$|A_{res}|^2 = \frac{(\Gamma_n)^2}{(E - E_n)^2 + (\Gamma n/2)^2} \tag{11.85}$$

Let us consider the following three cases:

A. NEAR RESONANCE. $E \cong E_n$. Near the resonances $A_{res} \gg A_{pot}$, and hence

$$\sigma_{s,0} = \pi\lambda^2 |A_{res} + A_{pot}|^2$$

after neglecting A_{pot} it takes the form

$$\sigma_{s,0} = \frac{\pi\lambda^2 (\Gamma_n)^2}{(E - E_n)^2 + (\frac{1}{2}\Gamma_n)^2} \tag{11.86}$$

This is the well known *dispersion formula*, as in the case of damped forced oscillations. At or near the resonance, $E = E_n$, hence

$$A_{res} = 2$$

and

$$\sigma_{s,0} = 4\pi\lambda^2 \tag{11.87}$$

while

$$A_{pot} = e^{2ikR_x} - 1 \simeq 2ikR_x \tag{11.88}$$

which is very small, because $kR_x \ll 1$. Thus near resonance, the total scattering cross-section is given by Eq. (11.87).

B. FAR FROM RESONANCE. Somewhere in between the resonances, the function f_0 will be very large, and hence A_{res} will be very small. Thus the scattering will be due only to hard sphere scattering and for low energies

$$A_{pot} = e^{2ikR_x} - 1 \simeq 2ikR_x$$

and

$$\sigma_{s,0} = \pi\lambda^2 |A_{pot}|^2$$
$$= \pi\lambda^2 |2ikR_x|^2$$

or

$$\sigma_{s,0} = 4\pi R_x^2 \tag{11.89}$$

C. INTERMEDIATE REGION.   For the intermediate region where $E - E_n > \dfrac{\Gamma_n}{2}$, the two amplitudes A_{res} and A_{pot} have opposite signs for $E < E_n$ and have the same sign for $E > E_n$. The result of the change in signs is the interference between the two amplitudes as shown in Fig. 11.6.

The scattering cross-section as a function of energy for the three regions is shown in Fig. 11.7. The experimental result of this behavior is shown in Fig. 11.8[8] for the scattering and absorption of protons at 985-kev resonance in (Al^{27} + p).

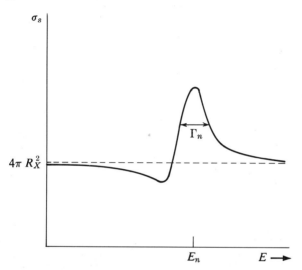

FIG. 11.7 Variation of the elastic scattering cross-section for $l = 0$ neutrons near resonance. Note that far away from resonance the cross-section is $4\pi R_x^2$.

We shall now extend this simple picture of resonances to the case of higher energy incident particles. As the energy of the particle increases, channels other than the entrance channel become available. Thus the reaction cross-section σ_r is no longer zero. The first reaction channel, β, to open will be the radiative capture process, and at higher energies particle emission will also take place. The wave function in the incident channel α is given by

$$u_l \sim e^{-ikr} + b\, e^{ikr}$$

where

$$b = e^{2i\zeta}e^{-2q}$$

instead of $b = e^{2i\zeta}$ as in the case of pure elastic scattering. Note that e^{-2q} is a real quantity and q is small. Thus the entrance channel wave-function is given by

$$u_l \sim e^{-ikr} + e^{i(Kr + 2\zeta + 2iq)} \tag{11.90}$$

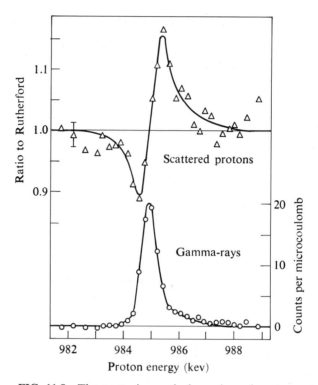

FIG. 11.8 The scattering and absorption of protons at 985-kev resonance in an (Al^{27} + p) compound nucleus. The variation in the cross section near resonance agrees with theoretical predictions (solid curve). [From Bender, R. S., F. C. Shoemaker, S. G. Kaufmann, and G. M. B. Bouricius, *Phys. Rev.*, **76**, 273, (1949).]

The function $f_0(E)$ is given by

$$f_0(E) = R_x \left(\frac{u'(r)}{u(r)} \right)_{r=R_x} = -KR_x \tan[Z(E) + iq] \qquad (11.91)$$

where $Z(E) = KR_x + \zeta(E)$. Once again, we proceed to calculate $\sigma_{s,0}$ and $\sigma_{r,0}$ as before. We assume that $|q| \ll 1$ and the resonances are defined by

$$f_0(E, q = 0) = 0 = -\tan Z(E) \qquad (11.92)$$

We expand $f_0(E, q)$ in a Taylor series in both q and E

$$f_0(E) = (E - E_n) \left| \frac{\partial f_0}{\partial E} \right|_{E=E_n, q=0} + q \left| \frac{\partial f_0}{\partial q} \right|_{E=E_n, q=0} + \cdots, \qquad (11.93)$$

Substituting the value of $(\partial f/\partial q)_{E=E_n, q=0}$, from Eq. (11.91) into Eq. (11.93), we get

$$f_0(E) = (E - E_n)\left(\frac{\partial f_0}{\partial E}\right)_{E=E_n, q=0} - iqKR_x \qquad (11.94)$$

Let Γ_n^s and Γ_n^r be the widths of the levels for the elastic scattering through channel α and the reaction width through channel β, respectively. We define (for $l = 0$)

$$\Gamma_n^s = \frac{-2KR_x}{\left(\dfrac{\partial f_0}{\partial E}\right)_{E=E_n, q=0}} \qquad (11.95)$$

and

$$\Gamma_n^r = \frac{-2qKR_x}{\left(\dfrac{\partial f_0}{\partial E}\right)_{F=E_n, q=0}} \qquad (11.96)$$

while the total level width is given by

$$\Gamma_n = \Gamma_n^s + \Gamma_n^r \qquad (11.97)$$

Making use of Eqs. (11.72), (11.73), and (11.74) leads to the following expressions for elastic scattering and single-reaction channel cross-sections for $l = 0$ particles near resonance, i.e., for $E \simeq E_n$

$$\sigma_{s,0} = \pi \lambdabar^2 \left| \frac{i\Gamma_n^s}{(E - E_n) + \frac{1}{2}i\Gamma_n} + 2kR_x \right|^2 \qquad (11.98)$$

and

$$\sigma_{r,0} = \pi \lambdabar^2 \frac{\Gamma_n^s \Gamma_n^r}{(E - E_n)^2 + \frac{1}{4}\Gamma_n^2} \qquad (11.99)$$

These are known as the famous *Breit-Wigner formulae*. Note that if we neglect the hard-sphere or potential scattering near resonance, we obtain

$$A_{\text{res}} = \frac{i\Gamma_n^s}{(E - E_n) + \frac{1}{2}i\Gamma_n} \qquad (11.100a)$$

and

$$\sigma_{s,0} = \pi \lambdabar^2 \frac{(\Gamma_n^s)^2}{(E - E_n)^2 + (\frac{1}{2}\Gamma_n)^2} \qquad (11.100b)$$

In these derivations we have assumed that the spin of the target nucleus is zero, i.e., $I = 0$. The Breit-Wigner formulae must be modified to take into consideration the spin, I, of the nucleus. The total angular momentum, S, in the entrance channel is either $(I + \frac{1}{2})$ or $(I - \frac{1}{2})$, where $\frac{1}{2}$ is the spin of a proton or a neutron with $l = 0$. Because each value of S has $(2S + 1)$ space orientations, the total number of possible space orientations is $[2(I + \frac{1}{2}) + 1]$ $+ [2(I - \frac{1}{2}) + 1] = 2(2I + 1)$. The relative probability, or the statistical weight, that the incident particle and the target, the entrance channel, has a spin S is

$$g(S) = \frac{2S + 1}{2(2I + 1)} \quad \text{for } S = (I + \tfrac{1}{2}) \quad \text{or} \quad (I - \tfrac{1}{2}) \qquad (11.101)$$

Inclusion of the statistical weight leads to the following expressions for the cross sections:

$$\sigma_{s,0} = g(S)\pi\lambda^2 \left| \frac{i\Gamma_n^s}{(E - E_n) + \frac{1}{2}i\Gamma_n} + 2kR_x \right|^2 + [1 - g(S)]4\pi R_x^2 \quad (11.102)$$

and

$$\sigma_{r,0} = g(S)\pi\lambda^2 \frac{\Gamma_n^s \Gamma_n^r}{(E - E_n)^2 + \frac{1}{4}\Gamma_n^2} \qquad (11.103)$$

It should be noted that s corresponds to α and r to β, in general. The formulae of Eqs. (11.98), (11.99), (11.102), and (11.103) have been experimentally verified for low energy incident particles. Fig. 11.9[9] shows the resonances in the case of a radiative capture reaction Al^{27} (p, γ) Si^{28}. Fig. 11.10[10] shows the resonances in the reaction Al^{27} (d, p) Al^{28} for an incident deuteron energy of 2.1 Mev. The corresponding level scheme is shown in Fig. 11.11[10]. The most stringent test of the equations is shown in Fig. 11.12[11], where the results of 2.33-ev resonance in $_{52}\text{Te}^{123}$ have been compared with the theory.

7. CONTINUUM THEORY

The picture of resonances on the basis of the compound-nucleus model holds well for very low energy incident particles (up to ~ 2 Mev). As the energy of the incident particles increases, the number of levels available to the incident channel becomes very large. Once the incident particle crosses the nuclear surface, it will be captured, and the probability that it is re-emitted into the entrance channel is negligible. There are no longer discrete levels in the quasi-stationary states of the compound nucleus. A large number of levels and the condition that $\Gamma \gg D$ lead to complete overlapping, and elastic scattering cannot be explained because the incident channel is no longer available. This implies that there will no longer be any sharp resonances, and thus the compound-nucleus hypothesis breaks down. But this is not so. An altogether different interpretation of the compound-nucleus hypothesis is sought in the following manner.

    We assume that the resonances are broad and completely overlapping. The compound nucleus is formed as a random mixture of different states.

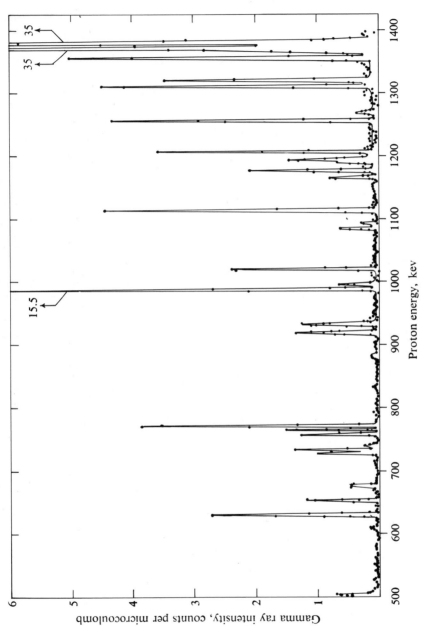

FIG. 11.9   Resonances obtained in the case of a radiative capture reaction Al^{27} (p, γ) Si^{28}. [From Brostrom, K. J., T. Huss and R. Tangen, *Phys. Rev.*, 71, 661, (1947).]

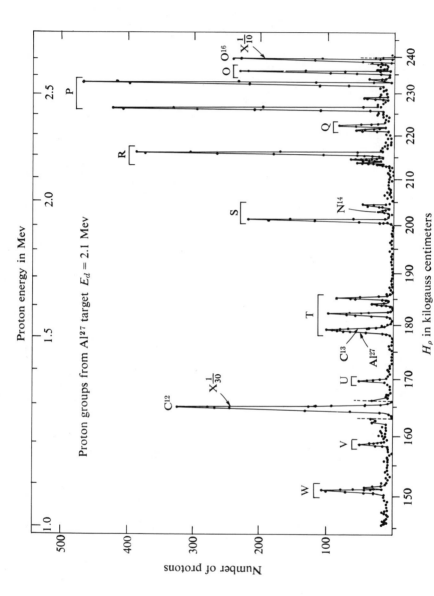

FIG. 11.10 (a) Both 11. 10 (a) and (b) represent resonances obtained in the reaction Al^{27} (d, p) Al^{28} for an incident deuteron energy of 2.1 Mev. [From Enge, H. A., W. W. Buechner and A. Sperduto, *Phys. Rev.*, **88**, 963, (1952).]

416

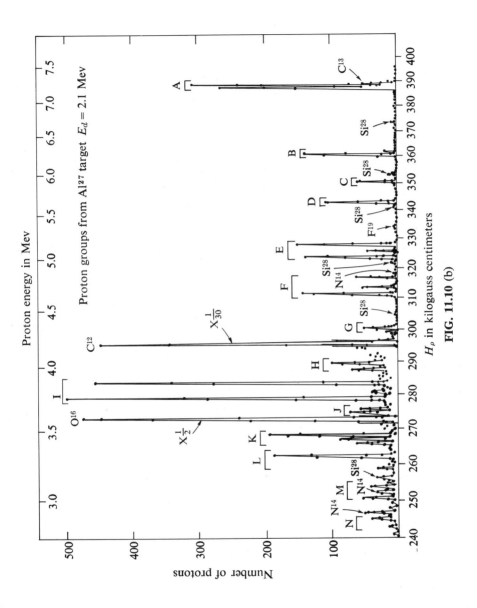

Proton energy in Mev

Proton groups from Al²⁷ target E_d = 2.1 Mev

H_ρ in kilogauss centimeters

FIG. 11.10 (b)

417

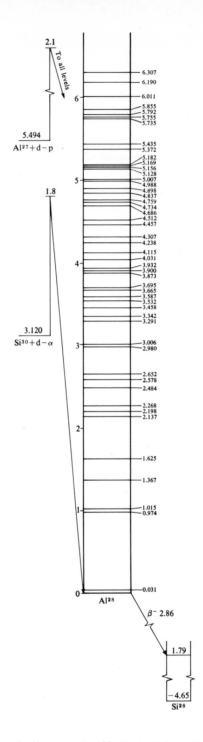

FIG. 11.11 Energy levels diagram of Al^{28} obtained from the resonance spectrum of Fig. 11.10. [From Enge, H. A., W. W. Buechner and A. Sperduto, *Phys. Rev.*, **88**, 963, (1952).]

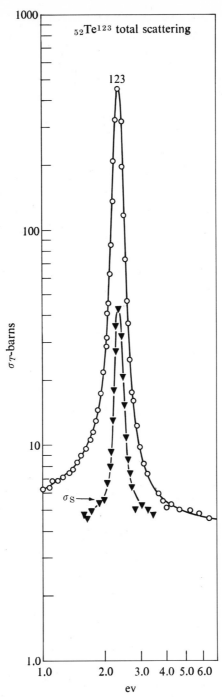

FIG. 11.12 The agreement between theoretical cross-sections predicted from Eqs. (11.102) and (11.103) and the experimentally measured cross-sections for the 2.33-ev resonance of Te^{123}. For $E_n = 2.33$ ev, the elastic scattering-width $\Gamma_n^{\alpha} = 0.0104$ ev, and the radiative capture-width $\Gamma_n^{\beta} = 0.104$ ev. S, the channel spin, $= 1$. [From Brookhaven Report BNL-325.]

Because the mixture is random, the probability of decay will be independent of the mode of formation; this justifies the compound-nucleus hypothesis. The cross-section for the formation of a compound nucleus $\sigma_c(\alpha)$ is equal to the reaction cross-section, σ_r. The elastic scattering on this model is explained by saying that the incident wave is reflected at the entrance channel without any formation of the compound nucleus.

The continuum theory works well for incident-particles energies of the order of a few Mev. Because of the resemblance of the energy distribution of the particles emitted from an excited nucleus in the continuum region with a thermodynamical system, different ways have been developed to interpret the energy spectrum[5]. We shall not go into the details of these interpretations but shall derive an expression for the cross section in the following manner.

For the sake of simplicity, once again we consider neutrons with $l = 0$. Because the entrance channel is no longer available, the wave function inside the nucleus is given by

$$u \sim e^{-iKr} \qquad \text{for } r < R_x \qquad (11.104)$$

where K is the wave number given by $\sqrt{2\mu E}/\hbar \simeq 10^{13}$ cm^{-1}. Once the compound nucleus is formed, there cannot be any elastic scattering. Eq. (11.104) gives

$$f_0 = -iKR_x \qquad (11.105)$$

and this, by the use of Eqs. (11.72) and (11.75), gives the following

$$\sigma_{s,0} = \pi\lambda^2 \left| \frac{2k}{K+k} + e^{2ikR} - 1 \right|^2 \qquad (11.106)$$

and

$$\sigma_{r,0} = \sigma_c(\alpha) = \pi\lambda^2 \frac{4kK}{(K+k)^2} \qquad (11.107)$$

We shall discuss Eq. (11.107) for $\sigma_{r,0}$ in some detail. We may write Eq. (11.107) as

$$\sigma_{r,0} = \pi\lambda^2 T_0(E_n) \qquad (11.108a)$$

where

$$T_0 = \text{Barrier Transmission factor} = \frac{4kK}{(K+k)^2} \qquad (11.108b)$$

Because the maximum value of T_0 possible is unity, therefore

$$\sigma_{r,0,\max} = \pi\lambda^2 \qquad (11.109)$$

For neutrons with $l \neq 0$, we may write

$$\sigma_{r,l} = \pi\lambda^2(2l+1)T_l \qquad (11.110)$$

where T_l is the barrier penetration factor due to potential discontinuity and is given by[5,12]

$$T_l = \frac{4kKv_l}{K^2 + (2kK + k^2v_l')v_l} \qquad (11.111)$$

where $v_l = v_l' = 1$ for $l = 0$ and for higher value of l, T_l are tabulated[5,12].

The total cross-section, σ, for the neutrons as a function of incident energies is plotted in Fig. 11.13[13] for different values of K_0 $[K = (k^2 + K_0)^{1/2}]$.

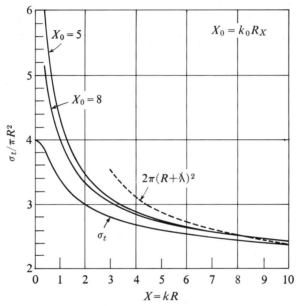

FIG. 11.13   Total cross-section for neutrons as a function of incident energy for different values of $K_0 R_x$. $K_0 R_x = \infty$ corresponds to a perfectly reflecting sphere. [From Feshbach, H., and V. F. Weisskopf, *Phys. Rev.*, **76**, 155, (1949).]

It is quite evident that for higher energies the cross-section is independent of K_0 and it looks as if the scattering is taking place from a perfectly reflecting sphere.

Let us now consider a special case of Eq. (11.107). For $k \ll K$, T_0 becomes

$$T_0 = 4kK/(K + k)^2 \simeq 4k/K$$

and because K does not vary much, we may say that $K = (k^2 + K_0^2)^{1/2} \simeq K_0$. This leads to

$$\sigma_{r,0} = 4\pi\lambdabar^2 \frac{k}{K} \simeq \frac{4\pi}{k^2} \frac{k}{K_0} \simeq \frac{4\pi}{K_0} \frac{1}{k}$$

or

$$\sigma_{r,0} \propto 1/v = \text{constant}/v \qquad (11.112)$$

that is, for small incident velocities of the neutrons, the reaction cross-section is inversely proportional to the velocity. As an example, Fig. 11.14[(14)] shows the total cross-section of iridium for slow neutrons. Variation of $\sigma_{r,0}$ as $1/v$ is quite clear at low energies.

Lastly, we shall discuss the emission of neutrons from a compound nucleus as an evaporation process analogous to the evaporation of a molecule from the surface of a liquid. The binding energy of a nucleon is similar to the latent heat of evaporation. On this thermodynamical model the energy spectrum can be explained in the following manner. It is difficult to concentrate a large amount of energy on a single nucleon, and the evaporated

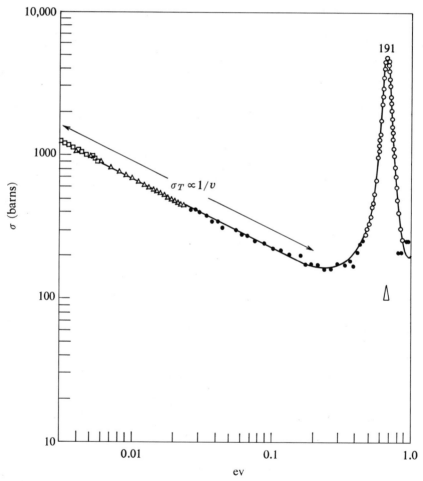

FIG. 11.14   Total cross-section, σ_T, of iridium for slow neutrons. It is evident that $\sigma_T \propto 1/v$ at low energies. [From Brookhaven Report, BNL-325.]

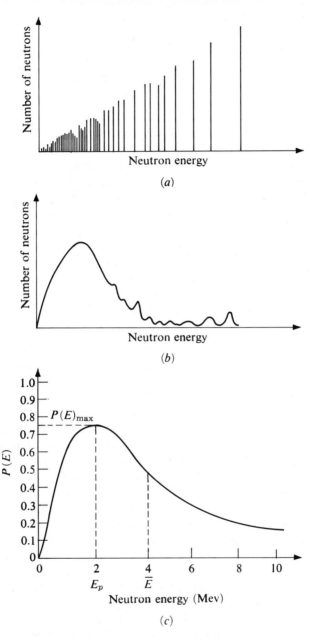

FIG. 11.15 (a) Energy distribution of emitted neutrons for infinite resolution. (b) Energy distribution of emitted neutrons for finite resolution. (c) Evaporated neutron-energy spectrum for nuclear temperature of 2 Mev. $\bar{E}$ = average energy, E_p = most probable energy. [From Blatt, J. M., and V. F. Weisskopf, *Theoretical Nuclear Physics*, p. 366, New York: John Wiley & Sons, (1958).]

nucleons, therefore, will be emitted primarily with low kinetic energies. This has been found experimentally to be true. The energy distribution of the emitted particles is a function of the temperature (in units of Mev) of the excited compound nucleus, as shown in Fig. 11.15(a), (b), and (c)[5]. For neutrons the energy spectrum may be written as

$$P(E) = Ee^{-E/T} \qquad (11.113)$$

where $P(E)$ is the probability that the neutron will be emitted with energy E and will leave the residual nucleus at a nuclear temperature, T. Fig. 11.15(c) is drawn for the case of a nuclear temperature $T = 2$ Mev, which shows that the most probable kinetic energy of the neutron is T Mev while the average energy is $2T$ Mev.

It may also be pointed out that the probability of emission of a charged particle at low energies is much less than a neutron emission. This is quite understandable because the charged particles have to cross the coulomb barrier as explained in Sec. 7, in addition to having the boundary (or potential) discontinuity factor as explained above (Eq. 11.111).

8. DIRECT NUCLEAR REACTIONS

The theory of the compound nucleus has been very successful in explaining many different types of nuclear reactions. As the energies of the incident particles increase, however, it becomes more and more difficult to account for the variations in the differential cross-sections. It seems that for incident particles of energies between 10 and 20 Mev, the angular distribution of the emitted particles can be explained by an altogether different process. This process is called *direct nuclear interactions* or *direct interactions*. According to the direct-interaction model, the transition from an incident channel to a reaction channel in a nuclear reaction takes place in one step without the formation of the intermediate compound-nucleus state. The outstanding features of the direct nuclear interaction processes are the following:

(a) Unlike the compound-nucleus model, the mean free-path is large, and the lifetime is very short. Therefore, at high energies, the direct-interaction processes do not show sharp resonances of the compound nucleus model. Instead the resonances are broad. (b) The relative number of high energy particles emitted is much higher than expected from the compound nucleus theory. (c) The differential cross-section strongly depends on the direction of emission of the reaction products. There is a strong forward-peaking of the higher energy particles. This is contrary to the symmetric angular distribution expected from the continuum theory.

The theory of direct nuclear interactions has been developed mostly by S. Butler[15,16] and his associates[17]. Without going into mathematical complexity, it is possible to predict some features by means of classical methods. According to Butler,[16] Fig. 11.16 shows an outline of the process. Collision of the incident particles takes place only in the surface of the nucleus while the core, shown shaded, does not contribute to the direct-interaction

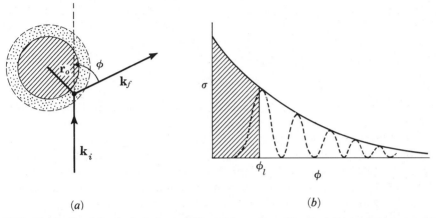

(a)   (b)

FIG. 11.16   Semiclassical picture of direct interaction. Classical theory is shown with solid lines; the direct-interaction mode is shown with broken lines (a) surface interaction and (b) differential cross-section versus θ. The shaded area is forbidden due to the conservation of angular momentum. [From Butler, S. T., *Phys. Rev.*, **106**, 272, (1957).]

processes. Any reaction taking place inside the core contributes to the compound-nucleus formation. There is a definite radius of interaction for the surface processes. Because it is assumed that the mean free-path is very large, the particles in the surface layer, after being struck by the incident particles, are emitted without the formation of the intermediate compound nucleus. Let k_i and k_f be the wave vectors of the incident and emitted particles. We assume that these particles cross the surface of the nucleus of radius R without being refracted. According to direct interaction theory, the collision may take place anywhere in the surface, say at a point P, a distance $\mathbf{r}$ from the center of the nucleus. From the conservation of linear momentum, the recoil momentum $q\hbar$ of the nucleus is given by the following equation:

$$q\hbar = (k_i - k_f)\hbar \tag{11.114}$$

or

$$q = k_i - k_f \tag{11.115}$$

For the (n, p) type reactions, the value of the angular momentum, $l\hbar$, imparted to the nucleus is limited by the condition

$$l_n + l_p \geqslant l \geqslant |l_n - l_p| \tag{11.116}$$

where l_n is the orbital quantum-number of the neutron in its final state after being captured and l_p is that of the proton in its initial state before the reaction.

Thus, from Eq. (11.115), and using Fig. 11.16(a), we may write

$$q^2 = k_i^2 + k_f^2 - 2k_i k_f \cos \phi$$
$$= (k_i - k_f)^2 + 4k_i k_f \sin^2 \phi/2 \qquad (11.117)$$

and

$$\mathbf{l} = \mathbf{q} \times \mathbf{r}\hbar \qquad (11.118)$$

$$l = qr \sin \beta \qquad (11.119)$$

According to Eq. (11.119), the direct interaction is limited to the points that lie on the surface of a cylinder of radius l/q. Because the nuclear core does not contribute to the direct interaction, only the points lying on the two end caps of the cylinder are effective for such processes. The waves originating at these two ends interfere to produce maxima and minima in the angular distribution of the emitted particles. This type of distribution is shown in Fig. 11.16(b).

The quantum-mechanical treatment of the direct interaction process gives the following expression for the angular distribution.

$$d\sigma \propto [j_l(qR)]^2 \, d\Omega \qquad (11.120)$$

where j_l are the spherical Bessel functions. The first maximum is determined by the argument (qR) given by the equation

$$qR = l \qquad (11.121)$$

From the angular distribution obtained experimentally, it is possible to determine the radius of interaction. The theory has been verified experimentally[16,18]. Fig. 11.17[16] shows the angular distribution for inelastic scattering of 31.5-Mev alpha particles from Mg^{24}.

There are four different types of nuclear reactions that may be explained by the direct interaction process.

(a) In *inelastic scattering*. The incident particle looses a part of its kinetic energy, thereby leaving the nucleus in the excited state. This is shown schematically in Fig. 11.18(a) where C represents the core of the nucleus, N the surface nucleon, and P the incident particle. Examples of such reactions are (α, α'), (p, p'), and the like.

(b) The *knock-out reactions* such as (n, p), (p, n) are shown schematically in Fig. 11.18(b).

(c) In *stripping reactions* the incident projectile loses a nucleon. The examples of such reactions are (d, p), (d, n), (α, p), among others. It is schematically shown in Fig. 11.18(c).

(d) The *pick-up reactions* are just the reverse of stripping. Two examples are (p, d) and (p, α), as shown in Fig. 11.18(d).

Theories of all these reactions have been worked out in detail at intermediate and high energies.[19] The most important of all the direct-interaction processes are the stripping reactions of the type (d, p) and (d, n), the theory for which was worked out first by S. Butler[15] in 1951. For such reactions, the conservation of angular momentum yields,

$$I_i + I_f + \tfrac{1}{2} \geqslant l \geqslant |\mathbf{I}_i + \mathbf{I}_f + \tfrac{1}{2}|_{\min} \qquad (11.122)$$

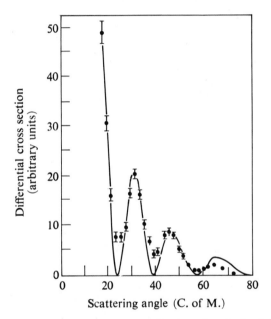

FIG. 11.17 Angular distribution for inelastic scattering of 31.5-Mev alpha particles from Mg^{24}; Mg^{24} (α, α') Mg^{24*}. [From Butler, S. T., *Phys. Rev.*, **106**, 272, (1957.)]

where I_i and I_f are the spins of the initial and final nuclei, respectively. $|\mathbf{I}_i + \mathbf{I}_f + \tfrac{1}{2}|_{\min}$ is the minimum possible vector sum. l must be even if the parities of the initial and the final states of nucleus are the same, and odd if they are different. As an example, consider the reaction C^{12} (d, p) C^{13} in which $I_i = 0^+$ and $I_f = \tfrac{1}{2}^-$. Thus there is a change in parity and l must have an odd value. According to Eq. (11.122), $0 + \tfrac{1}{2} + \tfrac{1}{2} \geqslant l \geqslant 0 - \tfrac{1}{2} + \tfrac{1}{2}$, i.e., $1 \geqslant l \geqslant 0$ or $l = 0, 1$. Because l must be odd, therefore, $l = 1$ and the last neutron in C^{13} is in the $p_{\frac{1}{2}}$ state.

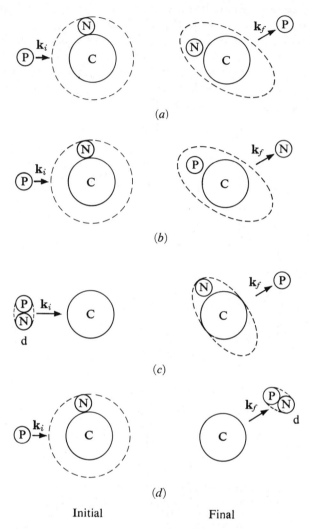

Initial   Final

FIG. 11.18 Schematic representation of (a) inelastic scattering, (b) knock-out reactions, (c) stripping reactions, and (d) pick-up reactions.

9. THE OPTICAL MODEL

The compound-nucleus model and direct-interaction process explain quite a large number of nuclear reactions. But one discomforting fact is that the assumptions made in these two models are altogether different. In the compound-nucleus model the mean free-path is very small while in the direct-interaction processes it is of the order of the nuclear diameter. Besides, there are many characteristics of nuclear reactions both at low and high energies that are not predicted by either of the two models. For example, according to the continuum theory the cross-section decreases steadily with increasing energy of the incident neutrons. More detailed investigations have revealed that there actually are broad maxima and minima in the cross-sections that are functions not only of the energies of the incident particles but also of the mass number. The resonance structure is more or less like that of a single particle as expected from the shell model. The cross-sections for 1-3 Mev neutrons were collected by H. Barschall[20]. K. Ford and D. Bohm[21] observed the discontinuities in the cross-sections versus mass number for different elements. Again, at very high energies the scattering of neutrons cannot be accounted for by the Bohr theory as we discussed in Sec. 6.4.

In order to account for different characteristics at various energies and mass numbers, including those of the compound nucleus as well as direct interactions, the Optical Model of the nucleus has been developed[22,23,24,25]. We have already discussed this model in some detail in Sec. 6.4 and we shall briefly outline it here again. According to this model the nucleus is treated as a cloudy crystal. A beam of light that falls on a crystal is partly absorbed and partly transmitted or diffracted, similarly a beam of particles that falls on a nucleus will be partly scattered. In order to account for both scattering as well as absorption, the interaction potential is represented as a sum of a real potential V_0 and an imaginary potential $i\xi V_0$. The real part of the potential accounts for the scattering and the imaginary part explains absorption. Thus the interaction potential is

$$V = -V_0(1 + i\xi) \qquad \text{for } r \leqslant R \leqslant r_0 A^{1/3}$$

$$V = 0 \qquad \text{for } r > R \qquad \textbf{(11.123)}$$

where $V_0 \simeq 42$ Mev and ξ is given by $0 < \xi \leqslant 1$. The wave equation for the neutron is then given (for $r < R$) by

$$\nabla^2 \psi + (2M/\hbar^2)(E + V_0 + i\xi V_0)\psi = 0 \qquad \textbf{(11.124)}$$

By adjusting the value of V_0 and ξ, the solution to different situations can be easily obtained. For example, if $\xi = 1$, the real potential is equal to the imaginary potential. This corresponds to a very short mean free-path and to high absorption. This is actually the strong-coupling model of Bohr. The value of ξ varies with the energy of the incident particle. Similarly, in the case of a weak coupling model, $\xi \langle\langle 1$ and this results in a very large mean free-path of the incident nucleon. This gives the necessary resonances in the cross-section at various mass numbers. The typical values are $V_0 \simeq 42$ Mev and $\xi = 0.03$. Again, ξ is not a constant.

The optical model has proven very successful for energies from a few Mev to a Bev. Fig. 11.19[26] shows the comparison between experimental results and the optical model. The agreement is quite obvious. In many cases the direct interaction theory is used with the optical-model potential for the interpretation of nuclear reactions.

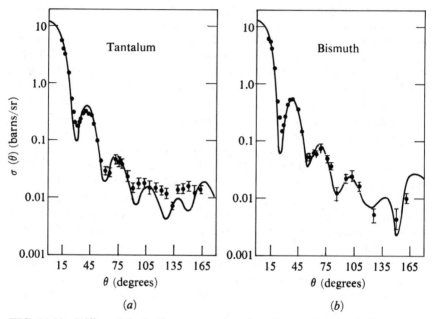

FIG. 11.19 Differential elastic cross-section for (a) tantalum and (b) bismuth for 15.2-Mev neutrons. The theoretical (solid) curve is calculated by using optical model parameters. [From: Hudson, Jr., C. I., W. S. Walker, and S. Berko, *Phys. Rev.*, **128**, 1271, (1962).]

10. HIGH-ENERGY NUCLEAR REACTIONS

The picture of nuclear reactions does not become any simpler as the energy of the incident particle increases. The compound-nucleus model becomes completely inadequate at very high energies. Above 50 Mev many types of inelastic collisions take place that, in most cases, can be explained with the help of the optical model. But as the energy of incident particles increases, the collisions become more complex[27]. In many cases the incident particles collide only with a few nucleons of a nucleus instead of with the whole nucleus. The cross-sections for the mass-yield change tremendously with the energy of the incident particles. As the energy increases, the yield of the lighter products increases. For example, 40 Mev protons bombarding a copper target may yield products with mass number as low as 40, and for protons of 5700 Mev, the yield of much lighter products, say from $A = 40$ to $A = 10$, is quite substantial. The reaction products are usually emitted anisotropically and primarily in the forward direction. The theoretical predictions are difficult to make. Usually statistical methods are applied and calculations are carried out by the Monte Carlo technique.

The most common inelastic processes that take place at energies greater than 50 Mev are the following:

(a) *Fission:* In this process the nucleus breaks up into two or more nearly equal masses. (b) *Fragmentation:* In this process the nucleus cracks and many fragments of light-weight nuclei result. (c) *Spallation:* In this process only a group of nucleons is emitted. It differs from fission in that one or more fragments are much less massive than a typical fission fragment. The nature of the process is determined by the energy of the incident particle and the mass number of the target.

As mentioned in Sec. 6.6, when the incident particles of energies greater than 300 Mev strike a heavy target, π-mesons are produced. Examples of such reactions are

$$p + p = \pi^+ + n + p$$

$$p + n = \pi^- + p + p$$

$$p + n = \pi^0 + p + n \qquad \textbf{(11.125)}$$

The production of pions and many other elementary particles takes place with increasing energies. We shall not become involved in their discussion until the last chapter.

PROBLEMS

1. Starting with Eq. (11.20) show that

$$\frac{2}{(2l+1)} a_l j_l(r) \sim \frac{1}{ikr} [e^{ikr} - e^{il\pi}e^{-ikr}]$$

2. Derive Eq. (11.28).
3. Combining Eq. (11.30) with Eq. (11.13), derive the expression for cross-section given by Eq. (11.31).
4. Derive the expression for $f(\theta)$ given by Eq. (11.38).
5. Starting with Eq. (11.38), derive the expression for σ_s given by Eq. (11.40).
6. Derive the expression for σ_r given by Eq. (11.42).
7. What is the maximum orbital angular momentum which may be brought into the Al^{27} nucleus by the capture of 40 Mev (LAB system) alpha particles?

8. Show that for thermal neutrons the reaction cross-section is inversely proportional to the square root of the kinetic energy. Evaluate the constant of proportionality.

9. What is the energy of the incident particle for which the compound nucleus will be left in the excited state at E_a?

10. A compound nucleus Y^* is formed by the capture of a neutron by the nucleus $_zX^A$. If the compound nucleus decays by alpha emission, what is the energy of the alpha particle? How do you decide whether the gamma emission in this case will compete with alpha emission or not?

11. Calculate the excitation energy of the compound nucleus formed by the capture of 8 Mev alpha particles by Al^{27}.

12. In the reaction Cu^{63} (p, n) Zn^{63} what are the compound and the residual nuclei? Calculate the excitation energy for the compound nucleus if the incident energy of the protons is 20 Mev (LAB system).

13. From the following data calculate the (n, γ) cross-sections of Ag^{109} for 0.10 ev and 0.15 ev and 0.20 ev neutrons. For (n, γ) cross-section the resonance at 5.12 ev has $\Gamma_n = 1.34 \times 10^{-2}$ ev and $\Gamma_\gamma = 0.136$ ev while the spins of Ag^{109} and the compound nucleus are $\frac{1}{2}^-$ and 6^+ respectively.

14. Te^{129} is formed by the capture of thermal neutrons (almost zero energy) by Te^{128}. What is the nuclear temperature corresponding to the excited nucleus Te^{129}?

15. What is the nuclear temperature of the excited nucleus Ag^{109} in Problem 13?

16. What is the relative probability (qualitative) for the occurrence of the reactions $X(n, n)$, $X(n, \gamma)$, $X(n, \alpha)$, $X(n, p)$, $X(n, 2n)$ if X is a medium weight nucleus and the energy of the incident neutron is (a) ~ 0.1 ev, (b) 2 Mev, (c) 10 Mev, (d) 50 Mev?

17. What theoretical model or models will you use in order to calculate the cross-section for neutron-induced reactions in (a) light nuclei, (b) medium weight nuclei and (c) heavy nuclei, if the energy of the neutrons is (i) less than 0.5 Mev, (ii) between 0.5 Mev and 10 Mev, (iii) between 10 Mev and 50 Mev, and (iv) greater than 50 Mev?

18. What is the maximum energy of the neutrons in $n - p$ scattering for which the condition $l = 0$ is satisfied?

19. Determine the most probable value of l_c in the stripping reaction Cl^{35} (d, p) Cl^{36}, where $J_i = \frac{3}{2}^+$ and $J_f = 2^+$.

20. Determine the most probable value of l_c in the stripping reaction O^{16} (d, p) O^{17}, provided the ground state spin of O^{17} is $\frac{5}{2}^+$.

REFERENCES

1. Schiff, L. I., *Quantum Mechanics*, Chapter 5, New York: McGraw-Hill Book Co., 1955.

2. Eisberg, R. M., *Fundamentals of Modern Physics*, pp. 534–558. New York: John Wiley & Sons, 1963.

3. Elton, L. R. B., *Introductory Nuclear Theory*, Chaps. 3 and 6. New York: Interscience Publishers, Inc., 1959.

4. Feshbach, H., C. E. Porter, and V. F. Weisskopf, *Phys. Rev.*, **96**, p. 448, (1954).

5. Blatt, J. M., and V. F. Weisskopf, *Theoretical Nuclear Physics*, Chapters, VIII, IX, and X, New York: John Wiley & Sons Co., 1952.

6. Bohr, N., *Nature*, **137**, p. 344, (1936).

7. Ghoshal, S. N., *Phys. Rev.*, **80**, p. 939, (1950).

8. Bender, R. S., F. C. Shoemaker, S. G. Kaufmann, and G. M. B. Bouricius, *Phys. Rev.*, **76**, p. 273, (1949).

9. Broström, K. G., T. Huss, and R. Tangen, *Phys. Rev.*, **71**, p. 661, (1947).

10. Enge, H. A., W. W. Buechner, and A. Sperduto, *Phys. Rev.*, **88**, p. 963, (1952).

11. Brookhaven Report BNL-325.

12. Bloch, I., M. M. Hull, Jr., A. A. Broyles, W. G. Bouricius, B. E. Freeman, and G. Breit, *Revs. Mod. Phys.*, **23**, p. 147, (1951).

13. Feshbach, H., and V. F. Weisskopf, *Phys. Rev.*, **76**, p. 1550, (1949).

14. (a) Butler, S. T., *Proc. Roy. Soc.*, (London) **A208**, p. 559, (1951).
    (b) Butler, S. T., *Phys. Rev.*, **106**, p. 272, (1957).
    (c) Butler, S. T., N. Austern, and C. Pearson, *Phys. Rev.*, **112**, p. 1227, (1958).
    (d) Watters, H. J., *Phys. Rev.*, **103**, p. 1770, (1956).

15. Butler, S. T., *Proc. Roy. Soc.*, **A208**, p. 559, (1951).

16. Butler, S. T., *Phys. Rev.*, **106**, p. 272, (1957).

17. Butler, S. T., N. Austern, and C. Pearson, *Phys. Rev.*, **112**, p. 1227, (1958).

18. Watters, H. J., *Phys. Rev.*, **103**, p. 1770, (1956).

19. Tobocman, W., *Theory of Direct Nuclear Reactions*, Oxford: Oxford University Press, 1961.

20. Barschall, H. H., *Phys. Rev.*, **86**, p. 431, (1952).

21. Ford, K. W., and D. Bohm, *Phys. Rev.*, **79**, p. 745, (1950).

22. Serber, R., *Phys. Rev.*, **72**, p. 1114, (1947).

23. Fernback, S., R. Serber, and T. B. Taylor, *Phys. Rev.*, **75**, p. 1352, (1949).

24. DeJuren, J., and N. Knable, *Phys. Rev.*, **77**, p. 606, (1950).

25. Feshbach, H., C. E. Porter, and V. F. Weisskopf, *Phys. Rev.*, **96**, p. 448, (1954).

26. Hudson, Jr., C. I., W. S. Walker, and S. Berko, *Phys. Rev.*, **128**, p. 1271 (1962).

27. Miller, J. M., and J. Hudis, *Ann. Rev. Nucl. Sci.*, **9**, p. 159, (1959).

SUGGESTIONS FOR FURTHER READING

1. Elton, L. R. B., *Introductory Nuclear Theory*, Chapters 3, and 6. New York: Interscience Publishers, Inc., 1959.

2. Eisberg, R. M., *Fundamentals of Modern Physics*, Chapter 15. New York: John Wiley & Sons, 1963.

3. Blatt, J. M. and V. F. Weisskopf, *Theoretical Nuclear Physics*, Chapters VIII, IX, and X. New York: John Wiley & Sons, 1952.

4. Bethe, H. A. and P. Morrison, *Elementary Nuclear Theory*, Chapter XX. New York: John Wiley & Sons, Inc., 1961.

5. Morrison, P., *Experimental Nuclear Physics*, ed. E. Segre, Vol. II, Part VI, (1953). New York: John Wiley & Sons.

6. Fermi, E., *Nuclear Physics*, Chapter VIII. University of Chicago Press, 1950. Notes compiled by J. Orear, A. H. Rosenfeld, and R. A. Schluter.

7. Endt, P. M. and M. Demeur, eds., *Nuclear Reactions*. New York: Interscience Publishers, 1959.

8. Tobocman, W., *Theory of Direct Nuclear Reactions*. Oxford: Oxford University Press, 1961.

9. Miller, J. M., and J. Hudis, *Ann. Rev. Nucl. Sci.*, **9**, 159 (1959).

XII

NUCLEAR FORCES

1. INTRODUCTION

The different fundamental forces that we have come across during our study of physics are (a) gravitational forces, (b) electromagnetic forces, (c) weak interactions, and (d) nuclear forces. A comparison of these forces was made in Sec. 8.9, and their relative order of strength was found to be, nuclear: 1; electromagnetic: 10^{-2}; weak interactions: 10^{-13}; and gravitational: 10^{-39}. Nuclear forces are necessary to explain many characteristics of the nuclei that cannot be accounted for by the other three fundamental forces. The gravitational forces are too weak to do so and are applicable only on the macroscopic scale, such as for astronomical objects. The mathematical structure used in such cases is classical Newtonian mechanics. The electromagnetic forces are not only weak but have a "wrong sign" because it will make the protons repel while the nuclear forces between protons are attractive. The weak interactions, as previously discussed, explain beta decay.

We had many occasions to mention some properties of nuclear forces, specifically that nuclear forces are strongly attractive and of short range. The purpose of this chapter will be to elaborate on these and other properties of nuclear forces. The aim of investigation has been to express the interaction between different nucleons of a nucleus in terms of a potential function, from which the force law may be derived. Many attempts have been made in this direction but the results are far from being complete. It is a lack of knowledge of the form of this potential function that compels one to formulate different nuclear models to explain different nuclear properties and nuclear reactions. In order to understand the nuclear interactions, attempts have been made from two different points of view. First, the qualitative aspects of nuclear forces may be deduced by observing the properties and regularities in the complex nuclei. Second, the quantitative aspects of nuclear interactions may be deduced from two-body problems either by the study of a bound state of a deuteron (a neutron and a proton bound together) or by scattering experiments such as neutron-proton or proton-proton scattering. (It is difficult to have a neutron target in order to perform neutron-neutron scattering.) Before we go into the details of the qualitative aspects of nuclear forces deduced from the properties of the complex nuclei, we shall explain here in brief what we mean by a two-body interaction and how to interpret it mathematically.

If we assume that the interaction is a two-body interaction, the presence of the third, fourth, or fifth body does not affect the interaction that exists between the two bodies. The neutron and proton are assumed to be structureless particles. The interaction between any pair of protons, neutrons, or a neutron-proton is not affected by the presence of other particles (protons or neutrons). An interaction between the pair is represented by a potential function, and, subsequently, the Schrödinger equation is used to solve the problem. The relativistic corrections are usually small (~ 5 percent) at low energies and, for the sake of simplicity, are neglected. The experimental and theoretical work indicates that the nucleon-nucleon forces are not simple. It looks as if many different types of forces are acting at the same time.

(i) *Central forces* are the simplest and most important forces. Their magnitude depends on the distance between the two nucleons and the orientation of their spins with respect to one another. The simplest types of central potential, satisfying the conditions that the nuclear forces are attractive and short range, that have been commonly used are

$$\left. \begin{aligned} V &= -V_0 \quad \text{for } r < \alpha \\ &= \quad 0 \quad \text{for } r > \alpha \end{aligned} \right\} \quad \text{square well}$$

$$V = -V_E \, e^{-r/\alpha} \qquad \text{exponential}$$

$$V = -V_G \, e^{-(r/\alpha)^2} \qquad \text{Gaussian}$$

$$V = -V_Y \, \frac{e^{-r/\alpha}}{r/\alpha} \qquad \text{Yukawa} \qquad \text{(12.1)}$$

and are shown in Fig. 12.1. V_0, V_E, V_G, and V_Y are the fixed potentials, and r is the distance between the two nucleons. Thus the force between the nucleons will be given by

$$F = -\partial V/\partial r \tag{12.2}$$

It can be shown[1] that at low energies any of the four potential forms may be used without affecting the results. The reason is that at low energies the wavelength is very large as compared to the range of the nuclear force. The

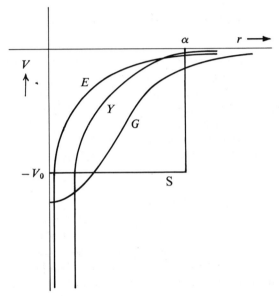

FIG. 12.1 The central potentials commonly used for representation of nuclear forces: (S) square well, (E) exponential, (G) Gaussian, and (Y) Yukawa.

shape of the potential is detected by the wavelength only if it is shorter than the range. More accurate and finer details are required to differentiate between different forms. The square well, exponential, and Gaussian forms of the interaction potential are used because of their mathematical simplicity. The Yukawa potential has a theoretical justification because it was predicted by the meson theory.

(ii) *Noncentral or tensor forces* are a function of the distance between the two nucleons and of the angle that their spins make with the line joining the two nucleons.

(iii) "*Hard-core*" *repulsive forces* act between two nucleons when they are very close ($\sim 0.5 \times 10^{-13}$ cm), and the repulsion increases as they come closer at high energies.

(iv) *Spin-orbit forces* depending on the angle between the spin and orbital angular momentum vectors.

(v) *Velocity-dependent forces* are a function of velocities of the nucleons.

(vi) *Many-body forces* are the forces that come into play for more than two nucleons.

(vii) *The exchange force* is that in which the particle exchanged is the meson.

2. QUALITATIVE ASPECTS OF NUCLEAR FORCES

Many important and significant aspects of nuclear forces may be deduced by observing the regularities in the complex nuclei. The nuclear forces between the nucleons inside the nucleus must be attractive (the average net-effect) because of the very existence of stable nuclei. If it were not the case the nuclei would have been disrupted because of the coulomb repulsion. From our knowledge of the stable nuclei as studied in the previous chapters, we are now in a position to establish some qualitative features of nuclear interactions.

A. STRENGTH AND RANGE OF NUCLEAR FORCES. We know that the forces between the nucleons are strongly attractive, but this cannot be completely true. There has to be a repulsive force even though the overall effect is the attractive force. If this were not so, the nucleus would collapse to the size of the nuclear-force range. This means that all nuclei would have the same size. This is not true, because the size is a function of the mass number,

$$R = r_0 A^{1/3} \tag{12.3}$$

i.e., the nuclear size is greater than the range of the nuclear force. We may get some idea of the magnitude of the attractive potential in the following way. The kinetic energy, K, of a nucleon that is confined to the nucleus is related to its wave length by the relation

$$\lambda = \frac{\hbar}{p} = \frac{\hbar}{\sqrt{2MK}} = \left(\frac{\hbar}{Mc}\right)\sqrt{\frac{Mc^2}{2K}} \tag{12.4}$$

where $\dfrac{\hbar}{Mc}$ = Compton wavelength of the nucleon = 2.1×10^{-14} cm. But the wavelength must fit into the nucleus, i.e.,

$$2\pi\lambda = 2R \tag{12.5}$$

where R is the radius of the nucleus $\sim 3 \times 10^{-13}$ cm. Combining Eqs. (12.4) and (12.5) one obtains $K \cong 25$ Mev. This implies that a potential energy greater than this is required to confine the nucleon in the nucleus. The binding energy is about 8 Mev per nucleon, and the potential energy is about -35 Mev per nucleon.

It has been established beyond a doubt that the range of the nuclear force is very short and is of the order of nuclear size. If this were not so, the nuclear forces would have definitely affected molecular interactions, but no such effect has ever been observed in the molecular structure. Thus the nuclear potential cannot have the form $V(r) \propto 1/r$, which is the long-range coulomb potential. One may attempt to explain the nuclear forces by the potential of the form $V(r) \propto 1/r^n$. But for $n \geqslant 2$, the Schrödinger equation breaks down for any solution. The difficulty is overcome if the potential is cut off at a certain range, α, as required.

The description of the nuclear potential requires two parameters: (i) the strength, or depth of the potential, V_o, and (ii) the range, α, of the potential beyond which the potential falls very rapidly to zero. In order to get some idea as to the magnitudes of these parameters, we start by looking at the binding energies of the lightest nuclei, as given in Table 12.1. We notice that as the

TABLE 12.1

ENERGY PER BOND AND BINDING ENERGY PER NUCLEON

Nucleus	Total Binding Energy (Mev)	Bond Diagram	No. of Bonds	Energy per Bond (Mev)	BE per Nucleon (Mev)
H^2	2.2	o——o	1	2.2	1.1
H^3, He^3	8	(triangle diagram)	3	2.7	2.7
He^4	28	(square with crossed diagonals diagram)	6	4.7	7.0

number of nucleons increases the total number of bonds also increases. Unlike chemical bonding, where the binding energy per bond is constant, the binding energy per bond in this case increases in the ratio $1:1.23:2.14$ for H^2, (H^3, He^3), and He^4, respectively.

The increase in binding energy per bond can be explained in terms of a potential that is narrow and deep and may take any one of the forms given by Eq. (12.1). For the deuteron, the wave function, as we shall see in the next section, extends well outside the range of nuclear interaction. As the number of nucleons increases inside the nucleus, the wave function is pulled more and more inside the range of interaction. This increases the potential energy (makes more negative) at a much faster rate than the kinetic energy, thereby increasing the binding energy per bond with an increasing number of nucleons.

The range, α, may be calculated in the case of deuteron in the following manner.

$$R \approx 2\alpha$$

$$2\pi\lambda = 2R = 4\alpha$$

From Eq. (12.4), using $\lambda = 4\alpha$ and reduced mass $\mu = M/2$, we get $K = \hbar^2/2\mu\lambda^2 = \hbar^2/M\lambda^2 = \pi^2\hbar^2/4M\alpha^2$. As already mentioned, in this case, the kinetic energy is approximately equal to the potential energy.

$$BE \approx 0 = KE + PE$$

$$V_0 \approx \pi^2\hbar^2/4M\alpha^2$$

$$V_0\alpha^2 \approx \pi^2\hbar^2/4M \qquad (12.6)$$

Because the right-hand side of Eq. (12.6) is constant, it implies that if V_0 increases, α decreases. It turns out that the range, α, of the potential is less than the dimensions of the nucleus, i.e., $\alpha \gtrsim 2.0 \times 10^{-13}$ cm.

B. SATURATION OF NUCLEAR FORCES. A second important property of nuclear forces is that of saturation, i.e., the number of nucleons with which a given nucleon interacts strongly is limited. In Chapter V, we established from the plot of BE/A versus A that for the most part the binding energy per nucleon is constant (≈ 8 Mev), or in other words

$$BE/A = \text{constant}$$

or

$$BE \propto A \qquad (12.7)$$

As already explained in Chapter V, the deviations at low A are due to a surface-tension effect and at large A due to coulomb repulsion. The coulomb forces, unlike the nuclear forces, are not saturated. These forces are long-range and act on every particle present in the range. Thus if there are A particles, every particle acts with each of the other $(A - 1)$ particles, resulting in a binding energy that is proportional to $A(A - 1)/2$. Thus if $A \gg 1$, BE (coulomb) $\propto A^2$.

Unlike the coulomb binding energy ($\propto A^2$), the nuclear binding energy is proportional to A, which implies that the nucleon is bound only to a limited number of nucleons in its neighborhood and not to every nucleon present in the nucleus. The addition of more nucleons increases the total binding energy, but the binding energy per nucleon remains almost constant. This property of the nuclear forces is called saturation.

Another argument for saturation of nuclear forces is the nuclear size. It is found that the nuclear radius is given by

$$R \propto A^{1/3}, \tag{12.8}$$

which means that the size of the nucleus increases with increasing number of nucleons, and the density of the nuclear material is constant. If the forces were unsaturated forces, the size of the nucleus per nucleon would have decreased with an increasing number of nucleons, but this is not so, and the volume per nucleon is found to be constant. The unsaturated nature of the coulomb force explains the constant size of all the atoms.

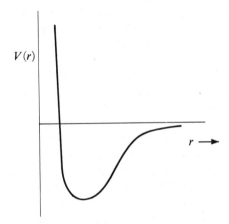

FIG. 12.2 Potential energy curve for molecular attraction; r is the separation between the two atoms of a molecule.

An interesting conclusion can be drawn from the observation that the binding energy per nucleon (Table 12.1) of 7 Mev for an alpha particle compares very well with the average binding energy per nucleon for other nuclei. We may say, therefore, that the average number of bonds per nucleon is the same as that for alpha particle, i.e., three bonds per nucleon. Actually the alpha particle forms a stable unit in accord with the Pauli principle that only two neutrons and two protons can occupy the same orbital state. Thus the binding energies of the heavier nuclei may be calculated in units of alpha particles, i.e., in units of four nucleons. We may conclude that saturation is caused because: *Nucleons attract each other strongly only if they are in the same orbital state.*

Saturation is not exclusive to nuclear forces; the forces between the molecules of a liquid drop also show saturation. The form of the potential-energy curve for the molecular attraction is shown in Fig. 12.2. If we assume this interaction-potential form for nuclear forces, the potential at large distances can explain the scattering experiments, and the minimum in the curve (~ 30 Mev) may correspond to the stable nuclei. The repulsive potential at very short distances is of the order of 300 Mev. Though at first glance it looks very unreasonable to assume a repulsive hard-core, this has been verified in very high energy (300–1000 Mev) scattering experiments. The alternative to the hard-core repulsive force at short distances (which is not predicted by meson theory) are (1) the exchange forces originally developed by Heisenberg, which will be discussed later (such exchange forces also exist in molecular bonding), and (2) the many-body forces.

C. CHARGE DEPENDENCE OF NUCLEAR FORCES. The third important problem of nuclear forces is to evaluate whether the forces are charge dependent or charge independent. There are three different forces. These are (i) the force between two protons denoted by p-p, (ii) the force between two neutrons, denoted by n-n, and (iii) the force between a neutron and a proton, denoted by n-p. If these forces are equal, i.e., p-p $\approx$ n-n $\approx$ n-p, we say that the forces are *charge independent*; and if only p-p $\approx$ n-n, then the forces are said to be *charge symmetric*. The evidence indicates, as we shall discuss below, that the forces are probably charge independent.

An examination of the chart of stable nuclei indicates that for light and intermediate stable nuclei we have $N = Z \simeq A/2$. This means that there is a tendency for neutrons and protons to go in pairs. The extraordinary stability of nuclei with $A = 4n$, where n is an integer (such as $_2\text{He}^4$, $_4\text{Be}^8$, $_6\text{C}^{12}$, $_8\text{O}^{16}$) indicates that neutrons and protons add in pairs of two. Thus

either	n-p $>$ n-n $\approx$ p-p
or	n-p $\approx$ n-n $\approx$ p-p

Additional evidence comes from the mirror nuclei (odd A) and the isobaric nuclei with even A. These two topics were discussed in Sec. 6.7 and Sec. 5.11, respectively. The total ground-state binding energies of each member of a set of mirror nuclei are found to be equal if corrections are made for the coulomb effect and the neutron-proton mass difference. One member of the pair of mirror nuclei has the same number of n-n interactions between nucleons in various quantum states as the number of p-p interactions between nucleons in the same quantum state for the other member, and vice versa. The neutron-neutron interactions, therefore, are equal to proton-proton interactions, i.e., n-n $\approx$ p-p. Because the number of n-p interactions is the same in the two members of the mirror pair, it is not possible to say anything about the n-p interaction. The detailed investigation of the isobaric nuclei with even A, in which the charge changes by units of two, may be used to show that the interactions are charge independent[2,3,4], i.e., n-p $\approx$ n-n $\approx$ p-p. There are two more interesting facts that may be mentioned here.

(i) For $A = 4$, He^4 is stable. For $A = 6$, $_2He^6$ (which consists of two neutrons more than $_2He^4$) and $_4Be^6$ (with two protons more than $_2He^4$) are both unstable while $_3Li^6$ (which has one proton and one neutron more than $_2He^4$) is stable. In the case of He^6 and Be^6 the spins of the last two neutrons or protons from Pauli's principle will have to be antiparallel, while for Li^6 the spins are parallel. Thus either n-p > n-n $\approx$ p-p, or the interaction is spin dependent, and it is stronger when they are parallel.

(ii) The existence of stable Be^9 (one neutron in addition to two He^4 nuclei) indicates that there is some attraction between nucleons in different states, but that it is small as compared with the very strong interaction between the nucleons in the same state.

An interesting question that might be asked is this: If n-p $\approx$ n-n $\approx$ p-p, and we have a stable deuteron, why there is no stable di-neutron or di-proton? It is not the weakness of the nuclear forces but the existence of Pauli's principle that prevents their formation. The existence of a di-neutron has been investigated but with negative results[5].

D. SUMMARY.   We may draw the following conclusions from the discussion of the qualitative aspects of nuclear forces:

(1) Nuclear forces are short range, the range of the interaction being less than the dimensions of the nucleus. Two parameters are required to describe the interaction potential.

(2) Nuclear forces show saturation and nucleons in the same orbital state interact more strongly than those in different orbital states.

(3) Aside from the coulomb effect, n-p $\approx$ n-n $\approx$ p-p, i.e., the forces are charge independent. There may be a spin-dependent interaction, i.e., the nucleons with parallel spins interact more strongly.

3. TWO-BODY BOUND STATE PROBLEM (DEUTERON)

In the previous section we have stated most of the information that can be obtained from complex nuclei. A detailed quantitative description of nuclear interactions may be obtained by investigating the two-body problem in the bound state or in the free state, i.e., in a scattering problem. We shall consider the bound state in this section and shall postpone the scattering problem for a later section.

Of the three possible two-nucleon systems, i.e., di-proton, di-neutron, and neutron-proton, the first two are unbound. The third one, the neutron-proton, forms a bound, stable state because of the nuclear force between the two, and the nucleus so formed is the deuteron nucleus denoted by $_1H^2$ or $_1D^2$.

If the forces are truly represented by a two-body interaction, we should expect to get information about both the depth (or strength) and the range of the interaction from the known properties of deuteron. But this is not so, and the information obtained from deuteron gives only the relation between the depth and range of the interaction.

We shall limit our discussion to the ground state of deuteron, which is the only bound state because the excited states are unbound. A deuteron in the ground state has the following properties.

mass of deuteron, $(M_{_1H^2})$	$= 2.014732$ amu
binding energy, B	$= (2.225 \pm 0.002)$ Mev
total angular momentum,	$= 1\hbar$
magnetic moment, μ_D	$= (0.857411 \pm 0.0000199)\mu_N$
electric quadrupole moment	$Q = +2.82 \times 10^{-27}$ cm^2

In terms of spectroscopic notation, there are four possible states in which a deuteron may exist resulting with a spin of 1 unit, i.e.,

$$^3S_1, \; ^1P_1, \; ^3P_1, \; ^3D_1$$

A deuteron cannot exist in the combination of all four states because the P states $(l = 1)$ have odd parity while the $S(l = 0)$ and $D(l = 2)$ states have even parity. Thus a deuteron may be in the $^3S_1$, $^3D_1$ states or $^1P_1$, $^3P_1$ states. The possibility of the P states is rejected on the ground that they do not give the value of the magnetic moment of the deuteron anywhere close to the measured value. Thus the deuteron may exist either in the $^3S_1$ state or $^3D_1$ state, or both. In order to simplify the problem we make the following assumptions.

(a) The force between the two particles is attractive, short range, and central, i.e., it acts along the line joining the two particles. This means that the ground state of deuteron is $^3S_1$. This is not exactly true because this state will give zero quadrupole moment. In order to get non-zero quadrupole moment there should be a deviation from spherical symmetry. This needs an addition of a noncentral-force term, and the existence of the deuteron in the $^3D_1$ state as well. For the time being we can assume that because the quadrupole moment is very small, it may be neglected. We shall make the correction later. Thus the deuteron being in the $^3S_1$ state implies that the spins of both the neutron and the proton are parallel and in a $l = 0$ state. The magnetic moment of the deuteron will then be the sum of the magnetic moments of a proton and a neutron. The actual difference is very small, i.e.,

$$\Delta\mu = \mu_D - (\mu_p + \mu_n)$$
$$= 0.857411 \pm 0.000019 - (2.7925 \pm 0.0001 - 1.9128 \pm 0.0001)$$
$$\Delta\mu = -(0.0223 \pm 0.0002)\mu_N \tag{12.9}$$

(b) The force is derivable from a potential. As we mentioned earlier, the form of the potential function is not important, and we may take any one of the potentials given by Eq. (12.1). For the sake of mathematical simplicity, we shall consider a square well potential given by

$$V(r) = -V_0 \quad \text{for } r < \alpha$$
$$\quad = \quad 0 \quad \text{for } r > \alpha$$

(c) A neutron and a proton have almost equal mass, so that the reduced mass, μ, is equal to $M/2$ where M is the mass of the nucleon, i.e.,

$$\mu = M_p M_n / (M_p + M_n) \cong M/2$$

We shall now proceed to solve the Schrödinger wave equation for the two regions shown in Fig. 12.3. For the S-state ($l = 0$) the wave function will not have any angular dependence, and

$$\psi = R(r) Y_{lm}(\theta, \phi)$$

reduces to

$$\psi = R(r) = u(r)/r \qquad \qquad \textbf{(12.10)}$$

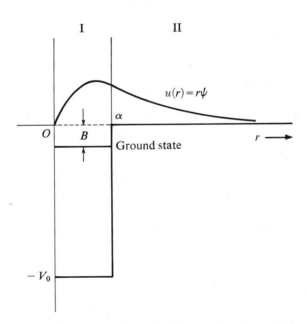

FIG. 12.3 The deuteron radial-wave function $u(r)$ is shown for two regions, inside the potential well and outside.

as before. The resulting modified radial wave equation

$$\frac{d^2u(r)}{dr^2} + \frac{2\mu}{\hbar^2}[E - V(r)]u(r) = 0 \tag{12.11}$$

takes the following form for the square well potential shown in Fig. 12.3. For $\mu = M/2$ and $E = -B$ we have

$$\frac{d^2u}{dr^2} + K^2u = 0 \qquad \text{for } r < \alpha \tag{12.12}$$

where

$$K = \frac{\sqrt{M(V_0 - B)}}{\hbar} \tag{12.13}$$

and

$$\frac{d^2u}{dr^2} - k^2u = 0 \qquad \text{for } r > \alpha \tag{12.14}$$

and

$$k = \frac{\sqrt{MB}}{\hbar} \tag{12.15}$$

The general solutions of Eqs. (12.12) and (12.14) are

$$u = A \sin Kr + F \cos Kr \quad \text{for } r < \alpha$$

and

$$u = Ce^{-kr} + De^{kr} \qquad \text{for } r > \alpha$$

respectively. But in order that $u(0) = 0$, i.e., the wave function must vanish at the origin, makes $F = 0$. Also the wave function must not diverge as $r \to \infty$, i.e., $u(\infty) = 0$, which makes $D = 0$. Thus the required solutions are

$$u(r) = A \sin Kr \quad \text{for } r < \alpha \tag{12.16}$$

and

$$u(r) = Ce^{-kr} \qquad \text{for } r > \alpha \tag{12.17}$$

We now impose the condition that u and du/dr muts be continuous at the boundary $r = \alpha$, i.e.

$$A \sin K\alpha = Ce^{-k\alpha} \tag{12.18}$$

and

$$AK \cos K\alpha = -Cke^{-k\alpha} \tag{12.19}$$

Dividing one by the other, we get

$$K \cot K\alpha = -k \tag{12.20}$$

This equation can be solved graphically by writing it in the form ($x = K\alpha$)

$$x \cot x = -k\alpha$$

and plotting $y = \cot x$ and $y = -k\alpha/x$. The solution gives the relation between V_0, α, and B. However, we shall proceed in a slightly different manner to get the relation between V_0 and α. Eq. (12.20) may be written as

$$\frac{\sqrt{M(V_0 - B)}}{\hbar} \cot\left(\frac{\sqrt{M(V_0 - B)}}{\hbar}\alpha\right) = -\frac{\sqrt{MB}}{\hbar} \qquad (12.21)$$

Because $V_0 \gg B$, we may write $\sqrt{V_0 - B} \simeq V_0$ and $B/V_0 \simeq 0$. Hence Eq. (12.21) takes the form

$$\cot\left(\frac{\sqrt{MV_0}}{\hbar}\alpha\right) \simeq 0$$

or

$$\frac{\sqrt{MV_0}}{\hbar}\alpha = \frac{\pi}{2}$$

or

$$V_0\alpha^2 \simeq \pi^2\hbar^2/4M \qquad (12.22)$$

This is the relation between V_0 and α which we discussed earlier in Sec. 12.2. Thus if we know the value of one, the other is automatically fixed. If we take $V_0 \simeq 35$ Mev, Eq. (12.22) gives a value of $\alpha \approx 1.8 \times 10^{-13}$ cm, which is in agreement with scattering experiments.

In order to plot the wave functions given by Eqs. (12.16) and (12.17), the values of the constants A and C may be evaluated by using Eq. (12.16) or (12.17) and the relation

$$\int |\psi|^2 \, d\tau = 4\pi \int_0^\infty u^2 \, dr = 1$$

The plot of the wave function inside and outside of the potential well is shown in Fig. 12.3. It is quite evident that for more than 50 percent of the time the neutron and the proton in the deuteron are separated by a distance that is more than the range, α, of interaction, i.e., the size of the deuteron $\simeq 2\alpha$. This explains why the deuteron is in a loosely bound state.

The deuteron does not have any bound excited states; even the ground state is loosely bound. The absence of the bound-singlet excited state, ^1S implies that the nuclear forces are spin dependent. In the ^1S state of the deuteron, the spins are antiparallel, and they do not interact strongly. More evidence for the spin-dependent interaction comes from scattering experiments.

In order to explain the quadrupole moment of the deuteron and a small discrepancy in the magnetic moment, noncentral forces come into play, which we will discuss now.

The very fact that the deuteron has a positive electric quadrupole-moment, even though it is very small, implies that the probability density is not spherically symmetric. Thus the deuteron ground-state cannot be completely an S-state. Though the central potential will be most predominant, it cannot account for the asymmetric distribution, and we require an introduction of a noncentral potential function[6,7]. The choice of the form of the noncentral potential function is limited because the deuteron is in a definite state and should be invariant under displacement, rotation, and reflection of coordinates (parity conservation) of the system. The potential is independent of velocity. These requirements put forth the condition that both central and noncentral potentials should be scalars. The scalars that satisfy these conditions are:

   (i) $V(r)$

   (ii) $\sigma_1 \cdot \sigma_2$

   (iii) $(\sigma_1 \cdot \mathbf{r})(\sigma_2 \cdot \mathbf{r})$, and

   (iv) $(\sigma_1 \times \mathbf{r}) \cdot (\sigma_2 \times \mathbf{r})$ $[= r^2 \sigma_1 \cdot \sigma_2 - (\sigma_1 \cdot \mathbf{r})(\sigma_2 \cdot \mathbf{r})]$ **(12.23)**

where σ_1 and σ_2 are the spin vectors of the two nucleons. (i) and (ii) represent the central potential, while (iii) and (iv) represent the noncentral. (iv) is actually a special form of (ii) and (iii), and we shall not carry it any further.

   $(\sigma_1 \cdot \mathbf{r})(\sigma_2 \cdot \mathbf{r})$ is the noncentral potential and is called the *tensor interaction*. The corresponding force is called the *tensor force*. The name tensor is misleading because the noncentral force is actually a scalar. The form of the tensor operator S_{12} is given by

$$S_{12} = \frac{3}{r^2} (\sigma_1 \cdot \mathbf{r})(\sigma_2 \cdot \mathbf{r}) - \sigma_1 \cdot \sigma_2 \qquad (12.24)$$

This is derived from the condition that the average of the noncentral potential over all directions of $\mathbf{r}$ vanishes. Thus the noncentral force is derivable from a potential

$$V^{(r)}_{\text{noncentral}} = V'(r)S_{12} \qquad (12.25)$$

Hence, the potential that describes the two-body interaction is given by

$$V = V(r) + V'(r)S_{12} = V(r) + V'(r)\left\{\frac{3}{r^2}(\sigma_1 \cdot \mathbf{r})(\sigma_2 \cdot \mathbf{r}) - \sigma_1\sigma_2\right\} \quad (12.26)$$

   In order to account for the noncentral force, the deuteron not only exists in the $^3S_1$ state, but also for a fraction of the time is in the $^3D_1$ state. It is found that if we use a mixture of $(0.96\ ^3S_1 + 0.04\ ^3D_1)$, i.e., 96 percent $^3S_1$ and 4 percent $^3D_1$, and use the potential given by Eq. (12.26), we get the required quadrupole moment of the deuteron and the correct[6,7] value of the magnetic moment. Because the measured quadrupole moment is positive, the shape of the charge distribution is ellipsoidal along the axis parallel to the line joining the spins of the two nucleons as shown in Fig. 12.4. Note that the resulting shape of the charge distribution is the effect of the noncentral force.

It may be mentioned here that the tensor force is not velocity-dependent, so that it does not become zero at low energies. The tensor force is not to be confused with the spin-orbit force. The spin-orbit force is velocity dependent and becomes zero at low energies. There is no tensor force for a singlet state because of the absence of a resultant spin and, as a consequence, there is no preferred spin axis.

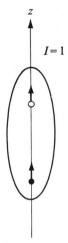

FIG. 12.4 The charge distribution for positive electric-quadrupole moment of deuteron for $I = 1$.

4. TWO-BODY SCATTERING AT LOW ENERGIES

In the previous section we consider the two-body problem for which $E < 0$, i.e., a bound state. We shall start now with the discussion of the two-body problem for which $E > 0$, i.e., the two-body scattering problem involving unbound states. The discussion of the two-body scattering will be divided into two parts: low-energy neutron-proton scattering, and low energy proton-proton scattering.

The theoretical treatment of the collision problem was discussed in Sec. 11.2, and it is given in some length at other places[8,9,10]. The experimental investigation involves the measurement of cross sections by the techniques used for scattering of particles by target nuclei. The usual experimental arrangements for low energy neutron-proton scattering and proton-proton scattering have been explained in several places[10-15]. We shall start with the discussion of low energy neutron-proton scattering.

A. Low Energy Neutron-Proton Scattering. To simplify the calculations, we shall put a lower and upper limit on the energy of the incident neutrons that are scattered by the protons.

A proton in a solid target is always in a bound molecular state with a binding energy of 0.1 ev. The calculation of the scattering cross-section of the neutrons by the bound protons is complicated. But if we assume that the incident neutron has an energy greater than 1 ev, the bound protons can be treated as free protons. Thus the lower limit on the neutron energy is 1 ev.

We have shown in Chapter XI that the scattering cross-section is given in terms of the phase shifts δ_l. The upper limit to the neutron energy is fixed by the requirement that only the first phase shift ($l = 0$) contributes to the scattering cross-section. We know that the interaction takes place only if the impact parameter is less than the range of interaction. Thus from Eq. (11.33) we have

$$\sqrt{l(l + 1)}\hbar = k\hbar\alpha$$

or

$$\sqrt{2} \simeq \frac{\sqrt{ME}}{\hbar}\alpha \tag{12.27}$$

This gives us the energy, E, in the CMCS and hence, $E_{\text{lab}} = 2E$. For values of α ranging from 1.4×10^{-13} cm to 2.0×10^{-13} cm the energy ranges from ~ 15 Mev to ~ 20 Mev. To be on the safe side let us say that the upper limit of the energy of the incident neutron is 5 Mev. Because the wavelength of a neutron with this energy is much larger than the range of the interaction, the zero range approximation ($k \to 0$) may be used. Thus we are dealing with S-state scattering, which is isotropic, and the contribution to the scattering cross-section comes only from the first phase shift, δ_0.

We shall still be dealing with a square-well potential as in the case of the deuteron, but our aim is to express δ_0 in terms of the binding energy of the deuteron. The results obtained in Chapter XI may be used because $|E| \leqslant V_0$, and it does not effect the shape of the wave function. One may be tempted to accept the conclusion that with the help of the deuteron binding-energy and the neutron-proton scattering cross-section, it may be possible to evaluate both V_0 and α. This is not true because, unlike the deuteron, the neutron-proton scattering takes place from both the triplet and the singlet S-states. The scattering is incoherent and is mixed in the ratio of their statistical weights $(2I + 1)$ for the $I = 1$ ($^3S_1$) and $I = 0$ ($^3S_0$) states, i.e., in the ratio of $3:1$. We shall derive an expression for the triplet state. The same expression holds for the singlet state as well, except the binding energy will be different.

The wave function inside the potential well is the same as Eq. (12.16)

$$u = A \sin Kr \qquad \text{for } r < \alpha \tag{12.28}$$

where
$$K = \sqrt{M(V_0 - B)}/\hbar$$
and the external wave-function is given by Eq. (11.27) for $l = 0$
$$u = r\psi = C \sin(kr + \delta_0) \qquad \text{for } r > \alpha \qquad (12.29)$$
where
$$k = \sqrt{2\mu E}/\hbar = \sqrt{ME}/\hbar$$
The amplitude $f(\theta)$ according to Eq. (11.30) for $l = 0$ is
$$f(\theta) = (1/2ik)(e^{2i\delta_0} - 1) \qquad (12.30)$$
and the cross-section according to Eq. (11.31) for $l = 0$ is
$$\sigma_T = (4\pi/k^2) \sin^2\delta_0 \qquad (12.31)$$
Applying the continuity condition $\dfrac{1}{u}\left(\dfrac{du}{dr}\right)_{r=\alpha}$ to Eqs. (12.28) and (12.29), we obtain
$$K \cot K\alpha = k \cot(k\alpha + \delta_0) \qquad (12.32)$$
But from Eq. (12.20)
$$K \cot K\alpha = -K' = \sqrt{MB}/\hbar \qquad (12.33)$$
Equating Eqs. (12.32) and (12.33)
$$k \cot(k\alpha + \delta_0) = -K' \qquad (12.34)$$
or
$$\delta_0 = \cot^{-1}(-K'/k) - k\alpha$$
$$\cong \cot^{-1}(-K'/k), \quad \text{for } k\alpha \ll 1 \qquad (12.35)$$
Thus the total cross-section is given by
$$\sigma = \frac{4\pi}{k^2}\sin^2\delta_0 = \frac{4\pi}{k^2}\frac{k^2}{k^2 + K'^2}$$
$$= \frac{4\pi}{k^2 + K'^2} = \frac{4\pi}{ME/\hbar^2 + MB/\hbar^2}$$
or
$$\sigma = \frac{4\pi\hbar^2}{M}\frac{1}{E + B} \qquad (12.36)$$

Note that E, the incident neutron energy, is in the CMCS. Thus if the scattering is taking place in the triplet state, Eq. (12.36) gives the value of the cross-section for $E < 1$ Mev, $\sigma \simeq 4\pi\hbar^2/MB \simeq 2.4 \times 10^{-24}$ cm^2 = 2.4 b. The experimental value of the cross-section for 1 ev neutrons is 20.4 b. The plot of cross-section versus energy is given in Fig. 12.5. The theoretical value is off by a factor of 10. Even more exact calculations do not give a better agreement. The answer to this discrepancy was given by E. Wigner.

According to Wigner the scattering takes place both in the triplet $^3S_1$-state as well as the singlet $^1S_0$-state in proportion to the statistical weight of the states, $(2I + 1)$. Thus

$$\sigma = (3/4)\,\sigma_t + (1/4)\sigma_s \qquad (12.37a)$$

or

$$\sigma = \frac{4\pi}{k^2}\,[(3/4)\sin^2\delta_{0t} + (1/4)\sin^2\delta_{0s}]$$

$$= \frac{\pi\hbar^2}{M}\left[\frac{3}{E + B_t} + \frac{1}{E + |B_s|}\right] \qquad (12.37b)$$

B_t is the binding energy of the triplet state and B_s that of the singlet state, where the sign of B_s is not determined. The indications are that the singlet and

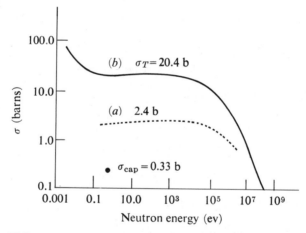

FIG. 12.5 Low energy neutron-proton cross sections: (a) theoretical scattering cross-section based on the assumption that the scattering is only from the triplet state and (b) experimentally measured total cross-sections. [From: Melkonian, E., *Phys. Rev.*, **76**, 1744, (1949).]

triplet phase-shifts are opposite in sign, and hence the singlet state of the neutron-proton system is a virtual state. Because the measured cross-section, σ_T, is 20.4 b and the calculated $\sigma_{triplet}$ is ~2 b, from Eq. (12.37a) we get $\sigma_{singlet} =$ 74 b. From Eq. (12.37b) the binding energy B_s may be calculated by substituting $\sigma = 20.4$ b and $B_t = 2.225$ Mev. It turns out that $|B_s| \cong 50$ kev as compared to $B_t = 2.225$ Mev. This is an indication that the interaction is spin dependent. It is strong when the spins are parallel and results in a large binding energy, as in the $^3S_1$-state, and it is weak when the spins are anti-parallel, as in $^1S_0$-state, which results in a smaller binding energy. Actually this results in different potentials and ranges for the singlet and the triplet states. A typical fit of Eq. (12.37) after some corrections yields the following values:

$$V_{0t} = 33.9 \text{ Mev}$$

$$\alpha_t = 2.05 \times 10^{-13} \text{ cm}$$

$$V_{0s} = 11.7 \text{ Mev}$$

$$\alpha_s = 2.9 \times 10^{-13} \text{cm} \tag{12.38}$$

It is clear that the singlet interaction is considerably weaker and, therefore, the nuclear forces are spin dependent.

The results given in Eq. (12.38) for the neutron-proton scattering are based on the *zero-range approximation*. Information about the range may also be obtained by calculating the cross-section by making use of the *effective-range theory*. We shall not go into the details of the calculations but will summarize the results. The relation for the phase shift according to the effective range theory is [16]

$$k \cot \delta_0 = -\frac{1}{a} + \frac{1}{2} r_0 k^2 + \cdots \tag{12.39}$$

and the expression for the cross-section is

$$\sigma = \frac{4\pi}{k^2} \sin^2 \delta_0 = \frac{4\pi}{k^2 + [\frac{1}{2} r_0 k^2 - (1/a)]^2} \tag{12.40}$$

where a is the scattering length (will be explained below), and r_0 is an effective range. The third term in the expansion of Eq. (12.39), which is not shown, will determine the shape of the potential. These third-order effects are hard to detect at low energies and we assume the shape independence of the potential by neglecting the third term in Eq. (12.39).

The *scattering length*, a, is defined in the following way. Assuming that δ_0 is small, we can expand $e^{2i\delta_0}$ in Eq. (12.30):

$$f(\theta) = \frac{1}{2ik} (e^{2i\delta_0} - 1) = \frac{1}{2ik} (1 + 2i\delta_0 + \cdots - 1) \cong \frac{\delta_0}{k}$$

We define the scattering length a as

$$a = \underset{k \to 0}{\text{limit}} f = \underset{k \to 0}{\text{limit}} \frac{\delta_0}{k} \tag{12.41}$$

Thus

$$\sigma(\theta)_{k \to 0} = a^2$$

and

$$\sigma_T = 4\pi a^2 \tag{12.42}$$

For the bound state of the deuteron, we may rewrite Eq. (12.39) as (triplet state)

$$K = \frac{1}{a_t} + \frac{1}{2} K^2 r_{0t} \qquad (12.43)$$

where $K = \sqrt{MB}/\hbar$ and B is the binding energy of the deuteron. a_t may be calculated from Eq. (12.42). Thus we can find the effective range r_{0t}. For the n-p scattering, the total cross-section is given by

$$\sigma_T = \frac{3\pi}{k^2 + [\frac{1}{2}r_{0t}k^2 - (1/a_t)]^2} + \frac{\pi}{k^2 + [\frac{1}{2}r_{0s}k^2 - (1/a_s)]^2} \qquad (12.44)$$

B. LOW ENERGY PROTON-PROTON SCATTERING[17,18]. Investigation of proton-proton scattering has many interesting points. Unlike neutrons, it is easy to produce a well-defined collimated beam of protons, and, in addition, the detection of the scattered protons is simple and accurate. The theoretical analysis of proton-proton scattering is much more complicated than the neutron-proton scattering. First of all, we are dealing with identical particles, and, secondly, the scattering is not due entirely to the nuclear potential. Because the two particles are charged, there is coulomb scattering superimposed on the nuclear scattering. We shall discuss the consequences of these two factors in detail.

The theoretical treatment of the low energy proton-proton scattering has been given by G. Breit, *et al.*[19,20] and others[21,22,23]. Because the two protons (each with spin 1/2) are identical particles, according to the Pauli exclusion principle, the total wave function of the system must be antisymmetric. Thus if the spatial part of the wave function is symmetric, the spin part of the wave function must be antisymmetric, and vice versa. The spatial part of the wave function is symmetric if the parity of the state is even $(l = 0, 2, 4, ...)(S, D, G, ...$ states) and antisymmetric if the parity is odd $(l = 1, 3, 5, ...)(P, F, H, ...$ states). Corresponding to these two divisions, the spin wave function will be antisymmetric or symmetric, respectively. Thus the different possibilities are ^1S, ^3P, ^1D, ^3F, ^1G, ^3H, etc. For incident-proton energies of less than 10 Mev, only the $^1S_0$-state contributes to the scattering. The absence of the $^3S_1$-state (not allowed by the exclusion principle) means that we have a single phase shift due to the $^1S_0$-state. This simplifies the problem to some extent.

The coulomb potential, $V(r) = e^2/r$, causes coulomb scattering, and in this case $rV(r)$ does not approach zero as $r \to \infty$. Coulomb scattering was discussed from a classical point of view in Sec. 6.2, and the same treatment is equally applicable here after making a proper correction. A more complete quantum-mechanical treatment has been discussed by N. Mott and H. Massey[24], and we shall not attempt to reproduce it here. The coulomb scattering interferes destructively with the nuclear scattering. As the result of this interference, it is possible to determine accurately the magnitude and sign of the nuclear interaction potential phase shift, and hence the nuclear parameters.

Let $f_C(\theta)$ and $f_N(\theta)$ denote the coulomb and the nuclear scattering amplitudes, respectively. If the potential changes the S-wave phase-shift, by $\delta_0 + \eta_0$, where η_0 is nuclear phase-shift and δ_0 coulomb phase-shift, we may write the total amplitude of the scattered wave as

$$f(\theta) = f_C(\theta) + f_N(\theta) = f_C(\theta) + \frac{1}{2ik} e^{2i\delta_0}(e^{2i\eta_0} - 1) \qquad (12.45)$$

For identical particles, if one particle is scattered at angle θ, the other is scattered at $(\pi - \theta)$. It is not possible to distinguish between the two. Thus the total scattering amplitude is given by $[f(\theta) \pm f(\pi - \theta)]$, not only by $f(\theta)$. The $+$ sign is for a singlet state, and the $-$ sign is for a triplet state (from the requirement of antisymmetry of the total wave-function for the proton-proton system). Because there is only a singlet-state scattering, the cross-section is given by

$$\sigma(\theta) = |f(\theta) + f(\pi - \theta)|^2$$
$$= |f(\theta)|^2 + |f(\pi - \theta)|^2 + 2 \text{ real part of } [f^*(\theta)f(\pi - \theta)] \qquad (12.46)$$

If the triplet state were also present, then

$$\sigma(\theta) = \tfrac{1}{4}|f(\theta) + f(\pi - \theta)|^2 + \tfrac{3}{4}|f(\theta) - f(\pi - \theta)|^2$$

A combination of Eqs. (12.45) and (12.46) can be used to calculate the cross-sections. Fig. 12.6 shows the plot of cross-section versus angle. As is

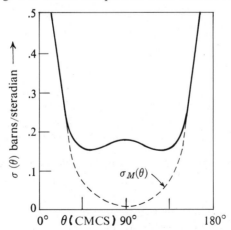

FIG. 12.6 The p-p differential scattering cross-section in the CMCS at 2.4 Mev. The broken line is the coulomb cross-section alone, while the solid line is the sum of the nuclear and coulomb scatterings.

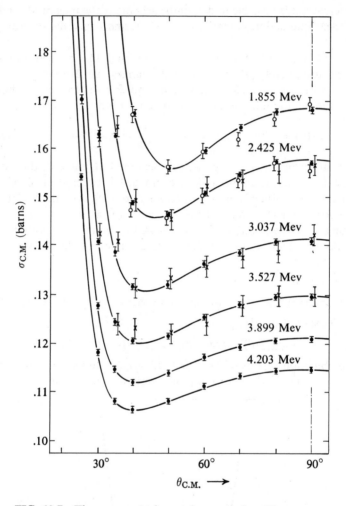

FIG. 12.7 The p-p scattering at low energies. The agreement between the experimentally determined differential cross-sections (points) and the theory (continuous curves) in the S-wave energy range is good. [From Breit G. and R. L. Gluckstern, *Ann. Rev. Nucl. Sci.*, **2**, (1953).]

evident, the scattering is symmetrical about 90°. The presence of the coulomb term makes the scattering anisotropic, and so we talk in terms of differential cross-sections. Many precise measurements on proton-proton scattering have been made up to a few Mev[25,26,27,28]. Fig. 12.7 shows the plot of $\sigma(\theta)$ as a function of energy and angle[29]. Agreement between the theory and the experiment is excellent. The values of the interaction potential and the range for the singlet state, i.e., V_{0s} and α_s have been derived from such analysis. It gives

$$V_{0s} = 13.3 \text{ Mev,}$$

and

$$\alpha_s = 2.58 \times 10^{-13} \text{ cm} \qquad \textbf{(12.47)}$$

which are in good agreement with the one derived from the neutron-proton scattering as given in Eq. (12.38).

Thus experiments show that the *two-body nuclear interactions are charge independent*, i.e., the interaction between any two nucleons is the same for low energies. This does not imply that the potential shapes are the same. All it means is that the same phase shift is produced due to the interaction between any two nucleons.

5. EXCHANGE FORCES[30]

Before we discuss the high-energy scattering problem, it will be worthwhile to study exchange forces. The exchange forces are important for two reasons: They help in explaining the saturation properties of nuclear forces, and they play a significant part in the nucleon-nucleon scattering at high energies. We also are concerned with the exchange forces in molecules. The saturation in this case is explained by the forces that are acting on the electron between the two atoms of a molecule. In this case, the two atoms share the same orbital electrons. Whenever two interacting particles can share a common property, the result is the exchange interaction.

It was first postulated by Heisenberg that there is an exchange force between two nucleons, and there is conclusive evidence of these forces from the angular distribution of nuetron-proton scattering at high energies. According to Heisenberg, the property being shared by the two nucleons was charge. The exchange of the charge according to field theory (Sec. 12.7) is explained in terms of the absorption and re-emission of virtual π-mesons (pions). The exchange of charge is equivalent to the exchange of position and spin. Thus the wave equation of the system of two nucleons is

$$\left(\frac{\hbar^2}{M} \nabla^2 + E\right)\Psi(\mathbf{r}_1, \sigma_1; \mathbf{r}_2, \sigma_2) = V_{12}\Psi(\mathbf{r}_1, \sigma_1; \mathbf{r}_2, \sigma_2) \qquad \textbf{(12.48)}$$

where $\mathbf{r}_1, \mathbf{r}_2$ are the position vectors of the two nucleons, and σ_1, σ_2 are the z-components of the spins of the two nucleons, with σ_1 pointing up and σ_2 pointing down. V_{12} is a two body potential that includes the central attractive-potential, $V(r)$, as well as the exchange operator. We shall find it convenient to split the wave function, Ψ, into a space-dependent part $\psi(r)$ and a spin-dependent part, χ_{12}, i.e.,

$$\Psi(\mathbf{r}_1, \sigma_1; \mathbf{r}_2, \sigma_2) = \psi(\mathbf{r})\chi_{12}(\sigma_1, \sigma_2) \qquad (12.49)$$

where $\mathbf{r}$ is the distance between the two nucleons.

Besides the charge, the other quantities that may be exchanged are spin or position. Four different types of exchange interactions have been developed and are named after the scientists who first investigated them.

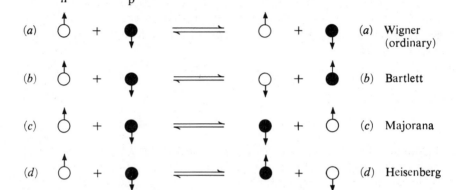

FIG. 12.8 Different types of exchange forces: ○ stands for a neutron and ● for a proton.

A. WIGNER (ORDINARY) FORCES—NO EXCHANGE. This is shown in Fig. 12.8(a) and mathematically expressed by

$$V_{12} = V(r)W \qquad (12.50)$$

where W is a unit operator. Hence, the exchanged wave-function is $\Psi(\mathbf{r}_1, \sigma_1; \mathbf{r}_2, \sigma_2)$ and the wave equation is

$$\left(\frac{\hbar^2}{M}\nabla^2 + E\right)\psi(\mathbf{r}) = V(r)\psi(\mathbf{r}) \qquad (12.51)$$

The forces are ordinary attractive forces.

B. BARTLETT FORCES—SPIN EXCHANGE. The exchange is shown in Fig. 12.8(b) and mathematically expressed by

$$V_{12} = V(r)B_{12} \qquad (12.52)$$

where B_{12} is an operator, which acting on the spin part of the wave-function, exchanges the spin, i.e.,

$$B_{12}\chi_{12} = \chi_{21} \qquad (12.53)$$

Hence, the exchanged wave function is $\Psi(\mathbf{r}_1, \sigma_2; \mathbf{r}_2, \sigma_1)$ and wave equation is

$$\left(\frac{\hbar^2}{M}\nabla^2 + E\right)\psi(\mathbf{r})\chi_{12} = V(r)\psi(\mathbf{r})\chi_{21} \qquad (12.54)$$

However, for a triplet state ($S = 1$) the spin wave-function is symmetric and, therefore, $\chi_{12} = \chi_{21}$, while for a singlet state ($S = 0$) the spin wave-function is antisymmetric and, therefore, $\chi_{12} = -\chi_{21}$ or $\chi_{21} = (-1)^{S+1}\chi_{12}$. Thus we may rewrite Eq. (12.54) in the following form

$$\left(\frac{\hbar^2}{M}\nabla^2 + E\right)\psi(\mathbf{r}) = (-1)^{S+1}V(r)\psi(\mathbf{r}) \qquad (12.55)$$

This implies that the Bartlett forces are attractive for triplet states and repulsive for singlet states.

C. MAJORANA FORCES—SPACE EXCHANGE.   The exchange is shown in Fig. 12.8(c) and mathematically expressed as

$$V_{12} = V(r)M_{12} \qquad (12.56)$$

where M_{12} operates on the space part only and corresponds to the inversion of coordinates (parity), i.e.,

$$M_{12}\psi(\mathbf{r}) = \psi(-\mathbf{r}) = (-1)^{\frac{1}{2}(1-P)}\psi(\mathbf{r}) \qquad (12.57)$$

where $P = \pm 1$ for even and odd parity states, respectively. Hence the exchanged wave function is $\Psi(\mathbf{r}_2, \sigma_1; \mathbf{r}_1, \sigma_2)$ and the wave equation is

$$\left(\frac{\hbar^2}{M}\nabla^2 + E\right)\psi(\mathbf{r}) = (-1)^{\frac{1}{2}(1-P)}V(r)\psi(\mathbf{r}) \qquad (12.58)$$

Thus Majorana forces are attractive for even parity states ($l = 0, 2, 4, ...$, i.e., S, D, G ... states) and repulsive for odd parity states ($l = 1, 3, 5, ...$ i.e., P, F, H... states).

D. HEISENBERG FORCE—SPACE AND SPIN EXCHANGE.   The exchange is shown in Fig. 12.8(d) and mathematically expressed as

$$V_{12} = V(r)H_{12} = V(r)M_{12}B_{12} \qquad (12.59)$$

The exchange wave function is $\Psi(\mathbf{r}_2, \sigma_2; \mathbf{r}_1, \sigma_1)$ and the wave equation is

$$\left(\frac{\hbar^2}{M}\nabla^2 + E\right)\psi(\mathbf{r}) = (-1)^{\frac{1}{2}(1-P)+S+1}V(r)\psi(\mathbf{r}) \qquad (12.60)$$

A close look at Eq. (12.60) reveals the following: The forces are attractive for even triplet states and odd singlet states. The forces are repulsive for odd triplets and even singlet states.

SUMMARY. In determining the potential energy or some other property, the field theory has been used in calculating the mixture of each of the forces present. It may appear that by taking a proper mixture, we may explain saturation and avoid the collapse of the nucleus to a small volume. As the nucleons are added up, there will be as many in the odd angular-momentum states as in the even angular-momentum states. Further, if we assume that Majorana forces predominate over Wigner forces, the repulsive forces will counterbalance the attractive forces, which leads to saturation. But actually Majorana forces do not predominate. The saturation is explained by adding a hard-core repulsive force (acting at distances of the order of 0.5×10^{-13} cm) to the already present interaction which also contains a certain degree of exchange interaction.

6. TWO-BODY SCATTERING AT HIGHER ENERGIES[31]

In order to get further information about nuclear forces, it is necessary to consider nucleon-nucleon scattering at higher energies. The work on neutron-proton scattering[32-34] and proton-proton scattering[35-38] has been carried out by many scientists. The results of all the experiments prior to 1958 have been summarized by W. Hess[31], and some of these we shall present here in graphical form. Below 290 Mev the scattering is completely elastic, while at 290 Mev and above, pion production takes place. Because we are interested in the study of nuclear structure, we shall limit our discussion to energies below the threshold for pion production.

The results of the differential cross-section for neutron-proton scattering at energies from 14 Mev to 580 Mev are shown in Fig. 12.9. The curves shown have been fitted to the experimental points (the points are not shown in the diagram). The particular features of these curves are (i) there is forward peaking as well as backward peaking in the cross-section, (ii) the minimum in the cross-section for all energies occurs at about 80° to 110°, and (iii) at a particular angle the cross-section varies as $1/E$.

The differential cross-sections for proton-proton scattering are shown in Fig. 12.10 for energies from ~ 9 Mev to ~ 460 Mev. Two features are quite obvious from these curves: The differential cross-section for angles greater than 30° at different energies is almost constant, and the sharp variation in the differential cross-section, due to coulomb scattering, is quite clear for angles less than 30°.

The total cross-sections for neutron-proton scattering and proton-proton scattering are shown in Fig. 12.11. We shall now see how some of the outstanding features of the scattering experiments may be explained by assuming different types of nuclear forces. As the energy of the system increases, the de Broglie wavelength decreases, and, therefore, it should be possible to observe more details of the nuclear potentials. But this is not so, because with increasing energy of the particles we have to consider the higher angular-momentum states as well, and this makes the problem more complicated, as we shall see.

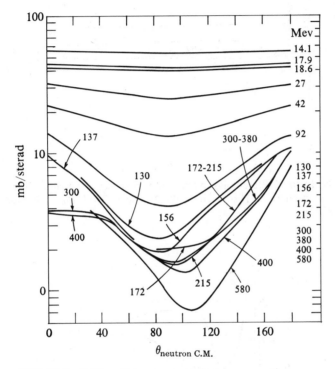

FIG. 12.9 Differential n-p scattering cross-section versus angle for different neutron energies. [From Hess, W. N., *Revs. Mod. Phys.*, **30**, 368, (1958).]

In the case of neutron-proton scattering, we expect that as the energy of the incident neutron increases there should be more and more forward scattering. The maximum energy that the protons may gain during the collision is equal to the interaction potential energy, which from our low energy scattering experiments is ~40 Mev. Thus the conservation law for elastic collisions requires that neutrons with energies $\geqslant 100$ Mev be scattered in the forward direction with angles less than $90°$ in the center-of-mass coordinates, or less than $45°$ in the laboratory-coordinate system. This is apparently not true, as shown in Fig. 12.9. There is as much scattering in the forward direction as in the backward, with a minimum at about $80°$ to $110°$,

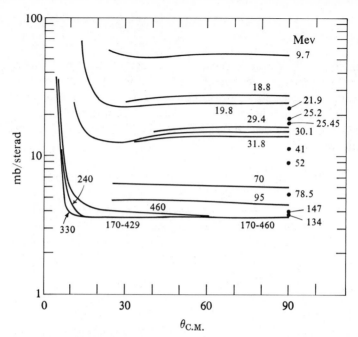

FIG. 12.10 Differential p-p scattering cross-section versus angle for different energies. [From Hess, W. N., *Revs. Mod. Phys.*, **30**, 368, (1958).]

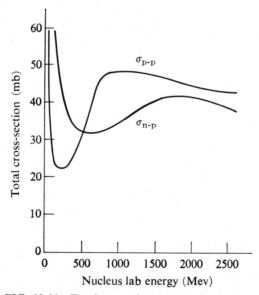

FIG. 12.11 Total experimental cross-sections for n-p scattering and p-p scattering at various energies. [From Chen, F. F., C. P. Leavitt and A. M. Shapiro, *Phys. Rev.*, **103**, 211, (1956).]

and it is almost symmetrical about this minimum. The ordinary central forces that predict a forward scattering cannot explain this. But it is possible to explain such a distribution with the help of exchange forces, according to which the neutron and proton exchange charge during the interaction as shown in Fig. 12.12. Thus the neutrons scattered in the forward direction are

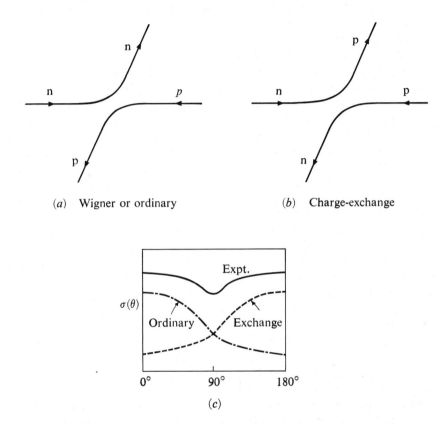

(a)   Wigner or ordinary

(b)   Charge-exchange

(c)

FIG. 12.12   (a) n-p scattering in ordinary, or Wigner force, without any exchange, (b) n-p scattering with charge exchange, and (c) experimental cross-section due to the ordinary and the exchange force.

due to ordinary force, and the ones scattered in the backward direction are due to exchange forces. The ordinary and the exchange forces mix to give equal contributions to the scattering. This results in the required distribution as shown in Fig. 12.12(c). The potential used is called the *Serber potential*, which is actually a mixture of the ordinary (Wigner) potential and the Majorana potential, i.e.,

$$V_{12} = \tfrac{1}{2}[(1 - a)W + aM_{12}]V(r) \tag{12.61}$$

where $a \simeq \frac{1}{2}$. For odd angular momentum states M_{12} and Eq. (12.61) give $V_{12} \simeq 0$. This means that for these states there is no interaction potential and the phase shifts δ_1, δ_3, δ_5, ... all vanish.

The absence of the odd angular-momentum states does explain the salient features of the neutron-proton scattering, but it does not explain the saturation property of the nuclei. The use of the Serber potential does reduce the attractive forces, but it does not introduce the repulsive forces that account for the saturation. Actually the interaction in the odd states, P, F, is not zero, but it is weak as compared to the even states, S, D.

The proton-proton scattering differential cross-section is shown in Fig. 12.10, and it looks to be quite different from the neutron-proton scattering. Aside from the cross-sections at small angles, which are due to coulomb scattering, the differential cross-section is isotropic at all energies. This may induce us to think that the scattering must be taking place in the S-state only. This is not true because the total S-wave scattering cross-section ($=4\pi/k^2$) is only half of the experimentally observed value. At a particular energy one could explain the isotropic scattering by introducing the P, D, ... waves as the interference terms, but this does not explain the isotropic distribution at all other energies.

An interesting and somewhat satisfactory explanation was given by R. Jastrow[39] in 1951 by the introduction of a repulsive core of the type shown in Fig. 12.13. Because this repulsive core is effective only at very short distances, it is only the S-wave that is affected in high energy scattering. In order to explain proton-proton scattering at high energies, one takes a potential that is a combination of the Serber potential and the repulsive-core potential. Of course, the contribution from the odd orbital states is small. The repulsive core affects the higher angular-momentum states (other than the S-state) only if the energies are much higher than the range we are considering. At low energies the attractive potential at large distances affects the phase of the S-wave, which is positive, and at high energies, due to the repulsive core, the S-phase is negative. Actually δ_0 first decreases to zero and then becomes increasingly negative. The fit to the experimental data shows that the radius of the repulsive core is $\simeq 0.5 \times 10^{-13}$ cm. To completely account for the phase shifts and total cross-sections, it is enough to consider only the S, P, and D states.

To explain the n-p and p-p cross-sections as well as the saturation properties, it has been found satisfactory to use the spin-dependent potential which will include (i) the exchange interaction (or the Serber potential), (ii) the repulsive core, (iii) the tensor force, and (iv) the spin-orbit interaction $V(r)\,\mathbf{L}\cdot\mathbf{S}$ which is a velocity-dependent potential and is attractive if $\mathbf{L}$ and $\mathbf{S}$ are parallel, repulsive if antiparallel. The differences in the results of n-p and p-p scattering are not due to the charge dependence of nuclear forces, but rather to the fact that p-p scattering involves identical particles.

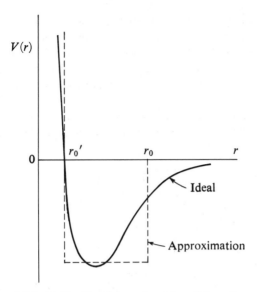

FIG. 12.13 The form of nuclear interaction potential, $V(r)$, that includes a repulsive core for distances shorter than r_0'. The broken line is an approximation to the ideal potential.

7. FIELD THEORY OF NUCLEAR FORCES

In the preceding sections we have discussed the properties of the nuclear forces and have tried to explain them by means of arbitrary potential functions. A first step in the development of a theory for the nuclear forces was the suggestion by Heisenberg, in 1932, that the nuclear forces have an exchange character. It was not clear at that time what was being exchanged. Finally in 1935 definite advances were made by H. Yukawa[40] that led to the establishment of meson field theory.

Yukawa proposed that when two nucleons are interacting, there is a field associated with this system, and the cause of the force between the two is an exchange of a quantum between them. A quantum is emitted by one nucleon and absorbed by the other. This is in analogy with the coulomb force between two electrically charged particles, where according to quantum mechanics, the interaction between the two is explained by saying that one charge emits a photon that is absorbed by the other. The zero mass of the photon explains the long-range nature of the coulomb forces. According to Yukawa, because the nuclear forces are short range, the quantum exchanged between the nucleons must have a finite mass. The mass of the quantum can be deduced from the range of the nuclear force, as we shall see later, and it turns out to be

$\sim 300 \ m_e$. The quanta involved in such interactions have been given the names pi-meson (or pion) denoted by π^0 (neutral pion), π^- (negative pion), and π^+ (positive pion). All three types of pions have been discovered experimentally; their masses and other properties have been measured. The interactions between the nucleons can be represented by means of equations as follows.

(1) The n-p interaction with no exchange of charge is represented by $n_1 \rightarrow n_1 + \pi^0$ and $\pi^0 + p_2 \rightarrow p_2$, i.e., emission and absorption which is shown in Fig. 12.14(a).

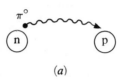

(a)

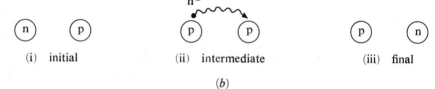

(i) initial   (ii) intermediate   (iii) final

(b)

FIG. 12.14 (a) The n-p interaction without exchange of charge and (b) the n-p interaction with exchange of charge.

(2) The n-p interaction with exchange of charge is given by $n_1 \rightarrow p_1 + \pi^-$ and $\pi^- + p_2 \rightarrow n_2$. This corresponds to the exchange of a proton and a neutron, and may be represented by three stages as shown in Fig. 12.14(b).

(3) Similarly, the p-n exchange can be explained by the emission and absorption of π^+ mesons, i.e., $p_1 \rightarrow n_1 + \pi^+$ and $\pi^+ + n_2 \rightarrow p_2$. It is the exchange of the momentum carried by the meson that causes the nuclear force.

There is another question we may ask ourselves: When a meson is emitted, will there be an apparent nonconservation of energy of the nucleon by an amount $\Delta E = m_\pi c^2$? The answer lies in the uncertainty principle which allows nonconservation of energy by an amount ΔE given by

$$\Delta E \Delta t \sim \hbar$$

or

$$\Delta t \sim \frac{\hbar}{\Delta E} = \frac{\hbar}{m_\pi c^2} \leqslant 4 \times 10^{-24} \ \text{sec} \qquad \textbf{(12.62a)}$$

or

$$(\Delta t)c \sim \frac{\hbar}{m_\pi c} \qquad \textbf{(12.62b)}$$

Thus if the meson comes back to the other nucleon within $\sim 10^{-24}$ sec, the nonconservation of energy will not be detected. During this time the maximum distance traveled by the meson will be $(\Delta t)c \sim 1.2 \times 10^{-13}$ cm, which is precisely the range of the nuclear forces. In the case of a single nucleon, the mesons are constantly emitted and absorbed by the same nucleon, i.e., a nucleon is surrounded by a cloud of mesons.

Whereas quantum electrodynamics has been completely successful in explaining all of the properties of the electromagnetic interaction, the same cannot be said of quantum mechanics for meson field theory. The difficulties are mathematical and not conceptional. It is not possible to go into the complete details of the theory in this text, but we shall go just far enough to show the relation between the range of the force and mass of the pion (m_π) and to find the coupling constant, i.e., the strength of the interaction[41].

According to relativistic mechanics, the total energy, E, the momentum, p, and the mass, m_π, are related by

$$E^2 - p^2c^2 - m_\pi^2 c^4 = 0 \tag{12.63}$$

By the rules of quantum mechanics, we replace E by $i\hbar\, \partial/\partial t$, and p by $-i\hbar\nabla$, and let $\phi(\mathbf{r}, t)$ be the function on which they operate, i.e.,

$$-\hbar^2 \frac{\partial^2 \phi}{\partial t^2} + \hbar^2 c^2 \nabla^2 \phi + m_\pi^2 c^4 \phi = 0$$

or

$$\nabla\phi^2 - \frac{1}{c^2}\frac{\partial^2 \phi}{\partial t^2} = \frac{m_\pi^2 c^2}{\hbar^2}\phi \tag{12.64}$$

Eq. (12.64) is the famous Klein-Gordon equation. For $m_\pi = 0$, this reduces to the wave equation of the electromagnetic field, i.e.,

$$\nabla^2\phi - \frac{1}{c^2}\frac{\partial^2 \phi}{\partial t^2} = 0 \tag{12.65}$$

Substituting $K = m_\pi c/\hbar$ in Eq. (12.64), we get

$$\left(\nabla^2 - \frac{1}{c^2}\frac{\partial^2}{\partial t^2} - K^2\right)\phi = 0 \tag{12.66}$$

For the static field, this takes the form

$$(\nabla^2 - K^2)\phi = 0 \tag{12.67}$$

Eq. (12.67) has a solution of the form

$$\phi = g\,\frac{e^{-Kr}}{r} \tag{12.68}$$

which is of the form shown in Fig. 12.15 and is the Yukawa potential. Comparing Eq. (12.67) with the static electric field for which $K = 0$, we get

$$\nabla^2 \phi = 0 \qquad (12.69)$$

which has a solution

$$\phi = e/r \qquad (12.70)$$

and gives the long-range coulomb potential.

From Eq. (12.62a) we define the range of the interaction as $\alpha = \hbar/m_\pi c = 1/K$. Hence Eq. (12.68) becomes

$$\phi = (g\ e^{-r/\alpha})/r \qquad (12.71)$$

where the range is of the order of 10^{-13} cm, and the coupling constant $g^2/\hbar c$ is about equal to unity.

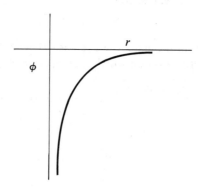

FIG. 12.15 The form of the Yukawa potential.

PROBLEMS

1. If the neutron-proton forces were much greater than the neutron-proton forces, how will it effect the plot of N versus Z for stable nuclei?

2. What information about the nucleon-nucleon interaction may be obtained by simply looking at the values of $\frac{v}{c}$ and λ for neutrons of energies 1 ev, 1 kev, 1 Mev, 10 Mev, 100 Mev?

3. Evaluate the constants A and C in Eq. (12.16) and Eq. (12.17) i.e., evaluate the normalized wave function for deuteron.

4. From the binding energy and potential V_0 for the deuteron, what information you can get about the radius of the deuteron nucleus? How does this compare with the values of r_0 obtained from other results?

5. Assume that the neutron and proton in a deuteron are about 3×10^{-13} cm aparat. If both are at rest and with spins parallel, what is the magnetic force exerted by the proton on the neutron? How does this affect the binding energy of the deuteron?

6. Assume that the potential

$$V = -V_0 \quad \text{for } r < \alpha$$
$$= \quad 0 \quad \text{for } r > \alpha$$

represents the triplet S, (n, p) scattering potential. Furthermore, if $\alpha = 1.72f$, what should be the value of V_0 which will agree with the deuteron potential?

7. In Eq. (12.26) what is the value of S_{12} for the following spin directions of neutron and proton in a deuteron:

(a)   (b)   (c)   (d)

8. An $(n\text{-}p)$ scattering is investigated by scattering neutrons from a target. If the target in addition to hydrogen atoms contains oxygen and nitrogen, how will you correct for these impurities?

9. In Eq. (12.44), is there any significant relation between r_{os}, r_{ot} and the nuclear radius? If we assume that there is a relation between r_{os}, r_{ot} and the nuclear radius, how does this effect the values a_s and a_t?

10. What type of experiment will you perform in order to find out if the scattering is taking place from (a) a central repulsive core surrounded by an attractive potential, or (b) a central attractive core surrounded by a repulsive potential?

REFERENCES

1. Elton, L. R. B., *Introductory Nuclear Theory*, p. 79. New York: Interscience Publishers, Inc., 1959.

2. Wigner, E. and E. Feenberg, *Rep. Prog. Phys.*, Vol. 8, p. 274, London: Physical Society, 1941.

3. Wigner, E. *Phys. Rev.*, **51**, p. 107, (1937).

4. Feenberg, E. and E. Wigner, *Phys. Rev.*, **51**, p. 95, (1937).

5. Jarmie, N. and R. C. Allen, *Phys. Rev.*, **111**, p. 1121, (1958).

6. Feshbach, H. and J. Schwinger, *Phys. Rev.*, **84**, p. 194, (1951).

7. Rarita, W. and J. Schwinger, *Phys. Rev.*, **59**, p. 436, (1941).

8. Frisch, O. R., *Prog. Nucl. Phys.*, **2**, (Squires) p. 89, (1952).

9. Breit, G. and M. H. Hull, Jr., *Am. J. Phys.*, **21**, p. 184, (1953).

10. Jackson, J. D. and J. M. Blatt, *Revs. Mod. Phys.*, **22**, p. 77, (1950).

11. Melkonian, E., *Phys. Rev.*, **76**, p. 1744, (1949).

12. Lampi, E. E., G. D. Freier, and J. H. Williams, *Phys. Rev.*, **80**, p. 853, (1950).

13. Bailey, C. L., W. E. Bennett, T. Bergstralh, R. C. Nuckolls, H. T. Richards, and J. H. Williams, *Phys. Rev.*, **70**, p. 583, (1946).

14. Frisch, D. H., *Phys. Rev.*, **70**, p. 589, (1946).

15. Blair, J. M., G. Freier, E. E. Lampi, W. Sleator, and J. H. Williams, *Phys. Rev.*, **74**, p. 553, (1948).

16. Sachs, R. G., *Nuclear Theory*, Chap. 4, pp. 79–88. Cambridge, Mass.: Addison-Wesley Publishing Co., Inc., 1953.

17. Worthington, H. R., J. N. McGruer, and D. E. Findley, *Phys. Rev.*, **90**, p. 899, (1953).

18. Hall, H. H. and J. L. Powell, *Phys. Rev.*, **90**, p. 912, (1953).

19. Breit, G., E. U. Condon, and R. D. Present, *Phys. Rev.*, **50**, p. 825, (1936).

20. Breit, G., H. M. Thaxton, and L. Eisenbud, *Phys. Rev.*, **55**, p. 1018, (1939).

21. Hoisington, L. E., S. S. Share, and G. Breit, *Phys. Rev.*, **56**, p. 884, (1939).

22. Jackson, J. D. and J. M. Blatt, *Revs. Mod. Phys.*, **22**, p. 77, (1950).

23. Yovits, M. C., R. L. Smith, M. H. Hull Jr., J. Bengston, and G. Breit, *Phys. Rev.*, **85**, p. 540, (1952).

24. Mott, N. F. and H. S. W. Massey, *The Theory of Atomic Collisions*, Chap. 3, 2nd Edition. Oxford: Clarendon Press, 1949.

25. Herb, R. G., D. W. Kerst, B. Parkinson, and G. J. Plain, *Phys. Rev.*, **55**, p. 998, (1939).

26. Heydenburg, N. P., L. R. Hafstad, and M. A. Tuve, *Phys. Rev.*, **56**, p. 1078, (1939).

27. Blair, J. M., G. Freier, E. E. Lampi, W. S. Sleator Jr., and J. H. Williams, *Phys. Rev.*, **74**, p. 553, (1948).

28. Worthington, H. R., J. N. McGruer, and D. E. Findley, *Phys. Rev.*, **90**, p. 909, (1953).

29. Breit, G. and R. L. Gluckstern, *Ann. Rev. Nucl. Sci.*, Vol. 2. Stanford: Annual Reviews, 1953.

30. Bethe, H. A. and P. Morrison, *Elementary Nuclear Theory*, Chap. XV, New York: John Wiley & Sons, Inc., 1961.

31. Hess, W. N., *Revs. Mod. Phys.*, **30**, p. 368, (1958).

32. Hadley, J., E. Kelly, C. Leith, E. Segrè, C. Wiegand, and H. York, *Phys. Rev.*, **75**, p. 351, (1949).

33. Kelly, E., C. Leith, E. Segrè, and C. Wiegand, *Phys. Rev.*, **79**, p. 96, (1950).

34. Wallace, R., *Phys. Rev.*, **81**, p. 493, (1951).

35. Fillmore, F. L., *Phys. Rev.*, **83**, p. 1252, (1951).

36. Binge, R. W., U. E. Kruse, and N. F. Ramsey, *Phys. Rev.*, **83**, p. 274, (1951).

37. Oxley, C. L. and R. D. Schamberger, *Phys. Rev.*, **85**, p. 416, (1952).

38. Chamberlain, O., E. Segrè, and C. Wiegand, *Phys. Rev.*, **83**, p. 923, (1951).

39. Jastrow, R., *Phys. Rev.*, **81**, p. 165, (1951); 636L, (1951).

40. Yukawa, H., *Proc. Phys., Math. Soc.*, Japan, **17**, p. 48, (1935).

41. Bethe, H. A. and P. Morrison, *Elementary Nuclear Theory*, Chap. XVIII. New York: John Wiley & Sons, Inc., 1961.

SUGGESTIONS FOR FURTHER READING

1. Elton, L. R. B., *Introductory Nuclear Theory*, Chaps. 3 and 4. New York: Interscience Publishers, Inc., 1959.

2. Blatt, J. M. and V. F. Weisskopf, *Theoretical Nuclear Physics*, Chaps. 2, 3, and 4. New York: John Wiley & Sons, 1958.

3. Preston, M. A., *Physics of the Nucleus*, Chaps. 2 and 5. Cambridge, Mass.: Addison-Wesley Publishing Co., Inc., 1962.

4. Behte, H. A. and P. Morrison, *Elementary Nuclear Theory*, Chaps. VIII–XVIII. New York: John Wiley & Sons, Inc., 1961.

5. Sachs, R. G., *Nuclear Theory*, Part I. Cambridge, Mass.: Addison-Wesley Publishing Co., Inc., 1953.

6. Fermi, E., *Nuclear Physics*, Chapter VI. University of Chicago Press, 1950. Notes compiled by J. Orear, A. H. Rosenfeld, and R. A. Schluter.

7. Ramsey, N. F., *Experimental Nuclear Physics*, ed. E. Segrè, Vol. I, Part IV, (1953). New York: John Wiley & Sons, Inc.

XIII

NEUTRON PHYSICS AND FISSION

1. INTRODUCTION

Since its discovery by J. Chadwick[1] in 1932, the neutron has played a significant role in the understanding of the structure of the nucleus. Starting with Chapter II, where we discussed in detail the discovery of the neutron, all through the text we have considered many aspects of neutron physics. The discussion in this chapter will be limited to topics not previously covered.

TABLE 13.1
DEFINITION OF NEUTRON ENERGY RANGES

Type	Energy
(a) slow neutrons	0–1000 ev
(b) thermal neutrons	$\sim$0.025 ev
(c) intermediate energy neutrons	$\sim$1–500 kev
(d) fast neutrons	$\sim$0.5–10 Mev
(e) high (or very high) energy neutrons	>10 Mev

This will involve, for example, the methods of production and detection of neutrons. Because neutrons are not deflected by an electric or magnetic field and also they do not produce appreciable ionization, special methods must be employed for the determination of neutron energies. Our next step will be the investigation of different aspects of neutron diffraction. Finally, we shall discuss fission produced by slow neutrons.

Since the methods of production and detection of neutrons and their interaction with matter depend strongly on the neutron energies, the preceding nomenclature (Table 13.1) has been used commonly for different energy ranges.

2. SOME PROPERTIES OF FREE NEUTRONS

In this chapter we are primarily interested in the study of free neutrons which differ in many aspects from bound neutrons. A few properties of free neutrons are discussed here.

A. CHARGE.   The neutron has been shown to be neutral. The absence of charge on the neutron makes it penetrating, and it may travel through several meters of air without producing more than one or two ion pairs[2]. It can also penetrate the nucleus even if its kinetic energy is very low because it encounters no coulomb barrier.

B. MASS.   The neutron mass may be determined by the methods of mass doublets or by nuclear reactions forming closed cycles as discussed in Chapter V. The latest accepted value of the neutron mass[3] is (on the C^{12} scale)

$$m(_0n^1) = 1.008665 \text{ u},$$

as compared to the proton mass

$$m(_1H^1) = 1.007825 \text{ u}.$$

C. SPIN AND MAGNETIC MOMENT.   As discussed in Chapter II, the neutron has a spin angular-momentum of $\frac{1}{2}\hbar$ and, being a Fermi particle, it obeys Fermi statistics and the Pauli exclusion principle. Though the neutron has no charge, it has been shown to have a magnetic moment. Its value has been found to be -1.9135 nuclear magnetons. The negative sign indicates that the direction of the magnetic moment is opposite to that of the spin direction (or as if the neutron had a negative charge).

D. WAVE AND POLARIZATION CHARACTERISTICS.   Like other particles, the neutron also exhibits wave properties. The wave length, λ, associated with a neutron is given by $\lambda = h/mv$, where m is the mass, and v is the velocity. The wave characteristic has been established by diffraction methods. Neutron diffraction has proved to be useful in the investigation of crystal structure.

An important aspect by which the neutron differs from the wave characteristic of other particles is the following: Because the neutron has no charge but does have a magnetic moment, a beam of neutrons after passing through strongly magnetized iron will show polarization effects.

E. RADIOACTIVE DECAY OF FREE NEUTRONS. That the mass of a neutron is slightly greater than the mass of a proton leads to an important consequence. According to the theory of beta decay, if energetically possible, the neutron should decay to a proton with an emission of an electron and an antineutrino represented by the following equation:

$$ {}_0\mathrm{n}^1 \to {}_1\mathrm{p}^1 + {}_{-1}\beta^0 + {}_0\bar{\nu}^0 + 0.782 \text{ Mev} $$

In order to observe the beta decay of free neutrons, one needs a high-intensity beam of thermal neutrons. Such beams have been made available by nuclear reactors. The first evidence of such a beta decay was obtained by the experiments of A. Snell, et al.[4,5]. More improved and quantitative measurements that confirmed this were carried out by J. Robson[6]. According to his measurements, free neutrons decay with a half-life of 12.8 ± 2.5 minutes. A more recent value reported[7] for the half-life is 12.0 ± 1.5 minutes.

3. INTERACTION OF NEUTRONS WITH MATTER

Because neutrons are neutral they scarcely interact with atomic electrons. A very weak interaction between them is due to their magnetic moments. On the other hand, neutrons have one big advantage over charged particles. Being neutral they do not have to cross a coulomb barrier, and, thus, even very slow neutrons may reach the nucleus without any difficulty. The slower the neutron is, the more probable is its capture by the nucleus. There are many different types of nuclear reactions that may be caused by neutrons. The probability of a particular nuclear reaction to take place strongly depends upon the type of the neutrons. We shall not elaborate here all the different kinds of reactions caused by neutrons, because most of them have already been discussed. However, because of their importance, we shall discuss elastic collisions in some detail.

A. SCATTERING OF NEUTRONS. Scattering may be elastic or inelastic. In the process of elastic scattering, the sum of the kinetic energies of the neutron and the nucleus is the same before and after the collision. In the case of inelastic scattering, some of the kinetic energy of the incident neutron is used in the excitation of the target nucleus. The excited nucleus then decays by gamma emission. It may be noted that only elastic collisions are possible between neutrons and protons, but with other nuclei, both elastic and inelastic collisions can take place. Since a larger energy is needed to cause excitation of a nucleus, for low energy neutrons (from ~ 0.1 to 10 Mev) elastic scattering predominates, while for neutrons of energy greater than 10 Mev, inelastic scattering is predominant.

In both elastic and inelastic collisions, the net effect is that the neutron loses energy and slows down. Elastic scattering plays an important part in the slowing down of fast neutrons produced in fission, and we shall investigate elastic scattering in more detail. It may be shown that if a neutron of kinetic energy, E_0, is deflected through an angle, ϕ, by an elastic collision with a stationary nucleus of mass M, the kinetic energy, E, of the scattered neutron is given by

$$\frac{E}{E_0} = \frac{v^2}{v_0^2} = \frac{M^2 + m^2 + 2Mm \cos \phi}{(M + m)^2} \tag{13.1}$$

where m is the mass of the neutron, and ϕ is the scattering angle in the center-of-mass coordinate system. Because, in amu, m is close to unity, and A is almost an integer, we may, without much error, write Eq. (13.1) as

$$\frac{E}{E_0} = \frac{A^2 + 1 + 2A \cos \phi}{(A + 1)^2} \tag{13.2}$$

The angle ϕ in CMCS is related to the angle θ in the laboratory system by the following equation:

$$\cos \theta = \frac{A \cos \phi + 1}{(A^2 + 1 + 2A \cos \phi)^{1/2}} \tag{13.3}$$

From Eq. (13.2), we see that energy lost will be maximum, or E will be minimum for $\phi = 180°$, i.e.,

$$E_{min} = E_0 \frac{A^2 + 1 - 2A}{(A + 1)^2}$$

$$E_{min} = E_0 \left(\frac{A - 1}{A + 1} \right)^2 \tag{13.4}$$

Thus neutron energy-loss in an elastic collision is a function of A. For very heavy nuclei, $E_{min} \simeq E_0$, i.e., there is no loss in the neutron energy. On the other hand, for $A = 1$ (hydrogen nucleus), $E_{min} = 0$, i.e., in a single collision, the neutron loses all its energy. Therefore, for slowing down fast neutrons, the light nuclei such as hydrogen (in the form of water), deuteron (in the form of heavy water), and carbon, all of which have very low absorption but high scattering cross-sections, are commonly used. For example, in the case of hydrogen, $\sigma_{scatt}/\sigma_{cap} \approx 200$, and it is still higher for D_2O. The process of slowing down continues until the neutrons are in thermal equilibrium ($E_{th} \simeq 0.025$ ev).

B. NEUTRON CAPTURE.   In this process the neutron is captured and a γ-ray is emitted. In most cases the residual nucleus is radioactive, and it usually decays by beta emission. The capture cross-sections for light nuclei are low. For slow neutrons, the capture cross-section increases for heavier nuclei. For slow neutrons the phenomenon of resonance capture is prominent. The neutron capture cross-sections of B, Cd, and Gd are exceptionally high.

C. PARTICLE EMISSION.   The reactions of the type (n, p), (n, α), (n, T) occur more often with light nuclei. The recoil nucleus may or may not be radio-active. For neutrons of energies greater than 10 Mev, the reaction of the type (n, 2n) is more common. In some cases more than two neutrons may be emitted. The recoiled nucleus is usually radioactive.

D. FISSION.   Some heavy nuclei split into two fragments when they capture neutrons. This process is fission and will be discussed later on.

4. PRODUCTION OF NEUTRONS

Depending upon the energy and the intensity of the neutron beam, different methods are used for neutron production. A brief description of various methods will be given here.

A. NEUTRONS FROM (α, n) REACTIONS.   Neutrons are produced by bombarding a light element by alpha particles. The most common reaction is one in which beryllium is used as a target:

$$_2He^4 + {_4}Be^9 \rightarrow {_6}C^{12} + {_0}n^1 + 5.71 \text{ Mev} \qquad (13.5)$$

Other light elements used are Li, F, and B. The alpha particles may be obtained from radium, polonium, or radon. The most useful source of neutrons is the radium-beryllium source that makes use of the reaction of Eq. (13.5) and is described here[8].

The alpha particles are absorbed in very short distances in solids, hence it is necessary to make an intimate mixture of radium and beryllium. Radium and its decay products emit alpha particles with energies from ~ 4.8 Mev to ~ 7.7 Mev. These alpha particles interact with beryllium atoms and produce neutrons with energies as high as 13 Mev; the largest fraction of neutrons have energies about 5 Mev. Since the half-life of Ra is long (about 1600 years), the number of neutrons in a beam from the Ra-Be source is fairly steady over long periods of time. From a mixture of one curie of Ra with Be, $\sim 1.7 \times 10^7$ neutrons per second have been obtained[9,10].

One big disadvantage of the Ra-Be source of neutrons is that it is accompanied by a large gamma flux. A Po-Be source is used if a low gamma flux is desirable. But the disadvantage of the Po-Be source is its short half-life (140 days) and low neutron emission rate ($\sim 3 \times 10^6$ neutrons per second).

A beam of thermal neutrons may be obtained by slowing down fast neutrons. This is accomplished by surrounding a Ra-Be source by water, paraffin, or some other hydrogenous material. By means of elastic collisions with protons, the fast neutrons are slowed down to thermal energies in very short distances. In the case of a 2-Mev neutron source, for example, the thermal-neutron flux is a maximum at a distance of ~ 10 cm from a Ra-Be source[10].

B. Neutrons From Photodisintegration[11,12]. Neutrons may be produced by the reactions of the type $_4Be^9(\gamma, n)_4Be^8$ and $_1H^2(\gamma, n)_1H^1$. The threshold energies for these two reactions are 1.67 Mev and 2.23 Mev, respectively. It is possible to obtain an intense gamma-ray beam from artificial radioactive nuclei produced in nuclear reactors. These in turn may be used to produce high-flux neutron beams by means of photodisintegration.

A convenient photoneutron source has been designed by B. Russell, et al.[13], and is shown in Fig. 13.1. A suitable source of γ-rays is surrounded by Be or D_2O and may produce as many as 10^7 neutrons per second. Several radioactive nuclides have been suggested[12,13,14] to be used as gamma sources. The neutrons produced by photodisintegration are more nearly monoenergetic than those from (α, n) reactions.

C. Neutrons From Particle Accelerators[15,16]. For the production of monoenergetic neutrons, the method most commonly used is the bombardment of certain targets by accelerated charged particles. The reactions usually employed are the following:

$$_1H^2 + d \rightarrow {}_2He^3 + n + 3.28 \text{ Mev} \tag{13.6}$$

$$_1H^3 + d \rightarrow {}_2He^4 + n + 17.6 \text{ Mev} \tag{13.7}$$

$$_4Be^9 + d \rightarrow {}_5B^{10} + n + 4.35 \text{ Mev} \tag{13.8}$$

$$_1H^3 + p \rightarrow {}_2He^3 + n - 0.764 \text{ Mev} \tag{13.9}$$

$$_3Li^7 + p \rightarrow {}_4Be^7 + n - 1.65 \text{ Mev} \tag{13.10}$$

$$_6C^{12} + d \rightarrow {}_7N^{13} + n - 0.26 \text{ Mev} \tag{13.11}$$

Of these, the first two reactions are used more frequently. Deuterons accelerated to energies of 100 to 200 kev may be used for a good neutron yield. In the reaction of Eq. (13.6) the target is in the form of heavy ice (or deuterium contained in paraffin) while in reaction of Eq. (13.7), the tritium is deposited on zirconium. From these reactions one may obtain neutrons in the energy range of 5 kev to 20 Mev. A neutron flux of the order of 10^8 is easily obtained.

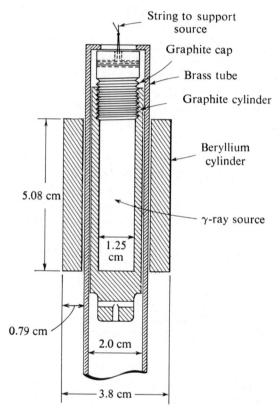

FIG. 13.1 The arrangement used for producing neutrons by means of photodisintegration of B or D_2O. [From Russell, B., D. Sacks, A. Wattenburg, and R. Fields, *Phys. Rev.*, **73**, 545, (1948).]

The energy of the neutrons emitted in the above reactions depends upon the angle of observation and the energy of the incident particle. This is given by the relation (from Sec. 4.2)

$$Q = K_y\left(1 + \frac{m_x}{M_Y}\right) - K_x\left(1 - \frac{m_x}{M_Y}\right) - \frac{2}{M_Y}(m_x m_y K_x K_y)^{1/2} \cos\theta \quad \textbf{(13.12)}$$

For convenience, the plots of K_y versus K_x have been made for different reactions and are shown in Fig. 13.2. The extent to which the neutrons are monoenergetic at a given angle depends upon the solid angle formed by the detector. The fast neutrons obtained by these methods have been used extensively in neutron research.

D. NEUTRONS FROM STRIPPING REACTIONS[17]. Very high-energy neutrons (of several hundred Mev) may be produced by means of stripping of deuterons.

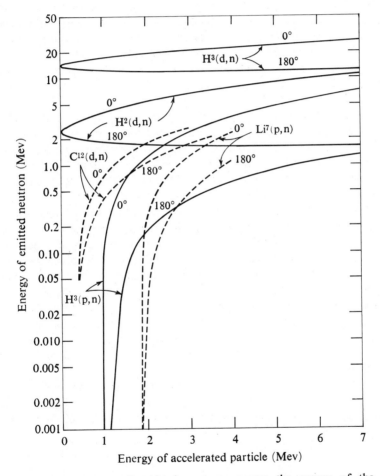

FIG. 13.2 Energy of emitted neutrons versus the energy of the bombarding particle for various common nuclear reactions. The upper curve in each case is for $\theta = 0°$ (in the direction of the incident beam), and the lower curve is for $\theta = 180°$ (opposite to the direction of the incident beam). [From Hanson, A. O., R. F. Taschek, and J. H. Williams, *Rev. Mod. Phys.*, **21**, 635, (1949).]

The deuteron consists of a neutron and a proton loosely bound together by an energy of only ~ 2.2 Mev. When a beam of very high-energy deuterons strikes a target, it is possible that the neutron and the proton may be separated. This results in the emission of the neutron in the forward direction with about half of the deuteron energy, while the proton may be captured by the target nucleus.

E. NEUTRONS FROM HIGH ENERGY PROTONS.   This is one of the simplest means of producing very high-energy neutrons by nucleon-nucleon interaction. It utilizes a head-on collision between a very-high energy incident proton and a single neutron of the target nucleus. The neutrons are knocked out in the forward direction carrying all the energy and the momentum of the incident proton. Neutrons of energy up to a few Bev may be produced by this method.

F. NEUTRONS FROM NUCLEAR FISSION REACTORS.   Most of the methods discussed so far produce high-energy neutrons with comparatively low fluxes. For producing low-energy neutron beams of high fluxes, nuclear reactors cannot be surpassed by any other method. Neutron fluxes of the order of 10^{14} neut./cm^2-sec. have been obtained from nuclear reactors as compared to $\sim 10^7$ neut./cm^2-sec from (α, n) sources and $\sim 10^8$ neut./cm^2-sec from the accelerators making use of $_1\text{H}^2(d, n)_2\text{He}^3$ and $_1\text{H}^3(d, n)_2\text{He}^4$ reactions. The energies of the neutrons emitted from fission vary from thermal energies to about 18 Mev, and with an average value of neutron energy of about 2 Mev.

Neutrons in the nuclear reactors are produced by the process of fission, which we shall discuss later in this chapter. It is sufficient to say here that in the process of fission, a neutron is absorbed by a fissionable nucleus, and it breaks the nucleus into two almost equal parts with an emission of more than one neutron for each neutron absorbed. For example, a thermal neutron absorbed by $_{92}\text{U}^{235}$ causes fission producing, on the average, 2.5 neutrons per fission. The neutrons produced may be further absorbed, and, thus, a chain reaction is set up.

In order to obtain a beam of thermal neutrons, as already mentioned, the source is surrounded by a material that will slow down the neutrons without absorbing them. Such materials are *moderators*, and include water, heavy water, and carbon.

5. DETECTION OF NEUTRONS

The detection of neutrons is a much more complex problem than the detection of charged particles and photons, because neutrons do not carry any electric charge and cause no direct ionization. Most of the methods to be discussed depend directly or indirectly on the following principles: (a) The interaction of a neutron with a nucleus, which includes elastic scattering, emission of a charged particle in a nuclear reaction caused by the neutrons, and the production of a radioactive nucleus, (b) the time-of-flight method, and (c) neutron diffraction. The method of detection used depends upon whether we are interested in determining the flux of the neutrons or both flux and energy. It may be noted that in most cases the energy of the neutrons is predetermined by the method of their production. Neutron detectors suitable for different experiments are the following.

A. RECOIL DETECTORS BASED ON ELASTIC SCATTERING.   This method is good for the detection of fast neutrons only, but it has the advantage that it may be used for energy as well as flux determination. This is essentially the method used in the discovery of the neutron. When an incident neutron of mass m and kinetic energy E_n collides with a nucleus of mass M, the energy E_r of the recoil nucleus at an angle ϕ with the incident neutron direction is given by

$$E_r = \frac{4mM}{(m + M)^2} E_n \cos^2 \phi \qquad (13.13)$$

There are three advantages of using recoil protons. First, the energy of the recoil protons is much higher than any other recoil nucleus. Second, the n-p elastic scattering cross-section is very high. And third, up to about 20 Mev the neutron-proton scattering has isotropic angular distribution in the center-of-mass coordinate system.

Thus in the laboratory coordinate system, the energy E_p of the recoiled proton is given by

$$E_p = E_n \cos^2 \phi \qquad (13.14)$$

The recoil protons will have maximum energy in a head-on collision, i.e., for $\phi = 0^\circ$, and hence $(E_p)_{max} = E_n$. The number of protons having energy between E_p and $E_p + dE_p$ is given by

$$dN(E) = \Phi N \frac{\sigma(E_n)}{E_n} dE_n \qquad (13.15)$$

where Φ is the incident neutron flux, N is the number of protons per unit volume and $\sigma(E_n)$ is the scattering cross-section at energy E. Thus, knowing the energy and the number of scattered protons, one can calculate the neutron energy and flux from Eqs. (13.14) and (13.15), respectively. The neutron-proton scattering cross-sections are known very accurately[18].

Determination of the number and energy of the recoiled protons, produced by allowing a beam of neutrons to fall on the counter filled with hydrogen gas or a block of hydrogenous material, like paraffin, placed in front of the counter window, may be made by one of the standard methods for charged-particle detection. These include the use of a cloud chamber, emulsion plates, solid-state counter, organic scintillator, ionization chamber, or proportional counter.

The cloud chamber filled with hydrogen used to be the most common method for observing the recoiled protons. This has been replaced by other improved detectors. It is still good for determining energies of extremely low-energy neutrons. For some time, emulsion plates were obsolete, but with tremendous improvements in emulsions, the plates loaded with hydrogenous material are again being used for very high-energy neutrons[19]. Proton

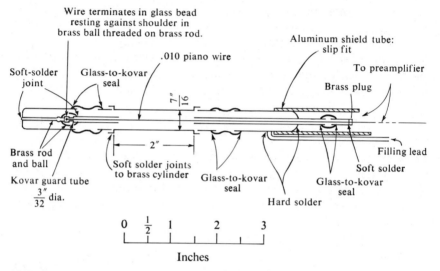

FIG. 13.3 A proton-recoil proportional counter. [From Frisch, D. H., *Phys. Rev.*, 70, 589, (1946).]

energies are determined by measuring their ranges in the emulsions. The use of solid state counters and scintillation counters is based on pulse-height analysis.

Ionization chambers or proportional counters filled with hydrogen are also used for observing proton recoils. The only limitation is that the neutrons must have high enough energy ($\gtrsim 35$ kev) so that the corresponding proton pulses are large enough as not to be confused with the background gamma pulses. A typical proton-recoil proportional counter, which has been designed by D. Frisch[20], is shown in Fig. 13.3.

Another form of a counter that is commonly used for energies above 20 Mev is the so-called "Counter Telescope"[21]. This uses metallic foils as absorbers for determining the range of protons emitted from a hydrogenous radiator in the forward direction. It may be pointed out that this method gives only a rough estimate of the neutron energy.

B. DETECTORS BASED ON NUCLEAR REACTIONS. Many detectors have been designed that are based on the emission of charged particles or gamma rays produced in nuclear reactions caused by incident neutrons. We shall discuss these methods in some detail.

1. Boron Detectors. These detectors utilize the reaction

$$B^{10} + n \rightarrow Li^7 + He^4 + 2.79 \text{ Mev}$$
$$\rightarrow Li^{7*} + He^4 + 2.31 \text{ Mev}$$
$$Li^{7*} \rightarrow Li^7 + \gamma + 0.48 \text{ Mev} \qquad \textbf{(13.16)}$$

For thermal neutrons, only a small fraction (~ 6.3 percent) decays directly to the ground state. The cross section for this reaction varies inversely with the velocity of the neutrons up to energies of about 1 kev. The cross section has been measured accurately by the crystal-diffraction method and has a value of ~ 4020 b for thermal neutrons (velocity $= 2200$ cm/sec and $E_n = 0.025$ ev, at 293°K). It is this high value of the cross section that makes boron a useful neutron detector. Even though natural boron contains only 19 percent of B^{10}, it is very easy to get enriched samples containing more than 90 percent of B^{10}. Although boron is essentially a slow-neutron detector, it is also possible to use it for fast neutrons. This is achieved by first slowing down the fast neutrons by elastic collisions with protons.

A typical boron detector consists of an ionization chamber or proportional counter filled with boron trifluoride (BF_3) gas or a boron-loaded scintillator counter. Fig. 13.4(a) shows a BF_3 proportional counter designed by A. Hanson and J. McKibben[22]. The detector may be used for measuring total-neutron flux or only fast-neutron flux. In order to remove thermal neutrons from the beam, a cadmium cap is provided in front of the detector. Because cadmium has a very high absorption cross-section for thermal neutrons, the pulses from the proportional counter will be due to fast neutrons only. Before the fast neutrons enter the BF_3 tube, they are slowed down by paraffin. Any stray neutrons from outside are slowed down by the surrounding paraffin and absorbed by B_2O_3.

The above counter used for flux determination is the *long counter* and as shown in Fig. 13.4(b), it has the great advantage of being almost energy-independent over a long range of up to about 5 Mev[23]. A shielded long counter is shown in Fig. 13.4(c)[22]. Efficiency for still faster neutrons decreases rapidly. Fast neutrons entering the counter are slowed down by paraffin and detected by the BF_3 counter. The whole paraffin block may be surrounded by a thin sheet of cadmium if it is necessary to absorb all thermal neutrons.

Other reactions in which charged particles are emitted, but infrequently used, are the following:

$$He^3 + n \rightarrow H^3 + p + 0.77 \text{ Mev} \qquad \textbf{(13.17a)}$$
$$Li^6 + n \rightarrow H^3 + \alpha + 4.64 \text{ Mev} \qquad \textbf{(13.17b)}$$
$$N^{14} + n \rightarrow C^{14} + p + 0.63 \text{ Mev} \qquad \textbf{(13.17c)}$$

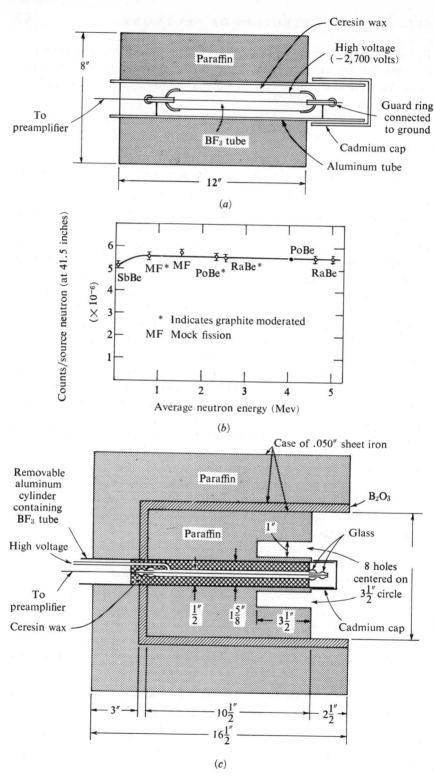

(a)

(b)

* Indicates graphite moderated

MF Mock fission

(c)

2. *Activation Method.* Many nuclei become radioactive by capturing neutrons and then decaying by gamma emission. The capture cross-section in general decreases with increasing neutron energy as the reciprocal of the velocity. Some nuclei have resonance absorption-peaks for incident neutron energies greater than 0.1 ev. These resonances have been successfully used for measuring neutron fluxes[24].

A thin foil of a material is immersed in a neutron flux for a definite time. The foil is removed and after a short waiting period, the gamma activity produced in the foil is measured, which, in turn, may be used to calculate the neutron flux. Shielding against thermal neutrons can be easily provided by using a cadmium cap. Some of the nuclei[25] commonly used for activation analysis are listed in Table 13.2. Of particular interest is indium, for which the variation in cross-section with energy is shown in Fig. 13.5.

TABLE 13.2

ISOTOPES USED FOR NEUTRON DETECTION BY ACTIVATION ANALYSIS

Isotope	Capture cross-section (barns)	Half-life	Radiation emitted (Mev)
In^{115}	154	54 m	$\beta^-(1, 0.8, 0.6)$ $\gamma(1.29, 1.10, ...)$
Co^{59}	18	10.5 m	$\beta^-(1.54)$ $\gamma(1.33)$
	19	5.26 y	$\beta^-(0.3)$ $\gamma(1.33, 1.17)$
Au^{197}	9	64.8 h	$\beta^-(0.96, 0.29, 1.37)$ $\gamma(0.412, 0.674, ...)$
Mn^{55}	13.3	2.58 h	$\beta^-(2.86, 1.05, 0.75)$ $\gamma(0.84, 1.81, 2.11)$

3. *Threshold Detectors.* There are some reactions that take place only if the neutrons have a certain minimum energy[26]. Thus it is possible to discriminate against different neutron energies by using a suitable reaction. The minimum neutron energy at which the reaction starts is called the effective threshold. The recoil nucleus is radioactive, and by measuring the intensity of the emitted radiation, one can estimate the flux of neutron energy above

FIG. 13.4 (a) A BF_3 proportional counter. [From Hanson, O. A., and J. L. Mckibben, *Phys. Rev.*, **72**, 673, (1947).] (b) Efficiency of a longer counter. [From R. A. Nobles *et al.*, *Rev. Sci. Inst.*, **25**, 334, (1953).] (c) A shielded long counter. [From Hanson and Mckibben, *Phys. Rev.*, **72**, 673 (1947).]

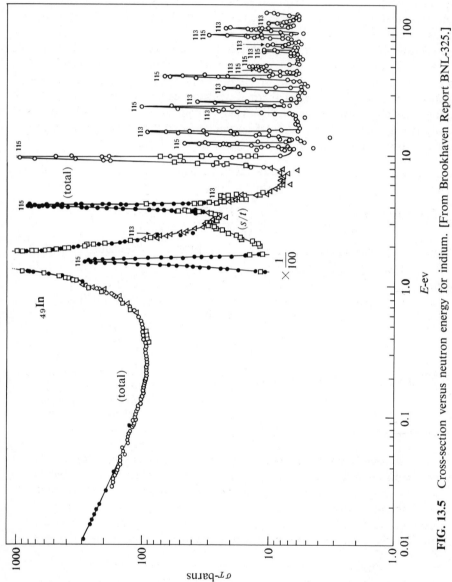

FIG. 13.5 Cross-section versus neutron energy for indium. [From Brookhaven Report BNL-325.]

TABLE 13.3

ISOTOPES USED AS THRESHOLD DETECTORS FOR FAST NEUTRON DETECTION

Isotope	Product nucleus	Effective threshold (Mev)	Average cross-section (barns)	Radiation emitted
P^{31}	Si^{31}	2	0.07	β^-
Al^{27}	Mg^{27}	4	0.08	β^-, γ
Cu^{63}	Cu^{62}	12	0.9	β^+, γ
Ni^{58}	Ni^{57}	13	1.1	β^+, γ
C^{12}	C^{11}	22	0.2	β^+

the threshold. Some properties of a few nuclei used in threshold detectors are given in Table 13.3.

4. Fission Detectors. These can be divided into detectors using (a) fission by thermal neutrons and (b) fission by fast neutrons. In the case of fast fission there is usually a certain threshold energy at which fission will occur. Apparatus usually consists of an ionization chamber lined with fissionable material. The energy released per fission is about 200 Mev, and most of it is taken away in the form of kinetic energy by the two main fission fragments, which, in turn, produce very large pulses in the ionization chamber.

For slow neutrons the most commonly used nucleus is U^{235}, while U^{238} and Th^{232} are used in fast fission. Properties of these and some other nuclei are listed in Tables 13.4 and 13.5. If a counter is lined with normal uranium, which is a mixture of U^{235} and U^{238}, it is possible to separate the slow and fast neutron fluxes by taking the ionization chamber reading with and without cadmium surrounding the ionization chamber. Cadmium has a very high absorption cross-section for thermal neutrons ($\sim 7 \times 10^3$ barns at 0.2 ev and 8 barns at 2 ev) and varies with neutron energy as shown in Fig. 13.6.

TABLE 13.4

PROPERTIES OF THERMALLY FISSILE NUCLIDES

Nuclide	Thermal neutron fission cross-section (Barns)	Fission cross-section for 3 Mev neutrons (barns)
U^{233}	520	1.9
U^{235}	590	1.3
Pu^{239}	730	2.0

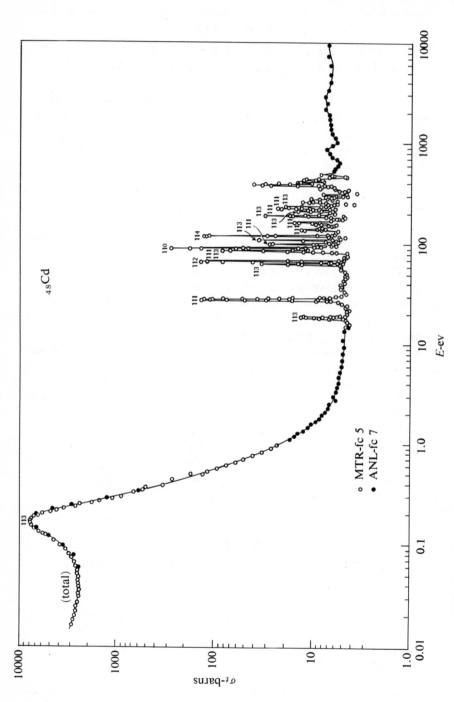

FIG. 13.6 Cross-section versus neutron energy for cadmium. [From Brookhaven Report BNL-325.]

TABLE 13.5

PROPERTIES OF FAST FISSILE NUCLIDES

Nuclide	Threshold Mev	Fission cross-section for 3 Mev neutrons (barns)
Th^{232}	1.3	0.14
U^{236}	0.8	0.85
U^{238}	1.2	0.55

C. THE TIME-OF-FLIGHT METHOD.   In recent years the time-of-flight method has become popular with the use of accelerators and reactions for measuring neutron cross-sections as function of energy. This method was developed independently by L. Alvarez[27], G. Fertel, *et al.*[28], and J. Milatz, *et al.*[29]

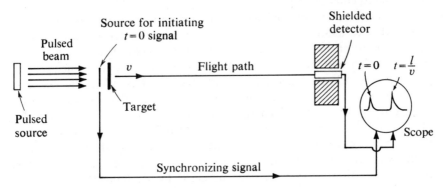

FIG. 13.7   A sketch of the experimental set-up for the time-of-flight measurements.

Although this method has been greatly improved, the principle still remains the same.

Neutrons produced in bursts travel a measured distance, *l*, (Fig.13.7) before reaching a detector. If the neutrons of energy E take a time t to travel the distance l, and if m is the mass of the neutron

$$E = \tfrac{1}{2}mv^2 = \tfrac{1}{2}m(l/t)^2 \qquad (13.18)$$

or

$$t = \sqrt{ml^2/2E} \qquad (13.19)$$

Thus if the detector is synchronized with the source and the output is a function of time, the time of arrival of neutrons at the detector is an inverse function of energy given by Eq. (13.19). If the neutrons are monoenergetic, they will all arrive at the same time. On the other hand, if the neutron pulse (or burst) produced at the source consists of neutrons of different energies, the higher-energy neutron group will reach the detector earlier than the lower-energy neutron group. In all the time-of-flight measurements, the following relations hold good if the neutron velocity v, energy E, and the flight time t are expressed in terms of m/sec, ev, and μsec/m, respectively:

$$v = 10^6/t \qquad (13.20a)$$

and

$$t = 72.3/\sqrt{E} \qquad (13.20b)$$

As an example, for a flight path of 10 meters the neutrons of energies 1 ev, 1 kev, and 1 Mev will take 723 μsec, 22.9 μsec, and 0.723 μsec, respectively. These times are easily measured. With the development of the techniques of nanosecond (i.e., 10^{-9} sec) resolving time circuits, the method has been extended to very fast neutrons ($\sim$ 150 Mev), and also the flight paths have been reduced considerably[30].

A typical outline of the experimental set-up is shown in Fig. 13.7. By pulsing the accelerator so that the target is bombarded periodically for only short intervals of time, bursts of neutrons are produced. The repetition rate may be as high as 1000 pulses per second. As soon as the pulse of neutrons is produced, a synchronizing signal is sent to the timing circuit of the detector. The subsequent arrival of the neutrons of different energies is measured with respect to a synchronizing signal. In many cases, in connection with the study of nuclear reactions, gamma rays may be emitted. In such cases the arrival of the gamma ray at the detector may be used as the base for the timing circuit of the detector. Fig. 13.8 shows a typical time-of-flight spectrum of neutrons from the reaction $F^{19}(\alpha, n)Na^{22}$ as obtained by R. Batchelor and J. H. Towle[31].

In nuclear reactors, neutrons are produced continuously. In order to make use of the time-of-flight method, a different arrangement is used. A device called a neutron beam "chopper," or velocity selector, is commonly used[32,33,34]. It consists of a disc made of cadmium and aluminum that is located in front of the neutron beam coming from the reactor and is rotated at a very high speed. The aluminum portion of the disc lets the neutrons pass through while the cadmium stops them completely. Thus the rotating disc works as a fast shutter and produces bursts of neutrons. By using this device with a multichannel analyzer it has been possible to measure neutron absorption cross-sections for various neutron energy ranges simultaneously.

C. OTHER METHODS.   There are two more methods which may be discussed here. One is the transmission method, which is the same as used with α, β, and γ rays. The other method is the diffraction of slow neutrons which we shall discuss in some detail in the next section.

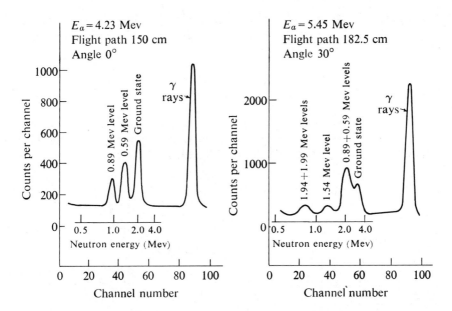

FIG. 13.8 A typical time-of-flight spectrum of neutrons from the reaction F^{19} (α, n) Na^{20}. [From Batchelor, R., and J. H. Towle, *Proc. Phys. Soc.*, **73**, 307, (1957).]

6. DIFFRACTION OF NEUTRONS

Even before the discovery of neutrons it had been experimentally verified that particles like electrons and protons exhibit wave characteristics including diffraction. W. Elsasser[35] and G. Wick[36] were the first to suggest that it might be possible to obtain a diffraction pattern by thermal neutron-scattering. According to the deBroglie hypothesis, a neutron of mass m, velocity v, and energy E will have a wave of length λ associated with it, i.e.,

$$\lambda = h/mv = h/\sqrt{2mE} \tag{13.21}$$

Thus, according to Bragg's condition, the diffraction angle, θ, (as defined in Fig. 13.9) is given by

$$n\lambda = 2d \sin \theta \tag{13.22}$$

where d is the spacing between different planes of the atoms in the crystal, and n is the order of diffraction. In order for diffraction to take place, the spacing must be of the order of the wave length of the incident particle. The method, therefore, is limited exclusively to very low neutron energies. It is possible to cause diffraction of neutrons whose energies are about 20 ev, and this limit is determined by the spacing of the crystal planes. Usually the observation of neutron diffraction is limited to the first order, $n=1$. For $n=1$, combining Eqs. (13.21) and (13.22), we obtain

$$E = \frac{h^2}{8md^2 \sin^2 \theta} \qquad (13.23)$$

It may be noted that there are three different kinds of neutron scattering[37] that may take place: (a) coherent scattering, in which neutrons are scattered in phase, (b) incoherent, or diffused, scattering in which neutrons

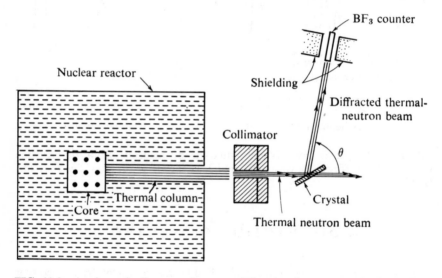

FIG. 13.9 A schematic diagram of neutron diffraction from a crystal. The angle of diffraction, θ, is determined by the Bragg's condition.

are scattered in random phase, and (c) inelastic scattering. It is coherent scattering that produces diffraction patterns by interference and is the one we are interested in here.

Neutron diffraction was first observed by D. Mitchell and P. Powers[38] and by H. Halban and P. Preiswerk[39]. Crystals like calcium fluoride, lithium fluoride, and magnesium oxide can cause appreciable amounts of diffraction of slow neutron beams. Though originally this method was used for getting a well-defined energy beam of neutrons, it is no longer used for this purpose. On the contrary, knowing the energy of the neutrons in the beam, it has been extensively used for the study of crystal structure. As the neutrons are scattered more often by nuclear centers than by the electrons, the method has proved useful in locating the position of atoms in crystals. With the availability of high intensity beams of thermal neutrons from the nuclear reactors, the investigation of crystal structure by this method has reached a high degree of perfection. Different arrangements have been used by W. Zinn[40], E. Wollan, C. Shull[41], and by others, and a typical schematic is shown in Fig. 13.9. A typical result obtained by Shull and Wollan[42] is shown in Fig. 13.10. Note that the effect of resonances also shows up if we are in the proper energy range.

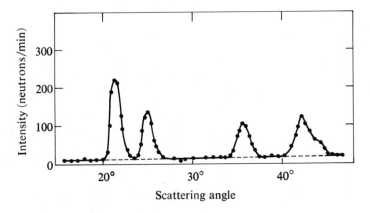

FIG. 13.10   The diffraction pattern of monoenergetic slow neutrons from powdered Pb. [From Shull, C. G., and E. W. Wollan, *Phys. Rev.*, **81**, 527, (1951).]

7. NUCLEAR FISSION

The discovery of fission was made by O. Hahn and F. Strassman[43] in 1939 and led to important applications of nuclear physics such as nuclear reactors and nuclear weapons. Hahn and Strassman bombarded uranium with slow neutrons and thought that the product nuclei were radium and actinium. By careful fractional crystallization they showed[44] that the new nuclei produced were isotopes of barium and lanthanum. For example, one of the activities observed had a half-life of 86 ± 6 min which is the same as that of Ba^{139} whose half-life is 85 min. Similarly, one of the nuclides was identified as La^{140}, which has a half life of 40 hours. It was also shown[45,46] with the help of ionization-chamber measurements that the products produced in fission carried away a very large amount of kinetic energy, and, in addition, pulses corresponding to 100 Mev were observed. *Fission* is a special type of nuclear reaction in which a nucleus frequently breaks into two comparable size fragments and a large amount of energy (~ 200 Mev) is emitted in each fission.

Uranium is not the only fissionable element. There are many other heavy elements that undergo fission. In addition to Ba and La, many isotopes of light elements in the range of $Z = 30$ (zinc) to $Z = 65$ (terbium) are emitted in the fission process.

A. Fissionable Materials.   So far, we have discussed the fission of U^{235} caused by slow neutrons. There are many other heavy nuclei that are fissionable, and the fission can be caused not only by slow neutrons, but also by fast neutrons, charged particles, and gamma rays.

The capture of a neutron by a nucleus may result either in fission or in the emission of a gamma ray. The later process is called radiative capture and is a complete loss of a neutron, as far as fission is concerned. The best nuclei for fission are those for which the fission cross-section is very high and, for thermal neutrons, the radiative capture cross-section is very small. There are a large number of isotopes[47,48] of $_{90}Th$, $_{91}Pa$, $_{92}U$, $_{93}Np$, $_{94}Pu$, and $_{95}Am$ that are fissionable. With the exception of three isotopes, $_{92}U^{233}$, $_{92}U^{235}$, and $_{94}Pu^{239}$, the others have either very short half-lives (most of them decay by α-emission) or have very small fission cross-sections for thermal neutrons. $_{92}U^{235}$ occurs naturally and has a half-life of 7.1×10^8 y. $_{92}U^{233}$ and $_{94}Pu^{239}$ can be produced artificially in large quantities and decay with half-lives of 1.62×10^5 y and 2.44×10^4 y, respectively. The fission cross-sections[47] of U^{233}, U^{235}, and Pu^{239} for thermal neutrons are 525 b, 582 b, and 742 b, while their total absorption cross-sections are 578 b, 683 b, and 1028 b, respectively. The fission cross-sections for U^{233} and U^{235} vary as $1/v$ at low energies to about 0.5 Mev. Up to about 20 ev, U^{235} has 20 resonance peaks.

As an alternative to alpha decay, some heavy nuclei decay by spontaneous fission, but their half-lives are very long. For examples, U^{235}, U^{238}, and Pu^{240} have half-lives 1.8×10^{17} y, 8×10^{15} y, and 5.5×10^{15} y, respectively for spontaneous fission decay. These spontaneous decay-products are completely identical with those produced by neutron-caused fission.

Many nuclei[49] like U^{234}, U^{236}, and U^{238} undergo fission only by fast neutrons. The threshold energy for these reactions is about 1 Mev and the fission cross section increases with increasing energy up to a few Mev and then levels off. Fission of nuclei with mass numbers $A \sim 200$ requires neutrons of energies about 40 to 50 Mev. The threshold for fission caused by charged particles like deuterons and alpha particles has been measured by J. Jungerman[50] for many nuclei. The threshold for fission by deuterons is about 8 Mev and by alpha particles is about 20 Mev. Photofission cross-sections have been measured by H. W. Koch, et al.[51], and it is found that threshold energies are about 5 Mev in most cases.

It may be pointed out that besides the emission of two large fragments in fission, neutrons and gamma rays are also emitted. For example, in the case of fission of U^{233}, U^{235}, and Pu^{239}, caused by thermal neutrons, on the average 2.51, 2.44, and 2.89 neutrons are emitted per fission, respectively. Sometimes, long-range alpha particles are also emitted in fission, but the probability is very low. Nuclei with mass numbers between 4 and 12 are emitted relatively infrequently. Fission in which three fragments of almost equal size are emitted, the so-called ternary fission, is not of very common occurrence. Besides the emission of different particles, an energy release of about 200 Mev per fission takes place, which plays an important part in the application of fission reactions.

Because of its natural occurrence and a very long half-life, U^{235} is commonly used for fission by thermal neutrons. Because the fission behavior of U^{233} and Pu^{239} is similar to U^{235}, we shall discuss the mass and energy distribution of U^{235} only. It is also important to note that natural uranium consists of only 0.72 percent of the U^{235} isotope. A complete separation of U^{235} from other U isotopes is a difficult and costly process. Usually natural uranium enriched in isotope U^{235} is used for fission and to obtain a chain reaction. See Sec. 14.7.

B. THE MASS AND ENERGY DISTRIBUTION OF FISSION FRAGMENTS. As mentioned earlier, the fission of U^{235} by slow neutrons results in the emission of a large number of different products varying from $A = 70$, $Z = 30$ (zinc); to $A = 160$, $Z = 65$ (terbium). There are more than 30 different modes of fission, and in each of them a different pair of nuclei is formed. Besides barium and lanthanum, some of the other common nuclei formed are bromine, molybdenum, rubidium, antimony, tellurium, krypton, iodine, xenon, and cesium. The neutron-to-proton ratio of U^{236} is $144/92 = 1.57$ while most of the stable isotopes of fission products have a neutron-to-proton ratio anywhere from 1.17 to 1.52. Thus the fission fragments produced have always an excess of neutrons, and they are, as a consequence, unstable. In order to get rid of excess neutrons, most of the fission fragments decay by β^- emission. In some instances where it is energetically possible, the fission fragments decay by neutron emission.

Because of the short half-lives of the fission fragments, it is difficult to separate and identify them. Most of these fragments go through many β^- decays before becoming stable isotopes. A series of products with the same mass number A is a fission chain. More than 60 such fission decay chains[52] have been established. One of the longest chains is the following:

$$_{54}Xe^{143} \xrightarrow[\text{1s}]{\beta^-} {}_{55}Cs^{143} \xrightarrow[\text{<1s}]{\beta^-} {}_{56}Ba^{143} \xrightarrow[\text{<0.5m}]{\beta^-} {}_{57}La^{143} \xrightarrow[\text{~19m}]{\beta^-}$$

$$_{58}Ce^{143} \xrightarrow[\text{33h}]{\beta^-} {}_{59}Pr^{143} \xrightarrow[\text{13.8d}]{\beta^-} {}_{60}Nd^{143} \text{ (stable)}$$

Some of the shortest chains like

$$_{60}Nd^{147} \xrightarrow[11\,d]{\beta^-} {}_{61}Pm^{147} \xrightarrow[4\,y]{\beta^-} {}_{62}Sm^{147} \ (\sim 10^{11}\,y)$$

and

$$_{42}Mo^{99} \xrightarrow[66\,h]{\beta^-} {}_{43}Tc^{99} \xrightarrow[2.2\times10^5\,y]{\beta^-} {}_{44}Ru^{99} \ (\text{stable})$$

are of particular interest because these have led to the establishment of new elements like Pm (promethium) and Tc (technetium), respectively.

Since most of the fission products have short half-lives, the aim of most experiments has been to measure the commulative fission yield of each chain. Suppose N_0 fissions take place in a given experiment and there are N_A fission fragments of mass number A formed. The fission yield $Y(A)$ is defined as

$$Y(A) = \frac{\text{number of nuclei of mass number } A \text{ formed in fission}}{\text{total number of fissions}} \times 100\%$$

$$= \frac{N_A\,100\%}{N_0} \tag{13.24}$$

Because in each fission, there are two fragments formed, therefore, the total yield is given by

$$\Sigma Y(A) = \frac{100}{N_0}\Sigma N_A\% = \frac{100 \times 2N_0}{N_0}\% = 200\% \tag{13.25}$$

The yields from different fissionable nuclei have been measured by several experimentalists[53,54]. The latest results of the fission yield from U^{236} have been obtained by H. Newson [54] and are shown in Fig. 13.11. It is quite clear from this figure that the fission of U^{235} by slow neutrons is completely asymmetric. Most of the fission products are divided into two groups, a light group, with mass number A from 85 to 104, and a heavy group, with mass number A from 130 to 149. These two groups account for 97 percent of the fission. The most probable type of fission corresponds to the two peaks in the two groups. The mass numbers of these two are 95 and 139 and occur in about 7 percent of the total fission. The other small peaks near the maxima are due to the shell-model effects.

Almost identical yield curves are obtained from the fission of U^{233} and Pu^{239} by thermal neutrons (as shown in Fig. 13.11). At these neutron energies the fission is asymmetric, and the symmetric fission, division into two equal fragments, takes place in less than 0.01 percent of the fissions. In almost all the cases, as the energy of the incident neutrons, or the charged particles causing fission, is increased, the fission becomes more and more symmetrical[55]. For example, with 100-Mev neutrons only one peak is observed for the distribution of fission fragments.

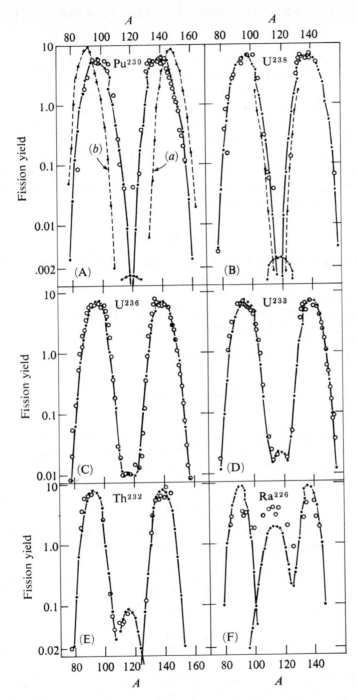

FIG. 13.11 Fission mass-yield curves for different fissionable nuclei. [From Newson, H. W., *Phys. Rev.*, **122**, 1224, (1961).]

In order to get some idea of the energy release in a fission process, consider the following: The binding energy per nucleon for U^{235} is about 7.6 Mev. The average binding energy of the fission fragments is about 8.5 Mev/nucleon. Thus the energy released in a single fission is $\sim 2 \times 118 \times 8.5 - 236 \times 7.6 \simeq 212$ Mev. More careful calculations show it to be about 200 Mev. This energy appears in the form of kinetic energy of fission fragments, kinetic energy of fission neutrons, γ-rays emitted in the fission, β- and γ-decay energies, and the energy taken away by the neutrinos. The distribution of this energy is shown in Table 13.6, and it shows that most of the energy is taken away by the fission fragments.

TABLE 13.6

ENERGY RELEASE IN THE FISSION OF U^{235} BY THERMAL NEUTRONS

1. kinetic energy of fission fragments	162 Mev
2. kinetic energy of fission neutrons (2.5 neutrons per fission each carry 2 Mev on the average)	5 Mev
3. prompt γ-rays	7 Mev
4. β^-- and γ^--decay energies (5 Mev each)	10 Mev
5. neutrinos energy	11 Mev
total energy per fission	195 Mev

The measurements of the energy distribution of the fission fragments from the fission of U^{233}, U^{235}, and Pu^{239} by thermal neutrons has been made by several experimentalists[56,57,58,59]. Assuming that the nucleus undergoing fission is initially at rest, the conservation of momentum gives

$$M_1 V_1 = M_2 V_2 \qquad (13.26)$$

where M_1, M_2 are the masses and V_1, V_2 are the velocities of the two fission fragments, respectively. The energies of the fission fragments are given by

$$\frac{E_1}{E_2} = \frac{\frac{1}{2} M_1 V_1^2}{\frac{1}{2} M_2 V_2^2} \qquad (13.27)$$

Combining Eqs. (13.26) and (13.27), we get

$$\frac{E_1}{E_2} = \frac{M_2}{M_1} \qquad (13.28)$$

Thus the kinetic energies of the fission fragments are inversely proportional to their masses. Experimental measurements have been made using single or back-to-back ionization chambers. The results obtained are shown in Fig. 13.12[59]. As is clear from this figure, the distribution is asymmetric. Again, as the energy of the incident neutrons increases the distribution becomes increasingly symmetric.

The velocity distribution of the fission fragments has been carried out by R. Leachman[60] by using a time-of-flight method. From the velocity distribution one can easily calculate the kinetic energies of the fission fragments. The results obtained are slightly higher (167 Mev) than those obtained with ionization chamber measurements (155 Mev).

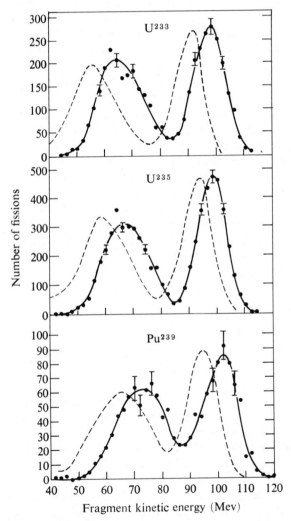

FIG. 13.12 Energy distribution of fission fragments produced in the fission of U^{233}, U^{235}, and Pu^{239}. [From Stein, W. E., *Phys. Rev.*, **108**, 94, (1957).]

C. NEUTRON EMISSION. As mentioned earlier, 2.5 neutrons, on the average, are emitted per fission. This is obvious from the fact that the two complementing fission fragments of U^{235} add up to a mass number of about 233 instead of 236. The average number of neutrons emitted per fission is denoted by v. The value of v has been measured for different fissionable materials for various neutron energies[61]. When the fission of U^{233}, U^{235}, and Pu^{239} is caused by thermal neutrons, the average value of v is 2.5, 2.44, and 2.9 respectively. The value of v for these and other fissionable materials increases with increasing neutron energy. The neutrons emitted in fission can be divided into two categories: prompt neutrons and delayed neutrons.

1. Prompt Neutrons. Prompt neutrons are those that are emitted within a very short interval after the fission takes place, say less than 10^{-14} sec. The prompt neutrons account for more than 99 percent of the total neutrons emitted in fission. The indications are that these neutrons are emitted from the fission fragments and not directly in the fission process. This is possible because the fission fragments are very unstable due to a high neutron-to-proton ratio and the availability of excess energy for neutron emission.

The energy distribution of the neutrons from the thermal neutron fission of U^{235} has been made[62,63,64]. It has been found that the neutrons are emitted with energies from a few kev to about 20 Mev. The neutron spectrum obtained from the measurements of D. Hill[63] and B. Watt[64] is shown in Fig. 13.13. The neutron intensity is maximum at about 0.075 Mev and decreases exponentially beyond 2 Mev. An empirical theoretical expression that fits the experimental data from 75 kev to about 20 Mev is given by Watt's formula, i.e.,

$$N(E) \, dE = A \, e^{-E} \sinh \sqrt{2E} \, dE \qquad (13.29)$$

where $N(E) \, dE$ is the fraction of neutrons with energies between (E and $E + dE$), and A is the constant given by

$$A = \sqrt{\frac{2\pi}{e}} \qquad (13.30)$$

The average neutron energy is about (2.0 ± 0.1) Mev. The same types of neutron spectrum and average neutron energy have been obtained for the fission of Pu^{239} by thermal neutrons.

2. Delayed Neutrons. Only about 0.64 percent of the total fission neutrons are delayed neutrons. These are called delayed neutrons because they are emitted with decreasing intensity for several minutes. Though the delayed neutrons form a very small fraction of the total neutrons emitted in fission, they play a very important part in the control of nuclear reactors. Because of their significant role, the characteristics of the delayed neutrons have been investigated in detail[65,66]. All the fissionable nuclei U^{233}, U^{235}, U^{238}, Pu^{239}, and Th^{232} seem to emit six groups of delayed neutrons with

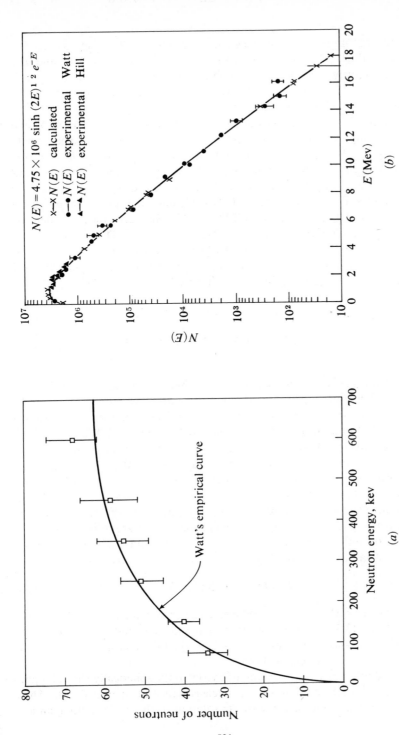

$N(E) = 4.75 \times 10^6 \sinh (2E)^{1/2} e^{-E}$ calculated

x—x $N(E)$ experimental Watt

●—● $N(E)$ experimental Hill

▲—▲ $N(E)$

(b)

(a)

FIG. 13.13 Energy distribution of the fission neutrons from 0.1 Mev to 17 Mev. [From: Watt, B. E., *Phys. Rev.*, **87**, 1037, (1952).]

respective half-lives of 0.2 sec, 0.6 sec, 2.1 sec, 5.6 sec, 22 sec, and 55 sec. The energies of the last five groups of neutrons are 0.42, 0.45, 0.41, 0.46, and 0.25 Mev, respectively. The intensity of different groups depends upon the type of fission nuclei. Three additional delayed neutron groups have been found[67] with extremely small intensities.

The two long-lived groups of delayed neutrons with half-lives of 55 and 22 sec are important for reactor control. The 55 sec group is associated with the decay of $_{35}Br^{87}$ produced in fission. Most of Br^{87} decays by β^- emission and γ-decay to the ground state of $_{36}Kr^{87}$. A small fraction (~ 2 percent) of the β^- decay of $_{35}Br^{87}$ leaves $_{36}Kr^{87}$ in the excited state. In this state the emission of a neutron is energetically possible and takes place with a half-life of 55 sec, i.e., with the β^- decay half-life of Br^{87}. Similarly, the 22 sec neutron group is the result of the decay of the 22 sec half-life I^{137}. The end products in the two cases are Kr^{86} and Ye^{136} both of which correspond to closed shells of 50 and 82 neutrons, respectively. Thus neutron emission takes place because of the one loosely bound excess neutron outside the closed shell.

8. THEORY OF FISSION

There is no theory in existence at present that can explain all the different aspects of fission, especially asymmetric fission. Many features can be explained by the liquid-drop model of the nucleus. The theory of fission is based on the liquid-drop model developed by N. Bohr and J. Wheeler[68] and, independently, by S. Frankel and N. Metropolis[69]. Since then many improvements on the model have been made that help to the understanding of fission process[70,71,72,73,74,75]. We shall briefly explain how the theory based on this model predicts fission.

In the ground state of the nucleus, the liquid drop is perfectly spherical. The two terms in the semiempirical mass formula that are responsible for the shape of the nucleus are the surface tension and the coulomb repulsion. For a nucleus of radius R, the total energy due to these two terms is

$$E = 4\pi R^2 O + 3Z^2 e^2/5R \qquad (13.31)$$

where O is the surface tension coefficient. The coulomb repulsion, the second term in Eq. (13.31), causes distortion of the nucleus and tries to deform its shape, but the surface tension effect overcomes this repulsion and keeps the nucleus in a perfectly spherical shape.

An addition of a small amount of energy to the spherically-shaped liquid-drop causes its deformation, and the nucleus is then in an excited state. These low lying excited states are due to the rotation of the nucleus along an axis perpendicular to its axis of symmetry. Mathematically, the deformed shape of the nucleus is represented by

$$R(\theta) = R_0[1 + a_1 P_1(\cos \theta) + a_2 P_2(\cos \theta) + ...] \qquad (13.32a)$$

or, by neglecting higher terms

$$R(\theta) = R_0[1 + a_2 P_2(\cos \theta)] \qquad (13.32b)$$

where $R(\theta)$ and θ are as defined in Fig. 13.14, and a_2 is a constant that is a function of the degree of deformation of the otherwise spherical nucleus of radius R_0. The first odd term $a_1 P_1(\cos \theta)$ has been omitted because it represents only the translation motion of the nucleus while the terms higher than $a_2 P_2$ $(\cos \theta)$ are unimportant for a low degree of excitation. Once the nucleus is excited, it can take different deformed shapes for different values of a_2 as shown in Fig. 13.14. The absorption of a neutron by a fissionable nucleus may lead to different deformed shapes in the sequence from (a) to (b) to (c) to (d). In (d), the shape is that which the nucleus may take for a sufficiently high degree of excitation. If, however, the surface tension is still more than coulomb repulsion, the nucleus will return to its original spherical shape and the extra energy is given out in the form of a gamma ray. This process is called neutron capture. Otherwise, the coulomb repulsion may lead to the breakdown of the drop as shown in Fig. 13.14(e), provided the repulsion is more than the surface tension attraction. Thus this leads to a symmetric fission. The probability of fission is a function of neutron energy as well as the type of the nucleus.

It can be shown that fission will not only be spontaneous, but instantaneous as well for nuclei for which the surface-tension effect is equal to or less than the coulomb repulsion. This happens for

$$Z^2/A > 50$$

i.e., for nuclei with $A > 390$ and $Z > 140$. For U^{238}, $Z^2/A = 36$, and the fission is certainly not instantaneous. The natural fission of U^{238} is due to the tunneling effect.

It is easy now to understand why some nuclei undergo fission by thermal neutrons while others do so by fast neutrons only. The potential energy of the drop for different degrees of deformation has been calculated[68,71] according to the Bohr-Wheeler theory. The plots of E_p, the potential energy, and R, the separation or deformation, for different types of nuclei are shown in Fig. 13.15. Curve (a) belongs to nuclei of the type with $A \sim 100$, curve (b) to $A \sim 235$, and curve (c) to $A \sim 390$. These curves can be understood more easily if we consider the process that is the reverse of fission. Suppose the nucleus (Z, A) has undergone fission and produced two fragments (Z_1, A_1) and (Z_2, A_2). The potential energy between these two fragments, which are spherical in shape, is zero when $R = \infty$ and increases as they are brought

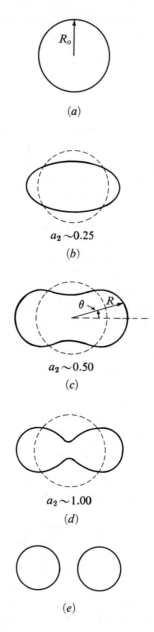

$a_2 \sim 0.25$

$a_2 \sim 0.50$

$a_2 \sim 1.00$

FIG. 13.14 Different shapes of the fissionable nucleus for different degrees of excitation, according to the liquid-drop model.

together. The coulomb energy E_c between the two drops when they are just touching is given by

$$E_c = \frac{Z_1 Z_2 e^2}{R_1 + R_2} \qquad (13.33)$$

If the drops are brought still closer, the potential energy is a complicated function of coulomb and surface tension. The variation of E_p between $R = 0$ and $R = R_1 + R_2$ depends on the type of the nucleus as shown in

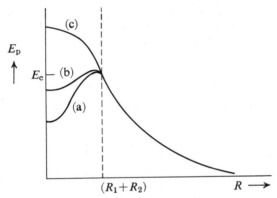

FIG. 13.15 Variation of potential energy of two fission fragments as a function of the distance between their centers.

Fig. 13.15 for three different cases. The nuclei of the type (a) lie about 50 Mev below E_c, the type (b) are about 6 Mev below E_c, and the type (c) lie above E_c and will undergo spontaneous fission. The type (b) are the nuclei such as U, Pu, or Th and need a few Mev energies to undergo fission. The energy needed by a nucleus to undergo fission is called the *activation energy* and is equal to $E_c - E_0$ where E_0 is defined as the energy of the compound nucleus formed by the capture of a neutron in the ground state, i.e.,

$$E_0 = [M(A, Z) - M(A_1, Z_1) - M(A_2, Z_1)]c^2 \qquad (13.34)$$

E_0 does not include the excitation energy resulting from the capture of a neutron. Now it can be made clear why some nuclei may undergo fission by the capture of thermal neutrons. In those cases the excitation energy resulting from the capture of slow neutrons (thus forming a compound nucleus in the excited state) is more than the activation energy, and, therefore, fission will take place. If the excitation energy is less than the activation energy, fast neutrons are used to make up for this difference in order to cause fission.

In order to explain asymmetric fission and some other properties of fission, two different approaches, one using shell-model effects[73] and the other using the collective model[72] have been applied.

PROBLEMS

1. Calculate the energy of neutrons produced in the forward direction by the following reactions if the energy of the incident deuterons is zero

    He^3 (d, n) He^4, Be^9 (d, n) B^{10}, C^{12}, (d, n) N^{13}.

2. Li^7 is bombarded by 3 Mev protons. What is the energy of the neutrons v̵...cn are emitted in this reaction and observed at (a) $45°$, (b) $90°$ and (c) $135°$ to the direction of the incident proton?

3. Calculate the energy of the deuteron beam necessary to produce 20 Mev neutrons in the forward direction by bombarding triton at rest.

4. Neutrons are produced by the reaction

    $$_1H^2 + d \rightarrow {}_2He^3 + n + 3.28 \text{ Mev}$$

    If the energy of the deuteron is increased from E_d to $E_d + \Delta E_d$ the neutron energy increases from E_n to $E_n + \Delta E_n$. Calculate the value of $\dfrac{\Delta E_n}{\Delta E_d}$ as a function of angle of emission of the neutrons.

5. Many (p, n) reactions are used for producing low energy neutrons. Show that minimum energy of the emitted neutron is given by $(E_n)_{min} = E_t/(A + 1)^2$, where E_t is the threshold energy and A is the mass number of the target.

6. A BF_3 counter 10 inches long and $\frac{1}{2}$ inch diameter and filled with BF_3 at 20 cm Hg is placed at a distance of 1 m from a neutron source. The overall efficiency of this detector is 2 percent. If the counter is reading 30, 500 counts per minute, what is the neutron flux? Also calculate the source strength, i.e., neutrons produced by the source per second.

7. Derive a mathematical expression to be used for calculating thermal neutron flux by activation analysis.

8. Show that in time of flight method the relation between E and t is given by

    $$E = 51.5 \times 10^2/t^2$$

9. If in a given experiment, the flight path is equal to 10 meters, what is the time interval between the arrival of neutrons of (a) 0.1 ev and 10 ev, (b) 10 ev and 10 Kev, (c) 10 Kev and 1 Mev, (d) 1 Mev and 10 Mev? Suppose the circuit used for time resolution has capability of 10^{-8} second, what should be the minimum flight path?

10. In measuring the neutron energy by crystal spectrometer, the uncertainty $\Delta\theta$ in the Bragg angle produces uncertainty in the energy. Show that the fractional uncertainty $\dfrac{\Delta E}{E}$ in energy is given by

    $$\frac{\Delta E}{E} = 2 \text{ Cot } \theta\Delta\theta \frac{2\Delta\theta}{\theta} \approx k\Delta\theta\sqrt{E}$$

    where k is a constant.

11. The reflecting planes in a crystal are Å apart. What are the Bragg's angles for the first order reflection of neutrons with energies 0.1 ev, 1 ev, 5 ev, and 10 ev. If the minimum angle which may be measured is 25 minutes, what is the maximum energy of the neutrons which may be diffracted?

12. In Problem 10, plot the fractional uncertainty $\frac{\Delta E}{E}$ for different energy neutrons if $\Delta\theta \approx 10'$?

13. What maximum energy neutrons may be filtered through a grating with spacing of 2.1Å between the reflecting planes?

14. Calculate the surface energies and coulomb energies of the following nuclei

$$U^{234}, U^{236}, Pu^{240}$$

Does this give any indication which nucleus will undergo fission easier than the others?

15. Calculate the binding energy of a thermal neutron added to the following nuclei

$$Th^{227}, U^{233}, U^{235}, Np^{236}, Pu^{239}, Pu^{242}, Cm^{240}.$$

Which of these will be easily fissionable by thermal neutrons?

16. The ratio of the masses of two fragments produced in the fission of U^{235} is 1.5. Calculate the ratio of their velocities.

17. One gram of U^{235} is completely fissioned by thermal neutrons. How much La^{139}, which is a stable end-product of the fission chain, will be produced?

18. A thermal neutron beam is incident on U^{235} sample. If ϕ is neutron flux and σ_f is the fission cross-section of U^{235}, calculate the yield of a nucleus $_zX^A$ if the chain yield of A is Y and the fractional yield for $_zX^A$ is Y.

19. For different values of a_2 [$a_2 = 0.1, 0.2, 0.3$] in Eq. (13.32b) draw the shape of the distorted nucleus.

20. Plot the shape of a distorted nucleus according to

$$R(\theta) = R_0[1 + a_2P_2(\cos\theta) + a_4P_4(\cos\theta)]$$

where a_4 is about 20% of a_2, and compare the results with Problem 19?

REFERENCES

1. Chadwick, J., *Proc. Roy. Soc.*, **A-136**, p. 692, (1932).
2. Dee, P. I., *Proc. Roy. Soc.*, **A-136**, p. 727 (1932).
3. General Electric Company, "*Chart of Nuclides*," Seventh Edition, 1964. Prepared by David T. Goldman.
4. Snell, A. H., and L. C. Miller, *Phys. Rev.*, **74**, p. 1217, (1948).
5. Snell, A. H., F. Pleasonton, and R. V. McCord, *Phys. Rev.*, **78**, p. 310, (1950).
6. Robson, J. M., *Phys. Rev.*, **78**, 311, (1950); **81**, 297, (1951); **83**, p. 349, (1951).
7. Sosnovskii, Spivak, Prokof'ev, Kutikov and Dobrynn; *Expt. Theoret. Phys.* (USSR), **35**, p. 1059, (1958).
8. Anderson, H. L., *Neutrons from Alpha-Emitters*, Preliminary Report No. 3 in Nuclear Science Series, Washington, D. C., National Research Council, 1948.
9. Anderson, H. L., and B. T. Feld, *Rev. Sc. Instr.*, **18**, p. 186, (1947).

10. Feld, B. T., *Experimental Nuclear Physics*, Vol. II, Part VII, New York: John S. Wiley & Sons, 1953.

11. Wattenberg, A., *Photo Neutron Sources*, Preliminary Report No. 6 in Nuclear Science Series. Washington, D.C., National Research Council, 1949.

12. Wattenberg, A., *Phys. Rev.*, **71**, p. 497, (1947).

13. Russell, B., D. Sacks, A. Wattenberg, and R. Fields, *Phys. Rev.*, **73**, p. 545, (1948).

14. Hanson, A. O., *Phys. Rev.*, **75**, p. 1794, (1949).

15. Hanson, A. O., and R. F. Taschek, *Monoenergetic Neutrons from Charged Particle Reactions*. Preliminary Report No. 4 in Nuclear Science Series. Washington, D.C., National Research Council, 1948.

16. Hanson, A. O., R. F. Taschek, and J. H. Williams, *Revs. Mod. Phys.*, **21**, p. 635, (1949).

17. Serber, R., *Phys. Rev.*, **72**, p. 1008, (1947).

18. Hughes, D. J., and R. B. Schwartz, *Neutron Cross Sections*, Brookhaven Report BNL-325, (1955).

19. Dilworth, C. C., S. J. Goldsack, Y. Goldsmith-Clermont, and F. Levy, *Phil. Mag.*, **41**, p. 1032, (1950).

20. Frisch, D. H., *Phys. Rev.*, **70**, p. 589, (1946).

21. *Nuclear Spectroscopy*, Part A, p. 365, New York: Academic Press, 1960.

22. Hanson, A. O., and J. L. McKibben, *Phys. Rev.*, **72**, p. 673, (1947).

23. Nobles, R. A., R. B. Day, R. L. Henkel, G. A. Jarvis, R. P. Kutarnia, J. L. McKibben, J. E. Perry, Jr., and R. K. Smith, *Rev. Sci. Inst.*, **25**, p. 334, (1954).

24. Feld, B. T., *Experimental Nuclear Physics*, ed., E. Segrè, Vol. II, Part VIII, p. 404, New York: John S. Wiley & Sons, 1953.

25. *Chart of Nuclides*, General Electric Company, Seventh Edition (1964).

26. Ajzenberg, F., and T. Lauritsen, *Revs. Mod. Phys.*, **24**, p. 321, (1952).

27. Alvarex, L. W., *Phys. Rev.*, **54**, p. 486, (1938).

28. Fertel, G. E. F., P. B. Moon, G. P. Thomson, and C. E. Wynn-Williams, *Nature*, **142**, p. 829, (1938).

29. Milatz, J. M. W., and D. Th. J. ter Horst, *Physica*, **5**, p. 796, (1938).

30. Rainwater, L. J., *Encyclopedia of Physics*, **40**, p. 373, (1957).

31. Batchelor, R., and J. H. Towle, *Proc. Phys. Soc.*, **73**, p. 307, (1959).

32. Seidl, F. G. P., D. J. Hughes, H. Palevsky, J. S. Levin, W. Y. Kato, and N. G. Sjöstrand, *Phys. Rev.*, **95**, p. 476, (1954).

33. Fermi, E., J. Marshall, and L. Marshall, *Phys. Rev.*, **72**, p. 193, (1947).

34. Hughes, D. J., *Scientific American*, p. 219, (1953).

35. Elsasser, W. M., *Compt. Rend.*, **202**, p. 1029, (1936).

36. Wick, G. C., *Z. Physik.* **38**, p. 403, p. 689, (1937).

37. Fermi, E., and L. Marshall, *Phys. Rev.*, **71**, p. 666, (1947).

38. Mitchell, D. P., and P. N. Powers, *Phys. Rev.*, **50**, p. 486, (1936).

39. Halban, H., and P. Preiswerk, *Compt. Rend.*, **203**, p. 73, (1936).

40. Zinn, W. H., *Phys. Rev.*, **71**, p. 752, (1947).

41. Wollan, E. O., and C. G. Shull, *Nucleonics*, **3**, p. 8, (1948).

42. Shull, C. G., and E. O. Wollan, *Phys. Rev.*, **81**, p. 527, (1951).

43. Hahn, O., and F. Strassmann, *Naturwissenschaften*, **27**, p. 11, (1939).

44. Hahn, O., and F. Strassmann, *Naturwissenschaften*, **27**, p. 89, (1939).

45. Frisch, O. R., *Nature*, **143**, p. 276, (1939).

46. Anderson, H. L., E. J. Booth, J. R. Dunning, E. Fermi, G. N. Glasoe, and F. G. Slack, *Phys. Rev.*, **55**, p. 511, (1939).

47. Hughes, D. J., and R. B. Schwartz, *Neutron Cross Sections*, Brookhaven Report, BNL-325, Supplement 1, (1960).

48. Hughes, D. J., *Nucleonics*, **17, No. 11,** p. 132, (1959).

49. Lamphere, R. W., *Phys. Rev.*, **104**, p. 1654, (1956).

50. Jungerman, J., *Phys. Rev.*, **79**, p. 632, (1950).

51. Koch, H. W., J. McElhinney, and E. L. Gasteiger, *Phys. Rev.*, **77**, p. 329, (1950).

52. Issued by the Plutonium Project, prepared by J. M. Siegel; *Revs. Mod. Phys.*, **18**, p. 513, (1946).

53. Katcoff, S., *Nucleonics*, **16, No. IV,** p. 78, (1958).

54. Newson, H. W., *Phys. Rev.*, **122**, p. 1224, (1961).

55. Jungermann, J., and S. C. Wright, *Phys. Rev.*, **76**, p. 1112, (1949).

56. Fowler, J. L. and L. Rosen, *Phys. Rev.*, **72**, p. 914, (1947).

57. Brunton, D. C., and G. C. Hanna, *Phys. Rev.*, **77**, 213, (1950); *Can. J. Research*, **A28**, p. 190, (1950).

58. Brunton, D. C., and W. B. Thompson, *Can. J. Research*, **A26**, p. 498, (1950).

59. Stein, W. E., *Phys. Rev.*, **108**, p. 94, (1957).

60. Leachman, R. B., *Phys. Rev.*, **87**, p. 444, (1952).

61. *Proceedings of the Second United Nations International Conference on the Peaceful Uses of Atomic Energy*, Paper No. 2187, **Vol. XV**, p. 353, (1958); Paper No. 2467, **Vol. XV**, p. 229, (1958).

62. Bonner, T. W., R. A. Ferrell, and M. C. Rinehart, *Phys. Rev.*, **87**, p. 1032, (1952).

63. Hill, D. L., *Phys. Rev.*, **87**, p. 1034, (1952).

64. Watt, B. E., *Phys. Rev.*, **87**, p. 1037, (1952).

65. Hughes, D. J., J. Dabbs, A. Cahn, and D. Hall, *Phys. Rev.*, **73**, p. 111, (1948).

66. Keepin, G. R., T. E. Wimett, and R. K. Zeigler, *Phys. Rev.*, **107**, p. 1044, (1957).

67. Kunstadter, J. W., J. J. Floyd, and L. B. Borst, *Phys. Rev.*, **91**, p. 594, (1953).

68. Bohr, N., and J. A. Wheeler, *Phys. Rev.*, **56**, p. 426, (1939).

69. Frankel, S., and N. Metropolis, *Phys. Rev.*, **72**, p. 914, (1947).

70. Frenkel, J., *J. Phys. U.S.S.R.*, **1**, p. 125, (1939).

71. Frankel, S., and N. Metropolis, *Phys. Rev.*, **72**, p. 914, (1947).

72. Hill, D. L., and J. A. Wheeler, *Phys. Rev.*, **89**, p. 1102, (1953).

73. Fong, P., *Phys. Rev.*, **102**, p. 434, (1956).

74. Halpern, I., *Ann. Revs. Nucl. Sci.*, **9**, p. 245, (1959).

75. Walton, G. N., *Quart. Revs.*, **XV**, p. 71, (1961).

SUGGESTIONS FOR FURTHER READING

1. Feld, B. T., *Experimental Nuclear Physics*, ed., E. Segrè, Vol. II, Part VII, New York: John S. Wiley & Sons, 1953.
2. Curtiss, L. F., *Introduction to Neutron Physics*, New York: D. Van Nostrand Company, Inc., 1959.
3. *The Encyclopedia of Physics* (*Handbuch der Physik*), Vol. 38, part 2, pp. 1–659, Berlin: Springer Verlag, 1959.
4. Bacon, G. E., *Neutron Diffraction*, Oxford: Clarendon Press, 1955.
5. Hughes, D. J., *Neutron Optics*, New York: Interscience Publishers, 1954.
6. Halpern, I., *Ann. Revs. Nucl. Sci.*, **9**, 245, (1959).
7. Frisch, O. R., *Progress in Nuclear Physics*, Vol. II, Oxford: Pergamon Press Ltd., 1952.
8. *Proceedings of the Symposium on the Physics of Fission*, (held at Chalk River, Ontario, May 1956) Chalk River, Ontario: Atomic Energy of Canada, Ltd. Report AECL–329, July, 1956.

XIV

PARTICLE ACCELERATORS AND NUCLEAR REACTORS

1. INTRODUCTION

Particle accelerators and nuclear reactors have developed to the extent that they may be no longer considered a part of nuclear physics. More correctly, their design may be considered as part of a branch of a service technology allied with nuclear physics. Because these machines provide probes for the investigation of nuclear structures, it is worthwhile to review the technology briefly. The development of particle accelerators has not only provided physicists with higher and higher energies, it has, in addition, opened a new field, particle physics. As we shall see in Chapter XV, the study of particle physics is basic to the exploration of the structure of nuclear matter.

The term "nuclear reactors" has been used commonly to mean fission nuclear reactors, but, actually, both fission as well as fusion reactors fall into this category. Fusion reactors, though not very successful at the present time, may become a major source of power in the near future. Fission reactors have already been successful in generating large amounts of power for industrial use. Fission reactors are used in nuclear physics to provide intense beams of slow neutrons and gamma rays. These, in turn, have been used in studying nuclear reactions and in the making of radioisotopes. The study of radioisotopes has provided us with the energy-level diagrams of a large number of isotopes, and radioisotopes have been used in medical treatment, as well as in tracer techniques.

2. DEVELOPMENT OF ACCELERATORS

The relation of an accelerator to a nuclear physicist is the same as that of a telescope to an astronomer or a microscope to a biologist. All through the text we have mentioned the use of these machines for the investigation of different aspects of nuclear structure, and it is unnecessary to emphasize once again the role of these accelerators.

The first use of high energy particles (α particles obtained from Po) was made by Geiger and Marsden in α-scattering experiments, which resulted in the establishment of the nuclear atom by Lord Rutherford in 1911. J. Cockcroft and E. Walton[1], on the instigation of Rutherford, developed a voltage multiplier that was successfully used in 1932 in accelerating protons and causing the first artificial transmutation. Within a few months a new machine, the cyclotron, that accelerated protons up to 1 Mev was developed by E. Lawrence and M. Livingston[2] at the University of California. Since then there has been great enthusiasm, except for a brief interruption during World War II, for the development of higher energy accelerators. In order to resolve the internal structure of a nucleus (or a nucleon) the wave length associated with the probe particle must be smaller than that of the structure to be resolved, a condition similar to that in optics. For example, the effective potential range of a proton or a neutron is $\sim 5 \times 10^{-14}$ cm; the wave length of an incident particle intended to probe the proton or neutron should be smaller than this. A wave length associated with a nucleon of 1 Gev ($= 10^9$ ev $= 1000$ Mev) is 1.1×10^{-14} cm.

The development of machines capable of producing high energy particles has resulted in the discovery of new particles like mesons (a particle of mass between an electron and a nucleon), hyperons (mass greater than a nucleon), antiprotons, antineutrons, and many others. Fig. 14.1[3] shows the tremendous development of accelerators that has taken place since 1930. Accelerators may be divided into the following four categories, each of which utilizes a different principle: direct-voltage accelerators, resonance accelerators, synchronous accelerators, and alternating-gradient accelerators. The only machine that has not been included in this list is the betatron. This is used for producing fast electrons, which, in turn, are used for producing high energy X-rays.

Fig. 14.2 shows the different types of machines that have been developed under each category. In the following sections we shall discuss these accelerators briefly.

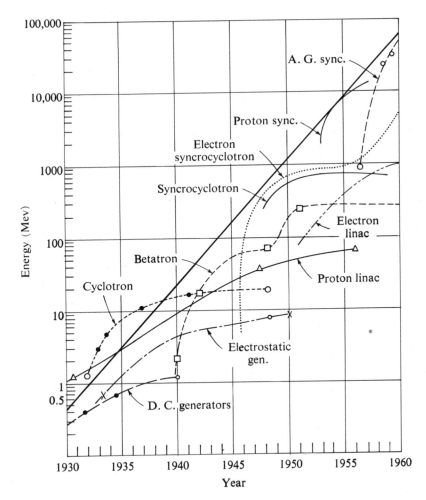

FIG. 14.1 Energies achieved by different types of accelerators since 1930. [From: Livingston, M. S., and J. P. Blewett, *Particle Accelerators*, p. 6. New York: McGraw-Hill Book Co., Inc. (1962).]

3. DIRECT-VOLTAGE ACCELERATOR

Direct voltage, or high voltage d.c., accelerators are presently more numerous than any other type of accelerators. There are three essential parts of this accelerator. First, the ion source[4,5] consists of a discharge tube with a small hole in the cathode, through which a beam of positive ions may be obtained. If electrons are to be accelerated, a heated filament may be used. Second, an

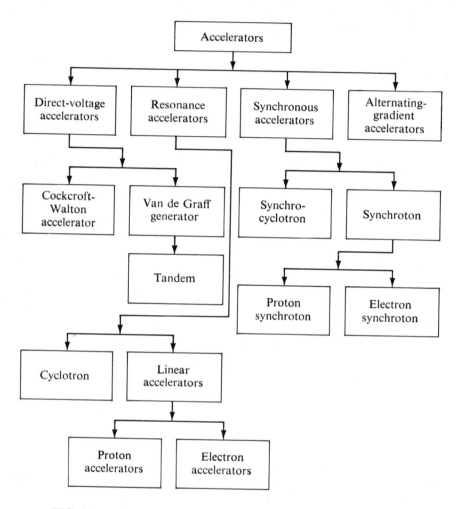

FIG. 14.2 A broad division of accelerators into different categories.

evacuated tube is provided, through which the particles are accelerated. At the end of the evacuated tube is placed a target to be bombarded. For obtaining a beam of uniform energy, usually a bending magnet is used for energy selection as shown in Fig. 14.3. Third, and most important, a source of high potential is included. If a particle of charge q is allowed to fall through a potential difference, ΔV, the kinetic energy, K, is given by

$$K = q \, \Delta V = Ze \, \Delta V \qquad (14.1)$$

where $q = Ze$, Z being the atomic number of the ion. Note that the final kinetic energy of the particle accelerated does not depend on the mass of the particle.

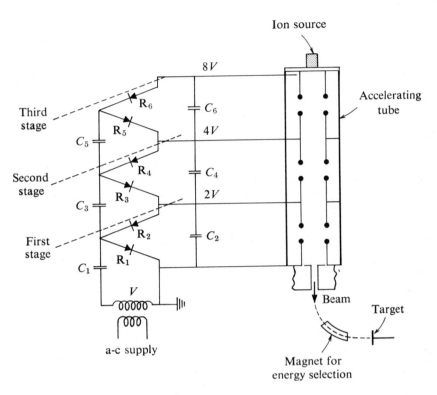

FIG. 14.3 A diagram of a Cockcroft-Walton accelerator.

A. COCKCROFT-WALTON GENERATOR.   A diagram of the apparatus used by Cockcroft and Walton is shown in Fig. 14.3. As a source of high potential difference, they used a voltage-multiplier circuit devised by H. Greinacher[6]. This circuit utilizes the principle in which the capacitors are charged in parallel and discharged in series, alternately, in order to multiply the voltage. The circuit consists of two stacks of series-connected capacitors C_1, C_3, C_5 ··· and C_2, C_4, C_6 ··· and a set of rectifiers R_1, R_2, R_3, ... connecting the two stacks of condensers in the manner shown in Fig. 14.3. As a result of the peak voltage, V, in the secondary coil of the transformer, the capacitor C_1 is charged to a potential, V, through R_1. Thus, during each cycle, the voltage across R_1 varies from 0 to $2V$. This voltage is applied to the circuit R_2C_2 resulting in the charging of capacitor C_2 to a voltage of $2V$. This process of mutiplication of voltage may be continued further, limited only by the breakdown of air between different components at high potentials. For n such stages, the potential achieved in the absence of a load is $2nV$.

In the first generator used by Cockcroft and Walton, protons were accelerated up to a voltage of 800 kev. These protons were utilized to study the reaction Li (p, α) He⁴. When operating in air, the practical upper voltage-limit for these generators is 1.5 Mev. By using gases under high pressure (at which they become insulators) the limit has been raised to about 2-Mev energies. These machines are commonly used for accelerating deuterons up to energies of ∼200 kev to ∼400 kev which, in turn, are used for producing neutrons by means of H^2 (d, n) He^3 and H^3 (d, n) He^4 reactions.

In addition to the voltage multiplier described, another type of circuit, called *cascade transformer*, has been developed by C. Lauritsen, *et al.*[7,8,9]

B. VAN DE GRAAFF ACCELERATOR.   This was the first machine that produced particles of energies greater than 1 Mev. The first 1.5-Mev Van de Graaff electrostatic generator was invented by R. Van de Graaff[10] in 1930. Many subsequent machines were constructed by Van de Graaff, *et al.*[11,12], R. Herb, *et al.*[13] and others[14,15]. Though the maximum attainable energy is only 10 Mev, it has many advantages over other machines. It can produce beams of high intensities (up to a few milliamperes), and it is very homogeneous in energies (up to 0.1 percent), highly stable, and easy to control. Another advantage is the absence of a ripple voltage, which is usually present in a Cockcroft-Walton generator.

The electrostatic generator is based on the principle that the charge resides on the outer surface of the conductor, irrespective of its potential. If a charged conductor is brought inside a hollow sphere (which may be at a higher potential), and the two are joined by means of a wire, the charge will flow from the conductor to the sphere. The practical form of this type of generator is shown in Fig. 14.4. A belt, B, of insulated fabric runs between two rollers, R and R'. A set of sharp spray points (corona points), S, is connected to the controllable spray voltage, P_1. The sharp points cause the ionization of the air and repel the positive ions. These positive ions are collected by the belt. The positive charges on the belt are collected by another set of sharp points, C, the collector points. These points convey the charge to the sphere, the high voltage terminal. By using a set of spray points, S', that spray negative charge, the charge-carrying capacity of the belt is doubled. The charge collection process at the high-potential terminal may be continued indefinitely. A limit is reached when the insulation breaks down and the loss of charge by corona currents is equal to the charge transferred by the belt. By filling the tank with air or nitrogen with 3 to 10 percent freon at very high pressure (∼15 atmospheres) and using insulators in small pieces, separated by corona rings, to support the high voltage terminal[13,14], protons have been accelerated up to about 8 Mev and currents up to about 100 μamperes have been obtained.

C. TANDEM VAN DE GRAAFF ACCELERATOR[16].   This is an ingenious modification of the conventional Van de Graaff generator in which particles may be

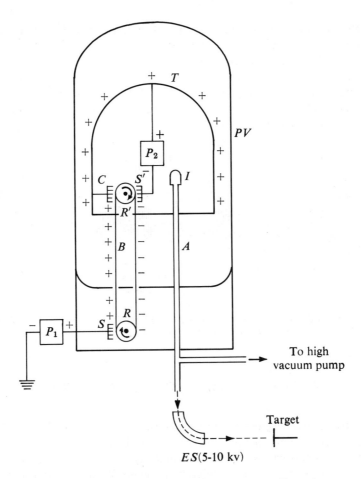

FIG. 14.4 A diagram of a typical Van de Graaff accelerator. P_1, P_2: controllable power supplies; S, S': spray points; C: collector points; T: high-voltage spherical terminal; I: ion source; PV: pressure vessel; A: accelerating tube; and ES: energy selector.

accelerated to energies twice as high as those in the conventional machines. Fig. 14.5 shows the tandem Van de Graaff machine. It consists of two insulating columns in one pressure tank. The common high-voltage terminal is charged by one belt as usual. The positive-ion source is replaced by a negative-ion source, produced by adding electrons to the positive ions outside the pressure vessel, as shown. These negative ions are accelerated to the positive high-potential terminal where they are stripped of their negative charge as well. These ions are now accelerated once again through the second column, the same as in the Van de Graaff machine. Thus, the ions are accelerated through voltages twice as high as in the conventional machine. Both ends of the tandem machine are at ground potential.

Protons have been accelerated to about 14 Mev with a tandem accelerator. The beam currents obtained are of the order of 1.5 μampere, which, though small, are sufficient for many precise studies. The latest design of this machine is the so-called "Emperor" tandem Van de Graaff accelerator, capable of accelerating protons to 20 Mev.

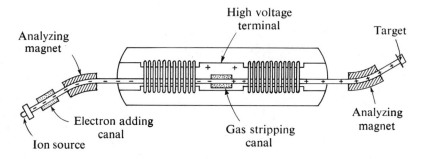

FIG. 14.5 A diagram of tandem Van de Graaff accelerator. [From R. J. Van de Graaff, *Nucl. Inst. and Methods*, **8**, 195, (1960).]

4. RESONANCE ACCELERATORS

The electrostatic generators previously described cannot be used to accelerate particles to very high energies because of the breakdown in the electrical insulation and corona discharge. This difficulty was overcome, however, by the discovery of an altogether different principle for accelerating particles. Particles are accelerated in steps, using the principle of resonance, by the repeated application of a relatively small voltage. This has led to the development of two different types of accelerators: the cyclic accelerator or cyclotron and the linear accelerator.

A. CYCLOTRON. The first cyclotron was constructed by E. Lawrence and M. Livingston[17] in 1932 by making use of the principle of magnetic resonance. A diagram of a typical cyclotron is shown in Fig. 14.6. A source, S, of positive ions, such as protons, deuterons, or alpha particles, is placed in the central region of the gap between two hollow metallic boxes, DD′, called *dees* because of their shape. The dees are connected to the terminals of an alternating high-frequency voltage, which produces an alternating field in the gap between the dees. When one dee is positive the other is negative, and vice versa. The dees are placed in an evacuated chamber, from which they are

FIG. 14.5   Model MP "Emperor" tandem Van de Graaff accelerator, rated to produce 20–Mev protons. (By courtesy of High Voltage Engineering Corporation.)

completely insulated. A uniform magnetic field is applied perpendicular to the whole cross-sectional area of the dees by placing the dees between the pole faces of a large magnet.

Suppose at the instant a positive ion is ejected from the source, S, D is positive and D′ is negative. The charge will be attracted towards D′ and, hence, accelerated across the gap. Once inside D′, it will not be influenced by

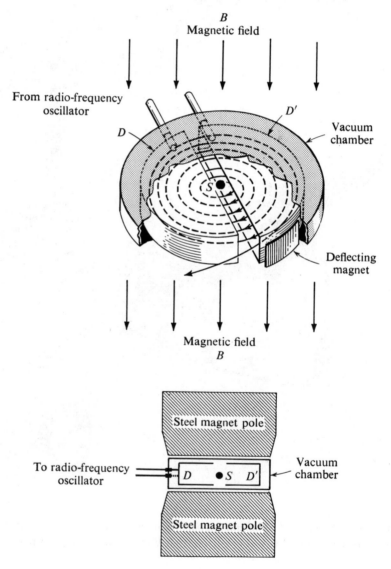

FIG. 14.6   A diagram of a typical cyclotron. (a) An outline sketch, (b) a side view.

the electric field because of the electrical shielding produced by the dees. However, the magnetic field will bend the path of the ion into a circular path. By
the time the ion is about to enter the gap again, if the frequency of the
alternating voltage is such that D is negative now and D' is positive, the ion
will be accelerated between the gap towards D. This process of acceleration
in steps continues every time the ion crosses the gap. As the velocity of the
ions increases, the magnetic field makes them move them into bigger and
bigger orbits. At the end, the ion beam is extracted from the chamber by
means of a deflecting magnet. The relation between the applied frequency of
the oscillator and the magnetic field may be obtained from simple considerations, as will be explained.

Suppose the positive ion of mass m and charge q is moving with velocity
v in a magnetic field of flux density B. The force acting on the ion is qvB. This
force is the centrifugal force mv^2/r, where r is the radius of the circular orbit.

$$qvB = mv^2/r$$

or

$$mv = qBr \tag{14.2}$$

The angular frequency, ω, the time period, T, for one revolution, and the
frequency, f, are given by the following relations.

$$\omega = v/r = qB/m \tag{14.3}$$

$$T = 2\pi/\omega = 2\pi m/qB \tag{14.4}$$

and

$$f = (1/2\pi)(q/m)B \tag{14.5}$$

Eq. (14.5) indicates that the frequency of circular motion is independent of
the velocity of the ions but that it depends upon the charge-to-mass ratio and
B. As the ions are accelerated between the gap, they attain higher velocities
and move in larger circular orbits. Every time the ions cross the gap, the orbit
size increases to a size given by Eq. (14.2). The resonance condition requires
that for the ions to be accelerated by the voltage applied to the dees, the
frequency of the alternating voltage must be the same as the natural resonance
frequency given by Eq. (14.5). If this condition is not satisfied, the ion will
get out of phase and may decelerate.

The maximum kinetic energy through which an ion may be accelerated in
a cyclotron depends upon B and the maximum radius, or the radius of the
dees, R, i.e.,

$$K_{max} = \tfrac{1}{2}mv_{max} = \tfrac{1}{2}(qBr_{max})^2/m$$

Because

$$r_{max} = R,$$

$$K_{max} = \tfrac{1}{2}(qBR)^2/m \tag{14.6}$$

In a typical cyclotron, for the maximum attainable flux density ($B \sim 2$ weber/m^2), the alternating voltage applied to the dees is ~ 200 kilovolts with an alternating frequency of ~ 10–12 megacycles per second. The diameter of the dees may be as large as 8 feet. This means the diameter of the pole faces will be also 8 feet, and the faces (iron) will weigh about 400 tons. The first cyclotron built by Lawrence and Livingston had 11-inch pole faces and produced 1.2-Mev protons. A later machine[18] with 60-inch pole faces produced 10-Mev protons, 20-Mev deuterons, and about 40-Mev alpha particles. The Oak Ridge National Laboratory 86-in cyclotron[19] produces 22-Mev protons. To achieve vertical stability and the focusing of the beam, the magnets are constructed in such a way that the field decreases by ~ 3 percent radially. This effect is called shimming. Though the energies obtained from the cyclotron are higher than those of the Van de Graaff generator, the beam intensity in the former is much lower, and the energy resolution is poor.

The upper limit to the energy obtainable from a cyclotron is due to relativistic effects and was first pointed out by H. Bethe and M. Rose[20] in 1937. According to Eq. (14.5), for low velocities the frequency is independent of the mass of the ion. However, at higher velocities the frequency takes the following form:

$$f = \frac{1}{2\pi} \frac{q}{m_0} \sqrt{1 - \frac{v^2}{c^2}} \, B \tag{14.7}$$

Thus, as the particles accelerate, their resonant frequency becomes lower. In order for the particles to arrive at the right time to be accelerated between the gap, the frequency of the voltage applied to the dees should decrease proportionately. The other alternative is to have a radially increasing magnetic flux, B. These possibilities were not recognized until the discovery of the phase-stability principle discussed in Sec. 14.5. The maximum proton energies obtainable from the cyclotron, ignoring relativistic effects, is ~ 22 Mev for protons. The cyclotron cannot be used for the acceleration of electrons because the relativistic change in mass becomes appreciable at very low energies (~ 0.51 Mev).

B. LINEAR ACCELERATORS[21,22,23]. As the name indicates, linear accelerators accelerate particles in straight-line paths using the principle of resonance. The principle of resonance was suggested by G. Ising[24] in 1924 and was tested on a small scale model by R. Wideröe[25] in 1925. The first successful linear accelerator, which was limited to the acceleration of very heavy ions such as mercury, was developed by D. Sloan and E. Lawrence[26]. Because of the tremendous difference between the masses of a proton and an electron, the construction of a proton accelerator is basically different from an electron accelerator.

1. Proton Accelerators. A diagram of a proton linear-accelerator is shown in Fig. 14.7. It consists of a large vacuum tank, along the axis of which are placed a number of cylindrical metal tubes as shown. These are called *drift tubes*. The odd-numbered drift tubes are connected to one terminal of the radio-frequency oscillator, while the even-numbered tubes are connected to each other. Suppose that when a beam of positive ions leaves tube 1, tube 2 is negative. The ions traversing the gap between 1 and 2 will, therefore, be accelerated. Once inside the tube, the ions are shielded, and thus they move with uniform velocity. If the length of the drift tube is such that the ions take

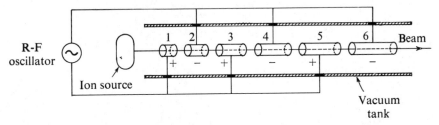

FIG. 14.7   A diagram of a proton linear accelerator. (Drift tube accelerator.)

the same time to travel the length of the tube as that required for the oscillator to change its polarity, tube 3 will be negative by the time ions leave tube 2. The ions will be accelerated once again across the gap. As the ions are accelerated, they move faster through the drift tubes. Because the frequency of the oscillator is fixed, the drift tubes must be of increasing length, so that the ions will cross each gap at the correct time. Let the velocity of the ions in the nth tube be v_n. The frequency of the oscillator is f, corresponding to time period τ and wave length λ. The length L_n of the nth drift tube is given as follows:

$$L_n = v_n(\tau/2) = v_n/2f = v_n\lambda/2c = \beta_n(\lambda/2) \qquad (14.8)$$

where $\beta_n = v_n/c$. If the applied voltage is V_0 (which is slightly less than the oscillator maximum output voltage), the velocity of the proton after crossing the nth gap is given by the following:

$$\tfrac{1}{2}Mv_n^2 = neV_0 \qquad (14.9)$$

Combining Eqs. (14.8) and (14.9), we obtain

$$L_n = \lambda\left(\frac{neV_0}{2Mc^2}\right)^{\tfrac{1}{2}} \qquad (14.10)$$

After the ions have reached velocities near the velocity of light, the lengths of the drift tubes become almost constant for further acceleration. Also Eq. (14.9) must be modified to take into account the relativistic change in mass.

FIG. 14.7 Overall view of the linear accelerator (linac) at Brookhaven National Laboratory. The linac boosts the energy of protons to 50 Mev and then injects them into the main alternating gradient synchroton accelerating ring. (By courtesy of Brookhaven National Laboratory.)

The first accelerator of Sloan and Lawrence[26] produced 2.9-Mev mercury ions. Further development of the linear ion accelerator was temporarily stopped because of the unavailability of very high frequency oscillators. However, after World War II, very high radio-frequency oscillators became available through the development of radar. This led to the construction of higher-energy ion accelerators using oscillators of the order of 200 megacycles per second. Modern linear accelerators, for example, the so-called proton *linac*, use the principle of cavity resonators. This is achieved by surrounding the drift tubes by a large coaxial cylinder with conducting walls. Standing electromagnetic waves are established in this large resonant cavity, and this has high efficiency in developing potentials between successive drift tubes. The largest linac at the University of Minnesota produces 68-Mev protons. In most of the high energy accelerators, protons are preaccelerated to a few Mev before entering the drift tube. This eliminates the necessity of having the first few drift tubes of very short lengths.

Focusing of the beam is always important in the accelerators. In linear accelerators it is done by applying one of two methods. One method is to place a wire grid at the entrance of each drift tube. The alternative method is to locate focusing magnets inside each drift tube. The first method is cheaper, but has the disadvantage of losing ions by scattering.

2. Electron Accelerators. Electrons accelerated to 2 Mev achieve a velocity very close to the velocity of light, i.e., 0.98 c. For further acceleration of electrons, therefore, the spacing between accelerating gaps is almost constant. This spacing will be very small if use is made of a very high radio-frequency oscillator such as the L-band (1200 megacycles per second) and S-band (2855 megacycles per second). This reduces the overall size of the electron accelerator by a large factor when compared to the proton accelerator.

The design of a linear electron accelerator is based on the traveling wave established inside resonant cavities, as contrasted to standing waves for a proton linac. The drift tubes are completely eliminated in an electron linear accelerator. It consists of a circular waveguide loaded with metallic annular discs as shown in Fig. 14.8. An electromagnetic wave travels along the axis of the tube. In order to reduce the phase velocity of the wave to that of the electrons, diaphragms are spaced at about one-third wave-length intervals. The

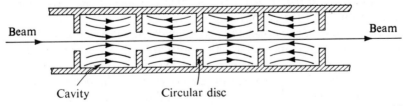

FIG. 14.8 A diagram of an electron linear accelerator (traveling wave guide accelerator).

electrons can be imagined as riding on the advancing wave front of the electromagnetic wave as surf riders ride on a water wave; see Fig. 14.8.

Many electron linear-accelerators based on this principle have been developed. The accelerators at Stanford University and in the U.S.S.R. both produce 100 Mev electrons and have lengths of 79 and 100 m, respectively. A 20 Gev (1 Gev or 1 Bev = 1000 Mev) electron accelerator is under construction at Stanford University and will have a length of 3000 m. All these accelerators use S-band frequencies.

5. SYNCHRONOUS ACCELERATORS

We showed in a previous section that the maximum energy to which a particle may be accelerated in cyclic accelerators is limited because of the relativistic increase in the mass. This limit is reached for protons at 22 Mev. If the

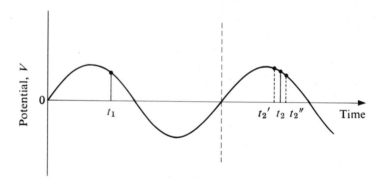

FIG. 14.9   Principle of phase stability.

particles are to be accelerated to a higher energy, in order to maintain the resonance condition it becomes necessary to decrease the applied frequency slowly or to increase the field (Eq. 14.7). The application of these methods to accelerate charged particles to very high energies was made possible by the discovery, made independently by V. Veksler[27], in the U.S.S.R., and by E. McMillan[28], in the United States, of the principle of *phase stability*, an inherent property of the cyclotron.

The principle of phase stability may be understood from Fig. 14.9, which shows the variation of potential with time across an accelerating gap in a cyclotron. Let t_1 and t_2 be the two successive times at which a particle is supposed to cross the gap, so that the energy gained at these times results in an acceleration that satisfies the resonance condition. If a particle crossing at the time t_1 has less energy than required by the resonance condition, this means that the particle will arrive at the next gap-crossing in a shorter time, such as t_2'. The particle, therefore, will receive energy at an increased rate to make up the deficit. Because of the additional gain in energy, the particle will take a longer time to arrive at the next gap-crossing and will correspond to the phase of the successive times t_1, t_2, t_3, ... Similarly, if initially the particle has more energy than necessary, it will arrive at a time corresponding to t_2'', and it will receive, therefore, less acceleration. In the subsequent crossing it will be back to its proper phase. *The energy tends to oscillate about the correct value.* This means that the stability in phase causes the motion of the ions to "lock in" to the applied frequency in such a way that the particles tend to seek a state of motion in which Eq. (14.5), $f = \dfrac{1}{2\pi}(qB/m)$, is satisfied. Note that the stability will break down if a rate of energy gain greater than the peak value of the potential curve is required.

Initially, f and B have values corresponding to the initial energy of the particle. Very high accelerations can be achieved by slowly varying f or B or both. It was pointed out by Veksler and McMillan that phase stability is preserved if the variations in f and B are very slow. Acceleration of the particle corresponds either to decreasing f or to increasing B. Two types of machines have been developed along this principle: (a) the synchrocyclotron, or frequency-modulated cyclotron, in which B is kept constant and f is varied, and (b) the synchrotron in which B is varied while f may or may not vary. For electron synchrotrons, f is kept constant while for the proton synchrotron, both f and B are varied. The variation of B is much more difficult.

A. SYNCHROCYCLOTRON. The synchrocyclotron, or FM cyclotron, was the first machine to make use of the principle of phase stability. The first test of this was made by converting, on McMillan's suggestion, the 27-inch cyclotron at the University of California at Berkeley. Immediately following the successful test, the 184-inch machine at Berkeley was converted into a FM cyclotron[29,30]. This machine produced 200-Mev deuterons and 400-Mev alpha particles. The deuterons and alpha particles were accelerated by using frequency modulation from 11.5 million cycles per second, at the time of injection, to 9.8 million cycles per second, at the time the particles reached the periphery of the dee. The magnetic field at the center was 15,000 gauss produced by a 4000-ton magnet. The dee voltage was 15 kv. The same machine produced 350-Mev protons with a frequency modulation of from 23 to 15.6 million cycles per second. The outline of the Berkeley FM cyclotron is shown in Fig. 14.10. In this machine only one dee is used, and the oscillating potential is applied between the dee and ground. Later modifications of the Berkeley machine raised the energy limit to 750 Mev for protons. A further increase in energy is possible, but it is not economically practical.

There are about two dozen FM cyclotrons in the world, of which, perhaps, eight are in the United States. Among the latter, the Berkeley machine has the highest energy. The machine at Dubna U.S.S.R. produces 680-Mev protons, while the one at CERN, the European Organization for Nuclear Research, Geneva, Switzerland produces 600-Mev protons.

There are many advantages of the synchrocyclotron. Though the use of a single dee gives half the acceleration per turn, this construction has many electrical and mechanical advantages. The shape of the magnetic field is not

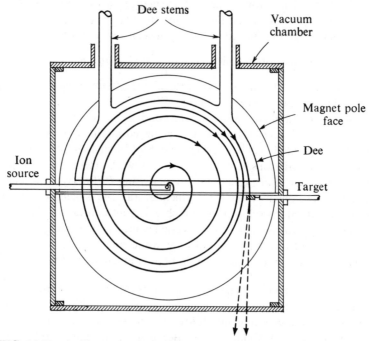

FIG. 14.10 A diagram of a synchrocyclotron (frequency-modulated cyclotron) showing the arrangement of the magnets within a vacuum chamber. [From Livingston, M. S., and J. P. Blewett, *Particle Accelerators*, p. 357. New York: McGraw-Hill Book Company, Inc. (1962).]

very critical. As long as good vacuum is established, there is no limit to the number of revolutions a particle may make. This allows the use of a low power radio-frequency oscillator (~ 15 kw), and high energies may be achieved by increasing the number of resolutions, say, to about 50,000.

With frequency modulation, the output intensity is very low because ions are captured in the stable orbits only during a small fraction of the modulation cycle. In addition, the beam is not continuous because a cycle of full-frequency modulation must be completed before starting another one from the initial frequency. The repetition rates are usually ~ 60 cycles per second, and the beam, appearing in the form of a pulse, is a few microamps. This is sufficient for many experiments.

B. SYNCHROTRONS. The success of phase stability led to the development of electron synchrotrons and proton synchrotrons capable of achieving very high accelerations for these particles. Because of a large difference between the mass of an electron and a proton, the construction of the two machines differs considerably. The electron synchrotron is simpler, and we shall discuss it first.

1. Electron Synchrotrons.[31] Electrons reach a velocity near that of light at small energies ($v = 0.98c$ for 2-Mev electrons), which eliminates the need of a variable radio-frequency source. A beam of electrons preaccelerated to about 2 Mev is injected in a circular orbit by means of electric deflection. The magnet that keeps the electrons in a fixed circular orbit is in the form of a ring. As the electrons are accelerated by passing through a radio-frequency source, the intensity of the magnetic field is modulated cyclically from low to high field-strength in order to maintain the orbits at constant radius. The applied frequency, f, is determined by the radius, r, of the orbit by the relation $f = c/2\pi r$, where c is the velocity of light. The ring-shaped magnet, formed of laminated iron to minimize eddy-current losses, is the most economical shape because the magnet need only provide the required orbit. Its field does not contribute to accelerating the particle. Fig. 14.11 shows an outline of a typical electron synchrotron. As in the case of FM cyclotron, the beam is in the form of pulses with a very low average current, but the energies attainable are very high.

The phase-stability principle is applied in this manner: When electrons cross the positive half-cycle of the electric field, they gain energy; in the other half-cycle, they lose energy. Electrons bunch together in a phase in which the rate of increase in energy by the r-f voltage matches the rising magnetic field. Under these circumstances, if an electron crossing the gap has excess energy, it will traverse a larger orbit, take longer to reach the gap, and receive less acceleration than an electron in the equilibrium phase. The converse happens with an electron of lesser energy. Phase stability, therefore, "locks in" the electrons around the equilibrium phase. After the magnetic cycle has been completed and the electrons have been accelerated to the required energies, the shape of the orbit may be distorted to get the beam out.

The maximum energy to which the electrons may be accelerated is limited by the radiation loss. No further acceleration is possible if the energy gain is equal to the energy loss by radiation. This sets a limit of ~ 1 Bev (1 Bev = 1000 Mev) to which electrons may be accelerated.

There are several electron synchrotrons[32] that have been constructed to produce energies from 50 Mev to ~ 1.2 Bev. This range has been extended to ~ 6 Bev by use of the alternating gradient method we shall discuss in the next section. The electron synchrotron of the California Institute of Technology, Pasadena, California, has an orbit radius of 3.76 m and produces electrons of 1.2-Bev energy.

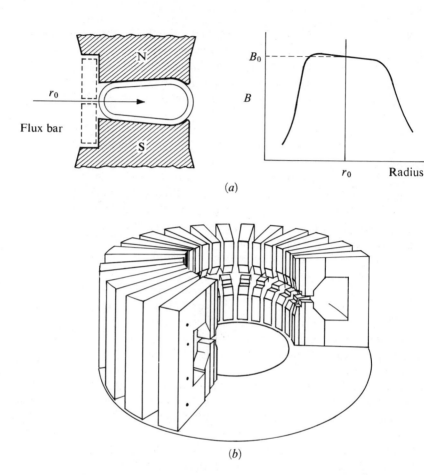

FIG. 14.11   A diagram showing the pole face and vacuum chamber for the MIT Electron Synchrotron. [From Livingston, M. S., and J. P. Blewett, *Particle Accelerators*, p. 412. New York: McGraw-Hill Book Co. Inc., (1962).]

2. Proton Synchrotron.[32,33]   Unlike electrons, protons can be accelerated to much higher energies. This is because of their higher mass, which implies that the energy losses (Chap. VIII) are not appreciable until energies much higher than 10 Bev are achieved.

Though the principle is the same, the design and construction of a proton synchrotron differs considerably from that of the electron synchrotron. The principle of phase stability is applied. The magnet is in the form of a ring. It is powered cyclically with current pulses, so that the magnetic field at the orbit increases during acceleration from a low value at injection of the particles to the maximum value at ejection with final energy. The vacuum chamber is of doughnut shape. The particles oscillate about an equilibrium orbit between the poles of the ring-shaped magnets inside the vaccum chamber. Unlike electrons, protons, as they gain energy, increase in velocity and frequency. This is because protons do not reach speeds near the speed of light for low energies (v =0.98 c for 2000 Mev). In the case of electrons the frequency is constant ($f = c/2\pi r$), but for protons it may change by a factor of 10 during acceleration. Thus the frequency of the applied electric field must also increase. In order to make use of phase stability, the orbital frequency must match the applied frequency of the applied electric field, and protons must be accelerated while the magnetic field is increasing. This requires an application of a precisely determined frequency-modulation schedule.

A low-energy proton beam is obtained from preacceleration and is injected into an orbit when the magnetic field will make the protons go into a proper orbit. After the protons have reached maximum energies, the orbit is distorted and the proton beam, in the form of a burst, is removed by means of an ejection device.

There are about a dozen proton synchrotrons[32] in the world at present in research use. The highest-energy proton synchrotron is the 10 Bev *synchrophasotron* at Dubna in the U.S.S.R. The *Bevatron* at the Lawrence radiation Laboratory, Berkeley, California produces 6.3 Bev protons. Fig. 14.12

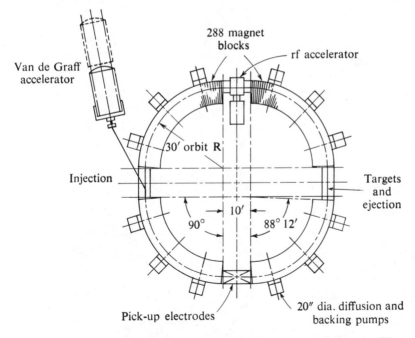

FIG. 14.12 A diagram of the Cosmotron (proton synchrotron). [From Livingston, M. S., J. P. Blewett, G. K. Green, and L. J. Haworth, *Rev. Sci. Inst.*, **21**, 7, (1950).]

FIG. 14.12 The Cosmotron at Brookhaven National Laboratory which accelerates protons up to 3 Bev. (By courtesy of Brookhaven National Laboratory.)

shows an outline of the Brookhaven National Laboratory *Cosmotron*, which produces 3 Bev protons[34,35]. It has a magnet that weighs about 2000 tons and has a maximum diameter of 75 feet. The magnet is in the form of a steel ring 8 ft by 8 ft in cross section. The magnet is divided into four quadrants separated by gaps of 10 ft. Protons of 3.5-Mev energy are pulsed into the synchrotron at which time the magnetic field is about 300 gauss. The maximum value of the magnetic field reached is 14,000 gauss. The r-f source is a high frequency resonant cavity that supplies about 3000 v per turn and is modulated from 0.37 mc to 4.20 mc per second. To attain maximum energy, the protons make about 3 million revolutions.

6. ALTERNATING-GRADIENT FOCUSING ACCELERATORS

Theoretically, it is possible to design synchronous accelerators for accelerating electrons and protons to much higher energies. But the cost of such accelerators increases tremendously with increasing energy, and it becomes uneconomical to construct huge machines. The size of the orbit becomes so large that the cost of the huge ring-magnets, alone, becomes impractical. A new principle of alternating-gradient (AG) focusing, as contrasted to the constant-gradient (CG) focusing used in synchronous accelerators, was proposed by E. Courant, M. Livingston and H. Snyder[36] at the Brookhaven National Laboratory in 1952. The principle of the fixed-field alternating-gradient (FFAG) synchrotrons is explained in the following.

The AG synchrotron uses a sequence of magnet sectors shaped in a way that the sense of the gradient alternates. By tilting the magnet-pole faces, the magnetic field gradient is made stronger on one side and weaker on the other. Thus the charged particles entering this field will have converging trajectories in the "positive" gradient and diverging trajectories in the "negative" gradient. Though there are now "focusing" and "defocusing" regions, the net effect is strong focusing in both transverse directions. The result of such strong focusing is that the particles oscillate with much smaller amplitudes about their equilibrium orbit. This permits a tremendous reduction in the cross section of the magnets and the vacuum chambers, thereby making it economically suitable to construct synchrotrons with much larger orbits for higher energies.

The highest energy electron and proton synchrotrons are of the AG focusing type. The first machine[37,38] that accelerated 50-Mev protons to 28 Bev was that of CERN, near Geneva, in 1959. The Brookhaven National Laboratory's AG synchrotron[39], which went into operation in 1960, accelerates protons to 30 Bev. A diagram of it is shown in Fig. 14.13. The protons are preaccelerated by means of a proton linac that has 124 drift tubes

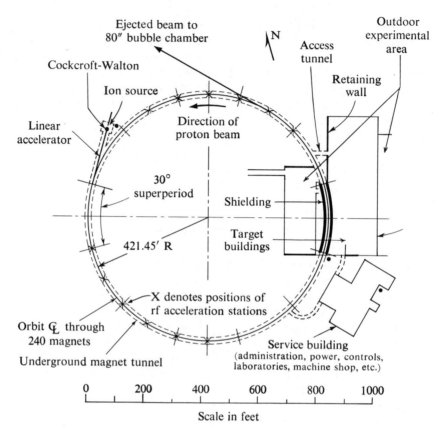

FIG. 14.13   A diagram of Brookhaven alternating-gradient synchrotron.

of a total length of 110 ft. 50-Mev protons are guided into the AG synchrotron by means of an elaborate system. The orbit has a diameter of 842.9 ft ($\sim \frac{1}{2}$ mile in circumference). The vacuum pipe is 7 inches wide and 2.75 inches high (as compared to 36 inches by 7 inches in the Cosmotron). The vacuum chamber is maintained at less than 10^{-5} mm Hg. Each of the 240 units of the main magnet weighs 60 tons.

Higher-energy machines are being thought of along the ideas of the so-called "colliding beams" but have not become practical as yet, because the intensity obtainable is very, very low.

7. BETATRON

The betatron is an electron accelerator. An outline sketch of the betatron is shown in Fig. 14.14. It operates on the same principle of electromagnetic induction as the transformer and hence may be categorized as an "induction machine." In a transformer the pulsed current in the primary coil produces a changing magnetic field. The changing magnetic flux in the core induces a voltage in the secondary coil that makes the electrons in the secondary coil move while the insulated copper wire wound around the core guides its motion. In a betatron the electrons are injected into a high vacuum glass or ceramic annular tube, "a doughnut-shaped chamber." This chamber is placed

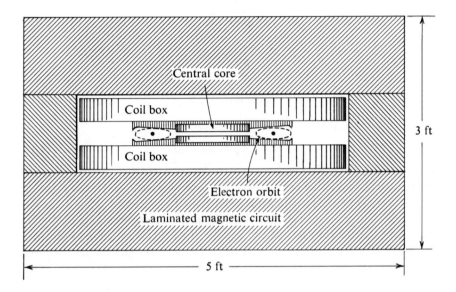

FIG. 14.14 A diagram of a betatron. [From Kerst, D. W., G. D. Adams, H. W. Koch, and C. S. Robinson, *Rev. Sci. Inst.*, **21**, 462, (1950).]

between the poles of an electromagnet. The pulsed current in the primary coil produces a changing magnetic flux. The electrons are accelerated by the electric field induced by changing magnetic flux within the orbit. The electrons travel thousands of revolutions in a circle of fixed radius and build up high energies without needing any insulation. The electrons are guided, kept in circular orbit or focussed towards it by a specially shaped magnetic guide field. There is a definite relation between the magnitude of the field and the flux through the orbit needed to maintain the circular path of constant radius for the electrons. We shall derive this condition below. Let Φ be the magnetic flux linking the orbit. The electric field E is given by

$$2\pi R E = \frac{d\Phi}{dt} \qquad (14.11)$$

where R is the radius of the electron orbit. The time rate of change of momentum, which is equal to the electrical force, is given by

$$\frac{dp}{dt} = eE = \frac{e}{2\pi R}\frac{d\Phi}{dt} \tag{14.12}$$

or

$$p = \frac{e}{2\pi R}(\Phi_2 - \Phi_1) \tag{14.13}$$

The magnetic field required to produce the circular orbit is given by

$$\frac{mv^2}{R} = evB$$

or

$$p = mv = BeR \tag{14.14}$$

Combining Eqns. (14.13) and (14.14), we get

$$\Phi_2 - \Phi_1 = 2(\pi R^2)B \tag{14.15}$$

This equation gives the relation between the magnetic flux through the orbit and the guide field at the orbit. This is the *betatron condition*. It states that the change in magnetic flux within the orbit must be twice the value if the flux density be uniform and equal to the field at the orbit (the guide field). The electrons enter the tube just when the magnetic field starts rising as shown in Fig. 14.15. The increasing field increases the potential which in turn increases

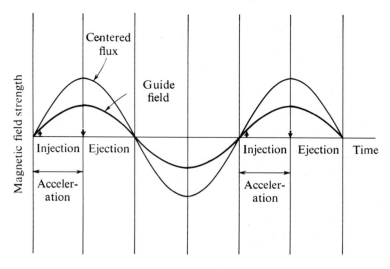

FIG. 14.15   The acceleration cycle of electrons in a betatron. The central flux and the guide field are in phase.

the energy of the electrons. The electrons are removed just when the field is at its peak. During this interval the electrons have gone through thousands of revolutions. Many betatrons have been constructed for accelerating electrons to 300 Mev[40,41,42].

With the availability of the more versatile and higher energy machines already discussed, the use of the betatron in nuclear physics research has been proportionately reduced. The beam of electrons may be used to produce high energy x-rays. In research the x-rays are used for investigation of such reactions as (γ, n), (γ, p), $(\gamma, 2n)$. These machines are being used in industry and medical technology where the x-rays are employed for radiography and cancer treatment.

8. FISSION REACTORS

The two important aspects by which nuclear fission differs from other nuclear reactions are the following: (1) In each fission more than one neutron is produced for each neutron absorbed. In the fission of U^{235} by thermal neutrons, for example, 2.5 neutrons, on the average, are emitted in each fission. This means that under proper conditions the fission can be made a self-sustaining reaction, and a chain reaction is possible. (2) In each fission about 200 Mev of energy is released, most of which (~ 165 Mev) is carried away by the fission fragments. This energy is available in the form of heat and may be utilized for the purpose of power production.

Fission nuclear-reactors are made possible for power production by utilizing these two characteristics. The self-sustained chain reaction is possible only if the number of neutrons produced in a given generation are more than, or equal to, the previous generation. An important quantity k, called the *reproduction factor* or *multiplication factor*, is defined as

$$k = \frac{\text{number of neutrons in the } (n+1)\text{th generation}}{\text{number of neutrons in the } n\text{th generation}} \qquad (14.16)$$

If the number of neutrons produced in any generation is equal to that of the previous generation, or if $k = 1$, the system is said to be *critical*. On the other hand, if $k < 1$, that is, the number of neutrons in any generation is less than that in the previous generation, the system is said to be *subcritical* or *convergent*.

The system in which $k > 1$, i.e., the number of neutrons in any generation is more than that in the previous generation, is called *supercritical* or *divergent*. In order to obtain a continuous, uniform supply of power from a fission reactor, the system must be critical. For a supercritical system the power will continuously increase, and it finally will become uncontrollable (resulting in an explosion as used in an atom bomb). In a subcritical system the power will continuously decrease and the system will eventually reduce the power level to zero. In a nuclear reactor, initially k is made slightly greater than unity, and after the desirable power level is reached, k is maintained at unity. The aim of a reactor designer, therefore, is to achieve a critical system.

The nucleus U^{235} is the only one occurring naturally that is fissionable by thermal neutrons. Natural uranium is a combination of the isotopes U^{235} and U^{238} in the ratio 1:138, which means that the abundance of U^{235} in natural uranium is only 0.71 percent by weight. Because of the identical chemical properties of the two isotopes, separation of U^{235} from U^{238} is a costly process. It is accomplished by making use of the small difference in their diffusion rates. It is not possible to achieve a critical system by using natural uranium for fission, because neutrons are absorbed in nonfission processes both in U^{235} and U^{238}. These processes can be understood by considering the life history of a neutron produced in fission.

A. LIFE CYCLE OF NEUTRONS PRODUCED IN FISSION.   Neutrons produced in fission may have energies anywhere from thermal to about 18 Mev. Let us consider a representative group of fast neutrons produced in fission and see what may happen to them in their subsequent life times. Because we are interested in producing fission of U^{235} by thermal neutrons, it is necessary to slow these neutrons to thermal energies by using some moderator (such as water, heavy water, or carbon) with the fissionable material.

We shall consider the life cycle of a single fast neutron of a given energy group.

1. Fast Fission (ε).   Because U^{238} is fissionable by fast neutrons, there is some probability that the fast neutron will cause fission. This probability is denoted by ε, called the *fast-fission factor*. Starting with one neutron, therefore, we have ($\varepsilon > 1$) neutrons.

2. Fast Nonleakage (P_f).   In the process of slowing down there is some chance that the fast neutrons will leave the system. If P_f represents the *fast nonleakage probability*, we shall be left with εP_f neutrons at the end, while $\varepsilon(1 - P_f)$ will leave the system.

3. Resonance Escape (p). U^{238} has several very strong resonance peaks in the energy range from 5 ev to 200 ev. Thus, before reaching thermal energies, some fraction of εP_f neutrons will be absorbed by these resonance absorptions. Let us call p the *resonance-escape probability*. On the average, $\varepsilon P_f p$ neutrons will reach thermal energies escaping resonance absorption. The fraction absorbed in the resonance peaks is $\varepsilon P_f(1 - p)$.

4. Thermal Nonleakage (P_t).   On the average, we have now $\varepsilon P_f p$ neutrons at thermal energies. Before these neutrons are absorbed in fissionable and nonfissionable processes, there is some probability that a fraction of them will leave the system. If we represent the *thermal nonleakage-probability* by P_t, we will be left with $\varepsilon P_f p P_t$ thermal neutrons available for absorption. The number of neutrons that leave the system at thermal energies is, thus, $\varepsilon P_f p(1 - P_t)$.

5. Thermal Utilization (f).   Not all the $\varepsilon P_f p P_t$ neutrons will be absorbed by uranium. A fraction of them will be lost by absorption in the moderating material, shielding, or other things. The fraction not lost in this way is denoted by f and is called the *thermal utilization factor*. The number of neutrons absorbed by uranium, therefore, is $\varepsilon P_f p P_t f$, while the average number of neutrons absorbed by materials other than uranium is $\varepsilon P_f p P_t (1 - f)$.

6. Fission. $\varepsilon P_f p P_t f$ thermal neutrons are absorbed by uranium. If v represents the number of neutrons produced in a fission of U^{235} by a thermal neutron ($v \simeq 2.5$ in this case), then the number of neutrons, η, produced per thermal neutron absorbed by uranium is given by

$$\eta = \frac{v\Sigma_f^{235}}{\Sigma_f^{235} + \Sigma_c^{235} + \Sigma_c^{238}}$$

$$= \frac{v\sigma_f^{235}}{\sigma_f^{235} + \sigma_c^{235} + (N_{238}/N_{235})\sigma_c^{238}} \qquad (14.17)$$

where σ_f^{235} is the fission cross-section of U^{235} for thermal neutrons, while σ_c^{235} and σ_c^{238} are the capture cross-sections for the nonfission processes by U^{235} and U^{238}, respectively. Σ's denote the macroscopic cross-sections. N_{238} and N_{235} are the number of atoms per unit volume of U^{238} and U^{235}, respectively. For U^{235}, in natural uranium, η is 1.3 even though $v = 2.5$ and $N_{238}/N_{235} = 0.00715$.

Thus for each fast neutron the total number of neutrons available at the end of the cycle is $\varepsilon P_f p P_t f \eta$ and is called the *effective reproductive constant* of the reactor, i.e.,

$$k_{eff} = \eta \varepsilon p f P_t P_f \qquad (14.18)$$

This is called the *6-factor formula*. All the above processes are illustrated schematically in Fig. 14.16. It may be noticed that the factors η and ε are each greater than unity, while all the other four, p, f, P_t, and P_f are each less than unity. Also η, ε, p, and f depend only on the properties and configuration of the reactor materials (fission fuel and moderator), while P_t and P_f depend upon the internal geometrical configuration and the overall size and shape of the reactor. If we assume that the overall size of the reactor is infinite, the total nonleakage probability, $P = P_t P_f$, will be equal to unity. Eq. (14.13) in such cases reduces to ($P_t = P_f = 1$),

$$k_\infty = \eta \varepsilon p f \qquad (14.19)$$

where k_∞ is called the *infinite reproductive constant*. Thus

$$k_{eff} = k_\infty P \qquad (14.20)$$

The design of a nuclear reactor is based on the 6-factor formula as we shall see.

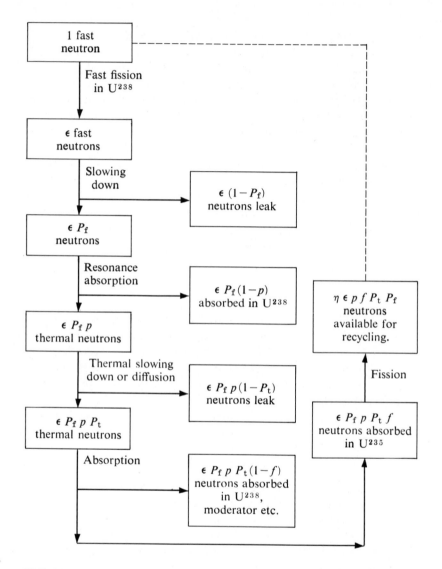

FIG. 14.16   Life cycle of a fast neutron in the process of producing fission.

B. DESIGN OF A NUCLEAR REACTOR.   The goal of a nuclear reactor designer is to adjust the six factors in Eq. (14.18) in such a way that $k_{eff} \geqslant 1$. As an example, we shall discuss the design of a nuclear reactor that uses thermal neutrons.

If the reactor fuel is natural uranium, it is not possible to achieve a chain reaction by using high or intermediate energy neutrons because of the high-resonance absorption cross-section of U^{238}. If the fast neutrons are allowed to slow down past the resonances without much absorption, a chain reaction is possible by thermal neutrons. In order to achieve rapid slowing down of the fast neutrons, a material of low mass number is used as a moderator with uranium. One may think that a high degree of slowing down will be achieved if uranium is mixed uniformly with the moderator. It is found that a divergent chain reaction is not possible because the resonance absorption of U^{238} is still very high. The uniform mixing of the moderator with the fuel increases the

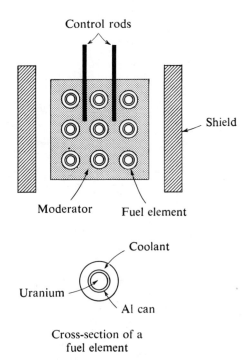

FIG. 14.17   A diagram of (a) the arrangement of the fuel elements in a nuclear reactor core and (b) the detail of an element.

absorption by the moderator as well. A divergent chain reaction, therefore, is not possible in a homogeneous thermal reactor using natural uranium.

A divergent chain reaction is possible with natural uranium only, if the reactor is of the *heterogeneous thermal reactor* type. In this kind of reactor, discrete lumps of uranium in the form of rods form a lattice in a matrix of the moderating material as shown in Fig. 14.17. This arrangement has an advantage that fast neutrons produced by fission in the rod leave the rod and are slowed down in the surrounding moderating material. The resonance absorption in U^{238} is reduced by a large amount because only the U^{238} on the surface of the rod is available. After being slowed down, the neutrons can easily go inside the fuel and produce fission, and a divergent chain reaction is produced.

The homogeneous thermal reactors are only possible with uranium enriched with the isotope U^{235}. It may appear that increasing the physical size of the reactor has an advantage because it makes P equal to unity. This advantage is offset by the fact that the size increases absorption in the non-fissionable materials and reduces f considerably. f varies, therefore, in exactly

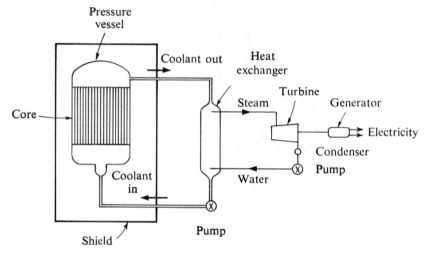

FIG. 14.18   A diagram of a typical nuclear power plant.

the *opposite* way to P with fuel element size and spacing. A compromise is made and a value of $P \approx f = 0.95$ is suitable for reactors using natural uranium with heavy water moderators.

The amount of power available from a nuclear reactor is tremendous. Each fission of U^{235}, for example, produces 200 Mev of energy, on the average, or 3.2×10^{-11} watt sec. One gram of U^{235}, if completely fissioned, will produce 8.2×10^{10} watt sec ≈ 1 MWD (mega watt days). As compared to this, one ton of coal produces ~ 0.36 MWD of heat. We may conclude that

$$1 \text{ ton of uranium} \equiv 2.7 \times 10^6 \text{ tons of coal.}$$

An outline of a typical nuclear power plant is shown in Fig. 14.18. The heat produced in the reactor core is taken away by the coolant, which, in turn, is used to produce steam. The steam runs a turbine and the electricity is made available through the generator as shown in the figure.

For the sake of convenience, nuclear reactors may be classified under two categories depending upon the type of neutrons used for fission and the purpose of the reactor.

A. *Chain reaction*

(i) *Fast reactors* are those in which fission is produced by neutrons of energies greater than 0.2 Mev.

(ii) *Intermediate reactors* are those in which fission is produced by neutrons of energies between 0.1 ev and 0.2 Mev.

(iii) *Thermal reactors* are those in which fission is caused by thermal neutrons (of energies less than 0.1 ev).

B. *Purpose*

(i) *Power* for industrial and everyday use.

(ii) *Research* uses are many and varied. Neutron and gamma beams produced in nuclear reactors, for example, are used in nuclear physics.

(iii) *Production of fissile material:* U^{233} and Pu^{239}, which do not occur naturally, but which are fissionable, may be produced through the following reactions from Th^{232} and U^{238}, respectively

$$Th^{232} + n \xrightarrow{\quad\quad} Th^{233} \xrightarrow[23 \text{ min}]{\beta^-} Pa^{233} \xrightarrow[27 \text{ days}]{\beta^-} U^{233}$$

$$U^{238} + n \xrightarrow{\quad\quad} U^{239} \xrightarrow[23 \text{ min}]{\beta^-} Np^{239} \xrightarrow[23 \text{ days}]{\beta^-} Pu^{239}$$

(iv) *Other purposes,* for example, the reactors may be used for the production of transuranium elements (very heavy nuclides) such as Cm, Cf, Fm, and others.

C. REACTOR CONTROL. One of the most difficult problems of the nuclear reactor is its control. For this purpose cadmium rods, the control rods, are inserted into the core of the reactor. Because cadmium has a very high absorption cross-section for neutrons, the rods may be adjusted to expose less or more of their length so that the corresponding neutron production rate can be increased or decreased. The rate of increase depends on the time lapse between the successive generations, which may be represented by τ. If the number of neutrons at time $t = 0$ is n_0, the number n at any subsequent time will be given by

$$n = n_0 \, e^{(k-1)t/\tau} \tag{14.21}$$

where $k(= k_{eff})$ of the system determines the neutron population with time.

If $k = 1$, $n = n_0$, and the power level remains constant. Suppose it is required to increase the power level. This will require the control rods being pulled out to make $k > 1$. The slowing down time of the fast neutrons is $\tau \sim 10^{-3}$ sec. The time allowed to raise the power level and then to maintain it at that level is too small for any mechanical arrangement to control the divergent reaction without letting the reactor run wild and explode. But the presence of a small fraction of delayed neutrons makes this mechanical control by Cd rod possible. Thus if d is a fraction of delayed neutrons produced in fission, then k may be divided into two parts: kd due to delayed neutrons, and $k(1-d)$ due to prompt neutrons. If $k(1-d)$ is less than unity, the increase in the number of neutrons is determined by the delayed neutrons for which the effective weighted average gives $\tau = 0.1$ sec. This time is large enough for mechanical controls to operate the reactor.

9. FUSION

Nuclear fusion is just the opposite of nuclear fission. In nuclear fusion, two very light-weight nuclei ($A \gtrsim 8$) combine together to form a heavy nucleus. The heavy nucleus, so formed, has much more binding energy than the combined binding energies of the two light nuclei. This results in conversion of some rest mass into energy, which, under special circumstances, may be made available. That energy is available in the process of fusion may be understood from the BE/A versus A plot shown in Fig. 5.6.

The energy radiated from the sun and the stars is the result of fusion reactions taking place in them. Because of very high temperatures inside the sun and other stars ($\sim 10^8$ °K), the atoms of the elements are completely ionized. A collection of bare nuclei and electrons are said to form a *plasma*. At such high temperatures the nuclei have very high velocities, and in the process of colliding can very easily cross the coulomb barrier. Thus the cross sections for nuclear fusion are very high, and because the reactions are exoergic, large amounts of energy are available. The reactions that take place by virtue of the very high temperatures are called *thermonuclear reactions*.

There are many different thermonuclear reactions that continuously take place inside the stars. The two most common cycles are the following:

Proton-proton cycle

$$H^1 + H^1 \rightarrow H^2 + \beta^+ + \nu + 0.42 \text{ Mev}$$
$$H^2 + H^1 \rightarrow He^3 + \gamma + 5.49 \text{ Mev}$$
$$He^3 + He^3 \rightarrow He^4 + 2H^1 + 12.86 \text{ Mev}$$

Carbon cycle

$$C^{12} + H^1 \rightarrow N^{13} + \gamma + 1.95 \text{ Mev}$$
$$N^{13} \rightarrow C^{13} + \beta^+ + \nu + 1.20 \text{ Mev}$$
$$C^{13} + H^1 \rightarrow N^{14} + \gamma + 7.55 \text{ Mev}$$
$$N^{14} + H^1 \rightarrow O^{15} + \gamma + 7.34 \text{ Mev}$$
$$O^{15} \rightarrow N^{15} + \beta^+ + \nu + 1.68 \text{ Mev}$$
$$N^{15} + H^1 \rightarrow C^{12} + He^4 + 4.96 \text{ Mev}$$

The amount of energy available in each of the above cycles is about 20 Mev. The study of fusion has been undertaken to utilize thermonuclear reactions in laboratories and to harness the available energy for useful purposes. There are many difficulties involved—primarily the containment of the plasma at temperatures of the order of 10^8 °K.

Where isotopes of light elements are made to undergo nuclear fusion with the production of more energy than that required to produce the reaction, controlled fusion has taken place. The study of controlled fusion reactions is well justified. With increasing population and power consumption, studies show that coal and oil will fall short of human needs in less than a century. The reserves of fissionable fuels are not very high, either. On the other hand, deuterium, alone, which may be used for fusion reactions and is available in large quantities in the world's oceans, is enough for billions of years, even if the power consumption rate goes as high as 1000 times the present one. In addition to the plentiful supply of fuel, fusion is attractive as a source of power because there are no radioactive waste disposal problems, in contrast to that of fission reactors, and, in addition, fusion admits of the possibility of direct conversion into electricity, with a high degree of efficiency.

The possible fusion reactions that use isotopes of hydrogen (deuterium, H^2, and tritium, H^3) are the following:

$$_1H^2 + {}_1H^3 \rightarrow He^4 + n \quad + 17.6 \text{ Mev}$$

$$_1H^2 + {}_1H^2 \rightarrow He^3 + n \quad + \; 3.2 \text{ Mev}$$

$$_1H^2 + {}_1H^2 \rightarrow H^3 \; + H^1 + \; 4.0 \text{ Mev}$$

The cross sections for the first two reactions, which are the most intensively studied, are shown in Fig. 14.19. A reaction between two protons either does not take place, or the cross section is extremely low.

There are many technical problems involved in achieving a controlled thermonuclear reaction. Unlike fission, where no initial heating is needed, fusion requires very high temperatures and confinement of the plasma becomes difficult. The *ignition temperature* is defined as that at which the nuclear power released becomes equal to the power lost due to *Bremsstrahlung*. Above this temperature the reaction not only sustains itself, it also releases extra energy.

This self-sustaining nuclear reaction is only possible if a minimum temperature of about 10^8 °K is achieved, and there are two more considerations. First, how long does the plasma have to be maintained at this temperature before it becomes self-sustaining? Second, what type of materials are we going to use for the walls that confine the plasma? The answer to the first problem is simple. The containment time may be calculated in a simple manner ($t = 1/n\bar{\sigma}v$) and turns out to be 10 and 1000 sec, respectively, for the $H^2 - H^2$ and $H^2 - H^3$ reactions. In practice, containment times of the order of 1/10 and 10 sec are enough. As for the second question, at present no suitable material is available for the walls. At such high temperatures, any material vaporises, permitting the plasma to disperse.

The alternative for a containment material is to confine the plasma at the center of a wide tube by means of external magnetic fields. (The method is currently in experiment.) The magnetic field confines the plasma by means of the *pinch effect*. Other magnetic systems used are named the *stellarator*, the *magnetic mirror system*, and the *astron system*. The study of fusion has been carried out as part of U.S. Government Projects Sherwood and Zeta, and the problem of containment still remains unsolved.

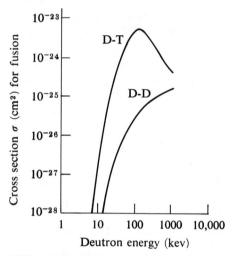

FIG. 14.19 Fusion cross-section versus deuteron energy: D-T and D-D reactions. From Bishop, A. S., *Project-Sheerwood-The U. S. Program in Controlled Fusion*, Reading, Mass: Addison-Wesley, (1958).

PROBLEMS

1. A flexible wire under tension T (newtons) and carrying current i (amperes) takes up the same path in a magnetic field as a charged particle of momentum p (kg-m/sec) moving in a magnetic field H. Show that the following relation is true (neglect the gravitational pull):

$$\frac{p}{e} = \frac{T}{i} \quad \text{where } e \text{ is the charge in coulombs.}$$

   [This floating wire technique is used in calibration.]

2. A particle of rest mass m_0 and charge q is accelerated to a potential of V volts. Taking into consideration the relativistic effects show that the moving mass m is given

$$m = m_0(1 + aV)$$

   where 'a' is constant expressed in terms of q, m_0 and c.

3. Consider an electrostatic generator with a sphere of capacity 200 *uuf*. What is the amount of charge it carries if operating at 0.5 Mev?

4. A Van de Graaff machine is being used for obtaining 6 μ amp, 2-Mev deuteron beam. Calculate the power needed to drive the belt. Assume 5% losses by friction, etc.

5. Protons, deuterons and helium ions are accelerated in a 48 in. cyclotron with a frequency of 10 megacycles per second. Calculate (a) the magnetic field required in each case, (b) the maximum energy to which each of these particles may be accelerated.

6. Design a cyclotron which will accelerate deuterons to 5 Mev.

7. In a cyclotron, what is the value of the small difference in the magnetic fields which are applied if the beam is shifted from (a) proton to deuteron and (b) deuteron to alpha particles?

8. In a frequency-modulated cyclotron for a given source the ratio H/n, where H is the applied magnetic field and n is the frequency of the applied voltage, is fixed. Derive this ratio for protons, deuterons, and helium ions.

9. A certain frequency modulated cyclotron is capable of accelerating protons to 500 Mev. What is the ratio of the highest to the lowest frequency needed to accomplish this?

10. What is the length of the last drift tube used for accelerating protons to 200 Mev. The applied frequency is 60 megacycles per sec.

11. A thermal nuclear reactor using natural uranium as fuel is operating at a power level of 500 megawatts. At what rate is U^{235} being consumed by fission?

12. In a homogeneous reactor containing U^{235} dissolved in water, what should the minimum ratio of U^{235} atoms to water molecules be so that the system is critical? Assume that the system is infinitely large.

13. If the efficiency for conversion from heat to electricity is only 5%, what is the fission rate of U^{235} to produce 500 megawatts of power?

14. Using Watt's formula for distribution of fission neutron, calculate the fraction of neutrons whose energies are greater than 2 Mev.

15. Four atoms of hydrogen form a helium atom by fusion. How much energy will be liberated if 1 gm of hydrogen atoms are converted into helium atoms by fusion? How does this energy compare with the energy liberated by a complete fission of 1 gm of U^{235}?

16. Calculate the total energy liberated in one complete carbon-nitrogen cycle and compare it with a proton-proton cycle.

REFERENCES

1. Cockcroft, J. D., and E. T. S. Walton, *Proc. Roy. Soc.*, **A 137**, p. 229, (1932); **A 136**, p. 619, (1932).

2. Lawrence, E. O., and M. S. Livingston, *Phys. Rev.*, **37**, p. 1707, (1931).

3. Livingston, M. S., and J. P. Blewett, *Particle Accelerators*, New York: McGraw-Hill Book Co. Inc., 1962.

4. Thonemann, P. C., et al., *Proc. Phys. Soc.*, **A 61**, p. 483, (1948).

5. Gow, J. D., and J. S. Foster, *Rev. Sci. Inst.*, **24**, p. 606, (1953).

6. Greinacher, H., *Z. Physik*, **4**, p. 195, (1921).

7. Lauritsen, C. C., and R. D. Bennett, *Phys. Rev.*, **32**, p. 850, (1928).

8. Lauritsen, C. C., and B. Cassen, *Phys. Rev.*, **36**, p. 988, (1930).

9. Lauritsen, C. C., and R. Crane, *Rev. Sci. Inst.*, **4**, p. 497, (1933).

10. Van de Graaff, R. J., *Phys. Rev.*, **38**, p. 1919, (1931).

11. Van de Graaff, R. J., K. T. Compton, and L. C. Van Atta, *Phys. Rev.*, **43**, p. 149, (1933).

12. Van de Graaff, R. J., J. G. Trump, and W. W. Buechner, *Rep. Prog. Phys.*, **XI**, p. 1 (1946).

13. Herb, R. G., C. M. Turner, C. M. Hudson, and R. E. Warren, *Phys. Rev.*, **58**, p. 579, (1940).

14. Parkinson, D. B., R. G. Herb, E. J. Bernet, and J. L. McKibben, *Phys. Rev.*, **53**, p. 642, (1938).

15. Wells, W. H., R. O. Haxby, W. E. Stephens, and W. E. Shoupp, *Phys. Rev.*, **58**, p. 162, (1940).

16. Van de Graaff, R. J., *Nucl. Inst. and Meth.*, **8**, p. 195, (1960).

17. Lawrence, E. O., and M. S. Livingston, *Phys. Rev.*, **40**, p. 19, (1932).

18. Lawrence, E. O., et al. *Phys. Rev.*, **56**, p. 124, (1939).

19. Howard, F. T., *Cyclotrons and High Energy Accelerators*, Oak Ridge National Laboratory Report No. ORNL 2644.

20. Bethe, H. A., and M. E. Rose, *Phys. Rev.*, **52**, p. 1254, (1937).

21. Slater, J. C., *Ann. Rev. Nucl. Sci.*, Vol. I. Palo Alto, California: Annual Reviews, Inc., 1952.

22. Slater, J. C., *Revs. Mod. Phys.*, **20**, p. 473, (1948).

23. Fry, D. W., and W. Walkinshaw, *Rep. Prog. Phys.*, **XII**, p. 9, (1949).

24. Ising, G., *Arkiv Mat., Astron. Fysik*, **18**, No. 30, p. 1, (1924).

25. Wideröe, R., *Arch. Elektrotech*, **21**, p. 387, (1928).

26. Sloan, D. H., and E. O. Lawrence, *Phys. Rev.*, **38**, p. 2021, (1931).

27. Veksler, V. I., *J. Physics U.S.S.R.*, **9**, p. 153, (1945).

28. McMillan, E. M., *Phys. Rev.*, **68**, p. 143, (1945).

29. Brobeck, W. M., E. O. Lawrence, K. R. MacKenzie, E. M. McMillan, R. Serber, D. C. Sewell, K. M. Simpson, and R. L. Thornton, *Phys. Rev.*, **71**, p. 449, (1947).

30. Henrich, L. R., D. C. Sewell, and J. Vale, *Rev. Sci. Instr.*, **20**, p. 887, (1949).

31. Oliphant, M. L., J. S., Gooden, and G. S. Hide, *Proc. Phys. Soc.*, **59**, p. 666, (1947).

32. Livingston, M. S., *ICSU Review of World Science*, **6**, p. 44, (1964).

33. Gooden, J. S., H. H. Jensen, and J. L. Symonds, *Proc. Phys. Soc.*, **59**, p. 677, (1947).

34. Livingston, M. S., J. P. Blewett, G. K. Green, and L. J. Haworth, *Rev. Sci. Instr.*, **21**, p. 7, (1950).

35. Blewett, M. H., *Rev. Sci. Instr.*, **24**, p. 725, (1953).

36. Courant, E. D., M. S. Livingston, and H. S. Snyder, *Phys. Rev.*, **88**, p. 1190, (1950).
37. (i) Adams, J. B., *Nature* **185**, p. 568, (1960) (ii) Livingston, M. S., and J. P. Blewett, *Particle Accelerators*, Chap. 15, New York: McGraw-Hill Book Co. Inc., 1962.
38. Proceedings of International Conference on High Energy Accelerators and Instrumentation of 1959, Geneva.
39. Kerst, D. W., G. D. Adams, H. W. Koch, and C. S. Robinson, *Rev. Sci. Instr.*, **21**, p. 462, (1950).
40. Kerst, D. W., G. D. Adams, H. W. Koch, and C. S. Robinson, *Phys. Rev.*, **78**, p. 297, (1950).
41. Westendrop, W. F., and E. E. Charlton, *J. Appl. Phys.*, **16**, p. 581, (1945).

SUGGESTIONS FOR FURTHER READING

1. M. S. Livingston, and J. P. Blewett, *Particle Accelerators*, New York: McGraw-Hill Book Co., Inc. (1962).
2. E. M. McMillan, *Experimental Nuclear Physics*, ed., E. Segre, Vol. III, Part XII, New York: John Wiley & Sons, Inc., (1959).
3. J. J. Livingood, *Principles of Cyclic Particle Accelerators*, Princeton: Van Nostrand Company, Inc., (1951).
4. M. S. Livingston, *High Energy Accelerators*, New York: Interscience Publishers, Inc., (1954).
5. S. Glasstone and M. C. Edlund, *The Elements of Nuclear Reactor Theory*, Princeton: Van Nostrand Company Inc., (1952).
6. S. Glasstone, *Principles of Nuclear Reactor Engineering*, Princeton: Van Nostrand Company Inc., (1955).
7. R. Stephensen, *Introduction to Nuclear Engineering*, 2nd Edition, New York: McGraw-Hill Book Co., (1958).
8. R. V. Meghreblian and D. K. Holmes, *Reactor Analysis*, New York: McGraw-Hill Book Co., (1960).
9. W. P. Allis, ed., *Nuclear Fusion*, Princeton: Van Nostrand Company Inc., (1960).
10. A. S. Bishop, *Project Sherwood, The U.S. Program in Controlled Fusion*, Reading, Mass: Addison-Wesley Publishing Company, Inc., (1958).
11. R. F. Post, "High Temperature Plasma Research and Controlled Fusion," *Ann. Rev. Nucl. Sci.*, **9**, p. 367, (1959).
12. D. J. Rose and M. Clark, Jr., *Plasmas and Controlled Fusion*, Cambridge, Mass: Technology Press of M.I.T. (1961).

XV

ELEMENTARY PARTICLES

1. INTRODUCTION

At the close of the last century, not much was known about the structure of the atom. But, as the result of J. J. Thomson's discovery of the electron in 1897, Ernest Rutherford's establishment of the nuclear model of the atom in 1911 and James Chadwick's discovery of the neutron in 1932, it was concluded that the only building blocks needed to make up the material world were electrons, protons, and neutrons, all being the constitutents of an atom. The only other particle known in the early 30's was the photon, a quantum of electromagnetic radiation. It should not be surprising to say that electrons, protons, neutrons, and photons are not the only particles present in the universe. There are many more, as we have seen. For example, the neutrino and antineutrino were needed to explain beta decay, positrons were formed in pair production, π-mesons were required to explain nuclear forces and μ-mesons formed μ-mesonic atoms. By 1947 the list had grown to about fourteen, and by 1957 there was a total of 32 basic particles. In 1965 the 1957 list had already more than doubled.

The questions that we ask ourselves today are: Is the list now complete?

Are these all fundamental (or elementary) particles? Do all these particles participate in the structure of matter? The answer to the first question is no, and there is no hope that there will ever be a complete list even though some physicists seem to be confident that there will. The definition of a fundamental particle is completely lost. It is hard to make rules for deciding what is fundamental and what is not. After all, what is the definition of a fundamental particle? It may be said that a particle is fundamental if it is not a composite of others. But this definition does not hold any more, for many particles have been called elementary even though they are a composite of others. Even nucleons have been found to have a definite structure.

The purpose of the closing chapter of this book is two-fold: First, to outline a historical sketch of the discovery of elementary particles and the measurement of some of their properties, and, second, to discuss the theoretical aspects by application of both the old and newly-discovered conservation laws and the way these lead to different classifications. It may be pointed out that no completely satisfactory theory has yet been devised. Before we discuss these two topics it is necessary to mention briefly the various factors that led to the discovery of different elementary particles and to the understanding of their characteristics.

2. THE REASONS FOR THE LONG LIST OF FUNDAMENTAL PARTICLES

It is true that many elementary particles were discovered in cosmic rays as a result of intensive investigation of these rays, but it is not possible to summarize all this work in this chapter. A brief mention of cosmic rays will be made in the next section in which we list all the elementary particles discovered up to 1957. Until 1947 the only source of elementary particles was cosmic rays, but a real break-through came with certain technical developments that enabled the production, detection, and analysis of high-energy particles in the laboratory. These developments include (a) high-energy accelerators, (b) new detection systems, and (c) data analysis techniques.

A. HIGH-ENERGY ACCELERATORS. Until the last decade or so, when the only source of elementary particles was cosmic radiation, it was impossible to readily control high-energy particles. With the recent development of man-made accelerators, however, very high-energy particles may be generated. These, in turn, may be used to produce fundamental particles in the laboratory. This makes it easier to investigate their properties. A detailed account of accelerators was presented in Chap. XIV. In this chapter we shall come across the use of accelerators in the field of elementary-particle physics. Even though very high-energy accelerators have been constructed, for the range of energies above the limits of these accelerators, cosmic rays are the only source. Though the costs are prohibitive, it is hoped that still higher-energy accelerators will be constructed, reaching energies of more than 100 Bev.

B. NEW DETECTION SYSTEMS. For more energetic particles, it became necessary to have more sophisticated detectors to investigate the details of the interactions of these short-lived fundamental particles with other long-lived particles. These detectors have been discussed in detail in Chap. III and their use in the field of elementary-particle physics will become obvious in this chapter. It may be pointed out that besides other detectors, the bubble chamber, spark chamber, and Čerenkov detector are especially useful in high-energy physics.

C. DATA ANALYSIS TECHNIQUES. Another major problem involved in the investigation of the fundamental particles is the analysis of the experimental data. The analysis in this field is much more complicated than most of the experiments in other branches of physics. Usually the data is in the form of thousands of tracks constituting only a fraction of an experiment, and analysis is a tedious job.

With the advent of high-speed computers, the task of analysis has been made much easier. Before the computer may analyze the data, the coordinates of the tracks must be transferred to punch cards. This is done by projecting the magnified tracks on a glass screen, and as a pointer is manually made to follow a track, the x-, y- and z-coordinates are automatically punched onto the data cards. The computer then analyzes the geometric data and presents it in the form of plots and histograms. Recently, a new method has been applied that does away with the manual transformation of the data onto punch cards. This automatic digitizer is called the Hough-Powell or Flying Spot Digitizer System.

Just to get an idea of the magnitude of analysis required at Berkeley, California, alone, in one year, about one million photographs were examined and about 100,000 events were processed by computer. This is data that otherwise might have taken a decade to analyze.

3. THE OLD FUNDAMENTAL PARTICLES

There are 32 "old" fundamental particles which are shown in Table 15.1. All except two (v_μ and $\bar{v}_\mu$) were discovered before 1957. The particles discovered after 1957 decay much faster than the old particles and have been called *resonance particles*, i.e., the resonant associates of the old particles. The old particles will be discussed in this section while the resonance particles will be taken up later on.

TABLE 15.1

THE THIRTY-TWO ELEMENTARY PARTICLES OF 1957

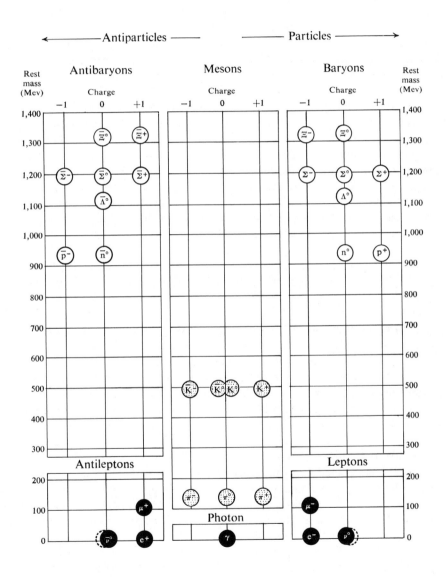

[From Chew, Gell-Mann and Rosenfeld, *Scientific American*, Feb. 1964.]

Of the 32 old fundamental particles, many were originally discovered in cosmic rays and later on produced in the laboratories. It may be said that cosmic radiation consists of very highly-energetic radiation coming from an unknown origin in outer space. There are many interesting aspects of the cosmic radiation, and they are discussed in detail in some other texts[1,2,3].

Because of the conflict between theoretical predictions and experimental discoveries, it is not possible to follow a strict chronological order in our discussion. It may be pointed out that if a particle is annihilated with another particle, the two are said to be a *particle and antiparticle*. Almost every particle has its antiparticle, except a few that are their own antiparticles.

A. ELECTRON, PROTON, AND PHOTON (e^-, p^+, γ). These were the only three particles known in 1930. The establishment of the electron and proton may be attributed to the work of J. J. Thomson in 1897 and E. Rutherford in 1910, respectively. Both the electron and proton have a spin of $\frac{1}{2}$ unit, while the mass of the proton is 1836 times that of the electron. The electron has a unit negative charge, while the proton has a unit positive charge. The work of Einstein in 1905 led to the establishment of the photon as a particle having zero rest-mass and a spin of 1 unit. The photon is its own antiparticle. The electron, proton, and photon are stable.

B. NEUTRON (n). The discovery of the neutron by Chadwick in 1932 led to the establishment of the neutron-proton model of the nucleus, as discussed in Chap. I. The mass of the neutron is very slightly larger than that of the proton and has a spin of $\frac{1}{2}$ unit. Even though the neutron is neutral overall, it has a negative magnetic moment. Both the neutron and the proton have a charge-bearing structure that has been experimentally verified[4]. A free neutron is not stable; it decays with a half-life of about 12 minutes to a proton with the emission of an electron and an antineutrino. A bound neutron is stable, because the energy that had been available for decay to a proton has been used for binding. The theoretical considerations of the substructure of the nucleons led to the eventual discovery of the *rho* and *omega* mesons.

C. POSITRON (e^+). As mentioned in Chap. IX, the positron was postulated by Dirac and discovered experimentally by Anderson in 1932. It has the same mass and spin as the electron and has equal and opposite charge. Because a positron is annihilated with an electron, it is the antiparticle of an electron. In the absence of an electron, the positron will be stable. Dirac's theory predicts antiparticles for other particles as well.

D. NEUTRINO AND ANTINEUTRINO ASSOCIATED WITH ELECTRONS (ν_e, $\bar{\nu}_e$). As already discussed in Chap. VIII, to explain the conservation of linear momentum, angular momentum, and energy in beta decay, Pauli introduced, in 1931, a particle that is emitted in beta decay and has zero rest mass, no charge, and a spin of $\frac{1}{2}$ unit. This particle was named neutrino by Fermi in 1932 and was used by him in developing a satisfactory theory of beta decay. It was also established that the neutrino interacts very weakly with matter. For the next twenty years there was no direct experimental evidence for the existence of the neutrino and antineutrino. In 1957 the existence of the two was finally established by the experiment of Cowan and Reines. These and other experiments concerning the neutrino and antineutrino were discussed in Chap. VIII. Both the particles were found to be chargeless, massless, stable, and to have spin of $\frac{1}{2}$ unit. One is the antiparticle of the other. The beta-decay reactions in which these particles participate may be written as

$$n \rightarrow p + e^- + \bar{\nu}_e$$
$$p \rightarrow n + e^+ + \nu_e$$
$$p + e^- \rightarrow n + \nu_e \tag{15.1}$$

E. Mu Mesons (μ^+, μ^-)[5]. As noted in Chap. XI, one of the physics puzzles of the 1930's, and of the present, is the explanation of the nature of nuclear forces. In order to explain different characteristics of the nuclear forces, Heisenberg, in 1933, suggested that the attraction between a neutron and a proton might be ascribed to the exchange of a charged particle from one nucleon to the other. This is in analogy with the electromagnetic interaction where an exchange of a photon is responsible for the force between charged particles. Yukawa, in 1935, published a theory in which he postulated that the force between the nucleons was due to the exchange of a new type of particle. Because of the short range of nuclear forces, the particle would not be massless. This particle would have a mass of about 270 m_e and would interact readily with matter. The search for this type of particle led to many interesting discoveries which we shall discuss now.

In 1937, S. Neddermeyer and C. Anderson[6], of the California Institute of Technology, who were actively engaged in the study of cosmic radiations, placed a lead plate in their cloud chamber in order to observe the energy losses of cosmic rays passing through it. Some of the photographs indicated the presence of particles that were less ionizing than protons. These particles could not be identified as electrons because the energy loss was much less than it would be if caused by electrons. The same sort of observations were made independently by J. Street and E. Stevenson[7], at Harvard University, who used a cloud chamber in a magnetic field. Further investigations led to the conclusion that the particles came with either unit positive or unit negative charge; and that they had a mass less than a proton, but more than an electron, which was found to be about 200 m_e (207 m_e is a closer value of the mass of a muon). This particle was called a meson, but with the discovery of pi mesons (which we shall discuss next), the name was changed to mu meson, or muon. There are two mu mesons: μ^+ and μ^-. No neutral mu meson has been found. For a long time mu mesons were taken for the Yukawa particles needed to explain the nuclear forces, but in 1947, when a pi meson was discovered, it was realized that it is the pi mesons, and not the mu mesons, that are responsible for nuclear forces.

Cosmic radiation at sea level consists of two parts: the so-called "soft component" and the "hard component". The soft component consists of electron-photon showers, while the hard component consists of muons.

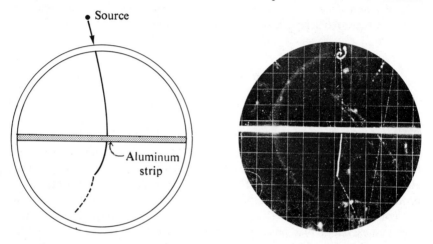

FIG. 15.1   A mu meson entering a cloud chamber filled with argon. After passing through an aluminum strip 0.63 cm thick, it stops. An emerging electron bends in the same direction as the muon, indicating a positive charge. [From R. W. Thompson, *Phys. Rev.*, **74**, 490, (1948).]

Apparently, muons travel all through the atmosphere without being absorbed much. From this we must conclude that muons do not take part in nuclear interactions. This is another reason why muons are not the mesons of the Yukawa theory. Muons lose energy only through the electromagnetic interaction. Because of their mass, they are not deflected by nuclei as the electrons are, and for this reason they do not produce many photons.

Mu mesons are unstable and are observed to decay with the emission of an electron near the end of their paths. The mean lifetime of spontaneous decay is found to be 2.2×10^{-6} sec. A cloud-chamber photograph of a muon decay taken by R. W. Thompson[8] of M.I.T., in 1948, is shown in Fig. 15.1. The energy measurements of the product electrons show a range of 9 Mev to 55 Mev. It looks as if, as in beta decay, muon decay is a three-body problem. The reactions proceed in the following fashion

$$\mu^\pm \to e^\pm + \nu_\mu + \bar{\nu}_e \qquad (15.2)$$

Muons have a spin of $\frac{1}{2}$ unit and are considered to be in the category of leptons. The neutrino and the antineutrino associated with the decay of a muon have almost zero rest-mass, no charge, and each has a spin of $\frac{1}{2}$ unit. Note that we have been particular to distinguish between the neutrino and the antineutrino. By this we imply that there are two types of neutrinos and anti-neutrinos even though they are all identical in mass, charge, and spin. If the neutrino and the antineutrino in Eq. (15.2) were identical, they would annihilate one another and produce photons. But this does not happen. We shall establish this difference more firmly after we have discussed the existence of another type of meson, the π-meson.

It may be pointed out that when mesons pass through medium-weight nuclei, only the μ^--mesons are easily observed. This is because the μ^--meson forms a mesonic atom as discussed in Chap. VI, and they decay in

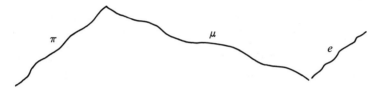

FIG. 15.2   A pion decaying into a muon, and a muon decaying into an electron. [From *Nature*, **163**, 47, (1949).]

$\sim 2.2 \times 10^{-6}$ sec. The capture cross section varies as Z^4 and takes the form of the following reaction

$$\mu^- + p \rightarrow n + \nu_\mu \qquad\qquad (15.3)$$

F. Pi Mesons (π^+, π^-, π^0)[9]. The pi meson was discovered by C. Lattes, G. Occhialini, and C. Powell[10] in 1947. They exposed some newly improved nuclear emulsion plates to cosmic rays at high altitude. Several tracks of the form shown in Fig. 15.2 were observed. The rate of increase in grain density in the first part of the track indicates a particle of mass several hundred times that of an electron. Another particle was emitted at the end of the track, where the first particle came to rest. This second particle came to a stop after traveling a distance of 0.5 mm. This indicates that it was also several hundred times heavier than the electron. Finally, the third particle produced, after traveling a certain distance, came to rest without further decay. The experimenters arrived at the conclusion that the first particle was a heavy meson, which decayed into a lighter meson. The heavier meson was different from the lighter one, because it did not decay to an electron. The heavier meson (mass = 273 m_e as we shall show) was named the pi meson (or pion) while the lighter meson is called mu meson (or muon), the one already discussed. These newly discovered pi mesons are the mesons postulated by Yukawa to explain nuclear forces. Both π^+ and π^- mesons were formed in these tracks.

It was found that the muon emitted in the decay of the pion always had the same kinetic energy—equal to 4.2 Mev. No photons were observed to be emitted in the decay of the pion, and therefore, the conservation of momentum and energy requires emission of another particle in the decay of the pion. It is found that the π^+-meson decays in the following manner

$$\pi^+ \to \mu^+ + \nu_\mu \tag{15.4}$$

while the decay of the μ^+ is given by Eq. (15.2), i.e.,

$$\mu^+ \to e^+ + \nu_\mu + \bar{\nu}_e$$

Like the negative muon, the negative pion is also captured easily by matter, and the energy released in the capture produces a "star" type pattern in the emulsion. The π^--mesons, therefore, are observed while decaying in flight according to the reaction

$$\pi^- \to \mu^- + \bar{\nu}_\mu \tag{15.5}$$

Finally, the π^0-meson (neutral pion) was discovered in 1950 by a group at M.I.T. That the neutral pion would decay into photons had already been postulated, by J. Robert Oppenheimer. In 1950, a group at M.I.T. found that interaction of cosmic rays with matter produced pi mesons as well as photons. These photons, which were assumed to arise from the decay of the neutral pi meson, initiated cascades of electron-positron pairs and lower energy photons.

The charged as well as neutral mesons have been produced in the laboratory. In 1950, J. Stellar, J. Steinberger, and W. Panofsky, at the University of California at Berkeley, produced neutral pi-mesons by bombarding a hydrogen or beryllium target with 330-Mev x-rays from a synchrotron. The gamma photons produced in the decay were detected by means of scintillation counters. The charged pions have also been produced in the laboratory by reactions similar to those shown here:

$$h\nu + p \to \pi^0 + p$$
$$h\nu + d \to \pi^0 + (n + p)$$
$$h\nu + d \to \pi^0 + d$$
$$p + p \to \pi^+ + (n + p)$$
$$p + p \to \pi^+ + d$$
$$h\nu + p \to \pi^+ + n$$
$$h\nu + n \to \pi^- + p \tag{15.6}$$

The neutral pion decays into gamma photons

$$\pi^0 \to \gamma + \gamma \tag{15.7}$$

while the charged pions decay according to Eqs. (15.4) and (15.5).

We shall now proceed to discuss methods for the determination of the masses and lifetimes of pions. We shall not discuss the methods for the determination of the spins, but it may be pointed out that all the pions have zero spins.

Fig. 15.3 shows an experimental arrangement[11] for one of the most accurate methods of determining the mass of the charged pi-mesons. The charged pi-mesons are produced by bombarding a carbon target with high energy protons. The pions travel in a semicircular path in a cyclotron and are detected by means of nuclear emulsion plates. In order to avoid errors in

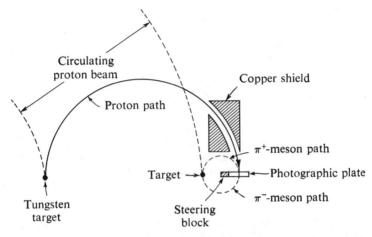

FIG. 15.3 Experimental arrangement for the mass determination of charged pi mesons. [From *Am. J. Physics*, **20**, 8, (1952).]

the determination of the intensity of the magnetic field, the emulsion plates are simultaneously exposed to protons scattered from a thin tungsten target placed in the path of the protons. The scattered protons that have the same velocity as the pions, therefore, reach the nuclear emulsion plates with the pions. The mass of the pions is determined by measuring the ranges of the protons and the pions, and by making use of the fact that for particles of the same velocity, ranges are proportional to masses. This resulted in a value of $273\ m_e$ for the mass of the charged pi mesons. The mass of the neutral pi meson has been found to be slightly less than the mass of the charged pi meson, i.e., $m_{\pi^0} = 264\ m_e$. The difference in mass is believed to be due to the difference in their interactions.

The lifetimes of charged pi mesons have been determined by making use of the decay of these particles in flight. The method used by R. Durbin, H. Loar, and W. Havens[12] is shown in Fig. 15.4. A beam of charged pi mesons is obtained by bombarding a beryllium target with 385-Mev protons from the Nevis cyclotron. The beam of pions, after emerging through a concrete shield, was deflected by a magnet and directed through three stilbene scintillation counters C_1, C_2, and C_3 as shown in the figure. Another scintillation detector, 8 inches in diameter, filled with xylene, was placed at a distance L from the C_3 counter. The counters C_1, C_2, and C_3 are all in coincidence, and thus they define the beam that comes out of C_3. The difference in the counting rates of C_1, C_2, C_3, and C_4 represents the number of mesons that decayed along the distance L. Knowing the average velocity and the mean free-path, the mean lifetime can be easily calculated. The mean lifetimes for

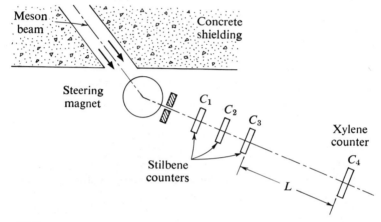

FIG. 15.4 Experimental arrangement for measuring the lifetimes of charged pi mesons. [From Durbin *et al.*, *Phys. Rev.*, **88**, 180, (1952).]

the positive pions and the negative pions are found to be almost identical, i.e., 2.54×10^{-8} sec and 2.44×10^{-8} sec, respectively. The lifetime of the neutral pion is much shorter and is found to be about 2×10^{-16} sec.

G. Neutrino and Antineutrino Associated with Mesons (v_μ, $\bar{v}_\mu$). In the previous discussion, we have been particular to distinguish between two types of neutrinos and antineutrinos. We shall now establish this difference clearly. The several modes of decay already mentioned in which neutrinos are emitted are the following:

$$n \rightarrow p + e^- + \bar{v}_e$$

$$p \rightarrow n + e^+ + v_e$$

$$p + e^- \rightarrow n + v_e \tag{15.1}$$

$$\pi^+ \rightarrow \mu^+ + v_\mu \tag{15.4}$$

$$\pi^- \rightarrow \mu^- + \bar{v}_\mu \tag{15.5}$$

$$\mu^\pm \rightarrow e^\pm + v_\mu + \bar{v}_e \tag{15.2}$$

The electron and the muon are apparently identical in all respects except that the muon is about 207 times heavier than the electron. For every reaction involving an electron there is a corresponding reaction involving a muon. As seen from Eqs. (15.1), in beta decay, neutrinos are emitted with electrons; similarly in Eq. (15.5), in pion decay, neutrinos are emitted with muons. In order to establish that neutrinos emitted from these two types of decays are different, let us consider the decay of a μ^--meson as given by Eq. (15.2). If the two neutrinos were identical, the muon should occasionally decay into an electron and gamma ray, i.e.,

$$\mu^- \rightarrow e^- + (\bar{v} + v) \rightarrow e^- + \gamma$$

virtual

process   **(15.8)**

Even though neutrinos are governed by weak interactions, and photons by electromagnetic interactions, the two-body decay of the meson given by Eq. (15.8) should be possible if the neutrino and antineutrino are antiparticles. This is possible because neutrinos can form an electron-positron pair which, in turn, will annihilate one another and emit gamma rays. But such a two-body decay, into an electron and a photon, has not been observed, and so the neutrinos are not identical. As a matter of fact, certain paradoxes in the theory of weak interactions at high energy could be resolved if it were assumed that the neutrino and antineutrino of the muon decay do not annihilate one another because they are of a different species. One may say that one neutrino in Eq. (15.2) belongs to the decay (or disappearance) of the muon, while the other belongs to the newly created electron.

In order to confirm this two-neutrino hypothesis, an experiment was performed using the 30-Bev Brookhaven synchrotron. An intense beam of pions is produced by this machine. The decaying pions produce muons and neutrinos. The best way to distinguish between the two types of neutrinos is to look for the inverse reaction. For this purpose the neutrinos produced in the pion decay are allowed to produce reactions of the type

$$v_\mu + n \rightarrow p + \mu^-$$
$$\bar{v}_\mu + p \rightarrow n + \mu^+ \qquad \textbf{(15.9)}$$

or

$$v_\mu + n \overset{?}{\rightarrow} p + e^-$$
$$\bar{v}_\mu + p \overset{?}{\rightarrow} n + e^+ \qquad \textbf{(15.10)}$$

Thus if the muon neutrinos are identical with the electron neutrinos, both types of reactions given by Eq. (15.9) and Eq. (15.10) would be produced equally. The results of the following experiment indicate that only reactions given by Eq. (15.9) take place and, hence, the two types of neutrinos are essentially different.

An experimental arrangement is shown in Fig. 15.5[13,14]. A 15-Bev proton beam produced by the Brookhaven A.G.S. machine was directed to a beryllium target, resulting in the production of pions of about 3 Bev. A part of the pion beam was allowed to fall on a spark chamber (the detector) placed at a distance of 20 m away. The decaying pions produced muons and neutrinos. By using an armor plate 13.5 m thick as shielding between the target and the spark chamber, only the neutrinos (mostly of the muon type) entered the spark chamber, while every other particle was stopped by the shielding.

The spark chamber consisted of 90 aluminum plates, one-inch thick by four feet square in 10 modules of 9 plates each. The plates were separated by

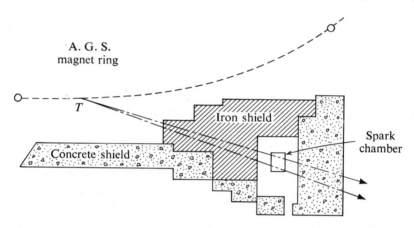

FIG. 15.5 Experimental layout for Brookhaven A.G.S. machine for the two-neutrino experiments. [From R. D. Hill, *Tracking Down Particles*, New York: W. A. Benjamin, Inc. (1962).]

3/8-inch thick transparent plastic spacers. The space between the plates was filled with neon. The volume of the detection system provided 10 tons of protons and neutrons for hard-to-capture neutrinos. By using short pulses (3 μsec long and 1.2 sec apart) from the synchrotron, it was possible to minimize the contribution of the cosmic-ray muons. The experiment started in September, 1961 and ended in June, 1962, consuming 25 good days of 20 hours each. 3000 pulses per hour containing 10^{14} neutrinos passed through the chamber. The yield was expected to be 25 reactions. Of the 5000 photographs taken, only 51 showed neutrino collisions. Of these, 29 showed muon tracks and 22 showed muon tracks with pion or other tracks. A few electron tracks observed could be explained as a result of some other reactions. (The paths due to muons are straight and strong while electrons produce erratic tracks.) The experiment clearly established that there are two types of neutrinos. The neutrinos in this experiment are of the muon type, because they cannot and did not produce electrons by reacting with neutrons.

H. STRANGE PARTICLES. After the discovery of π-mesons in 1947, many other new particles were discovered. These particles were completely unexpected, and their properties were confusing and not explainable by the existing theories. The new particles were detected from the showers of particles produced when cosmic rays pass through lead plates placed in cloud chambers. In 1947, G. Rochester and C. Butler[15] of a cosmic-ray group at the University of Manchester announced some startling results. Among the many tracks in their photographs, they found two tracks of charged particles forming curious two-prong or V-shaped patterns. They named these *V particles*.

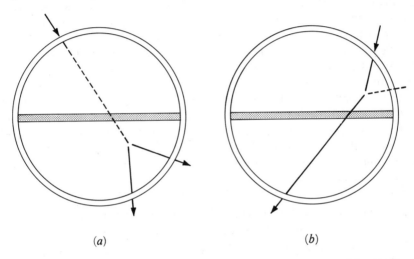

(a)   (b)

FIG. 15.6   (a) Cloud chamber diagram of a decaying lambda particle. (b) Cloud chamber diagram of a decaying sigma particle $\Sigma^+ \to n + \pi^+$. [From Butler and Rochester, *Nature*, **160**, 855, (1947).]

Considering all possible interpretations, the conclusion was that an unknown neutral particle that did not leave any track in the cloud chamber decayed into two charged particles as shown in Fig. 15.6(a). The neutral particle was named the *lambda particle* and was found to decay into a proton and a negative pi meson

$$\Lambda^0 \to p^+ + \pi^-$$ (15.11)

The other illustration, Fig. 15.6(b), showed an unknown charged particle suddenly changing direction in the cloud chamber. The only conclusion was that some unknown charged particle decayed into a charged particle and a neutral particle as shown in the figure. The particle was named the *positive sigma particle* and it decayed into a neutron and a positive pi meson

$$\Sigma^+ \to n + \pi^+$$ (15.12)

Soon afterwards another particle was found, which was called a *neutral K*, and which decayed into a positive and a negative pion

$$K \to \pi^+ + \pi^-$$ (15.13)

Once the road to new particles was opened, many more were discovered. On the basis of their masses, they were classified into two categories: (1) the *hyperons*; the particles with masses greater than the mass of the proton. [Some of these are lambda (Λ^0); sigma (Σ^+, Σ^-, Σ^0); and the negative and neutral *xi* (Ξ^-, Ξ^0) particles.] (2) the *heavy mesons*; the particles with masses less than that of the proton and more than that of the π-meson (K^0, K^+, K^-, belong to this group.) Before we discuss some properties of these particles, we shall explain what we mean by *strange particles*.

Besides many undesirable properties, the newly discovered particles, like the Λ and the K, have a peculiar property concerning their decay times. These particles are made by the strong interactions, the time scale of which is 10^{-23} seconds. Their lifetimes, as shown in Table 15.2, range from $\sim 10^{-8}$ to 10^{-10} seconds, which is on the time scale of weak interactions. Thus, the particles are produced by strong interactions, but they decay by weak interactions. But according to the fundamental principle of reversibility, a particle made in a strong interaction should decay by a strong interaction.

TABLE 15.2

MASSES AND MEAN LIVES OF THE ELEMENTARY PARTICLES

	Particle	Particle charge states	Antiparticle charge states	Mass (Mev)	Mean life (seconds)
Leptons	Neutrino	ν_e, ν_μ	$\bar\nu_e, \bar\nu_\mu$	0	stable
	Electron	e^-	e^+	.51	stable
	Muon	μ^-	μ^+	105.66	2.2×10^{-6}
Bosons	Photon	γ	γ	0	stable
	Pion	π^0	π^0	135	2.3×10^{-16}
		π^+	π^-	139.6	2.6×10^{-8}
	K-meson	K^+	$\bar K^-$	494	1.2×10^{-8}
		K^0	$\bar K^0$	497.8	6×10^{-8} 1×10^{-10}
Baryons	Proton	p^+	$\bar p^-$	938.2	stable
	Neutron	n^0	$\bar n^0$	939.5	1×10^3
	Lambda	Λ^0	$\bar\Lambda^0$	1115.4	2.5×10^{-10}
	Sigma	Σ^+	$\bar\Sigma^-$	1189.4	$.8 \times 10^{-10}$
		Σ^0	$\bar\Sigma^0$	1191.5	$<.1 \times 10^{-10}$
		Σ^-	$\bar\Sigma^+$	1196	1.6×10^{-10}
	Xi	Ξ^0	$\bar\Xi^0$	1311	1.5×10^{-10}
		Ξ^-	$\bar\Xi^+$	1318.4	1.3×10^{-10}

[From R. D. Hill, *Scientific American*, Jan., 1963.]

It is this great discrepancy between their expected and observed lifetimes (they live 100,000 billion times longer than they should!) that has earned them the name "strange" or "queer" particles.

A. Pais[16] and many others offered a solution to this paradox. They said that strange particles are produced in groups of two or more. It implies that strong interactions that manufacture strange particles work on more than one at a time. This concept is known as *associated production*. For example, an ordinary K-particle must be produced with its antiparticle or with an ordinary hyperon. An anti-K particle will be associated with an anti-hyperon, not with an ordinary hyperon. After the production, unless the associated particles manage to locate one another (which is improbable), their decay is a comparatively slow process. The principle of reversibility is automatically satisfied because a strong process of this kind would not be reversible due to a lack of energy. The strange particles produced by strong interactions do not have enough energy to decay by strong interactions, and they move away from each other after creation. Moving away keeps them from decaying by a strong interaction at that time, but they are caught up later by weak processes, i.e., they decay by weak interactions.

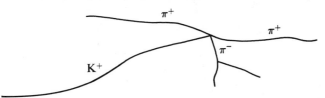

FIG. 15.7 The decay of a K meson. [From *Nature*, **163**, 82, (1949).]

I. K MESONS (K^+, K^-, K^0, $\overline{K}^0$). In 1949 C. Powell's group [17] at the University of Bristol discovered a new particle whose emulsion photographs showed tracks of the form shown in Fig. 15.7. The mass of this particle was found to be between a pi meson and a proton. This new charged particle, when it came to rest in the emulsion, decayed into three pi mesons in the same plane. Of the three pions produced, one stopped in the emulsion leaving the characteristic star of a negative-pion capture as shown in the figure. From the measurement of the masses of the products, the mass of the decaying particle was found to be 964 m_e. The charged particles were given the names *positive K meson* and *negative K meson*, and each decayed into three pions by the following reactions

$$K^\pm \to \pi^\pm + \pi^\pm + \pi^\mp \tag{15.14}$$

Originally $K^\pm$ mesons were called *tau* (τ) and *theta* (θ) *mesons*, but at present tau and theta are just two different modes of decay[18] of K^+ and K^- mesons, respectively. These two decay schemes are shown in Fig. 15.8 and Fig. 15.9.

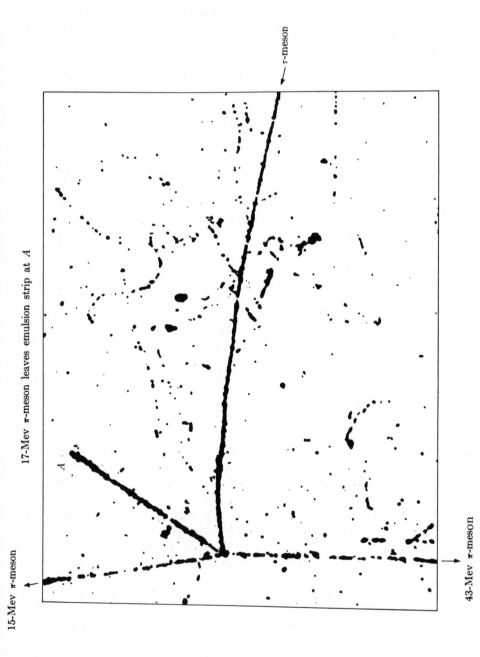

17-Mev π-meson leaves emulsion strip at A

15-Mev π-meson

43-Mev π-meson

τ-meson

FIG. 15.8 Decay of the K^--meson by τ-mode into three mesons. [Courtesy of the Brookhaven National Laboratory, Upton, New York.]

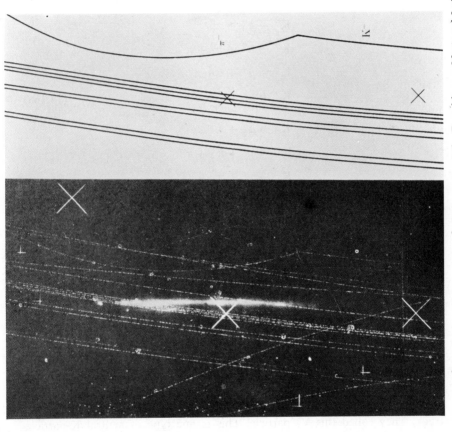

FIG. 15.9 Decay of the K^--meson by θ-mode, i.e., $K^- \rightarrow \pi^- + \pi^0$. [Courtesy of the Brookhaven National Laboratory, Upton, New York.]

The two corresponding reactions are the following:

$$K^+ \to \tau \to \pi^+ + \pi^- + \pi^+ \tag{15.15a}$$

$$K^- \to \theta \to \pi^- + \pi^0 \tag{15.15b}$$

There are many other alternatives by which these K mesons decay; for example,

$$K^+ \to \mu^+ + \nu$$

$$K^+ \to \pi^+ + \pi^0$$

$$K^+ \to \pi^+ + \pi^0 + \pi^0$$

$$K^+ \to \mu^+ + \nu + \pi^0$$

$$K^+ \to e^+ + \nu + \pi^0 \tag{15.16a}$$

and

$$K^- \to \mu^- + \bar{\nu}$$

$$K^- \to \pi^- + \pi^+ + \pi^-$$

$$K^- \to \pi^- + \pi^0 + \pi^0$$

$$K^- \to \mu^- + \bar{\nu} + \pi^0$$

$$K^- \to e^- + \bar{\nu} + \pi^0 \tag{15.16b}$$

One of the reasons why K mesons were difficult to detect is that there are so many modes that are available for their decay.

In addition to the two charged K mesons, there is a third one, the neutral K meson (K^0). As in pions, all the three K mesons have zero spin. As previously mentioned, charged K-mesons can decay in a number of ways, with a lifetime of 1.2×10^{-8} sec. The neutral K meson is a very strange one. Unlike the neutral pi mesons, the neutral K meson is not identical with its antimatter counterpart ($\overline{K}^0$). The reason for the lack of identity between K^0 and $\overline{K}^0$ is explained below.

G. Rochester and C. Butler[19] observed a particle which in 1×10^{-10} second decayed into a positive and a negative pi meson, forming a V-shaped track. They called this V_1^0 particle. This is one type of neutral K-particle and was called K_1^0. The other neutral particle, which is called K_2^0, decays in 6.1×10^{-8} sec into one of the following three products: (1) three pi mesons, (2) one pi meson, one mu meson, and one neutrino, and (3) one pi meson, one electron, and one neutrino. It is because of these two neutral particles, K_1^0 and K_2^0, that the difference between K^0 and $\overline{K}^0$ exists. Both K^0 and $\overline{K}^0$ are mixtures of K_1^0 and K_2^0, and the properties of these mixtures were predicted by M. Gell-Mann[20]. The view that K^0 is not identical with its antiparticle, $\overline{K}^0$, was supported by Gell-Mann[20], because experimentally these two had no tendency to be produced equally in certain reactions.

J. HYPERONS (Λ^0, Σ^+, Σ^0, Σ^-, Ξ^0, Ξ^-). Hyperons fall into three groups designated as lambda (Λ), sigma (Σ) and xi (Ξ). Because of the nature of their decay, all hyperons seem to be composed of nucleons and mesons. The tracks of these particles from cosmic ray investigation had been seen long ago, but they were not actually identified till 1956, when most of these particles were theoretically postulated by M. Gell-Mann[20] and independently by K. Nishijima[21]. These particles were produced in the laboratory by means of high-energy accelerators, the hyperons always being produced in association with K-mesons. With the construction of still higher-energy machines, it has been possible to produce hyperon pairs instead of hyper-K-meson pairs.

All the hyperons and antihyperons are strange particles, and thus they decay through weak interactions. The only exception is the sigma-zero, Σ^0, particle for which the electromagnetic decay route is open, i.e.,

$$\Sigma^0 \to \Lambda^0 + \gamma \tag{15.17}$$

We shall now discuss briefly the discovery of some of these hyperons.

The lambda particle occurs only as a neutral particle. It was one of the original V particles and was named V_2^0. Being neutral, its presence was inferred from its decay products—a negative meson and a proton—as given by Eq. (15.11). The alternative decay mode is to a neutral pion and a neutron. There is a very small probability of Λ^0 decaying into a proton, an electron, and a neutrino.

The lambda particle was produced in the laboratory for the first time in 1953 by W. Fowler, R. Shutt, and A. Thorndike[22]. A beam of 1.5-Bev pi mesons was allowed to enter a cloud chamber containing hydrogen at 18 times atmospheric pressure in a field of 11,000 gauss. The pion interacts with a proton producing a hyperon and a K^0-meson, as shown in Fig. 15.10.

$$\pi^- + p \to \Lambda^0 + K^0 \tag{15.18}$$

From momentum and energy conservation, the lambda particle was found to be 1.26 Bev. It traveled a distance of 0.65 cm before decaying into two charged particles—a proton and a π^--meson. The lifetime of the Λ^0 was found to be 2×10^{-11} sec. Both Λ^0 and $\overline{\Lambda}^0$ have a spin of $\frac{1}{2}$.

The sigma hyperons exist in three forms: positive, Σ^+; negative, Σ^-; and neutral, Σ^0. They have almost equal masses, with Σ^- being the heaviest, i.e., $m_{\Sigma^-} = 1196$ Mev. The mean lifetimes of Σ^+, Σ^-, and Σ^0 are $\sim .8 \times 10^{-10}$ sec, $\sim 1.6 \times 10^{-10}$ sec, and $< 0.1 \times 10^{-10}$ sec, respectively. Some of the decay modes of these hyperons are the following:

$$\Sigma^+ \to p + \pi^0$$
$$\Sigma^+ \to n + \pi^+$$
$$\Sigma^- \to n + \pi^-$$
$$\Sigma^0 \to \Lambda^0 + \gamma \tag{15.19}$$

With the availability of very high-energy beams of charged particles, it has been possible to produce Σ^+ in the laboratory by the following reaction[23].

$$\pi^+ + p \to \Sigma^+ + K^+ \tag{15.20}$$

A beam of pions was produced by bombarding a polyethylene target with a proton beam from the Brookhaven cosmotron. Pions of definite energy and momentum were allowed to enter a bubble chamber placed in a magnetic field of 17,000 gauss. The K^+ produced in the reaction leaves the chamber, while Σ^+ decays into a positive pion and a neutral particle.

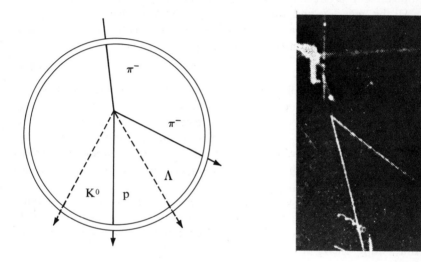

FIG. 15.10 Production of a lambda particle in a cloud chamber. [From Fowler *et al.*, *Phys. Rev.*, **91**, 1287, (1953)].

The xi hyperons (Ξ) are the heaviest and exist only as two types: negative, Ξ^-, and neutral, Ξ^0. Theory does not predict Ξ^+, and none have been observed as yet. The xi hyperons are also called *cascade particles* because of their lengthy decay. For example, a negative xi-particle decays in about 0.1×10^{-9} sec into a lambda particle and a negative pi meson. The lambda particle further decays as previously explained. The decays of neutral and negative xi hyperons are as follows:

$$\Xi^- \to \Lambda + \pi^-$$
$$\Xi^0 \to \Lambda + \pi^0 \tag{15.21}$$

Xi hyperons as well as their antiparticles have a spin of $\frac{1}{2}$.

All the particles just discussed and some others, which we shall discuss next, are shown with their characteristics and decay products in Tables

15.1–15.3. Keeping in chronological order, we will next discuss antinucleons and anti-xi minus and anti-xi zero particles—the last two being strange particles.

K. THE ANTIPROTON ($\bar{p}$). The theoretical formulation by Dirac led to the differential equation of an electron, which predicted an antiparticle of the electron. This antiparticle, the positron, was detected by Anderson in 1932.

TABLE 15.3
SPINS AND DECAY PRODUCTS OF THE ELEMENTARY PARTICLES

Particle		Spin	Decay products
Xi	Ξ^-	$\frac{1}{2}$	$\Lambda^0 + \pi^-$
	Ξ^0	$\frac{1}{2}$	
Sigma	Σ^+	$\frac{1}{2}$	$p + \pi^0 \quad n + \pi^+$
	Σ^-	$\frac{1}{2}$	$n + \pi^-$
	Σ^0	$\frac{1}{2}$	$\Lambda^0 + \gamma$
Lambda	Λ^0	$\frac{1}{2}$	$p + \pi^- \quad n + \pi^0$
Proton	p	$\frac{1}{2}$	
Neutron	n	$\frac{1}{2}$	$p + e^- + \bar{\nu}$
K meson	K^+	0	$\mu^+ + \nu \quad \pi^+ + \pi^0 \quad \pi^+ + \pi^+ + \pi^-$
			$\pi^+ + \pi^0 + \pi^0 \quad \mu^+ + \nu + \pi^0 \quad e^+ + \nu + \pi^0$
	K^-	0	$\mu^- + \bar{\nu} \quad \pi^- + \pi^0 \quad \pi^- + \pi^- + \pi^+$
			$\pi^- + \pi^0 + \pi^0 \quad \mu^- + \bar{\nu} + \pi^0 \quad e^- + \bar{\nu} + \pi^0$
	K^0_1	0	$\pi^+ + \pi^- \quad \pi^0 + \pi^0$
			$\pi^+ + e^- + \bar{\nu} \quad \pi^- + e^+ + \nu \quad \pi^+ + \mu^- + \bar{\nu}$
	K^0_2	0	$\pi^- + \mu^+ + \nu \quad \pi^+ + \pi^- + \pi^0 \quad \pi^0 + \pi^0 + \pi^0$
Pion	π^+	0	$\mu^0 + \nu$
	π^-	0	$\mu^- + \bar{\nu}$
	π^0	0	$\gamma + \gamma$
Muon	μ^-	$\frac{1}{2}$	$e^- + \nu + \bar{\nu}$
Electron	e^-	$\frac{1}{2}$	
Neutrino	ν	$\frac{1}{2}$	
Photon	γ	1	

[From Gell-Mann and Rosenbaum, *Scientific American*, July, 1957.]

Similar formulation for the proton, which also has a spin $\frac{1}{2}$, predicted an antiparticle of the proton, the so called *anti-proton*[24,25,26,27]. The almost 20-year search for this particle ended in 1955.[25,26] According to theory it should have the same mass as a proton, equal and opposite charge, and should be stable. It should have the same spin as a proton, but opposite magnetic moment. The antiproton should be mutually annihilated by a proton, and it should be generated as one member of a proton-antiproton pair.

Before 1955, there were indications of the presence of the antiproton from cosmic ray studies in nuclear emulsions[24]. In 1955, when the bevatron at the University of California started producing highly energetic particles, antiprotons were produced. Before describing this experiment, we shall show that the energy required to produce an antiproton is about 6 Bev. The antiproton is produced from a proton-proton collision according to the following reaction.

$$p + p \rightarrow p^+ + p^+ + p^+ + \bar{p}^- \tag{15.22}$$

Note that an antiproton must always be produced in a proton-antiproton pair with a new proton. One might think that if the incoming proton has energy equal to twice the rest mass energy of the proton, i.e., $2 \times 938 = 1876$ Mev, the reaction will start. But this is not possible because the momentum will not be conserved. The final products will be produced at rest while the initial system is not at rest. Let us say that the most efficient way to distribute the initial momentum, p_i, is for each of the final protons to share it equally, say p_{1f}, i.e.,

$$p_{1f} = p_i/4 \tag{15.23a}$$

Thus the minimum initial bombarding-energy, E_i, of the proton must be

$$E_i = 4E_{1f} + 2M_0 c^2, \tag{15.23b}$$

where M_0 is the rest mass of the proton. But from relativity, the relation between the momentum, kinetic energy E_K total energy, and mass is the following

$$E_K + M_0 c^2 = \sqrt{M_0^2 c^4 + p_{1f}^2 c^2} \tag{15.23c}$$

or

$$p_{1f} c = \sqrt{(E_K + M_0 c^2)^2 - M_0^2 c^4} \tag{15.23d}$$

Substituting (15.23d) into (15.23a), with $E_K = E_i$, we get the following

$$(E_{1f} + M_0 c^2)^2 - (M_0^2 c^4) = \tfrac{1}{16}[(E_i + M_0 c^2)^2 - M_0^2 c^4] \tag{15.23e}$$

Substituting for E_i from (15.23b) and solving for E_{1f} we get,

$$E_{1f} = M_0 c^2 \tag{15.24}$$

Thus the minimum initial kinetic energy required, from Eq. (15.23b), is the following

$$E_i = 4M_0 c^2 + 2M_0 c^2$$
$$= 6M_0 c^2 \simeq 5628 \text{ Mev} \tag{15.25}$$

An experimental arrangement used by E. Segrè and C. Wiegand[25,26] for the production and detection of antiprotons is shown in Fig. 15.11. A beam of 6-Bev protons was obtained from the bevatron at the University of California. In proton-proton collisions, as many as $\sim 100,000$ mesons (μ^-, K^-, π^-) and e^- were produced for each proton-antiproton pair produced. A system of deflecting magnets, M_1 and M_2, was used to select a beam of some particular momentum and energy. The time-of-flight method used is shown in the figure. The negative-beam momentum was 1.19 Bev/c, which corresponds to a velocity of 0.99 c for π^--mesons and 0.78 c for antiprotons. The scintillation counters S_1 and S_2 were placed 12 meters apart, which corresponds to a time-of-flight of 51 nanoseconds and 40 nanoseconds for the antiproton and the π^--meson, respectively. In order to observe coincidences between the pulses from S_1 and S_2, the signal from S_1 was delayed for 51 millimicroseconds. To reduce the background still further, two Čerenkov detectors, C_1 and C_2, were used. The counter, C_1, was designed to respond only to particles with a velocity greater than 0.78 c, while C_2 was designed to detect particles with velocities between 0.75 c and 0.78. c The counter, C_1,

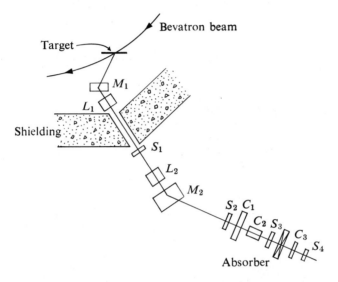

FIG. 15.11   The experimental arrangement of a mass spectrograph used for the detection of the antiproton. [From Segrè and Wiegand, *Scientific American*, June, 1956.]

worked as an anticoincidence counter for the coincidence between S_1 and S_2, while C_2 was used as a further check on the coincidences between S_1 and S_2. A real antiproton, therefore, had three conditions to fulfill—a delayed coincidence between S_1 and S_2, with a delay time of 51 millmicroseconds, no coincidence with C_1, and a coincidence count with C_2. Typical oscilloscope traces are shown in Fig. 15.12, and the experimental results are shown in Fig. 15.13. It may be pointed out that there were as many as 40,000 mesons for each antiproton detected.

The annihilation of an antiproton was also investigated at Berkeley. A beam of 6.2-Bev protons was incident on an emulsion. One of the particles produced was an antiproton. It traveled in the emulsion, producing a star that was initiated by the annihilation of a proton-antiproton pair. About 20 such tracks of antiprotons were observed.

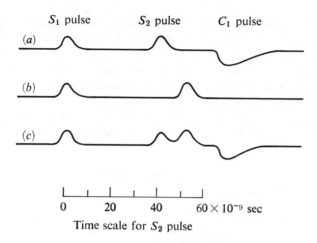

S_1 pulse S_2 pulse C_1 pulse

(a)

(b)

(c)

0   20   40 60×10^{-9} sec

Time scale for S_2 pulse

FIG. 15.12 Diagram of oscilloscope traces for (a) meson traversal, (b) antiproton traversal, and (c) accidental coincidence. [From O. Chamberlain, E. Segrè, C. Wiegand and T. Ypsilantis, *Phys. Rev.*, **100**, 947, (1958).]

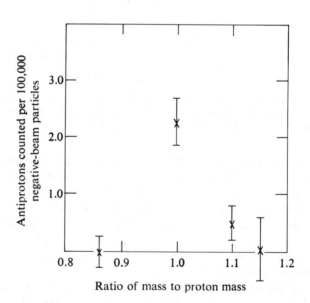

FIG. 15.13 Plot of the experimental counting rate of antiprotons versus the ratio of mass to proton mass. [From O. Chamberlain, E. Segrè, C. Wiegand and T. Ypsilantis, *Phys. Rev.*, **100**, 947, (1958).]

L. THE ANTINEUTRON ($\bar{n}$)[27,28]. The antineutron is supposed to have the same mass as the neutron, no charge, and it should be unstable—decaying by positron emission with the same half-life as the neutron. The detection of the antineutron is difficult, because it leaves no track until it is annihilated. The discovery of the antineutron was made from a propane bubble-chamber photograph. An incoming antiproton interacts with a proton, giving up its charge and forming a neutron-antineutron pair. The pair annihilates one another, giving rise to a star.

M. ANTI-XI PLUS ($\bar{\Xi}^+$). This is also sometimes written as anti-xi minus because $\bar{\Xi}^+$ is an antiparticle of Ξ^-. The anti-xi minus is the next-to-the-last strange particle predicted by Gell-Mann and Nishijima and was found[29] in 1962. The experiments were done in the United States using the 30-Bev machine at Brookhaven and in Europe by using the accelerator at CERN. The anti-xi plus is created, along with its antiparticle, the xi-minus, by the collision of a high-speed antiproton with a proton. The anti-xi particle decays into an antilambda and a pi meson in about one billionth of a second. The anti-lambda then decays into an antiproton and a pi meson. It is this complex mode of decay, as shown in Fig. 15.14, that had made them known as cascade particles.

A team of scientists from Yale examined about 34,000 photographs of bubble chamber tracks, each showing 14 antiproton tracks, and they found one anti-xi minus ($\bar{\Xi}^+$) event. It may be pointed out that the energy available from these machines was barely adequate.

N. ANTI-XI ZERO ($\bar{\Xi}^0$). This is an antiparticle of xi-zero and is the last of the expected strange elementary-particles. This was found in 1963 by a team of 13 physicists[30] from Yale and Brookhaven. The 30-Bev synchrotron at Brookhaven was used to produce a beam of antiprotons with an energy of 3.69 Bev. A 20-inch hydrogen-filled bubble chamber was used as a target and detector. The interaction of an antiproton with a proton produces an anti-xi zero, and the latter, being neutral, is difficult to detect. Its immediate decay products, the antilambda-zero and the neutral pi meson, are both neutral and also hard to detect, but the decay of the antilambda-zero to an antiproton and a positive pion, both of which produce tracks, may be observed. Fig. 15.15 shows the production and decay of the anti-xi zero particle.

Of the 300,000 photographs made from September 1961 until sometime in 1963, only three events showed the rare anti-xi zero particle. The appearance and configuration of these tracks was enough to convince the Yale group that they had detected the anti-xi zero.

O. SUMMARY[31]. Tables 15.1–15.3 show all the elementary particles discovered up to the early 1960's. Some of the particles not discussed in detail here are

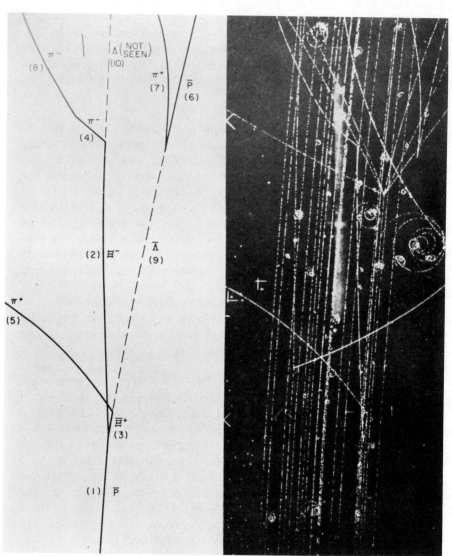

FIG. 15.14   Sketch and bubble chamber photograph of paths of an anti-xi-minus particle produced by the reaction $\bar{p} + p \rightarrow \Xi^- + \overline{\Xi}^+$. The photograph also shows the subsequent decays of Ξ^- and $\overline{\Xi}^+$. [From *Phys. Rev. Letters*, **8**, 255, 1962.]

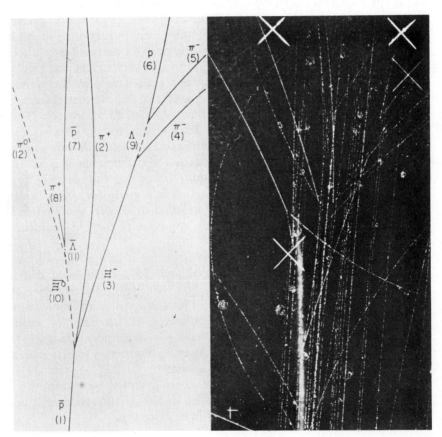

FIG. 15.15 Sketch and bubble chamber photograph of paths of an anti-xi-zero particle produced by the reaction $\bar{p} + p \rightarrow \bar{\Xi}^0 + \pi^+$. The photograph also shows the subsequent decays of Ξ^- and $\bar{\Xi}^0$. [From *Phys. Rev. Letters*, **11**, 165, 1963.]

also shown in the tables. This list includes all the particles except another new class of particles, the resonance particles, which we shall discuss in the next section. Also included in these tables are the masses, spins, lifetimes, and re-actions of the particles. In general, the elementary particles have been classi-fied into baryons, mesons, and leptons. The photon falls in a separate group by itself. The classification of these particles will be taken up in detail later.

4. RESONANCE PARTICLES[32,33,34]

In the late fifties, the list of the fundamental particles was almost static, and for the moment many physicists firmly believed that the list was complete. These fundamental particles may be called stable, because they decay in about a ten-billionth of a second. This time is long enough for the particles to travel appreciable distances in various detectors, so that their tracks are visible. A new class of particles, which caused quite a stir among physicists during the 1950's and 1960's, was slowly becoming apparent. One common character-istic of the new particles is their decay time of about 10^{-23} seconds. This time is so small that the particles travel a distance equal to only a few nuclear diameters. This is too short a time for tracks to be visible. The only way to detect the particles is by their decay products. The question one may ask is: Did these particles really exist autonomously before decaying, or were they just a group of particles that moved together in a group for a short while before they decayed? This is a very hard question to answer, and physicists have avoided answering it by calling this new class of particles resonance particles.

The first indication of resonance particles came from a group, working with the cosmotron at Brookhaven in 1952 and 1953, who showed that a very strong resonance peak occurred at about 169 Mev in the scattering of positive and negative pions from protons. This was a strong indication that a meson and a nucleon may exist in a short-lived excited state for about 10^{-23} seconds and may be regarded as having an independent existence. It was believed that the resonance peak was due to a momentary formation of a resonance particle from pi-mesons and nucleons.

Later, many more resonances were discovered that were formed by K-mesons with hyperons. It is not possible to discuss all these resonances here. The experimental details of a few will be given here.

A. THE Y* RESONANCE. The first resonance particle was observed by the bubble-chamber group at the Lawrence Radiation Laboratory in 1960. Using high energy K-minus mesons aimed at liquid hydrogen in a bubble chamber, they (L. Alvarez, P. Eberhard, M. Good, W. Graziano, H. Ticho, and S. Wojcicki) observed the following reaction:

$$\overline{K}^- + p^+ \to \Lambda^0 + \pi^+ + \pi^- \tag{15.26}$$

The energy and momentum represented by the visible pion tracks were analyzed with the aid of a computer. In a certain fraction of the few hundred events
observed, they discovered that one of the charged pions was recoiling from
one rather than from two other particles. This was a conclusion drawn from

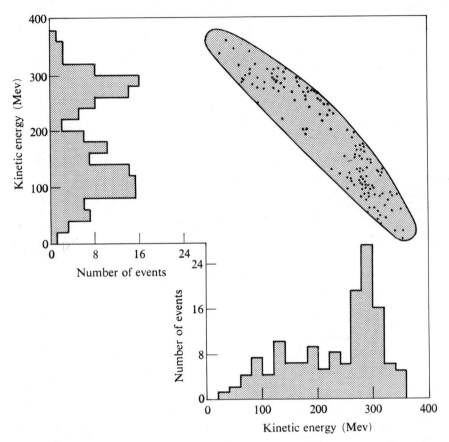

FIG. 15.16 The interaction of a negative K-meson and a proton as observed
by the bubble-chamber group under Alvarez is shown in the form of Dalitz plot.
The distribution indicates that two particles, rather than three, are produced in
the reaction $\bar{K}^- + p^+ \rightarrow Y^* + \pi$. The width, 60 Mev, of the strongest resonance
peak corresponds to an average lifetime of 10^{-23} second for the Y*. [From
R. D. Hill, *Scientific American*, Jan., 1963.]

the analysis of the energy spectrum. The implication was that the other pion
and the lambda did not break apart immediately but remained together as
one unit long enough for the other observed pion to recoil from it. The results
of the computer analysis are shown in Fig. 15.16, while the reaction is shown
in Fig. 15.17. In those few selected events, the reaction was thought to have

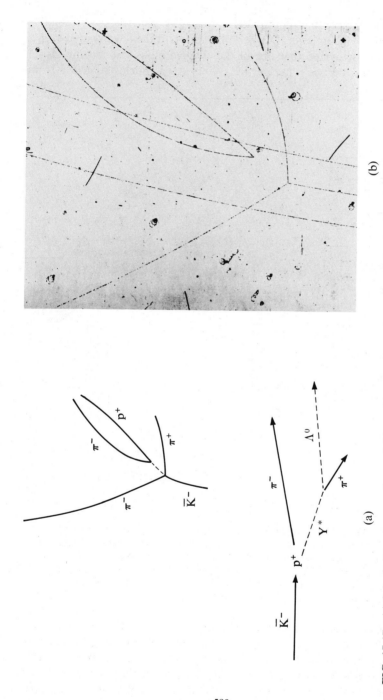

(a)

(b)

FIG. 15.17 (a) Schematic representation and (b) a bubble-chamber photograph (with a sketch) of a Y* resonance particle produced by a collision of $\bar{K}^-$ with p^+. Before Y* can produce a track it disintegrates into a neutral lambda particle (broken line representing no track) and a positive pion. The neutral lambda subsequently decays into p^+ and π^- as shown. [From R. D. Hill, *Scientific American*, Jan., 1963.]

taken place in the following manner:

$$\overline{K}^- + p^+ \rightarrow Y^{*\pm} + \pi^\mp \qquad (15.27)$$

In a time so short that Y* leaves no observable track, the reaction is followed by

$$Y^{*\pm} \rightarrow \Lambda^0 + \pi^\pm \qquad (15.28)$$

Calculations of the energies and momenta involved indicated a mass of 1384 Mev for Y*. This mass is made up of the rest masses of the two particles (Λ and π) into which Y* decays and the kinetic energies with which these two particles fly apart. Because there was not an infinitely sharp "spike" in the spectrum, there was an uncertainty of 60 Mev in the mass. This uncertainty in the mass corresponds to an uncertainty of 10^{-23} seconds in the time. This period is the lifetime of Y*.

Is the Y* an elementary particle, which decays into a lambda and pion, or is it just a combination of the two traveling together for a short while? The only answer is that these particles are classed as resonance particles.

B. THE N* RESONANCE. Once the Y* resonance was established, its discoverers at once pointed to a previously known resonance between a pion and a nucleon—the so-called N* resonance. In 1952, Enrico Fermi and his colleagues at the University of Chicago, and, later, another group at the Carnegie Institute of Technology, found that the scattering cross-section of pions from protons increased from 100 Mev to 200 Mev, the highest-energy pion beam available at that time. Later experiments by L. Yuan and S. Lindenbaum using higher energy pion beams from the Brookhaven cosmotron showed that the cross section reached a distinct maximum at 195 Mev and then fell off quite sharply after that. It was suggested by Keith A. Brueckner that there was an unusually strong interaction between the pion and nucleon at this energy. The phase of the scattered pion was shifted 90° at resonance, increasing and decreasing on each side of the peak. Thus it was established that N* behaves as a resonance particle of mass 1237 Mev and has a lifetime slightly shorter than that of Y*.

C. THE RHO AND OMEGA RESONANCES. In the late 1950's, experiments revealed that the proton and the neutron both had magnetic properties over a finite region of space instead of at a point. Such an electromagnetic structure of the nucleons led to certain ideas, dividing the nucleon charge into three parts, as follows: (1) There is a small central core accounting for 1/4 of the total charge. (2) A vector portion, (+ for the proton and − for the neutron) extending over the whole nucleon, accounts for 1/2 of the total charge. (3) There is a positive scalar portion extending over the whole particle and contributing to 1/4 of the charge.

As discussed in Chap. XII, the Yukawa forces are responsible for the nuclear interaction. The force is caused by the exchange of π-mesons. This leads to the belief that there is a cloud of π-mesons surrounding the nucleons. In 1959 it was proposed[35] that the vector part of the charge and the magnetic properties could be explained if two of the pions emitted formed a resonance of mass at 600 Mev while in the cloud.

Such predictions led to the search for a 600-Mev resonance. The experimental results showed that when a high-energy pion produces a pion by colliding with a proton, there is a strong attraction between the pions. Eventually,

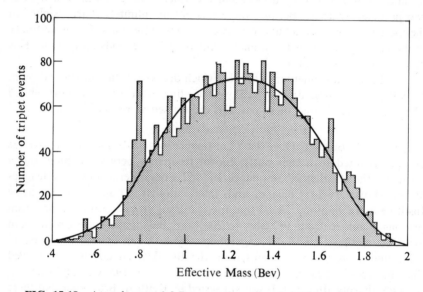

FIG. 15.18 A peak near 0.8 Bev corresponding to a three-pion resonance called the "omega resonance particle" was observed in experiments carried out at the Lawrence Radiation Laboratory. [From R. D. Hill, *Scientific American*, Jan., 1963.]

an analysis of the type used in the discovery of Y* was applied to these experiments. In 1960, this led to the discovery of a resonance known as the *rho resonance*[36], which has a mass of 760 Mev.

Considerations similar to the discovery of the rho resonance led to the discovery of another resonance called the *omega resonance*. In 1959, G. Chew pointed out that the scalar part of the electromagnetic structure of the nucleon could be due to a three-pion resonance of approximately the same mass as the two pion resonance state. This resonance was finally discovered[37] in 1961 at the Lawrence Radiation Laboratory. In studying the annihilation of protons and antiprotons in the 72-inch liquid-hydrogen bubble chamber, some reactions were observed producing four-pion tracks. Conservation of momentum and energy indicated, actually, five-pions according to the following reaction:

$$p^+ + \bar{p}^- \rightarrow \pi^+ + \pi^- + \pi^0 + \pi^+ + \pi^- \qquad \textbf{(15.29)}$$

A computer analysis (Fig. 15.18) for every possible combination of three of the five pions revealed that only the combination of π^-, π^0, and π^+ led to a mass-value group having a peak characteristic of a resonance particle. The observed mass was found to be 790 Mev, and its lifetime was found to be $\sim 4 \times 10^{-23}$ seconds.

D. OMÉGA MINUS (Ω^-)[38]. The discovery of the omega-minus resonance-particle will conclude the discussion of experimental discoveries. This particle was predicted from theoretical considerations required by the eight-fold way to complete a supermultiplet (to be discussed later) of 10 particles sharing the same basic characteristics. Gell-Mann and Susumu Okubo of the University of Rochester predicted its mass to be 1676 to 1680 Mev. (i.e. larger than the xi doublet).

TABLE 15.4

RESONANCE PARTICLES AS OF 1963

Resonance particle	Isotopic spin	Total angular momentum	Mass (Mev)	Particle production
$\eta(\pi^+\pi^-\pi^0)$	0	0	550	$\pi^+ + d^+ \rightarrow \eta^0 + p^+ + p^+$
$\rho(\pi\pi)$	1	1	760	$p^+ + \bar{p}^- \rightarrow p^0 + \pi^+ + \pi^-$ $\pi^\pm + p^+ \rightarrow p^\pm + p^+$
$\omega(\pi^+\pi^-\pi^0,\pi^0\gamma)$	0	1	790	$p^+ + \bar{p}^- \rightarrow \omega^0 + \pi^+ + \pi^-$ $\pi^+ + d^+ \rightarrow \omega^0 + p^+ + p^+$
$K^*(K\pi)$	1/2	1	880	$\bar{K}^- + p^+ \rightarrow K^* + p^+$ $\pi^- + p^+ \rightarrow K^* + \Sigma$
$K\bar{K}$	?	?	1,020	$\pi^- + p^+ \rightarrow \bar{K}^0 + K^0 + n^0$ $\bar{K}^- + p^+ \rightarrow \bar{K}^- + K^+ + \Lambda^0$
$N^*(\pi N)$	3/2	3/2	1,237	$\pi^\pm + p^+ \rightarrow \pi^\pm + p^+$
$Y^*(\pi\Lambda,\pi\Sigma)$	1	3/2	1,384	$\bar{K}^- + p^+ \rightarrow Y^* + \pi$ $\pi^- + p^+ \rightarrow Y^* + \bar{K}$
$Y^{**}(2\pi\Lambda,\pi\Sigma)$	0	1/2	1,405	$\bar{K}^- + p^+ \rightarrow Y^{**} + \pi$
$N^{**}(\pi N)$	1/2	3/2	1,516	$\pi^- + p^+ \rightarrow N^{**} + \pi$
$Y^{***}(\pi\Lambda,\pi\Sigma,KN)$	0	3/2	1,520	$\bar{K}^- + p^+ \rightarrow Y^{***} + \pi$
$\Xi^*(\pi\Xi)$	1/2	$>1/2$	1,535	$\bar{K}^- + p^+ \rightarrow \Xi^* + K$
$N^{***}(\pi N)$	1/2	5/2	1,683	$\pi^- + p^+ \rightarrow N^{***} + \pi$

[From R. D. Hill, *Scientific American*, Jan., 1963.]

TABLE 15.5

STRONGLY INTERACTING PARTICLES AS OF 1964

STRONGLY INTERACTING PARTICLES are presented with a new naming system. The 82 particles and antiparticles in this chart include only those with a rest mass below 2,000 million electron volts (Mev) and with atomic mass number (A) of -1, 0 or $+1$. Their existence has been predicted by the "eightfold way." The mass assignments are averages for the members of a charge multiplet, or family of states differing only in their electric charge. Multiplets that have the same spin angular momentum (J) and parity (P) are assigned a common mark. The same mark is also assigned to "recurrences" of these particles. Recurrences are particles with 2, 4, 6 (and so on) more units of spin than their "ground" states of lowest mass. BARYONS: Ξ Xi, Σ Sigma, Λ Lambda, N (Nucleon), Δ Delta, Ω Omega; MESONS: η Eta, π Pi, κ Antikappa, κ Kappa; COLLOQUIAL NAMES: ϕ Phi, ω Omega, ρ Rho. Letter A = Atomic mass, or baryon, number. Parentheses contain: (rest mass in million electron volts, spin angular momentum, parity). [From Chew, *et al.*, *Scientific American*, Feb., 1964.]

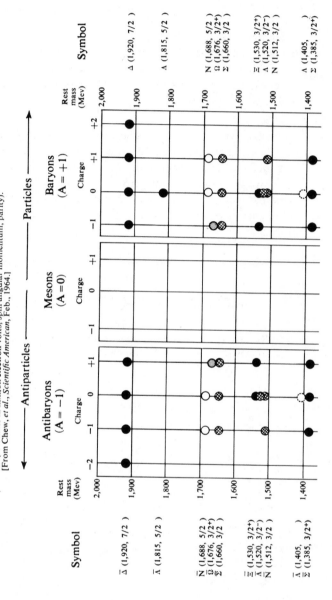

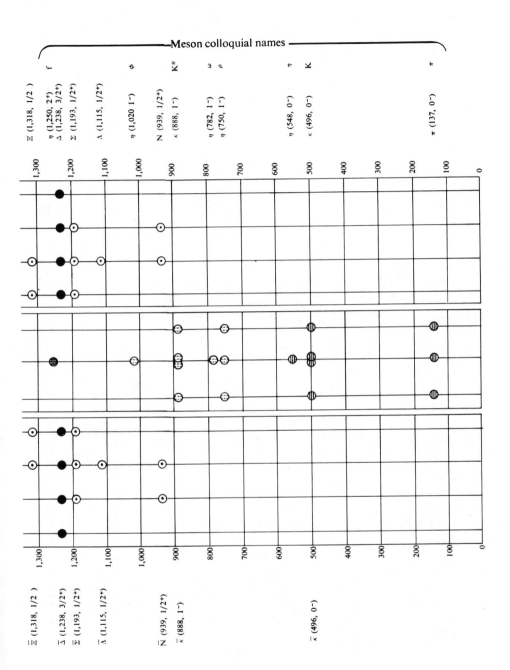

Meson colloquial names

Ξ (1,318, 1/2)

η (1,250, 2⁺)
Δ (1,238, 3/2⁺)

Σ (1,193, 1/2⁺)

Λ (1,115, 1/2⁺)

η (1,020 1⁻)

N (939, 1/2⁺)
κ (888, 1⁻)

η (782, 1⁻)
η (750, 1⁻)

η (548, 0⁻)
κ (496, 0⁻)

π (137, 0⁻)

f

φ

K*

ρ

η   K

π

Ξ̄ (1,318, 1/2)

Δ̄ (1,238, 3/2⁺)

Σ̄ (1,193, 1/2⁺)

Λ̄ (1,115, 1/2⁺)

N̄ (939, 1/2⁺)
κ̄ (888, 1⁻)

κ̄ (496, 0⁻)

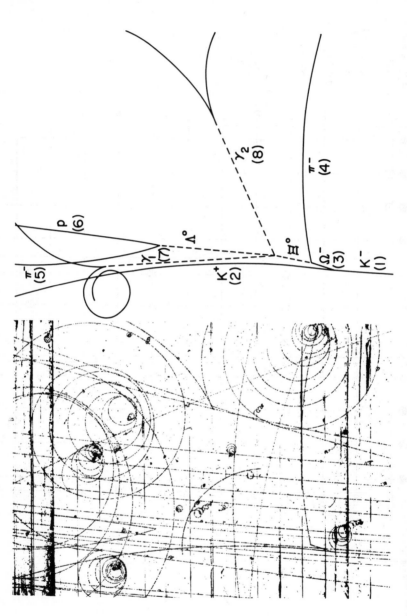

FIG. 15.19 Photograph and line diagram of event showing the decay of Ω^-. [From V. F. Barnes *et al.*, *Phys. Rev. Letters*, **12**, 204 (1964).]

   The Brookhaven team used the AGS for producing 33-Bev proton bursts every 2.5 seconds. The beam hitting the tungsten target produced K^--mesons and a few π^--mesons. The K^--mesons were separated from the beam by 450 feet of focusing and bending magnets, collimators, and separators. This, in effect, produced a beam of 5-Bev K^--particles, which entered the 80-inch hydrogen bubble-chamber where they reacted with protons. Every 2.5 seconds about 10 K^--particles entered the chamber. If an omega-minus is really created, it would decay by one of three kinds of reactions

$$(1) \quad \Omega^- \rightarrow \Xi^0 + \pi^-$$
$$(2) \quad \Omega^- \rightarrow K^- + \Lambda^0$$
$$(3) \quad \Omega^- \rightarrow \Xi^- + \pi^0 \qquad \textbf{(15.30)}$$

After taking 100,000 photographs, reaction (1) was discovered in January 1964, and the reaction (2) was found in February 1964. Reaction (3) was discovered in November 1964. The mass of the omega-minus was found to be 1686 ± 12 Mev with a lifetime of 0.7×10^{-10} seconds. A photograph and a line diagram of event (1) are shown in Fig. 15.19.

   Once a few of the resonances were established, it led to the discovery of many more. Table 15.4 shows a list of the resonances observed until 1963. A more recent list, resulting from intensive investigations, is much larger and is shown in Table 15.5.

5. OLD PARTICLE CLASSIFICATION AND INTERACTIONS

The detailed investigation of the properties of the original thirty-two "elementary particles" brought to light the fact that these particles can be classified into four groups

   Baryons. These are relatively heavy particles with a half-integral angular momentum. Protons, neutrons, and lambda, sigma, and xi particles all belong to this group. Also included in this list are the antiparticles of the above, the *antibaryons.*

   Mesons. The particles in this group have intermediate masses, i.e., less than the proton and greater than that of pi mesons. They have integral angular momentum. Included in this group are the pi mesons, the K mesons, and their antiparticles. These particles are sometimes classified as *bosons.*

   Leptons. These are the lightest particles, with masses less than pions and with half-integral angular momentum. The interaction of these particles with baryons and mesons is much weaker as compared to the interaction of mesons with baryons. Included in this list are the electrons, the mu-mesons, the neutrinos (two types), and their antiparticles. These particles are also referred to as "Fermi particles" or *fermions*.

Photon. The photon has a zero rest-mass and is assigned an integral value of angular momentum.

The production and decay of any particle in these groups is governed by one or more of the four different types of interactions discussed in Chap. IX. Because of their importance we shall review these interactions in some detail. It may be pointed out that the concepts of force and interaction are used interchangeably without any confusion.

A. THE STRONG INTERACTION. The strong interactions, or nuclear forces, are the strongest of the four basic interactions, and, as discussed earlier, are responsible for holding the nucleons together. These strong interactions are also responsible for the production of the baryons and the K-mesons. The range of these interactions is very small and is of the order of 10^{-13} cm, the diameter of a strongly interacting particle. As explained in Eq. (12.7), nuclear forces result from the virtual emission and absorption of pions. These interactions are called "strong" because of their very short reaction time. Suppose a particle is traveling at a speed of 10^{10} cm/sec. In order to go across a nucleon of diameter 10^{-13} cm, it takes 10^{-23} sec. Even though this time, 10^{-23} sec, is a very small time for contact, the interaction between the two does take place. Thus the reaction time of the strong interactions is of the order of 10^{-23} sec.

B. THE ELECTROMAGNETIC INTERACTION. These forces are 137 times weaker than the strong interactions. This force acts between all charged particles and particles having electric or magnetic moments. The uncharged photon is the carrier of an electromagnetic field. The electromagnetic force follows the inverse-square law, and, hence, its range is infinite. These forces are responsible for the binding of electrons in atoms and for the formation of molecules. The reaction time of electromagnetic interactions is of the order of 10^{-21} sec. These interactions are also sometimes referred to as "Dirac interactions."

C. THE WEAK INTERACTION. These forces are about 10^{-14} times weaker than strong interactions, and they are characterized by a reaction time of $\sim 10^{-8}$ seconds. As discussed earlier, this interaction is a point interaction, and it is responsible for beta decay and the behaviour of leptons. It also governs the decay of some of the strongly interacting particles—the strange particles. This interaction is also sometimes called the "Fermi interaction."

D. THE GRAVITATIONAL INTERACTION. This is the weakest of all the four, and it is 10^{-39} times the strength of the strong interaction. It is always attractive, but its effects on the scale of the atomic nucleus or elementary particles are neglegible and undetectable.

An elementary particle may be associated with some or all of the four interactions. The proton, for example, which is strongly interacting, has an electromagnetic interaction because of its charge. The proton is produced from the decay of a neutron, which is governed by weak interactions. And finally, like any other matter, the proton will have a gravitational interaction. Neutrinos and antineutrinos, on the other hand, feel only the weak and gravitational interactions.

The collection of experimental data has revealed many new characteristics of all the strongly interacting particles. These characteristics have to do with conservation laws and symmetry principles. This has, in turn, led to the grouping of the particles having similar properties, and, hence, provides a new classification scheme for naming these particles.

6. CONSERVATION LAWS AND SYMMETRY PRINCIPLES

Some conservation laws appear to be universal and are obeyed by all the four basic interactions. These include the conservation of energy, linear momentum, and angular momentum, as well as that of electric charge. There are other conservation laws that are not necessarily obeyed by all four. It may be pointed out that a conserved quantity appears in quantum mechanics as a quantum number.

A. CONSERVATION OF ENERGY AND MOMENTUM. That the description of a physical process is invariant to displacement in time results in the conservation of energy. The invariance of the physical system under translation in any direction gives rise to the conservation of linear momentum in that direction. Similarly the invariance under rotation of a system requires the conservation of angular momentum. These conservation laws have been verified to better than one part in 1,000 by the recently discovered Mössbauer effect.

It is not necessary that energy and momentum be the only criteria to tell us whether a given reaction will take place or not. An electron, for example, could decay into a neutrino and a gamma ray and still conserve momentum and energy. But this reaction does not take place, because it is believed to be forbidden by another conservation law.

B. CONSERVATION OF CHARGE. Conservation of charge is required by the invariance of electromagnetic interactions under a gauge transformation. It is this conservation law that forbids the decay of an electron into a neutrino and a gamma ray.

The charge on the electron seems to be the basic charge, which has been verified to one part in 10^{17}. The two kinds of charges are produced in equal amounts. This law states that the total charge before the reaction is equal to the charge at the end of the reaction. Thus if the electron decays, it must decay into charged particles. But there are no charged particles with mass less than the electron mass, and, hence, the electron does not decay.

C. THE CONSERVATION OF PARITY. Parity is that quantity that is invariant when nature makes no distinction between left and right. We may say that parity is the quantity conserved because of the invariance of a system when the coordinates are inverted.

The conservation of parity holds only approximately, breaking down on one time-scale and holding up on another. Conservation of parity holds for strong interactions with a time period of 10^{-23} seconds, while it breaks down in weak interactions, which have a time scale of about 10^{-8} seconds. The experimental verification of this has already been discussed in Eq. (8.13).

D. THE CONSERVATION OF BARYON NUMBER. This quantity, the *baryon number*, is defined as the number of baryons minus the number of antibaryons, or the atomic-mass number. The law states that the total value of A can never change in an interaction, which means that baryons cannot be created or destroyed except when a baryon-antibaryon pair is created or when the pair is annihilated. For baryons, $A = +1$ and for antibaryons $A = -1$, while for mesons $A = 0$. If it were not for the conservation of baryon number, nothing would prevent the proton from decaying into a positron and a gamma ray. The baryon number has no known properties other than the fact that it satisfies a conservation law. It cannot be defined or measured independently and has no simple theoretical justification.

Similar laws have been observed for the lepton and muon and are known as the "conservation of lepton number" and "conservation of muon number". The justification for these laws is that certain reactions would not be forbidden if it were not for these laws.

E. THE CONSERVATION OF ISOTOPIC SPIN. The isotopic spin, denoted by I, has nothing to do with spin or angular momentum. The concept of isotopic spin was introduced to emphasize the fact that the nucleon exists in two charged states, one positively charged (the proton) and the other neutral (the neutron). As far as strong interactions are concerned, these two states are alike and are related to each other by the symmetry of the isotopic spin. If the electromagnetic interaction observed the same symmetry, the proton and the neutron would have the same mass. It is because of the violation of the isotopic-spin symmetry by the electromagnetic interactions that the neutron is 1.3 Mev more massive than the proton. If the electromagnetism could be turned off in the laboratory, then the neutron and the proton would be indistinguishable. Hence, the nucleon can be thought of as a "charge doublet" with one state representing the proton and the other state the neutron.

Heisenberg expanded this idea and constructed a mathematical description of a nucleon by using a variable having two values. One value represents the proton and the other the neutron. He called this quantity the isotopic spin—a mathematical device to distinguish between the two states. The name "spin" has been used because of its close analogy to real spin, even though it is merely a mathematical quantity. The isotopic spin of the nucleon is $\frac{1}{2}$ with components of $+\frac{1}{2}$ and $-\frac{1}{2}$. The reference direction for the isotopic spin is along the z-axis. Thus for $I = \frac{1}{2}$, $I_z = \pm \frac{1}{2}$, and we have the two isotopic-spin components for the nucleon with $-\frac{1}{2}$ for the neutron of zero charge and $+\frac{1}{2}$ for the proton of $+1$ charge; i.e., the nucleon forms a charged doublet. Similarly, pions constitute a charged triplet of neutral, positive, and negative charge. Again in analogy with real spin, the isotopic spin of the charged triplet is 1 with $I_z = \pm 1$, 0, the three components being given by $M = 2I + 1$, where M is the multiplicity.

The conclusion that can be drawn from this is that strong interactions are charge independent and conserve isotopic spin.

F. CHARGED MULTIPLETS AND DISPLACED MULTIPLETS. The grouping of particles into charged doublets and triplets is a convenient way of identifying them. If we say, for example, that the nucleon is a charged doublet with a center of charge at $+1/2$, where

$$\text{center of charge} = \frac{0 + (+1)}{2} = +\frac{1}{2},$$

this means that the charges are 0 and $+1$, the isotopic spin $\frac{1}{2}$ and the I_z's are $+\frac{1}{2}$ and $-\frac{1}{2}$. On the contrary, for an antinucleon, the center of the charge is at $-\frac{1}{2}$ or

$$\frac{0 + (-1)}{2} = -\frac{1}{2}$$

with isotopic spin $1/2$ and the I_z's are $-\frac{1}{2}$ and $+\frac{1}{2}$, as shown in Fig. 15.20. Similarly, the pion is a triplet with its center of charge at 0,

$$\frac{+1 + (0) + (-1)}{3} = 0$$

corresponding to states with charge $+1$, 0, and -1; isotopic spin 1; and I_z's of ± 1, 0.

Originally it was thought that for all the multiples of heavy particles, the center of charge will be at $+\frac{1}{2}$, the same as for the nucleon. This is not so; the centers of charge of these heavy-particle multiplets are actually displaced

Particle	Isotopic spin	Strangeness	Charge				
			-1	$-1/2$	0	$+1/2$	$+1$
Nucleon	1/2	0			n°		p°
Anti-nucleon	1/2	0	$\bar{p}^-$		$\bar{n}^\circ$		
Lambda	0	-1			Λ°		
Anti-lambda	0	$+1$			$\bar{\Lambda}^\circ$		
Sigma	1	-1	Σ^-		Σ°		Σ^+
Anti-sigma	1	$+1$	$\bar{\Sigma}^-$		$\bar{\Sigma}^\circ$		$\bar{\Sigma}^+$
Xi	1/2	-2	Ξ^-		Ξ°		
Anti-xi	1/2	$+2$			$\bar{\Xi}^\circ$		$\bar{\Xi}^+$
Pion	1	0	π^-		π°		π^+
K	1/2	$+1$		K_1° K_2°	K°		K^+
Anti-K	1/2	-1	$\bar{K}^-$		$\bar{K}^\circ$	K_1° K_2°	

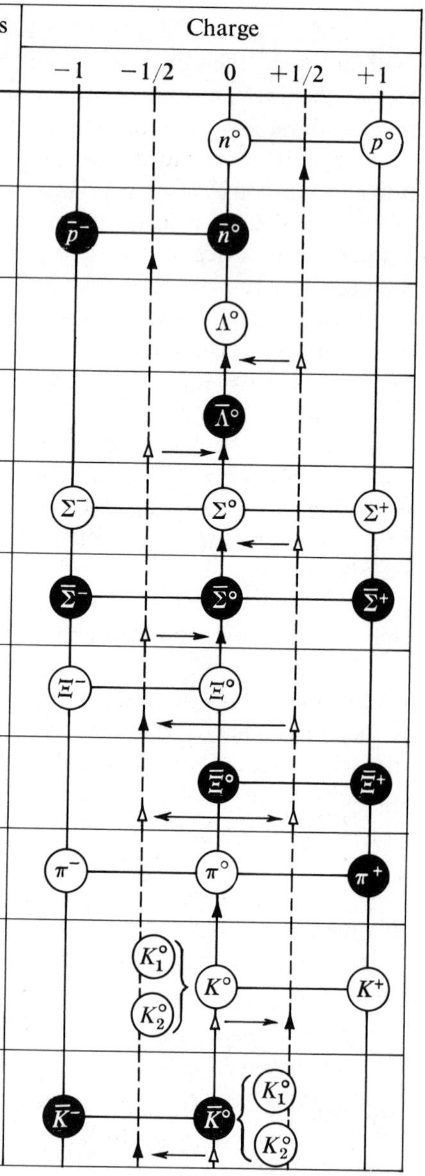

FIG. 15.20 Strangeness is illustrated in tabular form. Particles (*white circles*) and antiparticles (*black circles*) are grouped in multiplets with their charges indicated by the vertical lines. The solid carets mark the charge center of each multiplet; open carets mark the "expected" location of charge centers (1/2 for heavy particles, $-1/2$ for heavy antiparticles and 0 for mesons). Horizontal arrows show the displacement of each center from the expected position. The strangeness equals twice the value of this displacement. [From M. Gell-Mann and E. P. Rosenbaum, *Scientific American*, Jan., (1957).]

from the nucleon doublet at $+\frac{1}{2}$. For example, for neutral lambda, Λ^0, which is a singlet, the center of charge will be at 0. Thus the lambda is "displaced" by $-\frac{1}{2}$ charge unit. It is this displacement of the heavy particles from the nucleon center-of-charge that, perhaps, may be the cause of the strange behaviour of the strange particles. For the sake of mathematical convenience, the strangeness is defined as twice the displacement. Thus the strangeness of the Λ^0 is -1. Similarly, the antilambda whose center is also at zero, but is displaced by $+\frac{1}{2}$ from the center of charge of the antinucleons, will have a strangeness of $+1$. For the sigma triplet (Σ^+, Σ°, Σ^-) the center of charge is at zero, and hence the strangeness is -1. Similarly, the xi doublet, Ξ^-, Ξ°, will have its center of charge at

$$\frac{0 + (-1)}{2} = -\frac{1}{2},$$

which is displaced by -1 unit from $+\frac{1}{2}$, and will have a strangeness of -2. Many more examples are shown in Fig. 15.20. For mesons, the pion triplet provides a reference for the measurement of the displacement of mesons. By definition, the strangeness of nucleons and pions is zero. It may be pointed out that many particles corresponding to different multiplets were predicted before they were actually discovered.

G. THE CONSERVATION OF STRANGENESS. This has come to stand as an experimental law, and we can assign a strangeness number to all the strongly interacting particles. It can be shown that the strangeness must be conserved both in strong as well as in electromagnetic interactions. This means that in any reaction of these two types, the total strangeness of the particles entering the reaction must be equal to the total strangeness of the particles leaving the reaction. This conservation law is useful in explaining many characteristics of the strange particles.

The conservation of strangeness automatically explains "associated production". Because strange particles are produced by means of ordinary particles that have zero strangeness, the reaction products must contain at least two strange particles with equal and opposite strangeness in order to conserve the strangeness, i.e., the strangeness of the product particles is zero. Now it is also possible to explain why the strange particles produced by strong interactions decay by weak interactions. An isolated particle whose strangeness is not zero cannot decay into particles each with zero strangeness by means of a strong or electromagnetic interaction. while the decay by a weak interaction is possible because it does not require conservation of strangeness. The strangeness number, S, is connected with the charge center-of-gravity, or average charge, $\bar{Q}$, of the multiplet; the hypercharge $Y(=2\bar{Q})$; and the baryon number, or mass number, A; by the following relation

$$S = Y - A = 2\bar{Q} - A \qquad (15.31)$$

TABLE 15.6

THE QUANTITIES CONSERVED IN STRONG INTERACTIONS

Conserved quantity	Symbol	Observed values	Description	Examples proton	Examples negative pion
Electric charge	Q	$0, \pm 1, \pm 2, \pm 3 \ldots$	Represents the number of electric-charge units carried by a particle, or atomic nucleus, in units of the positive charge on the proton. Charge multiplets, such as the neutron-proton doublet or the pion triplet, can be assigned an average charge, $\bar{Q}$.	$Q = +1$ $\bar{Q} = +1/2$	$Q = -1$ $\bar{Q} = 0$
Atomic mass number, or Baryon number	A	$0, \pm 1, \pm 2, \pm 3 \ldots$	Represents the familiar atomic mass number long used for nuclei. For uranium 235, $A = 235$. For baryons, $A = +1$; for anti-baryons, $A = -1$; for mesons, $A = 0$.	$A = +1$	$A = 0$
Hypercharge (Related to average charge, $\bar{Q}$, and to strangeness, S)	Y	$-2, -1, 0, +1$	Defined as twice the average charge, $\bar{Q}$, of a multiplet. Strangeness, S, is hypercharge minus the atomic mass number ($S = Y - A$).	$Y = +1$ $S = 0$	$Y = 0$ $S = 0$
Isotopic spin (Related to multiplicity, M)	I	$0, 1/2, 1, 3/2$	Groups nuclear states into multiplets whose members differ only in electric charge. The number of charge states, or multiplicity, M, is related to I by the equation $M = 2I + 1$.	$I = 1/2$ $M = 2$	$I = 1$ $M = 3$
Spin angular momentum	J	$1/2, 3/2, 5/2 \ldots$ $0, 1, 2, 3 \ldots$	Indicates how fast a particle rotates about its axis, expressed in units of Planck's constant, $\hbar$.	$J = 1/2$	$J = 0$
Parity	P	$-1, +1$	An intrinsic property related to left-right symmetry.	$P = +1$	$P = -1$
G	G	$-1, +1$	An intrinsic property found only in mesons with zero hypercharge.	not defined	$G = -1$

[From Chew et al., *Scientific American*, Feb., 1964.]

The quantum numbers commonly used in classifying strongly interacting particles, which we shall discuss in the next section, are the following:

A — the atomic mass number or baryon number
Y — the hypercharge
I — the isotopic spin
J — the spin angular momentum
P — the parity
Q — the electric charge
G — a number assigned a value of ± 1 for mesons having $Y = 0$.

The relations between these quantum numbers and their meanings are briefly explained in Table 15.6.

7. THE NEW CLASSIFICATION

Since 1964, in the new system for naming strongly interacting particles, five different quantities are used. These five quantities A, J, P, I, and Y (or S or $\bar{Q}$) are all conserved in strong interactions, but not necessarily in weak interactions. The close relation between the symmetries and conservation laws allow either to be referred to in any particular case. The mass number, A, can be 0, ± 1, etc. $A = 0$ stands for mesons as well as for leptons. $A = 1$ represents baryons with a mass-number one, and $A = -1$ is for antibaryons. There is a close relationship between J and P, and for a given state it is usually written in the form J^P, i. e., for a proton $J = \frac{1}{2}$, $P = +1$, therefore $J^P = \frac{1}{2}^+$. For a state with isotopic spin, I, the multiplicity is given by $M = 2I + 1$. Lastly, Y, S, and $\bar{Q}$ are all related and any one of the three may be used.

The three numbers A, Y, and I provide the basis for the new naming system. It can be seen that mesons and baryons occur in charge multiplets differing only in their charge. The number and charge of particles occur in patterns of singlets, doublets, triplets, and quadruplets. Only ten different patterns are known, or can be predicted by this method, and each one of them represents a different set of values for A, Y, and I.

These ten patterns are divided into two groups. One group, the mesons, for which $A = 0$ has four patterns named by the Greek letters eta (η), pi (π), kappa (κ), and antikappa ($\bar{\kappa}$). The other group, the baryons, for which $A = 1$ has six patterns named by the Greek letters lambda (Λ), sigma (Σ), xi (Ξ), omega (Ω), delta (Δ), and the English letter (N). The values of Y and I for the two groups of mesons and baryons with different multiplicities are shown in Table 15.7. These ten symbols include all kinds of mesons and baryons known as of February 1964 as shown in Tables 15.8 and 15.9.

It is now easy to see the difference between the old and the new systems of naming. For example, in the old system the symbol π stood for a group of three pions of rest mass equal to 137 Mev. According to the new system, the symbol π stands not only for a group of the same three mesons, but also a new group of three with the same A, Y and I having rest mass of 750 Mev. Similarly, in the old system N stands for two nucleons of mass 939 Mev, while in the new system N stands for the nucleons as well as two new doublets of mass 1512 Mev and 1688 Mev. The old names, therefore, now stand for all the particles with the same values of A, Y, and I. In order to distinguish between the particles of the same family, after the family name the value of

TABLE 15.7

NAMES OF MESONS AND BARYONS

Mesons	Y	I	M	Baryons	Y	I	M
η	0	0	1	Λ	0	0	1
π	0	1	3	Σ	0	1	3
κ	+1	1/2	2	N	+1	1/2	2
$\bar{\kappa}$	−1	1/2	2	Ξ	−1	1/2	2
				Ω	−2	0	1
				Δ	+1	3/2	4

[From Chew *et al.*, *Scientific American*, Feb., 1964.]

the mass, and/or the value of J^P of the particle is written in parentheses. The different families of baryons and mesons are shown in the form of multiplets in Tables 15.8 and 15.9 respectively.

Our next aim will be to discuss briefly the different classifications that have been developed in the last few years and are still in the process of improvement.

A. REGGE TRAJECTORIES. With the recent increase in the number of strongly interacting particles, physicists have tried to find a new scheme that would predict new particles on the basis of the properties of those already known. The first such useful method was proposed by Italian physicist Tullio Regge in 1959.

It was observed that as the particles increased in mass, their J value also increased. Regge showed that certain properties of particles can be regarded as mathematical functions of J that vary continuously as J varies. But, according to quantum mechanics, the physical meaning is given only to half-integral and integral values of J. The curve that gives the physical mass for particles sharing the same numerical values of all of the quantum numbers except J is

TABLE 15.8

BARYON MULTIPLETS

(Baryon multiplets resulting from the same values of Y and I. Only six different combinations are possible. Each of these combinations is denoted by an upper-case Greek letter.) Ω^- which is marked "predicted," has since been discovered.

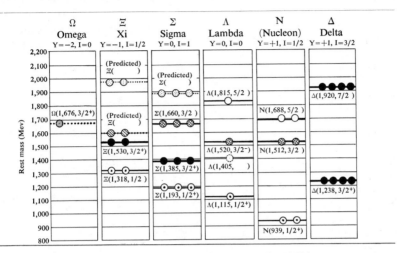

[From Chew *et al.*, *Scientific American*, Feb., 1964.]

TABLE 15.9

MESON MULTIPLETS

(Meson multiplets resulting from the same values of Y and I. Four possible combinations are denoted by the lower-case Greek letters.)

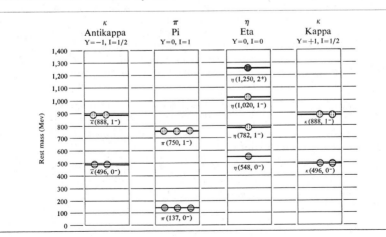

[From Chew *et al.*, *Scientific American*, Feb., 1964.]

called a *Regge trajectory*. Fig. 15.21 shows these trajectories for strongly interacting particles, the baryons. Fig. 15.22 shows the Regge trajectories for the mesons. Note that in the case of mesons, quantum mechanics requires the use of mass-squared rather than mass on the horizontal scale.

In Fig. 15.21, for the strongly interacting particles, the trajectories travel across the boundary from the stable to the unstable. It can be shown that for these particles a trajectory can join up real states for either odd or even values of *J*, but not for both. This implies that an interval of two units of *J* must

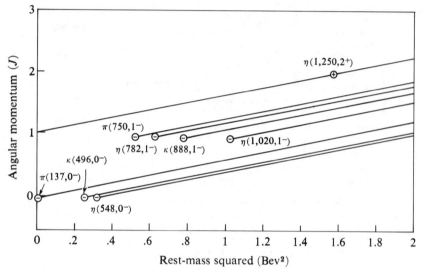

FIG. 15.21   Regge Trajectories for mesons are shown for eight well-established particles. They are all in the ground state; no recurrences have yet been identified. It can be shown that the highest η trajectory (that is, a trajectory with a *Y* and *I* of 0) should have an unreal intersection at *J* of 1 and mass 0. A line drawn through that point and η (1,250, 2$^+$) indicates the probable slope of Regge trajectories for mesons. The parallel lines for other trajectories are hypothetical. Their intersections with a *J* of 2 or 3 predict where Regge recurrences are likely to be found. The lowest-lying recurrence should be a $\pi(2^-)$ of about 1,700 Mev. [From G. F. Chew, M. Gell-Mann and A. H. Rosenfeld, *Scientific American*, 74, Feb. (1964)].

intervene between states on the same trajectory. Using this rule and extending the trajectories to high multiples of *J*, the trajectories are useful in indicating where to search for baryons of higher *J*.

One of the best evidences for the existence of a Regge trajectory for mesons is based on the prediction of a meson of $J = 2$, called η (1250, 2$^+$), which has been experimentally discovered.

B. THE EIGHT-FOLD WAY. Another scheme that has proved useful in classifying the existing particles and predicting particles previously undiscovered is the *eight-fold way*. This theory finds some relation between particles of different mass, Y, and I, but with the same values of J and P. On the contrary, the Regge trajectories connected particles of different J, but with otherwise identical quantum numbers. As an indication that the eight-fold way theory works let us consider an example. The N, Λ, Σ, and Ξ members of the baryon family are separated in mass difference by about a factor 10 greater than the mass separation within the various multiplets. These four baryons all seem to have the same value of $J^P(=\frac{1}{2}^+)$. Thus some scheme seems to be at work.

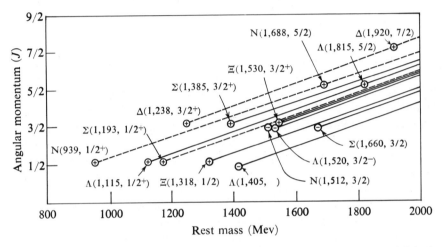

FIG. 15.22 Regge Trajectories for baryons are shown for 14 well-established baryons with mass less than 2,000 Mev. Slanting broken lines connect three occurrences with their Regge recurrences. For baryons spin angular momentum (J) is half-integral (1/2, 3/2, 5/2 and so on). Recurrences must have, 2, 4, 6 and so on more units of spin than their ground states (occurrences) of lowest mass. Spins for $\Lambda(1,815, 5/2)$ and $\Delta(1,920, 7/2)$ are uncertain, but they probably satisfy this requirement. Slanting solid lines show the probable Regge trajectories for other baryons. Circled symbols indicate parity; where not yet established, it has been guessed. [From G. F. Chew, M. Gell-Mann and A. H. Rosenfeld, *Scientific American*, 74, Feb. (1964).]

As we observed previously, it is possible to regard the mass difference between the proton and neutron as a splitting caused by the nonconservation of isotopic spin in the electromagnetic interaction (due to the electric charge). If the violation of isotopic spin could cause the mass difference within a multiplet, perhaps the violation of some other quantum numbers may be the cause of a mass difference between multiplets themselves. A scheme according to the above theory should require the conservation of Y and I in strong interactions, but violation of some other conservation laws of symmetry. If these new quantum numbers corresponding to the violation of the symmetries could be found, it might be possible to group baryon multiplets into supermultiplets with different values of Y and I, but with the same J and P values. This system could connect different Y and I values in the same way as the isotopic spin connects various electric-charge values. In other words, this new aspect of strong interactions would split each supermultiplet into charged multipets of different masses. The scale of mass splitting between the multiplets would be much greater than the splitting within a multiplet, partly because the forces at work are stronger than the electromagnetic forces.

The idea of the system of symmetries and the pattern of particular violations that explained the new supermultiplets was first developed in 1961 independently by M. Gell-Mann and Y. Ne'eman. This theory got its name, the eight-fold way, because its operation involves eight quantum numbers. (Perhaps an attribute to Buddha's "eight-fold way of life," namely: right views, right intention, right speech, right action, right living, right effort, right mindfulness, and right concentration) The basis of the eight quantum-number theory is the algebra of Lie groups that was developed by the Norwegian, Sophus Lie, in the 19th century. The simplest Lie algebra involves three operators corresponding to a quantum-mechanical symmetry operation. The algebra of the Lie group is that of a specialized unitary group for 2×2 arrays, called SU_2. The word "specialized" is used because there is one condition that will reduce the four components to three.

The eight-fold way uses a little more complicated algebra—that of SU_3. In this case, the Lie group consists of a special unitary group for 3×3 arrays with a condition that reduces the nine components to eight; each component corresponds to a certain conserved quantity. The eight components of SU_3 are the isotopic spin I (three components I_z, I_+, I_-); the hypercharge, Y, (one component); and four more. Two of these four change Y from up or down by one unit without changing the electric charge. The other two change both Y and the charge by one unit. The violation of the last four components by part of the strong interactions will change the masses of the multiplets, forming a supermultiplet. The example of the four baryons, as mentioned before, forms an octet or supermultiplet. This and other supermultiplets are shown in Fig. 15.23.

The violations suggested by the eight-fold way lead to a rule connecting masses within a supermultiplet, if the violations are not too drastic. Thus, for example, the rule for the baryon octet leads to the following relation, which is in good agreement with the actual masses.

$$\tfrac{1}{2}m_N + \tfrac{1}{2}m_\Xi = \tfrac{3}{4}m_\Lambda + \tfrac{1}{4}m_\Sigma \qquad (15.32)$$

In 1961, the only meson multiplets were the π, κ, and $\bar{\kappa}$, and they all have a J^P value of 0^-. These form an octet if a neutral meson of mass 563 Mev is added to this group as shown in Fig. 15.23. This neutral meson, predicted

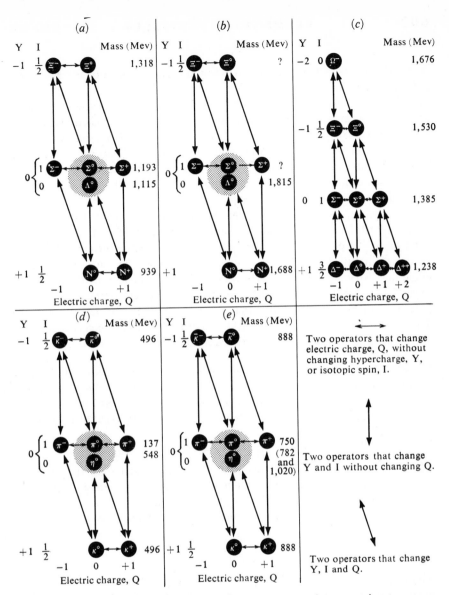

FIG. 15.23 "Eightfold Way" invokes a new system of symmetries to group multiplets of particles into "supermultiplets." The term "eightfold" refers to a special algebra showing relations among eight things, in this case eight conserved quantities. The new system of symmetries (*slanting arrows*) connects different values of hypercharge (Y) and isotopic spin (I) in the same way that isotopic-spin symmetry (*horizontal arrows*) connects different values of electric charge. Four of the diagrams (a, b, d, e) show supermultiplets with eight members; another group (c) contains 10 members. Several new particles are predicted by the eightfold way, notably $\Omega(1,676, 3/2^+)$, which appears in c. Note that the η meson in e is given two mass values, which leads to the "identity crisis" described in the text. [From G. F. Chew, M. Gell-Mann and A. H. Rosenfeld, *Scientific American*, 74, Feb. (1964).]

601

by the theory, was discovered and was found to have a mass of 548 Mev, and a J^P value of 0^-.

Unfortunately, there have been some disagreements between the theory and the experiments. For example, mesons of $J^P = 1^-$, which includes π (750, 1^-), κ (888, 1^-), and $\bar{\kappa}$ (888, 1^-), lead to another meson octet, if a neutral singlet of mass 925 Mev is postulated. This particle was found experimentally and was named η (1^-). The only trouble is that this new particle has a mass of 782 Mev instead 925 Mev. Several explanations have been advanced.

Lastly, we shall consider another example that also points to the success of the eight-fold way. The delta baryon is a quartet and doesn't belong to an octet or singlet pattern. It must then fit into a 10 member group, a decuplet as shown in Fig. 15.23. For a decuplet of this type, the mass rule predicts equal mass spacing among its members. This was confirmed by the discovery of the Ξ (1530, $\frac{3}{2}^+$) with $J^P = 3/2^+$. This rule also correctly predicted an omega particle with mass of 1676 Mev that would be a singlet of negative charge. Thus we conclude that even though the eight-fold way has been successful in classifying and predicting new particles, it has some shortcomings.

C. BOOTSTRAP THEORY. Over the last thirty years, experimentalists have verified the Yukawa hypothesis concerning the forces between strongly interacting particles. In modern terms this associates nuclear forces with the existence of antiparticles through the concept of crossing reactions. Consider the reaction

$$a + b \rightarrow c + d,$$

where the probability of the reaction occurring is given by the absolute square of the reaction amplitude $A(E_a, E_b, E_c, E_d)$. The crossing principle says this same function describes two crossed reactions that correspond to replacing outgoing particles by ingoing antiparticles and vice versa, i.e.,

$$a + \bar{c} \leftrightarrow \bar{b} + d$$
$$a + \bar{d} \leftrightarrow \bar{b} + c$$

The three above-mentioned reactions are differentiated by the sign of the energy variable, positive or negative for ingoing and outgoing particles, respectively.

An example of crossed reactions is shown in Fig. 15.24 for the nucleons. The pictures show (a) $n + p \leftrightarrow n + p$ and (b) $n + \bar{n} \leftrightarrow p + \bar{p}$, and they differ only in the direction in which they are read. The second drawing (b) can be interpreted as the contribution from the meson intermediate state. In general, if there is a particle that permits it to communicate with both sides of the reaction, this contribution is present in the reaction amplitude. This is given by the Breit-Wigner formula and such coupling strengths are called *partial widths*.

In Fig. 15.24 (a) we say that a meson is exchanged in a scattering collision, and this exchange constitutes a force between the interacting particles. This is the Yukawa force. Thus a single figure corresponds to both a force in one reaction and an intermediate particle in the corresponding crossed reaction. No additional forces have been found and it is possible to believe that all forces between strongly interacting particles arise by the Yukawa mechanism.

The bootstrap hypothesis essentially is the same as the notion of a democracy of particles governed by Yukawa forces. Strongly interacting particles

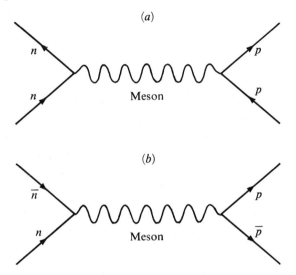

FIG. 15.24   Crossed nuclear reactions. [From G. F. Chew, M. Gell-Mann and A. H. Rosenfeld, *Scientific American*, 74, Feb. (1964).]

are all dynamical structures that owe their existence to these forces, through which they mutually interact. Each strongly interacting particle is considered to be a bound state of channels with which it communicates, existing entirely due to forces associated with the exchange of particles communicating with "crossed" channels. Each of these particles owes its existence to forces to which the original particle makes a contribution. This means each particle helps to generate particles which in turn help to generate it. If this is true, then there may be no free parameters, and the only self-consistent set of particles is the one we find in nature. Investigations of this are being carried out.

If the system is self-determining, perhaps the special strong interaction symmetries are not imposed from outside but will emerge as necessary components for self-consistency. The subject of symmetry groups and their place in the pattern of elementary particles will be discussed next.

8. SYMMETRY GROUPS

In recent years a group theoretic approach to the pattern of particle relationships has been attempted. As in the eight-fold way, it hopes to classify the particles from the "broken multiplets" of some symmetry group, even if the group origin and the nature of the interaction causing the symmetry breaking is unknown.

One investigates a symmetry property of any physical system by "rotating" the coordinate to see if the Hamiltonian looks the same in the new position. To carry out this process a group of operators is used which change the coordinates of a system by a certain amount. The entire set of such operators is called a mathematical group of operators known as a symmetry group. Symmetry groups operating on geometric coordinates are those of rotation, translation, and inversion. Those that operate on coordinates such as charge and baryon number are less familiar. To preserve total probability and normalization, these groups must be unitary, i.e., $UU^\dagger = 1$. (In some special cases such as time inversion operators, these groups may be anti-unitary.)

The groups in physics are those of operations or transformations. These form a group if every operator in the group has an inverse operator, the unit operator is contained in the group, and every product of the operators is found in the group (closed multiplication).

A finite group has only a finite number of elements as, for example, the parity group of P and P^2 (where $P = P^{-1}$, and $P^2 = 1$). To investigate the invariance of a system under an arbitrary transformation, a continuous group of operators is needed. An example of this type is the rotation operator of quantum mechanics. $R(\theta) = e^{i\theta J}$. Because the angles have an infinite range, the rotations are infinite in number. The J's are Hermitean, so the operator is unitary if the angle is real.

Rotations about a single axis form a group of operators that have only one parameter and these are called Abelian groups, and all its members commute. In physics, usually we have n parameters upon which the set of operators depends, as the three parameters of the isotopic spin group (I_+, I_-, I_z) and the eight parameters of the SU_3 group.

An invariant subspace is useful for physical situations, and it means that any operator of the group operating on the subspace will produce another vector in the subspace. The group may operate on all space of which this subspace is one part. No matrix elements connect the subspace with the outside if it is an invariant subspace. A multiplet is an irreducible invariant subspace. It contains no smaller invariant subspace. Using the example of the four-dimensional orthogonal vectors $Y_{1m} = Y_{11}$, Y_{10}, Y_{0-1}, Y_{00}, we see that J operating on each gives one of the other (changing m but not l). But this subspace is reducible to a triplet (Y_{10}, Y_{11}, Y_{1-1}) and a singlet (Y_{00}), which are irreducible. Because $J_1 Y_{10} = Y_{11} + Y_{1-1}$, the triplet is irreducible. There are no connecting elements between the singlet and the triplet. We can note this by Y_{11}, Y_{1-1}, Y_{10}) $\oplus$ $Y_{00} = (Y_{00}$, Y_{1-1}, Y_{11}, Y_{10}). This definition indicates a similarity between members of a multiplet. The term multiplet is from spectroscopy where the $\mathbf{L} \cdot \mathbf{S}$ symmetry breaking interaction splits the group (labeled $\mathbf{L}$, $\mathbf{S}$ without spin-orbit coupling) into several small sets labeled J. As the ^2P state splits into $^2P_{\frac{1}{2}, \frac{3}{2}}$, $J = \frac{1}{2}, \frac{3}{2}$. It is this set of close energy levels that produces a multiplet of spectrum lines.

In a group theoretic sense, it is the set of degenerate states that is called a multiplet. The lambda particle is an isotopic spin singlet, while the pions are an isotopic triplet. For some special continuous groups the multiplets can be found in a known way. The rotation group mentioned before, labeled j, has $2j + 1$ degenerate eigenstates of J^2. Thus $j = 0$, $\frac{1}{2}$, $1 \dots$ gives a singlet, doublet, triplet, and so forth. The SU_3 is another group in this class and its multiplets are labeled with two quantum numbers. Sometimes adding operators to a group to form a new group will mix the original multiplets forming new supermultiplets. For example, enlarging the isotopic spin group to SU_3 by adding strangeness operators will cause the multiplets of the lambda singlet, nucleon and xi doublet, and sigma triplet to coalesce into a super octet.

The groups used in physical systems study are the Lie groups. The n operators called the generators of the group are defined as

$$L_i = \frac{\partial U}{\partial \alpha_i}\bigg|_{\bar{\alpha} = 0}$$

where the continuous groups are given by $U(\bar{\alpha}) = U(\alpha_1, \dots \alpha_n)$. These generators form a commutator such that $[L_i, L_j] = \sum_{k=1}^{n} C_{ijk} L_k$. The numbers C_{ijk} are the structure constants of a Lie group. The rank of a Lie group is defined as the number of mutually commuting generators it possesses. The SU_3 is of rank two because T_3 and the strangeness S commute. If no operators commute it is of rank 1.

Sometimes the Lie groups are too general for physical purposes and the restriction of semisimple Lie groups is imposed. If a group possesses no Abelian subgroup whose members A_i satisfy the condition $BA_iB^{-1} = A_j$, for B being any other element of the full group, it is semisimple. Simple groups possess no invariant subgroup at all, even Abelian.

If one constructs a larger group that summarizes the total properties of say G_a and G_b simultaneously, it is called a direct product group and is represented as $G_a \times G_b$. Its rank is the sum of the ranks of its factors.

As an example of groups in particle physics, let us consider the isotopic-spin group. This group will be regarded as one generated by physical operations on the charge of particles. If charge exists, there must be a Hermitean operator Q that counts it. So write

$$Q \mid m\rangle = m \mid m\rangle \tag{15.33}$$

To assure its conservation as experimentally observed, one may write

$$[Q, H] = 0 \tag{15.34}$$

Because certain particles can exist in one or more charged states, operators are needed to raise or lower the charge. So we define

$$Q_+ \mid m\rangle = \lambda_m \mid m + 1\rangle \tag{15.35}$$

Also,

$$[Q, Q_+] \mid m\rangle = \lambda_m \mid m + 1\rangle = Q_+ \mid m\rangle \tag{15.36}$$

If $\mid m\rangle$ is the highest state, then $Q_+ \mid m\rangle = 0$. Doing the same thing for Q_- gives the fact that

$$[Q, Q_\pm] = \pm Q_\pm \tag{15.37}$$

These operators could generate a Lie group of n-dimensions. Another condition is needed. It can be shown from Eq. (15.37) that

$$[[Q_+, Q_-], Q] = 0 \tag{15.38}$$

as $[Q_+, Q_-]$ has the same eigenvalues of Q and hence

$$[Q_+, Q_-] = f(Q) \tag{15.39}$$

The missing condition is given by Eq. (15.39). To determine what function of Q it is, we need to identify the fundamental multiplet from which all other multiplets can be obtained by multiplication.

It is known that the charged triplets and doublets exist as Σ^+, Σ^0, Σ^-; K^+, K, and so forth. They combine in a way similar to nuclear charged states that consist of nucleon doublets. Thus the attempts to apply isotopic-spin groups to elementary-particle multiplets also try to construct them from the charged doublets. This has worked and determines Eq. (15.39) and the groups uniquely. We now can determine $f(Q)$ in Eq. (15.39). Using the two charged states as a basis then

$$Q = \begin{pmatrix} m_1 & 0 \\ 0 & m_2 \end{pmatrix} \tag{15.40}$$

and from Eq. (15.35)

$$Q_+ = \begin{pmatrix} 0 & \lambda \\ 0 & 0 \end{pmatrix} \tag{15.41}$$

$$Q_- = \begin{pmatrix} 0 & 0 \\ \lambda' & 0 \end{pmatrix} \tag{15.42}$$

so that

$$Q_+Q_- = \lambda\lambda'\begin{pmatrix} 1 & 0 \\ 0 & 0 \end{pmatrix} = \frac{\lambda\lambda'}{m_1 - m_2}(Q - m_2 I) \qquad \textbf{(15.43)}$$

$$Q_-Q_+ = \lambda\lambda'\begin{pmatrix} 0 & 0 \\ 0 & 1 \end{pmatrix} = \frac{\lambda\lambda'}{m_2 - m_1}(Q - m_1 I) \qquad \textbf{(15.44)}$$

Taking $\lambda\lambda' = 1$ makes

$$[Q_+, Q_-] = \left(\frac{2}{m_1 - m_2}\right)(Q - \tfrac{1}{2}(m_1 + m_2)I)$$

$$= 2\{Q - \tfrac{1}{2}(m_1 + m_2)I\} \qquad \textbf{(15.45)}$$

because $m_1 - m_2 = \pm 1$. In order for Eq. (15.33) to hold, $+1$ is chosen here. Thus Eq. (15.45) shows Q, Q_+, and Q_- to be closed under multiplication from the definition of $Q_\pm$ and Eqs. (15.37) and (15.45). This means a Lie group of rank 1 is generated by these observable operators on charge (a rotation in charge space). By making the generators traceless on any multiplet in the group, the isotopic spin group is isomorphic to the SU_2 rotation group. The fundamental multiplet of SU_2 is the doublet, so the resulting mutliplets using the product of the doublet with itself are multiplets of SU_2.

If one introduces hypercharge $Y = S + B$, and the fact that for anti-particles $\overline{Y} = -Y$ and $(m_1 + m_2) \to -(m_1 + m_2)$ then Eq. (15.45) becomes, for a doublet of $Y = 1$

$$[Q_+, Q_-] = 2(Q - |m_1 + m_2|\tfrac{1}{2}YI) \qquad \textbf{(15.46)}$$

If in customary notation $T_\pm = Q_\pm$ and $T_3 = Q - |m_1 + m_2|\tfrac{1}{2}Y$ or $T_3 = Q - \tfrac{1}{2}Y$ for a doublet of charge 0 and 1 then

$$[T_3, T_\pm] = \pm T_\pm \text{ and } [T_+, T_-] = 2T_3 \qquad \textbf{(15.47)}$$

and Eq. (15.37) is not affected. Because the commutator of $T_\pm$ with H is 0, the mass is independent of the charge.

By analogy with the group theory for the shell model, some facts may be established. The shell model may be considered as a two-step theory of atomic nuclear-energy levels. The first step replaces the actual Hamiltonian by a single particle approximation.

$$H(1, 2, \dots n) \to H^0 = \sum_{i=1}^{n} H_i^0 \qquad \textbf{(15.48)}$$

where H_i^0 is the interaction felt by the particle i. The second step consists of putting $H = H^0 + H'$ and treating it by perturbation theory. The symmetry group of H^0 is given by

$$S^0 = R_3(1) \otimes R_3(2) \otimes \dots \otimes R_3(n) \qquad \textbf{(15.49)}$$

containing a small subgroup S' of the correct Hamiltonian $H = H^0 + H'$ or

$$S' = R_3\,(1,\,2\dots n). \tag{15.50}$$

The large multiplets of S^0 consist of degenerate eigenstates of H^0 and are called supermultiplets. Using the Peter-Weyl theorem we can arrive at this conclusion: If a supermultiplet S^0 containing n multiplets of S' is broken by turning on a symmetry-breaking interaction H', then the H^0 energy levels will split into n distinct levels of H.

For the specific example of two electrons outside a closed shell, we can conclude that H' will split the (pd) configuration into $P(1^-)$, $D(2^-)$ and $F(3^-)$ states of odd parity. For the elementary particles a pattern is needed at the level of understanding of the shell model. The pattern relating them is a common origin in a single supermultiplet of a larger group whose symmetry was broken by moving the particle into their final observed position.

Because spin, parity, baryon number, isotopic spin, and strangeness are empirically conserved by strong interactions, the product of their groups can be called S', and S^0 is the group of which it is a subgroup.

It is commonly believed that the operators added to enlarge S' to S^0 commute with J^2, P, B; then the particle multiplets of S^0 will all have the same J, P, B, if not the same spin and/or strangeness. However, the splitting interaction, H', shows signs of being large, and a fine structure of well-separated levels can not be the pattern by which the supermultiplets are recognized.

The present way out of the puzzle is to choose a promising group with reasonable multiplets and assume that H' transforms as a single multiplet of the group. This technique has been successful in classifying some presently known levels into a single group called SU_3, a rank-2 simple Lie group. It is a symmetry group on the strangeness and charge, and it appears at present to be a good possibility for the S^0. At the present time, a number of physicists are working on theories that they hope will provide answers to the many puzzles still remaining.

The SU_3 theory shows how particles can be regarded as members of a supermultiplet if they are alike in spin and parity and vary in hypercharge and isotopic spin. In the last few months, another more comprehensive scheme has won support. This is called the SU_6 theory, a special unitary group of six components that yields even bigger supermultiplets than in the SU_3 theory.

This new theory is based on the old idea of E. P. Wigner that the forces inside the nucleus might be independent of the spin of the nuclear components. This idea has been applied to the nuclear particles themselves. Particles in the octets have spin 1/2 and those of the decuplet have spin 3/2 and both have positive parity. This difference in spin can be considered a variation of a property that could help to group the octet and decuplet into a larger supermultiplet much like charge, hypercharge, and the like has been used before.

The octet has two spin states for each particle for a total of sixteen and each decuplet particle has four spin states for a total of forty in the SU_6 theory. Thus the eighteen members are now considered as fifty-six members of the supermultiplet whose symmetry operations can transform into each other.

Supermultiplets of twenty, thirty-five and seventy members transform similarly under the SU_6 theory. Thirty-five or fifty-six member multiplets can encompass most well-established particles. The seventeen known mesons of negative parity constitute a group of thirty-five members. Eight with spin of zero give eight states and nine of spin-one give twenty-seven states, so the total is thirty-five.

One triumph of the theory is the fact that it accounts for the ratio of the magnetic moment of the proton and neutron to within one part in one hundred. SU_6 combines features of the SU_3 and Wigner's theory of spin independence. That SU_3 treats all particles as composites of three fundamental "quark" particles seems to be only a useful mathematical concept. The SU_6 theory assumes each quark has two spin-states so that six states are available to form multiplets. Now the smallest supermultiplet of six states taken three at a time is twenty and the groups of thirty-five, fifty-six, and seventy are merely more elaborate combinations of the quarks taken three at a time. There is always the possibility that the present symmetry groups may be enlarged to form still more supermultiplets.

PROBLEMS

1. A mu-meson whose mass is 207 m_e decays into an electron, a neutrino and an anti-neutrino. Assuming that the rest mass of the neutrino and anti-neutrino is zero, what is the maximum momentum given to the electron? What will be the maximum energy of the electron?

2. In Problem 1, what would be the maximum energy of the electron if there were only one neutrino emitted instead of a neutrino and an anti-neutrino?

3. Calculate the amount of energy available when a pi meson at rest decays into a mu meson and a neutrino. How much energy is carried away by the muon?

4. A mu meson is moving with velocity 0.98c with respect to an observer. If the half-life of the meson at rest is 1.54×10^{-6} sec., what is its half-life as measured by the observer?

5. If a π^--meson with zero kinetic energy interacts with a proton at rest according to the reaction

$$\pi^- + p \rightarrow n + \gamma$$

what is the energy of the gamma ray?

6. Most probable values of the energies of the gamma rays produced in the following reaction are measured experimentally.

$$\pi^- + p \to \pi^0 + n$$
$$\pi^0 \to \gamma + \gamma$$

How would you proceed to calculate the rest mass of the neutral pi meson?

7. Calculate the mean distance traveled by 1.2 Bev pions before decay.

8. If the momentum of a proton is 1 Bev/c, what is its energy?

9. What is the value of the magnetic field required to bend a beam of 10 Bev protons through 20°?

10. Pions are produced by the reaction $p + p \to \pi + p + n$. What is the threshold energy for pion production?

11. Why do hypernuclei have *greater* stability against mesonic decay? Explain this according to strangeness.

12. What is the relation between the strangeness of a particle isotopic spin multiplet and the strangeness of an anti-particle isotopic spin multiplet?

REFERENCES

1. Rossi, B., *Cosmic Rays*, New York: McGraw-Hill Book Co., (1964).
2. Thompson, R. W., *Progress in Cosmic Ray Physics*, Vol. III, North Holland Publishing Co., (1956).
3. Singer, S. F., *Progress in Elementary Particle and Cosmic Ray Physics*, 4, p. 205, Interscience Publishers, Inc., New York (1958).
4. Littauer, R. M., H. F. Schopper, and R. R. Wilson, *Phys. Rev. Lett.*, 7, p. 144, (1961).
5. Penman, S., *Scientific American*, p. 46, July, 1961.
6. Neddermeyer, S. H., and C. D. Anderson, *Phys. Rev.*, **51**, p. 884, (1937).
7. Street, J. C., and E. C. Stevenson, *Phys. Rev.*, **51**, p. 1005, (1937).
8. Thompson, R. W., *Phys. Rev.*, **74**, p. 490, (1948).
9. Marshak, R. E., *Scientific American*, p. 45, April, 1957
10. Lattes, C. M. G., G. P. S. Occhialini, and C. F. Powell, *Nature*, **163**, p. 47, (1949).
11. Barkas, W. H., *Am. J. Phys.*, **20**, p. 8, (1952).
12. Durbin, R. P., H. H. Loar, and W. W. Havens, *Phys. Rev.*, **88**, p. 180, (1952).
13. Hill, R. D., *Tracking Down Particles*, New York: W. A. Benjamin, Inc., 1963.
14. Hill, R. D., *Scientific American*, p. 38, Jan., 1963.
15. Butler, C., and G. Rochester, *Nature*, **160**, p. 855, (1947).
16. Pais, A., *Phys. Rev.*, **86**, p. 513, (1952).
17. Lattes, C. M. G., H. Muirhead, G. P. S. Occhialini, and C. F. Powell, *Nature*, **159**, p. 694, (1947).

18. Brown, R., U. Camerini, P. H. Fowler, H. Muirhead, I. C. F. Powell, and D. M. Riston, *Nature*, **163**, p. 82, (1949).

19. Rochester, G. D. and C. C. Butler, *Nature*, **160**, p. 855, (1947).

20. Gell-Mann, M., *Phys. Rev.*, **92**, p. 833, (1953).

21. Nishijima, K., *Prog. Theor. Phys.* (Japan), **12**, p. 107, (1954); **13**, p. 285, (1954).

22. Fowler, W. B., R. P. Shutt and A. M. Thorndike, *Phys. Rev.*, **91**, p. 1287, (1953).

23. Fowler, W. B., R. P. Shutt, A. M. Thorndike, and W. L. Whittenmore, *Phys. Rev.*, **93**, p. 861, (1954).

24. Bridge, H., H. Courant, H. DeStaebler, and B. Rossi, *Phys. Rev.*, **95**, p. 1101, (1954).

25. Segrè, E., and C. E. Wiegand, *Scientific American*, p. 37, June, 1956.

26. Chamberlain, O., E. Segrè, C. Wiegand, and T. Ypsilantis, *Phys. Rev.*, **100**, p. 947, (1955).

27. Segrè, E., *Am J. Phys.*, **25**, p. 363, (1957).

28. Cork, B., G. R. Lambertson, O. Piccioni, and W. A. Wenzel, *Phys. Rev.*, **104**, p. 1193, (1956).

29. Brown, H. N., *et al.*, *Phys. Rev. Lett.*, **8**, p. 255, (1962).

30. Baltay, C., J. Sandweiss, and H. D. Taft, *et al.*, *Phys. Rev. Lett.*, **11**, p. 165, (1963).

31. Gell-Mann, M., and E. P. Rosenbaum, *Scientific American*, p. 72, July, 1957.

32. Hill, R. D., *Scientific American*, p. 40, Jan., 1963.

33. Chew, G. F., M. Gell-Mann, and A. H. Rosenfeld, *Scientific American*, p. 74, Feb., 1964.

34. Rosenfeld, A. H., A. Barbaro-Galtieri, W. H. Barker, P. L. Barstein, J. King, and M. Ross, *Revs. Mod. Phys.*, **37**, p. 633, (1965).

35. Littauer, R. M., H. F. Schopper, and R. R. Wilson, *Phys. Rev. Lett.*, **7**, p. 141, (1961).

36. Erwin, A. R., R. March, W. D. Walker and E. West, *Phys. Rev. Lett.*, **6**, p. 628, (1961).

37. Maglic, B., L. Alvarez, A. Rosenfeld and M. Stevenson, *Phys. Rev. Lett.*, **7**, p. 178, (1961).

38. Barnes, V. E., *et al.*, *Phys. Rev. Lett.*, **12**, p. 204, (1964).

39. McVoy, K. W., *Revs. Mod. Phys.*, **37**, p. 84, (1965).

SUGGESTIONS FOR FURTHER READING

1. Frisch, D. H., and A. M. Thorndike, *Elementary Particles*, Princeton: D. Van Nostrand Company, Inc., 1965.

2. Swartz, C. E., *The Fundamental Particles*, Reading, Massachusetts: Addison-Wesley Publishing Company, Inc., 1965.

3. Singer, S. F., *Progress in Elementary Particle and Cosmic Ray Physics*, New York: Interscience Publishers, 1958.

4. Yang, C. N., *Elementary Particles*, Princeton: Princeton University Press, 1962.

5. Feld, B. T., *Elementary Particle Physics*, Lectures given at CERN in 1961, CERN Report No. 62–14.

6. Williams, W. S. C., *An Introduction to Elementary Particles*, New York: Academic Press, 1961.

7. Ritson, D. M. ed., *Techniques of High Energy Physics*, New York: Interscience Publishers, Inc., 1961.

8. Fulton, T., G. Källen, J. D. Jackson and C. Fronsdal, *Elementary Particle Physics and Field Theory*, New York: W. A. Benjamin, Inc., 1963.

9. Prentki, J., ed., *1962 International Conference on High Energy Physics* at CERN, Geneva: European Organization for Nuclear Research, 1962.

10. Nishijima, K., *Fundamental Particles*, New York: W. A. Benjamin, 1963.

11. Ramakrishnan, A., *Elementary Particles and Cosmic Rays*, Pergamon Press, 1962.

12. McVoy, K. W., *Revs. Mod. Phys.*, **37**, p. 84, (1965).

13. Rosenfeld, A. H., A. Barbaro-Galtieri, W. H. Barkas, P. L. Bastien, J. Kirz and M. Ross, *Revs. Mod. Phys.*, **37**, p. 633, (1965).

14. Hill, R. D., *Tracking Down Particles*, New York: W. A. Benjamin, Inc., 1963.

15. The following articles from *Scientific American*: (a) R. E. Marshak, "Pions," January, 1957; (b) E. Gell-Mann and E. P. Rosenbaum, "Elementary Particles," July, 1957; (c) B. Rossi, "High Energy Cosmic Rays," November, 1959; (d) S. Penman, "The Muon," July, 1961; (e) L. Lederman, "Two Neutrino Experiments," March, 1963; (f) G. F. Chew, M. Gell-Mann and A. H. Rosenfeld, "Strongly Interacting Particles," February, 1964; (g) R. D. Hill, "Resonance Particles," January, 1963; (h) E. Segrè and C. E. Wiegand, "The Antiproton," June, 1956; (i) W. B. Fowler and N. P. Samios, "The Omega-Minus Experiment," October, 1964.

APPENDIX A

WAVE MECHANICS

One of the most important problems of physics that remained unsolved until 1924 was the explanation of the dual nature, wave and particle, of radiation. Instead of trying to seek an explanation for this problem, French physicist Louis de Broglie[1] postulated that the dual nature of electromagnetic radiation exists throughout the realm of all physics. De Broglie suggested the following:

(a) The motion of a particle of momentum p is guided by a wave whose wave length, λ, is given by

$$\lambda = h/p \qquad \textbf{(A.1)}$$

where h is Planck's constant.

(b) The square of the amplitude of the wave of wave length, λ, is proportional to the probability of finding a particle of momentum p, where

$$p = h/\lambda \qquad \textbf{(A.2)}$$

These suggestions were experimentally confirmed by C. S. Davisson and L. H. Germer[2] in 1927 and by G. P. Thomson[3] in 1928. They showed that a beam of electrons is diffracted and scattered just as are electromagnetic waves.

Another step in this direction was the development of a mathematical structure based on the premise of the dual nature of matter. Such a formulation, known as *wave mechanics* or *quantum mechanics* was developed by E. Schrödinger[4] in 1926. At the same time, M. Born, W. Heisenberg and P. Jordan[5] came out with another mathematical formulation called *matrix mechanics*. The results obtained by these two treatments are essentially the same. The development of the subject of wave mechanics is based on Schrödinger's wave equation (S.W.E.) of a particle and certain postulates that we shall examine. Schrödinger described the amplitude of a matter wave by a wave function of the state of a system, $\Psi(x,y,z,t)$. If the state of the system is stationary, the wave function will be independent of time and is denoted by $\psi(x,y,z)$.

The basic postulates of wave mechanics are the following:

I.   The wave function, $\psi(x,y,z)$, that describes the state of a system must satisfy two conditions:

   A. The wave function, ψ, must be well-behaved if it describes any physical system. It must, therefore, be single-valued and continuous, and it must satisfy the boundary conditions that ψ and its derivative, ψ', are continuous everywhere.

   B. It must satisfy the condition that the integral $\int \psi^*\psi \, dx \, dy \, dz$ has a finite constant value. If we set this arbitrary constant equal to unity, then

$$\int_{\text{all space}} \psi^*\psi \, dx \, dy \, dz = 1 \tag{A.3}$$

   is called the normalization condition. The quantity $\psi^*\psi \, dx \, dy \, dz$ is also interpreted, according to Born, as the probability of finding a particle in a volume element $dx \, dy \, dz$.

II. To every observable physical quantity there corresponds an operator. The choice of the operator is arbitrary as long as the result of the operation on the wave function gives back the observable quantity and the wave function. We may associate with the vector momentum, the operator

$$\mathbf{P} \equiv -i\hbar\mathbf{V} \equiv -i\hbar \text{ grad.} \tag{A.4}$$

Then the eigenvalue equation for momentum is

$$\mathbf{P}\psi = -i\hbar\mathbf{V}\psi = \mathbf{p}\psi \tag{A.5a}$$

with the solution

$$\psi = \exp(i\mathbf{p} \cdot \mathbf{r}/\hbar) \tag{A.5b}$$

This leads to the conclusion that the only possible experimental values are the eigenvalues of its operator, operating on the well-behaved eigenfunction ψ.

III. If a physical system is in a state represented by the function $\psi(x,y,z)$, the average value of an observable o whose corresponding operator is $\mathcal{O}$, is given by

$$\langle o \rangle = \frac{\int \psi^* \mathcal{O} \psi \; dx \, dy \, dz}{\int \psi^* \psi \; dx \, dy \, dz} \tag{A.6}$$

where $\langle o \rangle$ represents the weighted average of the observable, and the integration is performed over the whole space or over the region of interest.

We are now in a position to write the Schrödinger wave equation of a particle. Let a particle of mass m moving in a coordinate system xyz, have a velocity $\mathbf{v}$ and potential energy $V(x,y,z,t)$ at time t. The total energy E of the particle is given by

$$E = \frac{m}{2}(v_x^2 + v_y^2 + v_z^2) + V(x,y,z,t) \tag{A.7}$$

or

$$E = \tfrac{1}{2}mv^2 + V(x,y,z,t) \tag{A.8}$$

where v_x, v_y, and v_z are the components of $\mathbf{v}$. If we represent the momentum of the particle by $\mathbf{p}$, Eq. (A.8) takes the form

$$E = p^2/2m + V(x,y,z,t) \tag{A.9}$$

Let us replace the observables $\mathbf{p}$ and E by their corresponding operators

$$\mathbf{p} \to \mathbf{P} \equiv -i\hbar \left(\mathbf{l}\frac{\partial}{\partial x} + \mathbf{m}\frac{\partial}{\partial y} + \mathbf{n}\frac{\partial}{\partial z} \right) \tag{A.10}$$

and

$$E \to i\hbar \frac{\partial}{\partial t} \tag{A.11}$$

where $\mathbf{l}$, $\mathbf{m}$, and $\mathbf{n}$ are the unit vectors along the axes x, y, and z, repectively. Similarly p^2 is replaced by

$$p^2 = \mathbf{p} \cdot \mathbf{p} \equiv -\hbar^2 \left(\frac{\partial^2}{\partial x^2} + \frac{\partial^2}{\partial y^2} + \frac{\partial^2}{\partial z^2} \right)$$
$$= -\hbar^2 \nabla^2 \tag{A.12}$$

If Ψ represents the eigenfunction of the state, then on combining Eqs. (A.9) and (A.12), we get

$$-\frac{\hbar^2}{2m}\nabla^2\Psi + V(x,y,z,t)\Psi = i\hbar \frac{\partial \Psi}{\partial t} \tag{A.13}$$

or

$$H\Psi = E\Psi \tag{A.14}$$

where $H = -(\hbar^2/2m)\nabla^2 + V(x,y,z,t)$ is the *Hamiltonian operator*. Eq. (A.13) or (A.14) is the famous *time-dependent Schrödinger wave equation*.

In many situations, the system will not change with time, and, in addition, the potential energy, $V(x,y,z,t)$ may be independent of time. In such cases, we can apply the method of separation of variables to Eq. (A.13) to get the time-independent Schrödinger wave equation (S.W.E.), as shown below:

$$\Psi(x,y,z,t) = \psi(x,y,z)T(t) \qquad \textbf{(A.15)}$$

Substituting for Ψ in Eq. (A.13) and dividing by ψT, we get

$$-\frac{\hbar^2}{2m}\frac{\nabla^2\psi}{\psi} + V(x,y,z) = i\hbar\frac{1}{T}\frac{\partial T}{\partial t} \qquad \textbf{(A.16)}$$

Because the left side of Eq. (A.16) is a function of space coordinates, and the right side is a function of time only, each must be equal to a constant. This constant turns out to be equal to E, the total energy. Hence

$$-\frac{\hbar^2}{2m}\frac{\nabla^2\psi}{\psi} + V(x,y,z) = E$$

or

$$\nabla^2\psi + \frac{2m}{\hbar^2}[E - V(x,y,z)]\psi = 0 \qquad \textbf{(A.17)}$$

Eq. (A.17) is the *time-independent Schrödinger wave equation*.

Considering the right-hand side of Eq. (A.16), we get

$$i\hbar\frac{1}{T}\frac{\partial T}{\partial t} = E$$

which on integration gives

$$T(t) = \exp[-i(E/\hbar)t] \qquad \textbf{(A.18)}$$

or, because $E = \hbar\omega$

$$T(t) = \exp(-i\omega t) = \cos\omega t - i\sin\omega t \qquad \textbf{(A.19)}$$

Next, we shall consider some special cases of Eq. (A.17), the time-independent S.W.E., which in one dimension takes the form

$$\frac{d^2\psi}{dx^2} + \frac{2m}{\hbar^2}(E - V)\psi = 0 \qquad \textbf{(A.20)}$$

(a) If $E > V$, where V is a constant potential, then the solution of Eq. (A.17) is given by

$$\psi(x) = Ae^{ikx} + Be^{-ikx} \qquad \textbf{(A.21a)}$$

or

$$\psi(x) = A'\sin kx + B'\cos kx \qquad \textbf{(A.21b)}$$

where

$$k = \frac{\sqrt{2m(E - V)}}{\hbar}$$

and A, B, A' and B' are constants.

(b) If $E < V$, where V is again a constant potential, then rewriting Eq. (A.20) in the form

$$\frac{d^2\psi}{dx^2} - \frac{2m}{\hbar^2}(V - E)\psi = 0$$

or

$$\frac{d^2\psi}{dx^2} - k'^2\psi = 0$$

where

$$k' = \frac{\sqrt{2m(V - E)}}{\hbar}$$

gives the following solution of the S.W.E.:

$$\psi(x) = C \exp(k'x) + D \exp(-k'x) \tag{A.22}$$

where C and D are constants.

(c) If $V = 0$, i.e., a particle is moving in a potential-free region, the S.W.E. for free particle becomes

$$\frac{d^2\psi}{dx^2} + \frac{2mE}{\hbar^2}\psi = 0 \tag{A.23}$$

the solution of which is

$$\psi(x) = N \exp\left(\frac{\pm i\sqrt{2mE}}{\hbar} x\right) \tag{A.24}$$

where N is a constant.

An extensive use of wave mechanics is made in the treatment of two-body problems; such as the deuteron, neutron-proton scattering and proton-proton scattering. The Schrödinger wave equation, given by Eq. (A.17), must be modified before it can be applied to such cases. Classically, we know that two-body problems can be reduced to two equivalent one-body problems, involving the motion of the center of mass and the relative motion of the two bodies. Such reduction is also possible in wave mechanics, as we shall see in the case of time-independent systems.

Let us consider two particles of masses m_1 and m_2 and their corresponding space coordinates x_1, y_1, z_1 and x_2, y_2, z_2 respectively. If ϕ represents the time-dependent wave function of such a system, then

$$\phi = \phi(x_1, y_1, z_1; x_2, y_2, z_2; t)$$

The time-dependent Schrödinger wave equation takes the form

$$-\frac{\hbar^2}{2m_1} \nabla_1^2 \phi - \frac{\hbar^2}{2m_2} \nabla_2^2 \phi + V\phi = i\hbar \frac{\partial \phi}{\partial t} \quad \text{(A.25)}$$

where

$$\nabla_1^2 = \frac{\partial^2}{\partial x_1^2} + \frac{\partial^2}{\partial y_1^2} + \frac{\partial^2}{\partial z_1^2}$$

and

$$\nabla_2^2 = \frac{\partial^2}{\partial x_2^2} + \frac{\partial^2}{\partial y_2^2} + \frac{\partial^2}{\partial z_2^2}$$

We define the *relative coordinates*, x, y, and z by the relations

$$x = x_1 - x_2$$
$$y = y_1 - y_2$$
$$z = z_1 - z_2 \quad \text{(A.26a)}$$

and the *center-of-mass coordinates*, X, Y, and Z, by

$$(m_1 + m_2)X = m_1 x_1 + m_2 x_2$$
$$(m_1 + m_2)Y = m_1 y_1 + m_2 y_2$$
$$(m_1 + m_2)Z = m_1 z_1 + m_2 z_2 \quad \text{(A.26b)}$$

Substituting Eqs. (A.26a) and (A.26b) into Eq. (A.25) we obtain

$$-\frac{\hbar^2}{2M}\left[\frac{\partial^2 \phi}{\partial X^2} + \frac{\partial^2 \phi}{\partial Y^2} + \frac{\partial^2 \phi}{\partial Z^2}\right] - \frac{\hbar^2}{2\mu}\left[\frac{\partial^2 \phi}{\partial x^2} + \frac{\partial^2 \phi}{\partial y^2} + \frac{\partial^2 \phi}{\partial z^2}\right] + V\phi = i\hbar \frac{\partial \phi}{\partial t} \quad \text{(A.27)}$$

where $M = (m_1 + m_2)$ and the reduced mass $\mu = \dfrac{m_1 m_2}{m_1 + m_2}$.

Two separations of the Eq. (A.27) can now be carried out. First, the time-dependent part of the wave equation can be extracted. Further, if we assume that V is a function of the relative coordinates only, then a second separation can be made into a product of functions of the relative coordinates and the center-of-mass coordinates. The result is

$$\phi(x,y,z;X,Y,Z;t) = \psi(x,y,z)\chi(X,Y,Z) \exp\{[-i(E + E')t/\hbar]\} \quad \text{(A.28)}$$

$$-\frac{\hbar^2}{2\mu} \nabla^2 \psi + V\psi = E\psi \quad \text{(A.29)}$$

and

$$-\frac{\hbar^2}{2M} \nabla^2 \chi = E'\chi \quad \text{(A.30)}$$

where

$$\nabla^2\psi = \frac{\partial^2\psi}{\partial x^2} + \frac{\partial^2\psi}{\partial y^2} + \frac{\partial^2\psi}{\partial z^2}$$

and

$$\nabla^2\chi = \frac{\partial^2\chi}{\partial X^2} + \frac{\partial^2\chi}{\partial Y^2} + \frac{\partial^2\chi}{\partial Z^2}$$

Eq. (A.30) tells us that the center of mass of the system of two particles moves as a free particle of mass M. Eq. (A.29) describes the relative motion of the two particles and is the same as the equation for the motion of a particle that has the reduced mass, μ, as it moves in an external potential, V. This equation represents the behavior of the system as viewed from the center of mass, and evidently it is the only equation of interest in the two-body problems. Rewriting Eq. (A.29), we have

$$\left(\frac{\partial^2\psi}{\partial x^2} + \frac{\partial^2\psi}{\partial y^2} + \frac{\partial^2\psi}{\partial z^2}\right) + \frac{2\mu}{\hbar^2}(E - V)\psi = 0 \qquad \text{(A.31)}$$

where ψ and V are functions of the relative coordinates, x, y, and z only. V represents the interaction potential between the two particles of the system.

In many two-body problems in nuclear physics at low energies (~ 10 Mev) the potential V depends only on the magnitude of the vector distance and not on its orientation. In such cases the problem is simplified. Expressing the Laplacian operator, ∇^2, in spherical polar coordinates, Eq. (A.29) or Eq. (A.31) take the form $[\psi(x,y,z) \rightarrow \psi(r,\theta,\phi)]$

$$\left[\frac{1}{r^2}\frac{\partial}{\partial r}\left(r^2\frac{\partial\psi}{\partial r}\right) + \frac{1}{r^2\sin\theta}\frac{\partial}{\partial\theta}\left(\sin\theta\frac{\partial\psi}{\partial\theta}\right) + \frac{1}{r^2\sin^2\theta}\frac{\partial^2\psi}{\partial\phi^2}\right]$$

$$+ \frac{2\mu}{\hbar^2}[E - V(r,\theta,\phi)]\psi = 0 \quad \text{(A.32)}$$

If the potential, V, is not a function of θ or ϕ, i.e., $V = V(r)$ and, further, if the angular momentum, l, is zero, which implies spherical symmetry, the derivative of ψ with respect to θ and ϕ will be zero. Thus Eq. (A.32) reduces to

$$\frac{1}{r^2}\frac{d}{dr}\left(r^2\frac{d\psi}{dr}\right) + \frac{2\mu}{\hbar^2}[E - V(r)]\psi = 0 \qquad \text{(A.33)}$$

Let us now make the substitution

$$\psi(r) = u(r)/r \qquad \text{(A.34)}$$

where $u(r)$ is the *radial wave-function*, in Eq. (A.33); we obtain

$$\frac{d^2u}{dr^2} + \frac{2\mu}{\hbar^2}[E - V(r)]u = 0 \qquad \text{(A.35)}$$

We shall use this equation on many occasions while discussing two-body problems in the low energy region. Eq. (A.35) is equivalent to the one-dimensional motion of a single particle of mass μ moving in a potential, $V(r)$, and, hence, the wave function $u(r)$ can be evaluated if E and V are known.

A more general solution of the wave equation given by Eq. (A.32) is obtained by the following procedure of separation of variables. Let ψ be written as a product of two separate functions

$$\psi(r,\theta,\phi) = R(r)Y(\theta,\phi) \tag{A.36}$$

Also assume, as before, that V is a function of r only. Substitution of Eq. (A.36) into Eq. (A.32) yields

$$\frac{1}{R}\frac{d}{dr}\left(r^2\frac{dR}{dr}\right) + \frac{2\mu}{\hbar^2}[E - V(r)] = -\frac{1}{Y}\left[\frac{1}{\sin\theta}\frac{\partial}{\partial\theta}\left(\sin\theta\frac{\partial Y}{\partial\theta}\right) + \frac{1}{\sin^2\theta}\frac{\partial^2 Y}{\partial\phi^2}\right] \tag{A.37}$$

The left-hand side of this equation is a function of variable r only, while the right-hand side contains θ and ϕ. This is possible only if each side is equal to a constant. The suitable constant is found to be $l(l + 1)$, where l has been identified as the angular momentum quantum number. Thus we get the following two equations:

Radial Equation:

$$\frac{1}{r^2}\frac{d}{dr}\left(r^2\frac{dR}{dr}\right) + \frac{2\mu}{\hbar^2}\left[E - V(r) - \frac{l(l + 1)\hbar^2}{2\mu r^2}\right]R = 0 \tag{A.38}$$

The radial wave function $R(r)$ can be evaluated only if the form of $V(r)$ is known.

Angular Equation:

$$\frac{1}{\sin\theta}\frac{\partial}{\partial\theta}\left(\sin\theta\frac{\partial Y}{\partial\theta}\right) + \frac{1}{\sin^2\theta}\frac{\partial^2 Y}{\partial\phi^2} + l(l + 1)Y = 0 \tag{A.39}$$

The solution of this equation is

$$Y_{lm}(\theta,\phi) = N_{lm}P_l^m(\cos\theta)e^{im\phi} \tag{A.40}$$

where $l = 0,1,2,3, \ldots$ and m can have any value between $-l$ and l, i.e., $m = -l, -(l - 1), -(l - 2), \ldots, -2, -1, 0, 1, 2, \ldots (l - 2), (l - 1), l$. N_{lm} is the normalization constant given by

$$N_{lm} = \left\{\left[\frac{(2l + 1)}{4\pi}\right]\left[\frac{(l - |m|)}{(l + |m|)}\right]\right\}^{1/2} \tag{A.41}$$

and $P_l^m(\cos\theta)$ are the associated legendre functions[6].

Thus the complete solution is

$$\psi(r,\theta,\phi) = R(r)Y_{lm}(\theta,\phi)$$
$$= R(r)N_{lm}P_l^m(\cos\theta)e^{im\phi} \qquad \text{(A.42)}$$

For a special case when $l = 0$, it will require that $m = 0$ and also $P_0^0(\cos\theta) = 1$. This gives $Y_{00} = \sqrt{1/(4\pi)}$ and hence

$$\psi(r) = \sqrt{1/(4\pi)}R(r) \qquad \text{(A.43)}$$

Lastly, we shall discuss an important property of the eigenfunctions, and hence of the eigenstates, called parity, that has no equivalent in classical mechanics.

Parity is a property of a wave function that describes its behavior under inversion of the coordinate system, i.e., the behavior of the eigenfunction when the signs of the coordinates are changed. Furthermore, if I is the parity operator, or inversion operator,

$$I\psi(x,y,z) = \psi(-x,-y,-z) \qquad \text{(A.44)}$$

and

$$I\psi(-x,-y,-z) = \psi(x,y,z) \qquad \text{(A.45)}$$

Let K be the eigenvalue of I, then from Eqs. (A.44) and (A.45),

$$I^2\psi(x,y,z,) = IK\psi(-x,-y,-z)$$
$$= KI\psi(-x,-y,-z)$$
$$= K^2\psi(x,y,z)$$

i.e.,

$$K^2 = 1 \quad \text{or} \quad K = \pm 1 \qquad \text{(A.46)}$$

This leads to the definition of even and odd parity wave functions. If

$$\psi(-x,-y,-z) = +\psi(x,y,z) \qquad \text{(A.47a)}$$

the wave function is said to have *even parity*, and if

$$\psi(-x,-y,-z) = -\psi(x,y,z) \qquad \text{(A.47b)}$$

the wave function is said to have *odd parity*.

We shall now show that if the potential $V(r)$ is symmetrical about $r = 0$, the eigenfunctions satisfying the Schrödinger wave equation have definite parity. Changing the sign of r in the S.W.E.

$$-\frac{\hbar^2}{2m}\nabla^2\psi(r) + V(r)\psi(r) = E\psi(r) \qquad \text{(A.48)}$$

and because $V(-r) = V(r)$, we get

$$-\frac{\hbar^2}{2m}\nabla^2\psi(-r) + V(r)\psi(-r) = E\psi(-r) \qquad \text{(A.49)}$$

Thus $\psi(r)$ and $\psi(-r)$ satisfy the same wave equation, and must be related by a constant, i.e.,

$$\psi(-r) = K\psi(r) \tag{A.50}$$

Changing the sign of r again

$$\psi(r) = K\psi(-r) \tag{A.51}$$

and combining Eqs. (A.50) and (A.51), gives $K^2 = 1$ or $K = \pm 1$, which is the result we obtained in Eq. (A.46). The wave functions, therefore, have either even (for $K = +1$) or odd (for $K = -1$) parity.

In terms of spherical coordinates, the inversion gives

$$\psi(r, \pi - \theta, \pi + \phi) = (-1)^l \psi(r, \theta, \phi) \tag{A.52}$$

Thus the states with $l = 0,2,4,6, \ldots$ will have even parity, and states with $l = 1,3,5,7, \ldots$ will have odd parity.

REFERENCES

1. de Broglie, Louis, *Phil. Mag.*, **47**, p. 446, (1924).
2. Davisson, C. J. and L. H. Germer, *Phys. Rev.*, **30**, p. 705, (1927).
3. Thomson, G. P., *Proc. Roy. Soc.*, **117**, p. 600, (1928).
4. Schrödinger, E., *Ann. Physik*, **79**, p. 489, (1926).
5. Born, M., W. Heisenberg, and P. Jordon, *Z. Physik*, **35**, p. 557, (1926).
6. Jahnke, E., and F. Ende, *Tables of Functions*, Dover Publications, 1945.

APPENDIX B

RELATIVISTIC MECHANICS

From our knowledge of the special theory of relativity, we know that when a body approaches the velocity of light ($c = 3 \times 10^8$ m/sec), the relativistic effects must be taken into consideration. In nuclear physics we often deal with particles in the microscopic domain moving with velocities approaching that of light; therefore, the relativistic corrections do become significant and important. In this section we shall summarize the results of the special theory of relativity without going into the details of the development of the subject. The two fundamental postulates of relativity are the following:

    (a) *Principle of Equivalence:* The laws of physical phenomena are the same when stated in terms of two systems of reference in uniform translatory motion relative to each other.

    (b) *Constancy of Velocity of Light:* The velocity of light in a vacuum is a constant, independent not only of the direction of propagation but also of the relative velocity of the source and the observer.

The second postulate is more important and basic than the first, because, it is by means of the second that the theory deviates from Newtonian classical mechanics.

I.   Consider two inertial frames of reference $S(X,Y,Z;t)$ and $S'(X',Y',Z';t')$ so oriented that the velocity, v, of S' relative to S is in the positive X-direction [Fig. (B.1)]. By making use of the postulates, we get the following transformations, called the *Lorentz transformations*, between the two sets of coordinates

$$X' = \frac{X - vt}{\sqrt{1 - (v^2/c^2)}} \qquad\qquad X = \frac{X' + vt'}{\sqrt{1 - (v^2/c^2)}}$$

$$Y' = Y \qquad\qquad\qquad Y = Y'$$

$$Z' = Z \qquad\qquad\qquad Z = Z'$$

$$t' = \frac{t - (vX/c^2)}{\sqrt{1 - (v^2/c^2)}} \qquad\qquad t = \frac{t' + (vX'/c^2)}{\sqrt{1 - (v^2/c^2)}}$$

$$\text{(B.1)}$$

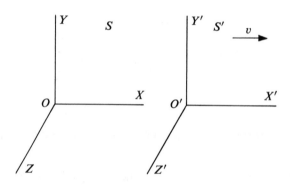

FIG. B-1

II.   If a particle moving in reference frame S has velocity components V_x, V_y, and V_z, then the velocity components $V_{x'}$, $V_{y'}$, and $V_{z'}$ in the reference frame S' are given by

$$V_{x'} = \frac{dX'}{dt'} = \frac{V_x - v}{1 - (vV_x/c^2)}$$

$$V_{y'} = \frac{dY'}{dt'} = \frac{V_y}{\gamma[1 - (vV_x/c^2)]}$$

$$V_{z'} = \frac{dZ'}{dt'} = \frac{V_z}{\gamma[1 - (vV_x/c^2)]}$$

$$\text{(B.2)}$$

where $\gamma = \dfrac{1}{\sqrt{1 - \beta^2}}$ and $\beta = v/c$.

III. By making use of the Lorentz transformation equations, it is shown that the classical rest-mass of a body is no longer constant; instead it is a function of velocity and is given by

$$m = \frac{m_0}{\sqrt{1 - (v^2/c^2)}} \tag{B.3}$$

where m_0 is the rest mass of the particle and m is its mass when moving with velocity v. Note that as $v \to 0$, $m \to m_0$.

IV. Variation in the mass of a body also changes the classical relation between the kinetic energy and the mass of the body. The expression for the kinetic energy K takes the form

$$K = mc^2 - m_0c^2$$

or

$$K = \frac{m_0c^2}{\sqrt{1 - (v^2/c^2)}} - m_0c^2 \tag{B.4}$$

It can be shown that when $v \ll c$, this expression reduces to the familiar classical expression for the kinetic energy, $K = \frac{1}{2}m_0v^2$. Rewriting Eq. (B.4) and substituting

$$E = mc^2 \tag{B.5}$$

we get

$$E = K + m_0c^2 \tag{B.6}$$

where E is the relativistic mass-energy (or the total energy) and is equal to the sum of the kinetic energy, K, and the rest-mass energy, m_0c^2. Eq. (B.5) is known as the famous *Einstein mass-energy relationship*. If, in addition to the kinetic energy, the particle also has potential energy, V, then the total energy of the particle is given by

$$E = mc^2 = K + V + m_0c^2 \tag{B.7}$$

In some cases it is more useful to know the relation between the total energy and the momentum of the particle. Such a relation is

$$E^2 = m^2c^4 = p^2c^2 + m_0^2c^4 \tag{B.8}$$

where p is the momentum of the particle defined by the following equation

$$p = mv = \frac{m_0v}{\sqrt{1 - v(^2/c^2)}} = m_0v\gamma \tag{B.9}$$

V. Finally, we shall summarize the transformation equations of momentum and energy that may be useful in collision problems. Referring again to Fig. B.1, the velocity of a particle of rest mass m_0 along the X-axis in the reference frame S is V, and that with respect to S' is V', also along the X'-axis. Then the relations

$$p_x = \frac{m_0 V}{\sqrt{1 - (V^2/c^2)}}, \quad p_y = 0, \quad p_z = 0; \quad E = \frac{m_0 c^2}{\sqrt{1 - (V^2/c^2)}} \quad \text{(B.10)}$$

and

$$p_x' = \frac{m_0 V'}{\sqrt{1 - (V'^2/c^2)}}, \quad p_y' = 0, \quad p_z' = 0; \quad E' = \frac{m_0 c^2}{\sqrt{1 - (V'^2/c^2)}} \quad \text{(B.11)}$$

can be combined together to give the equations relating the momenta and the energies in the two frames of reference. We get:

$$p_x' = \frac{p_x - (vE/c^2)}{\sqrt{1 - (v^2/c^2)}}$$

$$p_y' = p_y$$

$$p_z' = p_z \quad \text{(B.12)}$$

and

$$E' = \frac{E - p_x v}{\sqrt{1 - (v^2/c^2)}} \quad \text{(B.13)}$$

APPENDIX C

TABLES OF CONSTANTS AND CONVERSION FACTORS AS OF 1965†

TABLE I

DEFINED VALUES AND EQUIVALENTS

Meter (m)	1650763.73 wavelengths of the unperturbed transition $2p_{10}-5d_5$ in ^{86}Kr
Kilogram (kg)	Mass of the international kilogram
Second (s)	Astronomical 1/31 556925.9747 of the tropical year at 12^hET, 0 January, 1900 (yr = $365^d5^h48^m 45^s. 9747$)
	Physical 9192631770 cycles of the hyperfine transition $(4, 0 \rightarrow 3, 0)$ of the ground state of ^{133}Cs unperturbed by external fields

(Continued)

Degree Kelvin (°K)	In the thermodynamic scale, $273.16°K =$ triple-point of water $T(°C) = T(°K) - 273.15$ (freezing-point of water, $0.0000 \pm 0.0002°C$)
Unified atomic mass unit (u)	$1/12$ the mass of an atom of the ^{12}C nuclide
Standard acceleration of free fall (g_n)	9.80665 m s^{-2} 980.665 cm s^{-2}
Normal atmosphere (atm)	101325 N m^{-2} 1013250 dyn cm^{-2}
Thermochemical calorie (cal$_{th}$)	4.184 J 4.184×10^7 erg
Int. Steam Table calorie (cal$_{IT}$)	4.1868 J 4.1868×10^7 erg
Liter (1)	0.001000028 m^3 (recommended by CIPM 1950) 1000.028 cm^3
Inch (in.)	0.0254 m 2.54 cm
Pound (avdp.) (lb)	0.45359237 kg 453.59237 kg

† Taken from E. R. Cohen and J. W. M. DuMond, *Revs. Mod. Phys.*, **37**, 537, (1965). Reprinted with permission.

TABLE II
GENERAL PHYSICAL CONSTANTS

The digits in parentheses following each quoted value represent the standard deviation error in the final digits of the quoted value as computed on the criterion of internal consistency. The unified scale of atomic weights is used throughout ($^{12}C = 12$). C = coulomb; G = gauss; Hz = hertz; J = joule; N = newton; T = tesla; u = unified nuclidic mass unit; W = watt; Wb = weber.

Constant	Symbol	Value	Unit mksA	Unit cgs
Speed of light in vacuum	c	2.997925(1)	$\times 10^8$ m s^{-1}	$\times 10^{10}$ cm s^{-1}
Gravitational constant	G	6.670(5)^a	10^{-11} N m^2 kg^{-2}	10^{-8} dyn cm^2 g^{-2}
Elementary charge	e	4.80298(7)	10^{-19} C	10^{-20} emu
		1.60210(2)		10^{-10} esu
Avogadro constant	N_A	6.02252(9)	10^{26} kmole^{-1}	10^{23} mole^{-1}
Mass unit	u	1.66043(2)	10^{-27} kg	10^{-24} g
Electron rest-mass	m_e	9.10908(13)	10^{-31} kg	10^{-28} g
		5.48597(3)	10^{-4} u	10^{-4} u
Proton rest-mass	m_p	1.67252(3)	10^{-27} kg	10^{-24} g
		1.00727663(8)	u	u
Neutron rest-mass	m_n	1.67482(3)	10^{-27} kg	10^{-24} g
		1.0086654(4)	u	u
Faraday constant	F	9.64870(5)	10^4 C mole^{-1}	10^3 emu
		2.89261(2)		10^{14} esu
Planck constant	h	6.62559(16)	10^{-34} J s	10^{-27} erg s
	$h/2\pi$	1.054494(25)	10^{-34} J s	10^{-27} erg s
Fine-structure constant $2\pi e^2/hc$	α	7.29720(3)	10^{-3}	10^{-3}
	$1/\alpha$	137.0388(6)		
Charge-to-mass ratio for electron	e/m_e	1.758796(6)	10^{11} C kg^{-1}	10^7 emu
		5.27274(2)		10^{17} esu

(Continued)

Quantity	Symbol	Value		
Quantum of magnetic flux	hc/e	4.13556(4)	10^{-11} Wb	10^{-7} G cm^2
	h/e	1.379474(13)		10^{17} esu
Rydberg constant	R_∞	1.0973731(1)	10^7 m^{-1}	10^5 cm^{-1}
Bohr radius	a_0	5.29167(2)	10^{-11} m	10^{-9} cm
Compton wavelength of electron	$h/m_e c$	2.42621(2)	10^{-12} m	10^{-10} cm
	$\lambda_C/2\pi$	3.86144(3)	10^{-13} m	10^{-11} cm
Electron radius	$e^2/m_e c^2 = r_e$	2.81777(4)	10^{-15} m	10^{-13} cm
Thomson cross section	$8\pi r_e^2/3$	6.6516(2)	10^{-29} m^2	10^{-25} cm^2
Compton wavelength of proton	$\lambda_{c,p}$	1.321398(13)	10^{-15} cm	10^{-13} cm
	$\lambda_{c,p}/2\pi$	2.10307(2)	10^{-16} m	10^{-14} cm
Gyromagnetic ratio of proton	γ	2.675192(7)	10^8 rad s^{-1} T^{-1}	10^4 rad s^{-1} G^{-1}
	$\gamma/2\pi$	4.25770(1)	10^7 Hz T^{-1}	10^3 s^{-1} G^{-1}
(Uncorrected for diamagnetism H$_2$O)	γ'	2.675123(7)	10^8 s^{-1} T^{-1}	10^4 rad s^{-1} G^{-1}
	$\gamma'/2\pi$	4.25759(1)	10^7 HzT^{-1}	10^3 s^{-1} G^{-1}
Bohr magneton	μ_B	9.2732(2)	10^{-24} J T^{-1}	10^{-21} erg G^{-1}
Nuclear magneton	μ_N	5.05050(13)	10^{-27} J T^{-1}	10^{-21} s G^{-1}
Proton moment	μ_p	1.41049(4)	10^{-26} J T^{-1}	10^{-23} erg G^{-1}
	μ_p/μ_N	2.79276(2)		
(Uncorrected for diamagnetism in H$_2$O sample)		2.79268(2)		
Gas constant	R_0	8.31434(35)	J deg^{-1} mole^{-1}	10^7 erg deg^{-1} mole^{-1}
Boltzmann constant	k	1.38054(6)	10^{-23} J deg^{-1}	10^{-16} erg deg^{-1}
First radiation constant $(2\pi hc^2)$	c_1	3.74150(9)	10^{-16} W m^2	10^{-5} erg cm^2 s^{-1}
Second radiation constant (hc/k)	c_2	1.43879(6)	10^{-2} m deg	cm deg
Stefan–Boltzmann constant	σ	5.6697(10)	10^{-8} W m^{-2} deg^{-4}	10^{-5} erg cm^{-2} s^{-1} deg^{-4}

[a] The universal gravitational constant is not, and cannot in our present state of knowledge, be expressed in terms of other fundamental constants. The value given here is a direct determination by P. R. Heyl and P. Chrzanowski, *J. Res. Natl. Bur. Std.* (U.S.) **29**, 1, (1942).

TABLE III

ENERGY CONVERSION FACTORS

1 electron volt	$= 1.60210(2) \times 10^{-19}$ J
	$= 1.60210(2) \times 10^{-12}$ erg
	$= 8065.73(8)$ cm^{-1}
	$= 2.41804(2) \times 10^{14}$ s^{-1}
$V\lambda$	$= 12398.10(13) \times 10^{-8}$ ev cm
1 ev per particle	$= 11604.9(5)°$K
	$= 23061(1)$ cal$_{th}$ mole^{-1}
	$= 23045(1)$ cal$_{IT}$ mole^{-1}
1 amu	$= 931.478(5)$ Mev
Proton mass	$= 938.256(5)$ Mev
Neutron mass	$= 939.550(5)$ Mev
Electron mass	$= 511006(2)$ ev
Rydberg	$= 2.17971(5) \times 10^{-11}$ erg
	$= 13.60535(13)$ ev
Gas constant, R_0	$= 8.31434 \times 10^7$ erg mole^{-1} deg^{-1}
	$= 0.082053$ liter atm mole^{-1} deg^{-1}
	$= 82.055$ cm^3 atm mole^{-1} deg^{-1}
	$= 1.9872$ cal$_{th}$ mole^{-1} deg^{-1}
	$= 1.9858$ cal$_{IT}$ mole^{-1} deg^{-1}
Standard volume of ideal gas V_0	$= 22413.6$ cm^3 mole^{-1}

Taken from E. R. Cohen and J. W. M. DuMond., *Revs. Mod. Phys.*, **37**, 537, (1965). Reprinted with permission.

INDEX

non-coulomb cross-section, 147
one-quarter point recipe, 156
Counting, probability of, 69
Count rate:
 true, 69
 average, 69
Coupling constant, 261
Courant, E., 533
Cowan, C., 253, 305, 307
Critical condition for nuclear reactors, 537
Critical energy, 238
Crossed channels, 603
Crossed reactions, 602
Cross-section, 80, 97
 absorption, 100
 CMCS and LAB, 103
 D-D and D-T for fusion, 546
 differential, 101, 391
 geometrical, 400
 macroscopic, 99
 microscopic, 99
 neutrons from perfectly reflecting sphere, 421
 total, 101
 unit of, 99
Crystal diffraction spectrometer for gamma rays, 308
Curie, Crookes and Rutherford, 20
Curie, I. and F. Joliet, 12
Curie, Madame, 20
 identity of different types of radiation, 20
Curie, P., 20
Curie (unit), millicurie, microcurie, 38
Cyclotron, 518
 resonance frequency of, 521
 maximum frequency of, 521

D-lines sodium, 4
Dalton's atomic hypothesis (theory), 2, 110
Danysz, J., 227
Data analysis techniques, 552
Davey, W., 341
Davisson, C., 296, 306, 613
De Broglie's hypothesis, 10, 491, 613
Decay of free neutrons, 474
Decay probability, 390
Decay time, 390
Deformation parameter, 375
Deformed nucleus, 375
 deformation parameter of, 375
 moment of inertia of, 376
Degenerate gas and mean free path, 380
Degree Kelvin, definition of, 628
Delayed coincidence method, 338
Delayed neutrons and reactor control, 543
Delayed neutrons from fission, 501
 reactor control, 543
Delbruck scattering, 289
De Juren, J. and N. Knable, 163
Delta rays, 191
Dempster, A., 116
Dempster's mass spectrometer, 116
Depletion region, 62
Detection of neutrons, 480–491
Deuteron, two-body problem, 443–449
 angular momentum, 444
 binding energy, 444

electric quadrupole moment, 444
magnetic moment, 444
mass, 443
non-central force, 448
radial wave function, 445
tensor force, 448
Deutsch, M., 232, 312
Differential cross-section, 101
 scattering, 391
 variation with angle, 102
Differential-range curve for alpha particles, 188
Differential scattering cross-section, 391
Diffraction, cross-section and optical model, 163
Diffraction of electrons, 166–167
Diffraction pattern, experimental arrangement, 492
Diffusion chamber, 56
 recycling time of, 56
 sensitive volume of, 57
Dipole, 315
 electric, 320
 energy from oscillating, 320
 moment, 315
Direct interactions, 424–427
Direct-voltage accelerator, 513
Disintegration constant in alpha decay, 180
Disintegration energy, 81
 beta decay, 225, 226
Dispersion formula, 410
Dispersive power, 115
Displaced multiplets, 591
Donor, 62
Doppler effect, 341
Double focusing spectrometer, 233
Double values in nuclear reactions, 84, 91, 92
Drift-tube accelerators, 523
Du Mond, J., 230, 231, 309, 631
Durbin, R., 559

Effective range theory, 453
Eight fold way, 598–601
Einstein mass energy relation, 625
Elastic collisions of neutrons, 475
Elastic nuclear-potential scattering, 289
Elastic scattering cross-section, total, 392–395
Electric charge, 594
Electric dipole moment, 320
Electric moments and collective model, 377
Electric multipole transition probability, 321
Electric quadrupole moment, 319
 deuteron, 444
 shell model, 359, 372
Electromagnetic interactions, 588
Electrometer, 118
Electron, 16, 554
 charge, 16
 g-factor, 16
 magnetic moment, 16
 rest mass, 10, 16
 spin, 16
Electron accelerator, 525
Electron capture, 222
 disintegration energy of, 226
 theory of, 274

636

Resonance energies, 409
Resonance escape probability, 538
Resonance particles 552, 578–586
  N*, 581
  omega, 581
  properties of, 583
  rho, 581
  table of, 583
  Y*, 578–580
Resonance scattering amplitude, 408
Resonance, scattering theory of, 409
Resonances and compound nucleus, 401
Resonances in Al^{27}, 415, 416
Rest mass energy of electron, 10
Rho resonance, 581
Robson, J. M., 263, 474
Rochester, G., 562, 564, 579
Rodeback, G., 252
Root-mean-square deviation, 70
Rose, M., 330, 522
Rosenbaum, E. P., 571, 592
Rosenblum, E., 213
Rosenfeld, A. H., 553, 601
Rosseland, S., 327
Rotational levels and collective model, 374
Rotational quantum number, 375
Russell, B., 478
Rutherford:
  alpha particle scattering, 147
  nuclear atomic hypothesis, 1, 3
  proton-electron model, 11, 14
  unit, mrd, μrd, 38
Rutherford, E., 141, 201
Rutherford, E., and F. Soddy, 20
Rydberg constant, 4

Sacks, D., 478
Sargent, B., 256
Sargent plots, 257
Saturation of nuclear forces, 440
Scaler, 48
Scattering:
  alpha particles, 147–157
  amplitude, 391
  cross-section:
    collision, 161
    differential, 391
    elastic (theoretical), 392–395
    partial, 398
    total, 400
  fast neutron, 161
    radius from, 165
    sensitive area, 161
  hard sphere potential, 408
  length, 453
  neutron-proton, 449–457
  partial wave analysis, 390
  proton-proton scattering, 454, 455
  resonance, theory of, 409
  singlet state, 453
  triplet state, 453
  two body, 460
  wave mechanical treatment, 390–400
Scharff-Goldhaber, G., 329
Schmidt limits, 369
Schmidt, T., 369
Schrödinger, E., 614

Schrödinger wave equation:
  a particle, 616, 617
  alpha decay, 207
  center of mass coordinates, 618
  Fermi gas model, 380
  parity, 621
  relative coordinates, 618
  shell model, 359
  spherical polar coordinates, 619
  time dependent, 616
  time independent, 616
  two-body, 617, 618
Scintillation counter, 59
  energy resolution, efficiency, resolving
    time, sensitive volume, 59–61
Scintillation method for gamma rays, 313
Scintillators, 59
Second, definition of, 627
Secular equilibrium, 31, 32
Segrè, E., 572
Selection rules for beta decay (Fermi,
    Gammow-Teller), 272
Selection rules for gamma emission, 325–327
Selection rules for J and F, 6
Self energy, 129, 130
Self-quenching, 54
Self-sustaining fusion, 545
Semi-circular focussing spectrometer for beta
    particles, 228
Semi-empirical atomic mass formula, 132–
    136
  binding energy per nucleon, 135
  nuclear deformation, 136
  odd-even effect, 133
  pairing effect, 133
  shell structure, 136
  six term formula, 134
  surface tension, 133
  Weizsäcker, 132
Sensitive area, 97, 98
Serber, R., 162
Shape factors, 265
  Y^{91}, 265
Shapiro, A. M., 462
Shell model:
  electric quadrupole moment, 359, 372
  evidence for, 356–359
  harmonic oscillator potential, 362
  isomeric states, 371
  isomerism, 372
  magic numbers, 361, 363, 364
  non-central component, 363
  nuclear spin, 365
  order of levels, 364
  parity, 365
  Schrödinger wave equation, 359
  spin, 365
  spin-orbit coupling, 363
  square well potential, 361
Sherman, D., 357
Shimming, 522
Short chains, from fission, 496
Short half-life, measurement of, 338–340
  by delayed coincidence method, 338
  by nuclear resonance method, 340
Short lens spectrometer, 232
Shull, C. G., 493
Shull, F., 243

644